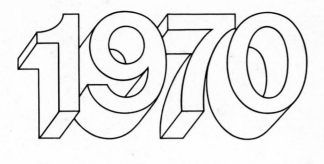

1970 Britannica Yearbook of Science and the Future

Encyclopædia Britannica, Inc.

William Benton, Publisher

Chicago Toronto London
Geneva Sydney Tokyo Manila

1970 Britannica Yearbook of Science and the Future

THE UNIVERSITY OF CHICAGO
The Britannica Yearbook of Science and the Future
is published with the editorial advice of the faculties of
the University of Chicago

Contents

About the Articles

Applications of Organic Forms
by Philip C. Ritterbush, page 14. The conscious transferrence of form from an object to a stone wall was the turning point for scientific understanding of design principles. The author of this pictorial essay is concerned with the way biological form—the form of living things—has had a cultural influence on art and design. Because form is a visual aspect of bodies, its study depends on the sensitivity of the observer's vision, that is, the observer's ability to perceive relationships between surfaces. The study of form is a meeting place for both scientists and artists because, to analyze form, both the objectivity of observation and the fanciful flight of imagination must proceed in tandem.

The Brain
by Robert W. Doty, page 34. Man's ability to comprehend the universe is, in the end, limited by the processes intrinsic to his brain. Thus, the study of this complex, miraculous organ is, indeed, "the ultimate science." For centuries, the relation of brain to mind remained too vague to penetrate the speculations of theology. But then came Darwin and the scientific revolution, in which the working of the brain began to be understood in intimate detail. As a result, man stands ready to answer some important questions concerning his identity: Is he a metaphysical or a physiological animal? Could a computer be programmed to write poetry? Would it be possible for an artificially manufactured human being to declare itself conscious?

Game Theory: Strategies for Resolving Conflict
by Anatol Rapoport, page 54. Game theory, which deals, in general, with the problems posed by rationally conducted conflict, is used by businessmen, politicians, diplomats, and generals to plan strategic decisions. Game theorists are not concerned with solving particular games, or with psychological evaluation. Instead, they analyze different games "in order to provide a clear perspective on the sort of problems that are involved in solving them." One insight of game theory, for example, is that the notion of "solution" has different meanings when applied to different kinds of games.

Man in America: The Calico Mountains Excavations
by Louis S. B. Leakey, Ruth DeEtte Simpson, and Thomas Clements, page 64. Generally, archaeologists accept 20,000 years ago as the approximate date of man's arrival in America. In recent years, however, Dr. Leakey and his colleagues, digging at a site in California, have uncovered materials that they maintain are remains of primitive tools made by Stone Age man. This evidence, which has indicated the possibility of an American Paleolithic occupation, has opened new areas for archaeological research. Further study of these "artifacts" could prove the authors' conviction that there were men in America as far back as 50,000 years ago.

Humanics and Genetic Engineering
by Joshua Lederberg, page 80. The author concedes that the term "genetic engineering" may conjure up the Frankenstein image of a mad scientist. But, in discussing some of the many possibilities of such engineering, he argues that humanics—the scientific study of human nature—has been both a conscious and an unconscious element in human cultural progress and that the most important ethical inference of human evolution is that man is still perfectible. Just as man has been able for some time to cultivate better grains and other foods by an almost unconscious use of genetic engineering, today he is able consciously to apply the same techniques to his own species.

Toward a Landfall in Space
by Jay Holmes, page 178. The guidance and navigation system of the Apollo command module that rocketed to the moon in 1969 is only about four feet high, two feet deep, and three feet wide. It is made up of no less than 40,000 parts, including a digital computer, a system of gyroscopes and accelerometers, optical viewing devices, supporting electronic equipment, and a display console and keyboards. This array of extremely sophisticated equipment in no way substitutes for the fact that, like sailors, astronauts must navigate by the stars. For this reason the age-old sextant, similar to the one used by seamen, is an essential part of Apollo's navigational equipment.

Life Beyond the Earth

by Norman H. Horowitz, page 192. Since the beginning of the Space Age, much fanfare has surrounded the technical challenges that have been mastered in man's effort to reach the moon. But a far more tantalizing space exploration is aimed elsewhere—at the possibility that there is life on planets other than our own. Of all the extraterrestrial objects within reach of present spacecraft, only Mars is conceivably capable of supporting life as we know it. Working with data gathered from telescopic observation from the earth and from flybys of Mariner space shots, and comparing this data with what they know about conditions under which life can exist, exobiologists speculate that Mars could support some form of life.

Urban Society: A Blueprint for the City of Tomorrow

by Philip M. Hauser, page 202. By the mid-21st century, urban man will be living in "superagglomerations" made up of several metropolitan areas and conceivably encompassing as many as 100 million people. Although the problems of such an urban mass are staggering to contemplate, the author of this article is optimistic. He predicts that, unlike the present urban system in which social, economic, and political forces clash, the city of tomorrow will be transformed, technologically and physically, and a new breed of city planners, called "social engineers," will construct an urban society far superior to the one we now know.

Nature on the Rampage

by Robert C. Cowen, page 226. Every year earthquakes, volcanic eruptions, tidal waves, hurricanes, and other violent natural forces claim thousands of lives and cause millions of dollars in property damage, thus mocking mankind's occasional boast that he has conquered nature. Although methods for predicting nature's vagaries have improved greatly, man remains largely at the mercy of the elements. Seismologists predict, for example, that California is "due" for a major earthquake soon, but they are unable to tell exactly when or where it will hit, or how severe it will be. And dormant volcanoes, located in many countries that border the Pacific, could erupt violently at any time.

Sleep and Dreams

by Julius Segal and Gay Gaer Luce, page 306. The discovery that heightened periods of dreaming are always accompanied by rapid eye movements (known as REM sleep) now draws hundreds of researchers around the world into sleep laboratories each night to observe the dreaming patterns of both animals and humans. Many hypotheses have been postulated as a result of this research. Physicians now suspect that violent or disturbing dreams during REM intervals may cause nocturnal heart attacks; psychologists believe that lack of REM sleep may cause mental illness. By a continued study of sleep and dreams, doctors hope to develop drugs that will ward off both physiological and psychological side-effects of poor sleeping habits.

Freud's Place in Modern Psychiatry

by Paul R. Miller, page 318. Sigmund Freud himself conceded that, over the years, new biological data would probably erode some of his theories. And this is exactly what has happened. Many of Freud's once sacrosanct explanations of human behavior have been found to be, in the words of the author of this article, "incorrect, equivocal, or metaphysical." Today, modern psychiatry is moving away from Freudian theory's preoccupation with the mind and is focusing instead on the behavioral sciences and their examination of the whole "biopsychosocial" spectrum of human behavior. Freud's place in psychiatry today is primarily a historical one.

Exploring the Ocean Frontiers

by Edward Wenk, Jr., page 328. Though man is primarily a terrestrial creature, he lives on a planet that contains 330 million cu mi of water covering almost 71% of its surface. For thousands of years, the mysteries of these depths were left largely unexplored or to such fantasists as Jules Verne. In recent years, however, oceanographers—working with deep-ocean submersibles, specially equipped ships, computers, and satellites—have opened up a vast underwater world with enormous potential for helping and serving mankind by supplementing the constantly dwindling food and mineral sources. The work that ocean scientists are doing covers many aspects of man's life and has worldwide implications.

When Young Children Go Hungry: Effects on Learning and Behavior

by Nevin S. Scrimshaw, page 344. Each year thousands of children may show signs of substandard mental development as a result of nutritionally deficient diets. Because more than ¾ of a child's brain size has been reached by the time he can talk, malnutrition early in life can have a permanent effect on his future mental abilities. Scientific research has also indicated that individual dietary history is an important factor in physical development as well. These facts alone point up the urgent need for immediate action by the world community to prevent malnutrition in young children.

The Mount Wilson and Palomar Observatories: Two Rooms with a View

by Jesse L. Greenstein, page 356. "My view is as old as civilization; the light I am seeing left the object 5,000 years ago." Thus, as he gazes at a star, the author gives an indication of the staggering dimensions of the cosmos that he and his fellow astronomers are probing with the powerful telescopes at these two observatories in southern California. With the more sophisticated instruments that have been made in recent years, scientists have been able to focus on such Space Age mysteries as quasars, pulsars, and other as yet unexplained astronomical phenomena.

A House for Living Molecules

by Max F. Perutz, page 364. Few researchers work closer to the frontiers of science than the 180 members of the Medical Research Council's Laboratory of Molecular Biology in Cambridge, Eng. By exploring life at the molecular level, they seek to explain the inheritance, development, and behavior of all living organisms in terms of the simple laws of physics and chemistry. These scientists have already determined the chemical structure of many proteins, established the molecular structure of DNA, and translated the genetic message by which DNA forms proteins. In the long run, their work in molecular biology may lead to the solution and prevention of many of medicine's yet unsolved problems.

A Scientific View of Race

by Raymond W. Mack, page 400. In the early part of the 20th century, scholars tended to overemphasize the importance of heredity in determining the human condition. In more recent decades, cumulative social science research has pointed up man's ability to alter his natural environment, and this has led to an exaggerated accent on the environmental factor in shaping the individual. The author of this article believes that "because all human beings are members of one species, and because the various stocks in that species have been mixing with one another for thousands of years, scientists have no set of 'racial' categories that are both exhaustive and mutually exclusive." Both heredity and environment work together to mold mankind.

Physical Sciences in the Soviet Union

by Mikhail D. Millionshchikov, page 414. A basic tenet of Marxism-Leninism holds that science is the most important component of man's efforts to remake his surroundings. In the U.S.S.R. today, some 700,000 scientists are pursuing thousands of research projects. Concentrating on the physical sciences, the author of this article, a noted Soviet scientist, describes some of the fundamental research by his colleagues in such fields as mathematics, astronomy, nuclear physics, chemistry, and the earth sciences. Dr. Millionshchikov speaks as a distinguished member of the Soviet science establishment, and the editors have not altered the point of view expressed in his original manuscript.

Toward Future Guidance of Science in Human Affairs

by Christopher Wright, page 428. Traditionally, scientists have claimed to be searching for objective truth, with little concern for the consequences of their discoveries. Over the years, they have justified the position by arguing that any contribution to the total fund of human knowledge would, in the long run, benefit man. But, as the development of nuclear weapons chillingly illustrates, science has a tremendous capacity to destroy. In this age of swift technological change, the author of this article feels that science has too many far-reaching moral and psychological implications to be left to the scientist alone.

Authors of Articles

Thomas Clements *Man in America: The Calico Mountains Excavations.* Formerly professor of geology and chairman of the geology department at the University of Southern California at Los Angeles, Dr. Clements is presently a consulting geologist specializing in engineering geology.

Robert C. Cowen *Nature on the Rampage.* Mr. Cowen, the natural science editor for the *Christian Science Monitor,* is a member of the American Meteorological Society, the American Association for the Advancement of Science, and the American Geophysical Union. He is the author of *Frontiers of the Sea,* a book on oceanography.

Robert W. Doty *The Brain.* Dr. Doty is professor of neurophysiology at the Center for Brain Research, University of Rochester, N.Y., and chief editor of *Neuroscience Translations.* He is also a member of the International Brain Research Organization, the International Primatological Society, the American Physiological Society, the Pavlovian Society, and the Visual Science Study Section of the National Institute of Neurological Diseases and Blindness.

Jesse L. Greenstein *The Mount Wilson and Palomar Observatories: Two Rooms with a View.* Professor of astrophysics and executive officer for astronomy at the California Institute of Technology, Dr. Greenstein is also on the staff of the Mount Wilson and Palomar Observatories and a member of the Observatory Council. Selected California Scientist of the Year in 1964, he is a member of the National Academy of Sciences and chairman of the U.S. National Committee for the International Astronomical Union.

Philip M. Hauser *Urban Society: A Blueprint for the City of Tomorrow.* Professor of sociology and director of the Population Research and Training Center at the University of Chicago, Dr. Hauser is also on the board of the National Assembly for Social Policy and Development. He has served as president of the American Sociological Association and the Sociological Research Association.

Jay Holmes *Toward a Landfall in Space.* Recognized as a specialist in the history of the U.S. National Aeronautics and Space Administration, Mr. Holmes is a science writer in the NASA Office of Manned Space Flight. He is a member of the National Association of Science Writers and the author of two books, *America on the Moon: The Enterprise of the Sixties* and *The Race for the Moon.*

Norman H. Horowitz *Life Beyond the Earth.* Dr. Horowitz is professor of biology at the California Institute of Technology and manager of the bioscience section at the Jet Propulsion Laboratory in Pasadena, Calif. He is a member of the National Academy of Sciences, the Genetics Society of America, and the American Society of Biological Chemistry.

Louis S. B. Leakey *Man in America: The Calico Mountains Excavations.* For his work on the origin and history of man, Dr. Leakey has been awarded numerous academic medals and honorary degrees. These include the Hubbard Medal of the National Geographic Society, the Swedish Vega Medal, and the Royal Medal of the Royal Geographic Society. Dr. Leakey is now director of the National Centre of Pre-History and Palaeontology in Nairobi, Kenya.

Joshua Lederberg *Humanics and Genetic Engineering.* Dr. Lederberg, a member of the National Academy of Sciences, shared the 1958 Nobel Prize for Physiology or Medicine for his studies on the organization of the genetic material in bacteria. He is professor of genetics and biology and chairman of the department of genetics at the Stanford University School of Medicine.

Gay Gaer Luce *Sleep and Dreams.* Mrs. Luce, a writer for the U.S. National Institute of Mental Health, has twice received the American Psychological Association prize for scientific writing in psychology. Her latest books (with Julius Segal) are *Sleep* and *Insomnia.*

Raymond W. Mack

A Scientific View of Race. Dr. Mack is professor of sociology, chairman of the department of sociology, and director of the Center for Urban Affairs at Northwestern University, Evanston, Ill. The author of the books *Transforming America* and *Our Children's Burden,* he is currently serving as editor of the *American Sociologist* magazine.

Paul R. Miller *Freud's Place in Modern Psychiatry.*

Dr. Miller is an assistant professor in the department of neurology and psychiatry at Northwestern University Medical School. He has served as senior assistant surgeon for the U.S. Public Health Service and is the author of *Sense and Symbol: A Textbook of Human Behavioral Science.*

Mikhail Millionshchikov

Physical Sciences in the Soviet Union. Dr. Millionshchikov, a specialist in mechanical and applied physics, is vice-president of the Academy of Sciences of the U.S.S.R. In addition to the Stalin and Lenin Prizes, he has also received the Hero of Socialist Labor Medal and was elected to membership in the Order of Lenin and the American Academy of Arts and Sciences.

Max F. Perutz *A House for Living Molecules.*

Dr. Perutz is founder and chairman of the Medical Research Council's Laboratory of Molecular Biology at Cambridge, Eng. A noted British biochemist and crystallographer, he shared the 1962 Nobel Prize for Chemistry for his work on the structure of hemoglobin.

Anatol Rapoport *Game Theory: Strategies for Resolving Conflict.*

A Fellow of the American Academy of Arts and Sciences, Dr. Rapoport is professor of mathematical biology at the University of Michigan's Mental Health Research Institute. He has been a visiting professor at the University of Warsaw, the Institute of Advanced Study in Vienna, and the Technical University of Denmark.

Philip C. Ritterbush

Applications of Organic Forms. The director of the Office of Academic Programs at the Smithsonian Institution in Washington, D.C., Dr. Ritterbush is also a member of the American Association for the Advancement of Science. He was a lecturer in the department of history of science and medicine at Yale University and a Rhodes scholar.

Nevin S. Scrimshaw *When Young Children Go Hungry: Effects on Learning and Behavior.*

Dr. Scrimshaw is professor of nutrition and chairman of the department of nutrition and food science at the Massachusetts Institute of Technology. He has been a consultant on food and nutrition to various United Nations organizations.

Julius Segal *Sleep and Dreams.*

Chief of the Program Analysis and Evaluation Branch at the U.S. National Institute of Mental Health, Dr. Segal was awarded the 1968 Superior Service Award by the U.S. Department of Health, Education, and Welfare for outstanding research and publication in the mental health field. The co-author (with Gay Gaer Luce) of two books about sleep, he also shared with her the American Psychological Association prize for the best popular scientific writing in the field of psychology.

Ruth DeEtte Simpson

Man in America: The Calico Mountains Excavations. The San Bernardino (Calif.) County Archaeologist for the San Bernardino County Museum, Miss Simpson is a specialist in Pleistocene archaeology in western North America.

Edward Wenk, Jr. *Exploring the Ocean Frontiers.*

In 1966 Pres. Lyndon B. Johnson appointed Dr. Wenk to the post of executive secretary of the National Council on Marine Resources and Engineering Development.

Christopher Wright

Toward Future Guidance of Science in Human Affairs. Formerly executive director of the Council for Atomic Age Studies at Columbia University, Mr. Wright is now director of the Institute for the Study of Science in Human Affairs at Columbia and a lecturer in the university's department of political science.

Contributors to The Science Year in Review

J. Garrott Allen *Medicine: Surgery.* Professor of Surgery, Stanford University Medical Center, Stanford, Calif.

Joel Allison *Behavioral Sciences: Psychology.* Research Associate, Psycho-Educational Clinic, Yale University, and Clinical Associate, Department of Psychiatry, Yale University, New Haven, Conn.

Joseph Ashbrook *Astronomy.* Editor, *Sky and Telescope,* Cambridge, Mass.

Walter Axelsen *Communications.* Technical Information Manager, Automatic Electric Company, Northlake, Ill.

Lowell K. Bridwell *Transportation (in part).* President, System Design Concepts, Inc., Washington, D.C.

John L. Buckley *Environmental Sciences: Ecology.* Technical Assistant, Office of Science and Technology, Executive Office of the President, Washington, D.C.

James C. Copeland *Molecular Biology: Molecular Genetics.* Assistant Geneticist, Division of Biological and Medical Research, Argonne National Laboratory, Argonne, Ill.

Andries van Dam *Computers (in part).* Associate Professor of Computer Science, Brown University, Providence, R.I.

Ralph Daniels *Chemistry: Organic Chemistry.* Professor of Chemistry, University of Illinois, Chicago.

Robert L. Davidson *Engineering: Chemical Engineering.* Managing Editor—News, *Chemical Engineering,* McGraw-Hill, Inc., New York City.

John M. Dennison *Earth Sciences: Geology and Geochemistry.* Professor of Geology and Chairman, Department of Geology, University of North Carolina, Chapel Hill.

Charles L. Drake *Earth Sciences: Geophysics.* Professor of Geology and Chairman, Department of Geology, Columbia University, New York City.

F. C. Durant III *Astronautics and Space Exploration: Earth-Oriented Satellites.* Assistant Director (Astronautics), National Air and Space Museum, Smithsonian Institution, Washington, D.C.

Robert G. Eagon *Microbiology.* Professor of Microbiology, University of Georgia, Athens.

Gerald Feinberg *Physics: High-Energy Physics.* Professor of Physics, Columbia University, New York City.

Herbert Friedman *Astronautics and Space Exploration: Space-Oriented Satellites.* Chief Scientist, E. O. Hulburt Center for Space Research, U.S. Naval Research Laboratory, Washington, D.C.

Joseph Gies *Engineering: Civil Engineering.* Senior

editor—Technology, Encyclopædia Britannica, Inc., Chicago, Ill.

Roy R. Grinker, Sr. *Medicine: Psychiatry.* Director, Institute of Psychosomatic and Psychiatric Research and Training, Michael Reese Hospital, Chicago, Ill.

Philip F. Gustafson *Molecular Biology: Biophysics; Future Trends in Molecular Biology.* Associate Director, Radiological Physics Division, Argonne National Laboratory, Argonne, Ill.

Philip Handler *The Science Year in Review: A Perspective.* President, National Academy of Sciences; Chairman, National Science Board, Washington, D.C.

Thomas W. Hunter *Fuel and Power.* Acting Head, Energy Analysis Group, Division of Mineral Studies, Mineral Resource Evaluation, U.S. Bureau of Mines, Washington, D.C.

Richard S. Johnston *Astronautics and Space Exploration: Manned Space Exploration.* Special Assistant to the Director, NASA Manned Spacecraft Center, Houston, Tex.

William L. Jolly *Chemistry: Inorganic Chemistry.* Professor of Chemistry, University of California, Berkeley.

Lou Joseph *Dentistry.* Assistant Director, Bureau of Public Information, American Dental Association, Chicago, Ill.

Sumner M. Kalman *Medicine: Pharmacology.* Professor of Pharmacology, School of Medicine, Stanford University, Stanford, Calif.

Robert Keller *Medicine: Immunology.* Associate Director, Department of Microbiology, Michael Reese Hospital and Medical Center, Chicago, Ill.

William W. Kellogg *Atmospheric Sciences.* Associate Director, National Center for Atmospheric Research, Boulder, Colo.

Richard M. Klein *Botany.* Professor of Botany, University of Vermont, Burlington.

Leonard J. Koch *Engineering: Nuclear Engineering.* Division Director, Argonne National Laboratory, Argonne, Ill.

Joyce C. Lashof *Medicine: Public Health.* Director, Community Medicine, Presbyterian-St. Luke's Hospital, Chicago, Ill.

Howard J. Lewis *Science, General.* Director, Office of Information, National Academy of Sciences—National Academy of Engineering—National Research Council, Washington, D.C.

C. Peter Lillya *Chemistry: Physical and Synthetic Chemistry.* Associate Professor of Chemistry, University of Massachusetts, Amherst.

J(ohn) David Lockard *Education, Science.* Associate Professor of Botany and Science Education and Director of the Science Teaching Center and The International Clearinghouse on Science and Mathematics Curricular Developments, University of Maryland, College Park.

Margaret Markham *Foods and Nutrition.* Executive

10

Director, Vitamin Information Bureau, New York City.

Donald N. Medearis, Jr. *Medicine: Introduction; Pediatrics.* Professor and Chairman, Department of Pediatrics, University of Pittsburgh School of Medicine, and Medical Director, Children's Hospital of Pittsburgh, Pa.

Thomas C. Merigan *Medicine: Infectious Diseases.* Associate Professor of Medicine and Chief, Division of Infectious Diseases, Stanford University Medical Center, Stanford, Calif.

Lorus J. Milne *Zoology (in part).* Professor of Zoology, University of New Hampshire, Durham.

Margery Milne *Zoology (in part).* Lecturer in Nature Recreation, University of New Hampshire, Durham.

Patricia Mitchell *Computers (in part).* Research Assistant, Department of Applied Mathematics, Brown University, Providence, R.I.

Henry L. Nadler *Medicine: Medical Genetics.* Associate Professor of Pediatrics, Northwestern University Medical School, and Head, Division of Genetics and Biochemistry, Children's Memorial Hospital, Chicago, Ill.

Willard J. Pierson, Jr. *Oceanography.* Professor of Oceanography, School of Engineering and Science, New York University, New York City.

Froelich Rainey *Archaeology.* Director, The University Museum, University of Pennsylvania, Philadelphia.

Thomas Ronningen *Agriculture.* Assistant Administrator, Cooperative State Research Service, U.S. Department of Agriculture, Washington, D.C.

Paul B. Sears *Environmental Sciences: Conservation.* Emeritus Professor of Conservation, Yale University, New Haven, Conn.

J. F. Smithcors *Veterinary Medicine.* Associate Editor, American Veterinary Publications, Santa Barbara, Calif.

William E. Spicer *Physics: Solid-State Physics.* Professor, Electrical Engineering and Materials Science, Stanford University, Stanford, Calif.

Robert E. Stoffels *Electronics.* Director, EAX Operations, Automatic Electric Laboratories, Inc. Northlake, Ill.

James Stouder Sweet *Molecular Biology: Biochemistry.* Science Editor, Office of Planning and Development, Northwestern University, Evanston, Ill.

Sol Tax *Behavioral Sciences: Anthropology.* Professor of Anthropology, University of Chicago.

H. E. Wegner *Physics: Nuclear Physics.* Senior Physicist, Project Manager of the Three-Stage Tandem Van de Graaff Facility, Brookhaven National Laboratory, Upton, N.Y.

David Gordon Wilson *Transportation (in part).* Associate Professor of Mechanical Engineering, Massachusetts Institute of Technology, Cambridge.

Comments from the Editor

Publishing a science yearbook is not usually a "stop press" operation. The editors of such a work tend to be more concerned with the stately progress of science over time than with the transient nature of day-to-day news events. In this as in other ways, however, the flight of Apollo 11 was unique. To cover man's first landing on the moon, the BRITANNICA YEARBOOK OF SCIENCE AND THE FUTURE extended its normal June 30 closing date to late July, holding open certain pages for text and pictures that record the beginning of a new era in the long history of mankind.

To obtain this information for our readers, I had the privilege of witnessing the Apollo 11 launch at Cape Kennedy and then following its subsequent progress from the space center at Houston, Tex. Since my return, many friends have asked me whether being there in person really made much difference, given its excellent coverage by television and the quantity of information provided by the press. The answer must be an unqualified "yes."

As one who deals constantly with the miracles of science, I should have been prepared for this experience. Yet no launch watched on a small screen can convey the silence of the crowd during the final countdown, the blast of heat and the immensity of the sound that engulfed the onlookers like a tidal wave, the agonizingly slow rise of the giant rocket as it pointed toward space. No descriptions, however detailed, can impart the suspense and excitement that pervaded the space center during this culminating flight, masked as they were by the laconic voices heard by the public. If television and press cannot communicate these things, neither, of course, can a yearbook.

To the materials here presented, the reader must add the ingredient of his own imagination. For, indeed, no matter how close one has been to Apollo 11, imagination is needed to comprehend it. We do not yet know how it will change man's view of his past or how it will affect his actions in the future. We only know that a door has swung open on the universe and man has taken his first steps, literally, out of this world.

Dick Young

RICHARD G. YOUNG
EXECUTIVE EDITOR

The Future
In Retrospect

"The future," Vladimir Nabokov has written, "is but the obsolete in reverse."

On occasion, I reflect on things and times now obsolete, usually without regret. But I felt a twinge of regret as I reviewed the contents of this *Britannica Yearbook of Science and the Future,* regret that this 1970 edition is only the second instead of the fiftieth since my graduation from Yale.

I never worry about my past mistakes, for the man who has not made mistakes has not made anything. I sometimes worry a bit about missed opportunities. What different perspectives potential opportunities can assume when examined in the context of deliberate and informed speculation and projections about the future!

Today's growing focus on questions dealing with the future, which makes possible rational exploration of "the obsolete in reverse," is a fairly new phenomenon. Until a decade or so ago the effort to pierce the shadows beyond the edge of tomorrow was confined largely to fortune-tellers and science fiction writers. The latter, among them distinguished scholars willing to venture their predictions only in the guise of fiction, were hardly regarded more highly than the former. But throughout my life I have been curious about, interested in—in today's phrase "hooked on"—the future. (That fact is what led me to urge Britannica editors to create this Yearbook, which attempts to blend the world of science and the world of the future.)

If in 1870 there had existed a Commission on the Year 1900—like Daniel Bell's present Commission on the Year 2000 and with comparable scientific insight—might not subsequent history have read very differently?

A few pioneers in what would come to be called sociology foresaw, in the turmoil of the Industrial Revolution, the creation of the American Federation of Labor in 1886. Suppose there had existed in 1870 a disciplined, widespread effort to peer into the future, reaching scholars, businessmen, and workers. How might the labor movement and the wrenching social dislocation and adjustment of its early years have been changed? Would the Haymarket riot in 1886 and the Homestead strike of 1892 have occurred as they did? Perhaps, but one must ask whether foreseeing the need for—and the likelihood of—social change would not have mitigated greatly the suffering and brutality, the human and economic waste, of the labor-management warfare that took place.

Perhaps there is an easier and closer example. Had there existed, in the 1920s, a growing body of knowledge and projection about the future of radio, it would have made a significant difference in my own life and in radio and TV as we know them today. Early in my career Chester Bowles and I founded the advertising agency of Benton and Bowles, which from the beginning of the Great Depression did much to develop radio as an entertainment medium. There was then no real discussion or thought about using radio as anything but an advertising medium or for purposes other than entertainment. After I retired from advertising in 1935 I watched the growing phenomenon of broadcasting with great interest. In my years as vice-president of the University of Chicago in the '30s and early '40s I attempted to develop the medium for education, and I hope some of our subscribers will remember "The University of Chicago Round Table" broadcasts. Later, I acquired the Muzak Corporation, which "piped" background music into homes and business places, and in 1943 I conceived the idea of "subscription radio," as I called it, now translated into "pay TV."

When I was named assistant secretary of state in 1945, I was on the verge of acquiring licenses for three FM radio stations, which would have formed the core of my own subscription radio network. These stations would have offered a choice among three different programs at all times, all without advertising and for only five cents a day. But upon my appointment by President Truman I abandoned my applications and simultaneously put the subscription-radio idea to the back of my mind. Had I pursued it, the course of the development of radio and TV might well have been different. Surprisingly, the pattern of radio was by then so firmly set that no one else picked up my idea.

Today, when I consider the development of Community Antenna Television and the still-lively potential for subscription television, I can tell you I regret that in 1945 there was no *Britannica Yearbook of Science and the Future,* no expanding wave of thought and concern and speculation about what the future might bring to replace the commonplace radio of that day, which has become today's commonplace TV.

In those years and before, informed speculation about tomorrow virtually belonged to scientists and inventors, to "crazy professors" and the authors of science fiction. They were lonely individuals, accustomed to the derision of their neighbors and even of their colleagues. They had not yet found a way to come together to publicize their concerns.

Even so, as individuals and as tiny groups, they knew that the midterm future must bring preoccupation with the more distant future. The late Will Ogburn, the great sociologist of the University of Chicago, was a futurist decades before the term was invented. He looked into the future and wrote of the social effects of cities, the social effects of radio and of airplanes. Thirty years ago he told me that there ought to be at least ten scholarly journals dealing with the future! Stimulated by Professor Ogburn, in the late '30s I tried to persuade my friend Henry Luce to change the name of his magazine *Fortune* to *Future.* I told him that the change would give his editors the right orientation; that the "future," to the man who could foresee it, was the clue to "fortune."

Today Ogburn's prescription is at last moving toward fulfillment. There is increasing attention to the future—including an occasional special issue entirely on the subject—in numerous professional journals basically committed to various scholarly disciplines. There are assorted commissions and organizations devoted entirely to predictions and speculations about the future—perhaps a dozen in America and Europe. And with the increasing attention to the future that these developments foreshadow and influence, it becomes increasingly possible not only for scholars and scientists and engineers but also for informed and curious laymen to have access to the best available thought about the future.

New terms—that speak of science and the future—have supplanted the old expressions of ignorance and incuriosity. Consider the topic of one of the articles in this book: humanics and genetic engineering. Another: exobiology, life elsewhere in the universe, outside our atmosphere. No one now calls the authors of such challenging and mind-stretching articles and the concepts behind them "crazy professors." What once was a scornful rejection of scholarly concern with the future has given way before the demonstrated accuracy of many fairly recent scientific forecasts. And the most exciting aspect of this increasing concern with the future, to me at least, is that it is engulfing us all, laymen and scholars alike.

Laymen, scholars—and children. The future has always belonged to our children, of course, but too often in the past it has belonged to them largely as the forbidden delight of daydreams. Nowadays we encourage our children to work to make their daydreams come true, and it is well that we do so.

The current prediction of many educators is that by the year 2000 our descendants will be able to achieve the equivalent of the present Ph.D. degree by the time they are 18 or 19 years old. Indeed, to help speed youngsters toward this goal, the Britannica is now preparing an encyclopaedia for preschool children who have not yet learned to read. The pace of life gathers speed, and as it does so it becomes increasingly imperative for us to examine the "obsolete in reverse."

It is to such examination, and to the speculation—and yes, the daydreams—that can spring from it, in your own home library, school, and office that I hope this *1970 Britannica Yearbook of Science and the Future* may usefully contribute.

Wm Benton

PUBLISHER

A Pictorial Essay

Applications of Organic Forms

by Philip C. Ritterbush

Natural organic forms, from the simplest microscopic organisms to the most intricate of structures, possess a beauty and elegance that man has applied aesthetically and functionally to art, architecture, and engineering.

"Form is the property of solid bodies relating their component parts in space . . . the study of form is an area where art and science meet." Below, photomicrographs by Roman Vishniac of organic substances: (top, left) beta lipoprotein; (bottom, left) cholesterol; (top, right) female hormone progesterone; (bottom, right) amino acid arginine. Opposite page, "St. Elmo's Fire," painting by Enrico Donati (1944).

Man's discovery of form in nature was not written down; probably it was not even recognized consciously for what it was. Nor do we know what impulses—religious or magical—led cavemen to paint the beasts of the hunt and Bronze Age Chinese to bury images with their dead. Yet this discovery—that form is a constant property of organic bodies that can be imitated in paint and stone and wood—was the beginning of insights that have been crucial for modern science, of design principles of the utmost importance for engineers, architects, and craftsmen, and of art.

Art is rooted in nature. The acanthus leaves of a Corinthian capital, the floral tracery ornamenting a medieval cathedral, the sinuous arabesques of art nouveau are only the most obvious uses of natural

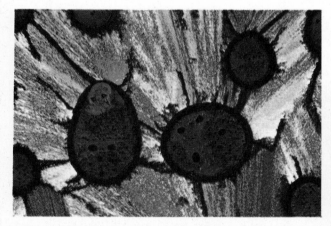
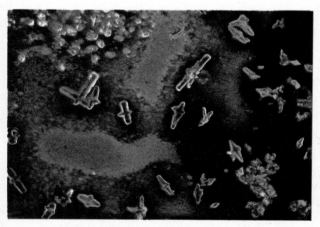
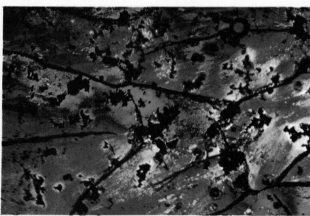

(Above and right) Roman Vishniac; (opposite page) Collection, The Museum of Modern Art, New York. Given anonymously.

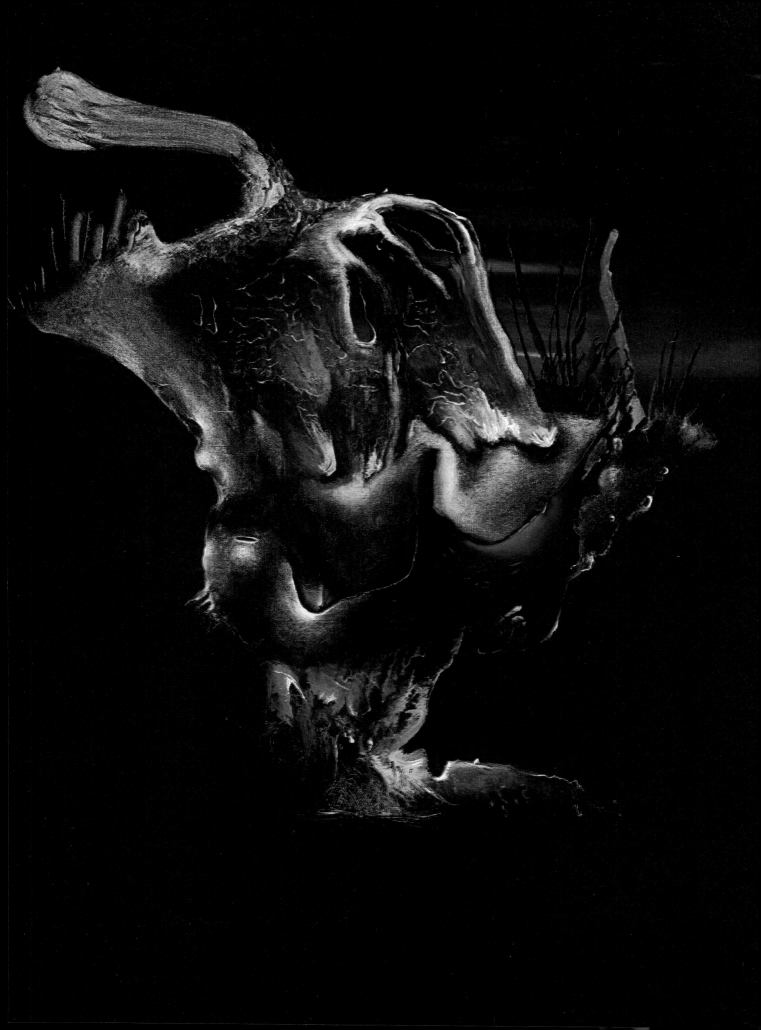

forms by artists. The curves and proportions of biological life are harmonious to the eye and, either intuitively or consciously, they have been repeated again and again.

Why this should be so—why men should call natural forms "beautiful"—is beyond the scope of this article. But at least a partial answer may have been suggested by the philosopher and educator Paul Weiss, who wrote:

Man . . . is a part of nature. So his artistic world cannot be one of sharply demarcated opposition to his natural world, but rather must be viewed as a fluid and continuous extension of his domain as an ordinary member of animate nature, subject to all the limitations of biological reality, into a realm of irreality of his own making, stripped of those limitations. And since artistic endeavor is thus a direct organic outgrowth of nature, its elements are of necessity the same as those of primitive biological experience. . . . Nature is credited with the supply of elements, but then man's fantasy is purported to take over to recombine them freely in novel patterns of his own creation. (Paul Weiss, "Organic Form: Scientific and Aesthetic Aspects," in Gyorgy Kepes, [ed.], *Visual Arts Today,* Wesleyan University Press, 1960.)

Form is the property of solid bodies relating their component parts in space. The form that objects assume depends not only on the arrangement of those parts, but also on the substances composing them, their manner of growth, their functions, and the shaping influence of the environment. These relationships, always empirically known to the artist, are also vital to scientific understanding, so that the study of form is an area where art and science meet.

"This discovery—that form is a constant property of organic bodies that can be imitated in paint and stone and wood—was the beginning of insights that have been crucial for modern science . . . and of art." Top, bronze tiger of the Chou dynasty, China, about the 10th century B.C. Bottom, Paleolithic paintings on the walls of the Lascaux cave, France.

Courtesy, Smithsonian Institution, Freer Gallery of Art

Ralph Morse, "Time," © 1959 Time Inc.

The bone and the crane: the secrets of organic structure

A century ago, the Swiss anatomist Hermann Meyer studied the internal fine structure of bones and discovered that regular, curving stress lines constituted one of their most significant features. One day a friend of his, a well-known engineer, entered the laboratory while cross sections of bones were being examined. The engineer had been calculating the pattern of forces in bridges and other structures, including the arm of a crane, and he saw at once that the tiny beams within the head of a thighbone represented a pattern of stress distribution similar to those he had been investigating. He stared for a moment and then cried out, "That is my crane!"

Nature's structural efficiency is evident throughout the organic world, even among the simplest living things. Single-celled plants that live suspended in water, for example, are spherical in shape—the form most readily assumed by one liquid suspended in another, but also the most efficient way to prevent the diffusion of body chemicals into the surrounding water. As soon as the structure of these tiny organisms came to be investigated, wonderfully integrated networks of plates and spanning ribs were discovered.

The single-celled marine animals known as radiolaria, studied by the German comparative anatomist Ernest Haeckel in the 19th century, were found to contain singularly beautiful meshes of great geometric regularity. In a classic work of scientific analysis, the

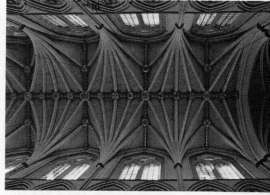

"The curves and proportions of biological life are harmonious to the eye and . . . they have been repeated again and again." Left, interior, cathedral at Cordoba, Spain (originally a mosque). Top, detail, Taj Mahal, near Agra, India. Center, 13th-century Gothic vaulting, cathedral at Ely, Eng. Bottom, left, capital of a Corinthian column, Corinth, Greece. Bottom, right, floor of the 8th-century palace of Caliph Hisham, Jericho, Israel.

British biologist D'Arcy Wentworth Thompson showed that these and many other natural structures could be understood as the most efficient solutions to problems of using space or of strengthening structural elements to the maximum extent consistent with the materials available. One frequently encountered feature in natural structure is the line that pursues the most direct course on a curved surface, found in microscopic filaments secreted between curving cells, in spiral elements within cylindrical plant cells, and in muscle fibers in the walls of curved organs. These so-called geodesic curves are often found in the radiolaria, which thus embody a highly efficient structural system and one capable of extension to the long-standing architectural problem of how to enclose large spaces without having to resort to using internal bearing members to support a building.

Working intuitively, the U.S. designer R. Buckminster Fuller developed the geodesic dome, a radically new method of construction, which *Architectural Forum* called "the highest practical point so far attained in the skeletal enclosure of space." The grid of the geodesic dome closely resembles the structural system of the radiolarian skeleton, although Fuller nowhere acknowledges a debt to Haeckel or Thompson. The parallels indicate, at least, that the principles governing natural form, if not the forms themselves, may provide clues to the most advanced design problems.

Among the most admired structures in nature is the bee's honeycomb. Some 18th-century writers were persuaded that the bee set the angles between adjoining rear faces of cells in the two layers of the honeycomb with a precision rivaling the finest clockwork in order to achieve walls containing maximum storage capacity while using the least amount of wax. What excited such admiration was the reali-

"Nature's structural efficiency is evident throughout the organic world." Stress patterns in the human thighbone (below), as drawn by Hermann Meyer, resemble those in the design for a crane by Karl Culmann. Right, drawing of a radiolarian by Ernest Haeckel, showing triangular outer skeleton and short, radiating spines. Far right, "Variation Within a Sphere, No. 10: The Sun," gold-filled wire construction by Richard Lippold (1956).

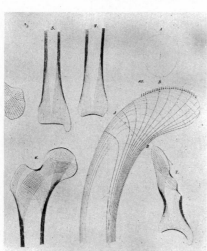

Courtesy, Smithsonian Institution

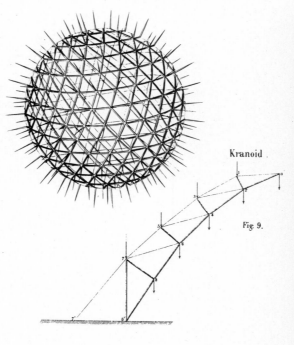

Kranoid

Fig. 9.

zation that, in theory, the cell would use a minimum of wax when its rear faces met at an angle of 109° 28′, and that the actual cells seemed to correspond to this measurement. The principle at work is not one of instinctive precision, however, but the far simpler physical tendency of fluid surfaces that enclose space, such as soap bubbles, to join together in the configuration with the least surface. Still, the regularity of the cells is a remarkable feature of natural architecture. To Eli Bornstein, a 20th-century Structuralist artist, the honeycomb's beauty could be viewed as a consequence of sustained harmony between the structure and function of an organism.

Form and function

In developing his theory of evolution by natural selection, Charles Darwin had to refute the notion that beautiful organisms reflect an aesthetic striving in nature. "Such doctrines, if true, would be ab-

"The principles governing natural form, if not the forms themselves, may provide clues to the most advanced design problems." Right, fire urchin from Mbéré Reef, New Caledonia. Left, Kaiser Aluminum building, Honolulu, a geodesic dome designed by R. Buckminster Fuller.

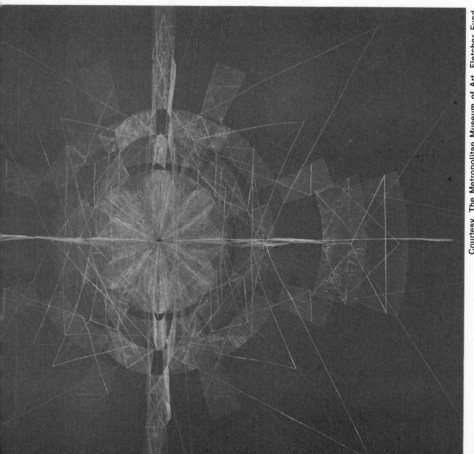

*"Among the most admired structures
in nature is the bee's honeycomb . . .
set . . . with a precision rivaling
the finest clockwork."*

solutely fatal to my theory," which held instead that the properties of organisms were selected from a range of varied characteristics according to their usefulness in the struggle for existence. Thus, colorful flowers were more successful in attracting the insects needed to pollinate them; the songs and plumage of birds and the magnificent colors of certain fish developed because of the consistent preference of females for mates with these characteristics.

The recognition that natural form and structure result from competition among organisms proved to have relevance for many problems of design. Among the first to see this was the architect Louis Sullivan, who conceived a fascination for natural forms as a child growing up near Wakefield, Mass. In high school he regularly heard lectures by Asa Gray, the foremost American botanist of the time, and he maintained his interest in biology while studying and later practicing architecture. Biology, he felt, offered "insight into the relationship of function and structure." Each plant reveals a distinctive shape indicating the functions it performs.

In a period when banks were built to look like Greek temples and colleges like Tudor mansions, Sullivan proposed that the space available for a building and the use to which it was to be put should determine its form, that each architectural problem contained the germ of its own solution and the task of the architect was to permit it to emerge. His central idea, "evolved through long contemplation of living things," was that "form follows function."

Sullivan was among the first to employ steel frame construction to overcome the limitations of exterior bearing wall structures, thus permitting clean and vertically soaring lines. He also developed a remarkable system of architectural ornamentation that reflected his deep interest in the symmetries and growth processes of plants. In these designs Sullivan was not copying superficially from nature. It was his achievement to carry the analysis of natural form to a deeper level of understanding. Sullivan's theories were crucial to the development of later architects, among them Frank Lloyd Wright, who felt that buildings should be an organic part of their environment. Of Wright, his wife Olgivanna wrote: "Every facet of a natural form was an inspiring circumstance to him. Affected first by its beauty in a spontaneous impact, he then drew knowledge which gave him insight into the very spirit of the form he had studied."

Nowhere is functionalism in nature better revealed than in the phenomenon of protective coloration. Most animals are darker above and lighter beneath to offset shadows cast by the sun. The mottled green frog on the leafy bank escapes the notice of passing insects until its tongue flicks out to capture them. The famous chameleon is only one of numerous creatures whose color and pattern change to blend with different backgrounds. An even more widespread principle, less obvious but more exciting, is the disruption of outline or form by contrasting patterns that are sometimes so brightly colored that they would seem to betray the wearer, but that actually serve to divert the eye, blur outlines, and seemingly allow parts of the background to be seen through the animal—a principle that was utilized by the military when it dazzle-painted ships to obscure their outlines and splotch-painted gun emplacements for concealment. It was a U.S. artist, Abbott H. Thayer, who in the 1890s first recognized the full importance of concealing coloration as a natural principle. Thayer wrote that the field of protective coloration "properly

"[Biology offers] insight into the relationship of function and structure." Details of buildings by Louis Sullivan: (top, left) People's Federal Savings and Loan Association building, Sidney, O. (1917); (top, right) Carson Pirie Scott building, Chicago (1899–1904). Houses by Frank Lloyd Wright: (bottom, left) the Mrs. Thomas Gale house, Oak Park, Ill. (1909); (bottom, right) Fallingwater, Bear Run, Pa. (1936).

(Top, left) G. E. Kidder Smith; (bottom right) Lee Boltin; (others) Dan Morrill

belongs to the realm of *pictorial art* and can be interpreted only by painters. For it deals wholly in optical illusion, and this is the very gist of a painter's life."

Form and imagination

Organic form is the very stuff of which the visual arts are made. Since the Stone Age, artists have portrayed the external appearance of plants and animals, and designers have used the curves and rhythms that occur in living forms. Artists have striven as well to portray the essence of the beings they painted or modeled—the beatitude of a Gothic saint, the earthy good humor of Frans Hals's peasants, the prosperous serenity of Constable's hayricks.

Modern science has reduced organic form to its essentials, making it possible to interpret the vast diversity of plant and animal forms in terms of such recurring themes as the division of cells, rhythms of growth, and the influence of the properties of fluids. Modern art, too, has attempted to see beyond the multiplicity of external particularities to the unity within, using abstracted principles of form without portraying realistic detail. Sometimes the borrowing from scientific analysis has been direct and obvious, as when Pavel Tchelitchew looks through the human body to the blood vessels. At other times the artist uses organic forms much as the submarine builder uses the form of the whale—because he intuitively knows or empirically finds that this is the right form for his purpose.

Both methods are perhaps embodied in the Swiss artist Paul Klee. Klee was no stranger to biology; he studied anatomy and on his own collected and studied seeds and shells. He sensed that there was a hidden harmony in nature answering to his own intuitions of complex rhythms, and spent his life attempting to express this harmony in a way that would be accessible to the untutored vision of a child. His paintings struck his contemporaries as wild flights of the imagination, but today we sense a correspondence between his abstract works

"Contrasting patterns that are sometimes so brightly colored that they would seem to betray the wearer . . . actually serve to divert the eye, blur outlines, and seemingly allow parts of the background to be seen through the animal." Below, Indian tiger. Center, top, mallard drake with the soberly colored female. Center, bottom, angelfish. Right, Pacific spadefish (above) and surgeonfish.

(Above) E. Hanumantha Rao from Photo Researchers; (above, right) Richard Keane; (right) courtesy, J. Prescott, Marineland of the Pacific; (far right) M. Woodbridge Williams

22

and the efforts of architects and designers to capture the essence of natural form. Many of his paintings show fruitlike forms seemingly cut open to reveal curves resembling lines of growth. Some include plantlike forms of different sizes connected by thin lines, as though to present a graph of the processes by which they had grown or might grow.

The whole movement of Surrealism, which attempted to portray inner, possibly subconscious, sensations visually, embodies this turning inward. Throughout the works of painters and sculptors associated with this movement we find curving shapes, outlines of liquid masses, branching structures that seem to indicate growth, as though to capture those very processes that science has identified as basic to life. The sculptor Jean Arp, whose smoothly curving works seem to embody many principles of biological form, wrote that "Art is a fruit growing out of a man like the fruit out of a plant, like the child out of the mother." May we not see in these works an effort to capture in art an image expressing the changeableness and vitality of the organic process?

FOR ADDITIONAL READING:

Collins, George R., "Antonio Gaudi: Structure and Form," *Perspecta,* No. 8, 1963, pp. 63–90 (Yale School of Architecture).

Kepes, Gyorgy (ed.), Vision and Value Series (George Braziller, 1965–66).

Peckham, Morse, *Man's Rage for Chaos: Biology, Behavior, and the Arts* (Chilton Books, 1965).

Ritterbush, Philip C., *The Art of Organic Forms* (Smithsonian Institution Press and Random House, Inc., 1968).

Sullivan, Louis H., *The Autobiography of an Idea* (Dover Publications, Inc., reprinted, 1957).

Thompson, D'Arcy Wentworth, *On Growth and Form* (Cambridge University Press, reprinted, 1952).

"Nowhere is functionalism in nature better revealed than in the phenomenon of protective coloration." Left, bullfrog on lily pads. Center, tree frog on bark. Bottom, seal on a rock. Below, milkweed bugs on a milkweed plant.

(Above) George Herben from Photo Researchers; (above, right) John Gerard; (others) W. E. Ferguson

"Modern art . . . has attempted to see beyond the multiplicity of external particularities to the unity within." Paintings by Paul Klee; (right) "Rock Flora" (1940); (below) "Things that Grow" (1932); (center) "Colored Circles with Colored Bands" (1914). Far right, "Hide and Seek," painting by Pavel Tchelitchew (1940–42). Bottom, right, "Birds in an Aquarium," painted wood relief by Jean Arp (c. 1920).

(Above) Courtesy, Museum of Fine Art Berne; (below and below, right) Courtesy, Paul Klee Foundation, Museum of Fine Art Berne

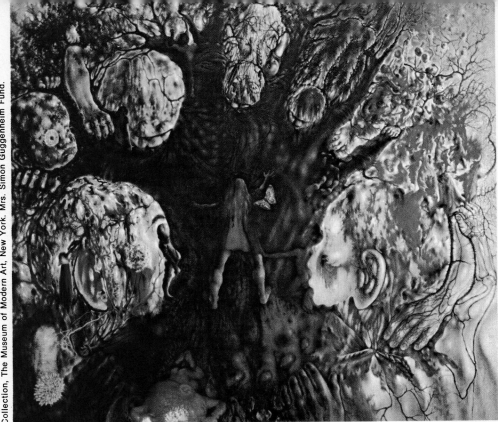

"Art is rooted in nature." Below, photograph of a leaf. Bottom left, "Blowing Leaves," painting by John Gernand (1944). Right, "Forest," painting by Max Ernst (1926). Far right, photograph of bamboo shoots. Bottom, center, "When They Shoot Me," painting by Yves Tanguy (1927). Bottom, right, photograph of sunlight reflected on water.

Ken Short

Collection, The Museum of Modern Art, New York. Purchase.

Courtesy, The Phillips Collection, Washington, D.C. Photo by Henry Beville.

Ken Short

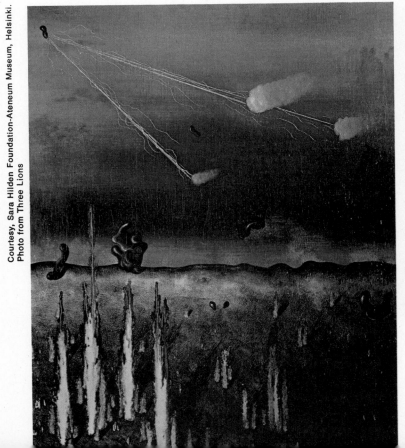

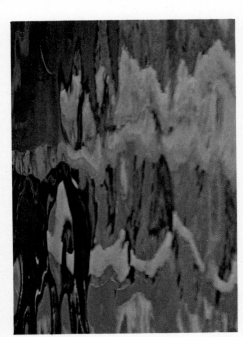

Roman Vishniac

Richard Keane

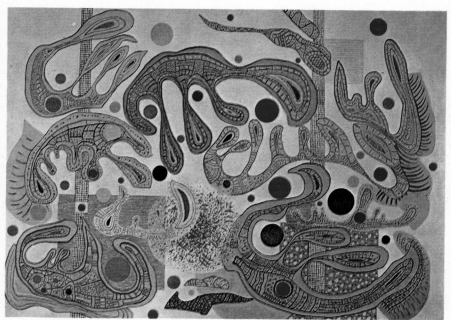

Courtesy, The Solomon R. Guggenheim Museum

Lee Boltin

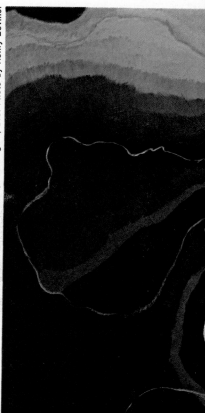

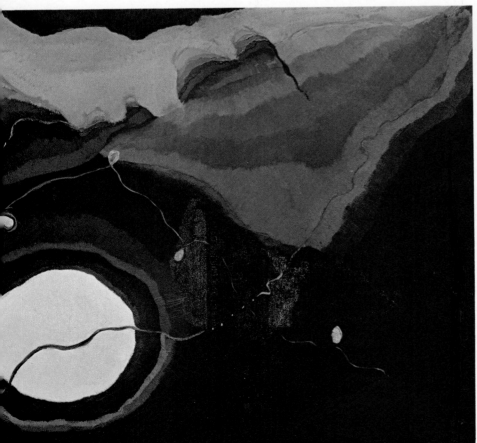

"[Man's] artistic world cannot
be one of sharply demarcated
opposition to his natural world,
but rather must be viewed
as a fluid and continuous extension
of his domain as an ordinary member
of animate nature." Left, top,
photograph of a sedum plant. Left,
center, "Capricious Forms," painting
by Wassily Kandinsky (1937). Left,
bottom, photograph of a polished
sample of jasper. Center, top,
"Thorn Heads," painting by Graham
Sutherland (1946). Paintings
by Arthur Dove: (left) "Rise
of the Full Moon" (1937); (above)
"Golden Storm" (1925).

The Future Is Here

In the 1950s, a decade that now seems as remote as the Stone Age, the nightclub satirist Mort Sahl could always get a laugh by reassuring his audiences that "the future lies ahead." It was a good joke, neatly skewering in one wry line mankind's age-old anxiety over what tomorrow may bring. In the relatively short time since, however, the quip may have become obsolete. For in that brief span, science and technology have taken such quantum leaps that, in a very real sense, the future no longer lies ahead but already has arrived.

To describe this new dawn, the intellectual community has invented a whole set of exotic labels—man is "post-Christian," the society "postindustrial," the age "technetronic," the world a "global village." It is all more than a little confusing. One thing is abundantly clear, however. "Humanity today," as political scientist Victor C. Ferkiss eloquently points out in his incisive book *Technological Man,* "is on the threshold of self-transfiguration, of attaining new powers over itself and its environment that can alter its nature as fundamentally as walking upright or the use of tools. No aspect of man's existence can escape being revolutionized by this fundamental fact."

The theme of man's attempts at "self-transfiguration" recurs throughout this edition of the *Britannica Yearbook of Science and the Future.* In almost every one of the 18 articles, the contributing scholar or scientist has attempted to predict what his particular field holds for the future. In addition, The Science Year in Review section underscores the role of the immediate past as prologue to the future by examining how developments during the year in the myriad scientific disciplines point toward the world of tomorrow. Inevitably, many of the predictions trigger a mixed reaction of hope and despair, but in no instance can they be ignored. For, as Joshua Lederberg writes in defending genetic engineering, "Man may have lived in a paradise of submissive ignorance before he ate from the tree of knowledge, but human civilization began just then and there is no return."

Perhaps the most optimistic contributor is Philip Hauser, whose enthusiastic blueprint for the city of tomorrow offers a badly needed tonic to today's harried city-dweller. Hauser predicts that the conventional politician, with his commitment to vested interest and tradition, will eventually give way to the "social engineer," who will work to solve the problems of the city through scientific knowledge. With this new breed leading it, writes Hauser, "the urban society of the future will be a society in which the social, economic, and political will have caught up with the transformed technological and physical world."

To many, Hauser's predictions will seem hopelessly wishful. Not a few serious scholars insist that man's tendency to crowd together in megalopolises and his increasing reliance on mechanization are two major causes of the numbing sense of alienation that now grips so much of the industrialized world. Hauser argues just the contrary, however. "Far from brutalizing and dehumanizing society," he writes, "technological advances that permit agglomerative living and the emergence of urban society will also generate changes in social organization and goals in the interest of the person and the urban society. . . .the inevitable and irresistible forces of urbanization will produce a society much more coeval and synchronous than present society."

Edward Wenk, Jr., brings the same sense of hopefulness to his look at the future of oceanography. He sees a day not too far off when man, using nuclear-powered deep submersibles and other sophisticated underwater technology, will be able to engage in oil production, mining, and other industry on the bed of the continental shelf "as easily as on land." Even more important for the future of mankind is the possibility that marine research will improve markedly the fish yield from the oceans. "Eventually," writes Wenk, "[man will] look to aquaculture to cultivate, augment, herd, and select fish. Raised in suitable estuaries, artificially cultured fish could yield more protein per acre than beef cattle or grain." Already, substantial efforts are being made to exploit this source of protein by grinding up whole fish into fish protein concentrate (FPC), a tasteless, odorless powder that provides a cheap source of protein.

The urgency of the need for inexpensive protein, as well as for other nutritional foods, is spelled out with grim clarity by Nevin S. Scrimshaw in his examination of the consequences of hunger among the world's children. Studies now indicate that malnutrition at an early age not only affects subsequent physical growth, but inhibits mental development as well. In the poverty pockets of industrialized societies, the implications of this are serious enough, but in the underprivileged nations the very stability of the future is at stake. "Experts estimate," writes Scrimshaw, "that millions of young children in less developed countries may be experiencing some degree of permanent retardation as a result of inadequate nutrition. These malnourished children of today will be the young adults on whose performance the economic and social progress of their countries will depend in the decades ahead."

In terms of the future, few areas of study offer as much scope for tantalizing speculation as the disparate fields of astronomy and molecular biology. The first looks outward and seeks to answer the question of whether life as we know it on earth exists anywhere else in the universe. The second looks inward in an attempt to define scientifically what "life as we know it" really is. Because of their importance and implications for tomorrow, the two subjects are covered in this edition of the Science Yearbook in a special section entitled Gateways to the Future.

In his discussion of the work being done at the Mount Wilson and Palomar Observatories, astronomer Jesse L. Greenstein describes how, in recent months, he and his colleagues have focused their telescopes and much of their attention on the Crab Nebula. At the center of that cloudlike mass of gas and dust, a faint star has been identified that seems to emit radio signals at short, regular intervals. Using the 200-in. telescope with complex photoelectric equipment, observers at Palomar confirmed the discovery of other astronomers that this source, known as a pulsar, also emits optical signals at the same regular intervals. Exactly what these cosmic blips mean is still a mystery. It is no doubt fanciful to regard them as emanating from another civilization out in the great void of space. And yet. . . .

As Norman H. Horowitz suggests in another article, evidence is accumulating that some form of life may, indeed, exist beyond the earth—if not in the vast reaches of the Crab Nebula, then perhaps on Mars and some of the other planets. As a result of telescopic observations and flybys by space probes, exobiologists now speculate that, though the Martian environment is severe, it could conceivably support some kind of microbial life. The U.S. Mariner program, which tentatively plans to land a vehicle on Mars in 1973, could go a long way toward providing a definitive answer by determining whether the "wave of darkening," a progressive change in the coloration of some portions of the planet, is caused by seasonal growth of vegetation.

Though we tend to take it for granted, life on earth is no less fascinating a puzzle. "The unity of life at the molecular level," writes Max Perutz as he looks toward the future through the "gateway" of the Laboratory of Molecular Biology, "gives the subject coherence and great conceptual beauty." Central to this sense of order is the molecular biologist's translation of complex biological processes into the terms of physics and chemistry. Nothing in recent years has illustrated this natural orderliness more dramatically than the laboratory's solution of the structure of deoxyribonucleic acid (DNA), the chemical substance in the genes that controls heredity.

For the short term, perhaps the most exciting possibilities opened up by this understanding of DNA are medical. Perutz foresees a time when answers to the great unsolved medical problems of cancer and heart disease will be sought by exploring pathological events at the molecular level. In fact, as Joshua Lederberg explains in his article on humanics and genetic engineering, studies of DNA specificity and of cell fusion are already beginning to revolutionize medical science's approach to disease. For example, such conditions as cystic fibrosis and mongolism now can be diagnosed prenatally by taking cell cultures from the amniotic fluid that surrounds the developing fetus.

For the long term, the scientific potential of genetic engineering extends far beyond medicine. Lederberg speculates that genetic intervention could eventually produce genes that would cause a bodily synthesis of amino acids, an ability man does not now appear to possess. Since lack of amino acids in available food is a primary cause of malnutrition, such a genetic feat would seem to be of incalculable benefit to mankind. In the minds of many, of course, genetic tinkering of any kind is repugnant. As Lederberg himself concedes, the phrase "genetic engineering" often conjures up images of "a technocratic dictator pushing the buttons that will control an assembly line of babies produced to order for service as infantrymen or storm troopers or docile subjects." Lederberg does not ignore the possibility that science will be bent to mean ends in the future, as it has been in the past. But to critics who insist that mankind is unequal to the task of dealing intelligently with the awesome implications of genetic engineering, he replies that "the consequences of ignorance are no less frightening [and] perhaps more unpredictable than those of scientific understanding."

Both ignorance and understanding are functions of the human brain, that unique and incredibly complex mechanism with which man now ponders his infinite future and which, not surprisingly, has an astonishing future all its own. As a result of the microminiaturization of electrical components, experiments are already being performed on monkeys to determine if some forms of epilepsy can be controlled by microelectronic devices inserted in the affected area of the brain. Microelectronics also offers hope for the development of prostheses for the blind and deaf and for modifying psychotic behavior and endocrinological disturbances. In his article on the brain, Robert W. Doty even suggests that some day " a pill might be developed that would in large measure accomplish quickly the same neurochemical changes as occur in sleep, thereby adding years to the effective life of each of us!"

A world of pill-induced wakefulness is no doubt intriguing. For the immediate future, however, man is destined to spend many conventional sleepless nights if his efforts to construct an "effective life" continue to fall short. That they do so often is the increasingly ironic tragedy of an age blessed with such promising scientific and technological possibilities. Science, as Christopher Wright reminds us in his article, remains a two-edged sword. "The perils [of science] will far outweigh the promises unless procedures can be devised that will integrate science with other human concerns while at the same time preserving its vitality."

Clearly, the future is here. But whether man will use the technology at his disposal to create a better world is still an open question—and one, as Thomas Huxley observed 80 years ago, "about which hangs a true sublimity and the terror of overhanging fate."

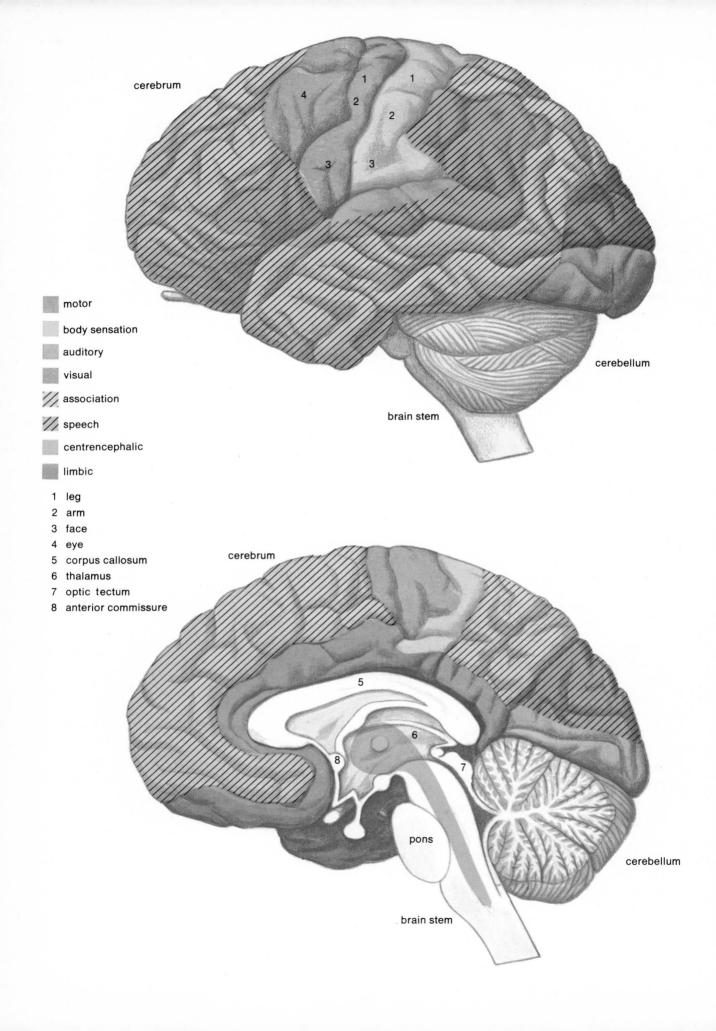

cerebrum

4
1 1
2
2
3 3

motor
body sensation
auditory
visual
association
speech
centrencephalic
limbic

1 leg
2 arm
3 face
4 eye
5 corpus callosum
6 thalamus
7 optic tectum
8 anterior commissure

cerebellum

brain stem

cerebrum

5
6
8
7

pons

cerebellum

brain stem

The Brain

by Robert W. Doty

The most important fact about the brain is that it is ourself. The "I" that feels and reacts—that experiences fear, love, or a mere elementary awareness—is somehow a manifestation of events in the brain. There is a profound mystery in this fact, in the creation of mind by a molecular machine, the brain. The challenge which this presents to human understanding still transcends the normal bounds of science and penetrates to man's deepest philosophical and religious convictions.

The relation of brain to mind is beyond question. Western man has understood this relationship for about 2,500 years, but only recently has it begun to condition his philosophy and hence his culture and behavior. Contemporary science has gone far in unlocking the incredibly complex secrets of the brain, and, as in other advanced research, the unlocking of one door has led to another more intriguing door. Still to be answered is that profound question that looms stark and insistent before all humankind: Is mind a mere molecular mechanism or is there in addition a transcendental quality to awareness? Is man's brain only a magnificently subtle computer or does the brain in its relationship with the mind act as the interchange between the physical and metaphysical?

It is well known that when people lose certain portions of the brain by either disease or accident, they also lose certain portions of their mental life. Perhaps the most dramatic illustration of this occurs in patients who have suddenly lost that part of the brain in which is "represented" one side of the body. Having been deprived of the relevant brain processes, such individuals neglect or even fail to recognize that side of their body as belonging to themselves! Without events in the brain experience of any kind is impossible.

The creation or deletion of various subjective experiences by the application of moderate electrical stimulation to the brain of conscious human patients provides further evidence of the coupling of neural and mental events. Sounds, for example, are heard upon excitation of the auditory areas; visions are seen upon excitation of visual areas. The effects of brain stimulation sometimes are startlingly realistic. In one patient stimulation produced the hallucination of a flitting butterfly which was so compelling that the patient reached out from the operating table to catch it. More uncanny still is the elicitation in man of past memories, of nameless terror, or of ineffable joy. Such stimulation guides the neurosurgeon in identifying functional and pathological areas of the brain.

On the opposite page, the human brain is viewed from the side. A rough indication of the functions of various areas is given. In the external view (top), only the repeated folds of the cerebral cortex can be seen. About two-thirds of the cortex is hidden in the depths of the folds. In a median section (bottom), the brain stem can be seen with the general location of the centrencephalic system indicated in blue. Also note the corpus callosum and anterior commissure, the great bands of nerve fibers that keep one half of the brain in communication with the other.

35

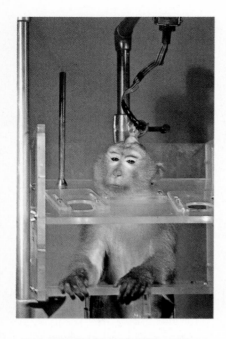

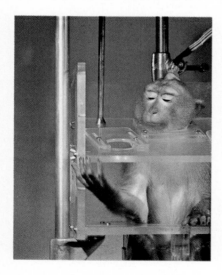

What is a brain that it is so miraculously capable of translating an electric current into objects, mood, or memory? No one can as yet explain the true nature of this transformation, but many of the general processes and functions of the brain are now fairly clear. As does the entire nervous system, the brain receives information from both internal and external senses, analyzes it, and then commands a response from muscles or glands in accordance with the analysis. Most of the analysis proceeds along predetermined lines with slight or occasional modification on the basis of past experience (memory).

The nervous system is organized into components that have evolved progressively from fish to man over the past half-billion years. Although the spinal cord, medulla, and tectal area account for most of the behavior of fish and amphibia, these centers are relatively minor in man, in whom the greatly developed forebrain overshadows all other portions of the nervous system. Yet these lower centers have not disappeared, and man's behavior is channeled through, or operates in conjunction with, the processes in these phylogenetically older structures. In other words, the evolutionary history of the brain is still written within each of us and forms a substrate for all perception and activity.

Neurons

The working units of the nervous system are bizarrely shaped cells called neurons. Each neuron consists of three parts: (1) a cell body, in which most of the intense chemical activity of the cell occurs; (2) an axon, a long extension from the cell body which contacts other neurons; and (3) dendrites, profuse extensions from the cell body which receive hundreds or thousands of contacts from the axons of other neurons.

The peculiar form of these nerve cells, or neurons, has changed little in the course of evolution. Indeed, it is strange to think that the quality of human life compared to that of a lizard may lie predominantly in the number and arrangement of neurons rather than in any great qualitative difference in their form or mechanism of operation! Certainly the number and complexity of neural connections in an organism match adequately the near infinite nuances of subjective experiences. While the brain of the lizard is so complex it defies detailed analysis, the brain of man is easily the most intricate entity in the known universe. The number of neurons in a single human brain exceeds the total human population of the world; and each neuron can be in communication with millions of others within a few thousandths of a second.

The wonder of this vast neural network is further increased by the fact that each neuron is itself an organization of extraordinary complexity. Each is packed with organelles, filaments, and tubules constructed from some 6 billion molecules of protein, 10 billion of fat, 600 billion of ribonucleic acid (RNA), and many other molecular substances, most of which are still unidentified. The neuron is a veritable cauldron of chemical activity and utilizes energy probably faster than any other type of cell in the body. Two-thirds of the weight of a neuron is made up of about 1,500 mitochondria, those microminiature factories in a cell that shuttle sugar through a maze of chemical reactions to yield energy. Each neural mitochondrion utilizes ten million atoms of oxygen per second; if oxygen is withheld from them for only ten seconds, neural functioning is so impaired that consciousness is lost.

This intense energy requirement stems from two properties of neurons, both related to their role in analyzing and transmitting signals. The first is the manufacture of chemicals which are passed from one neuron to another, exerting brief control over the electrical behavior of the recipient neuron and also determining which neuron is connected to which or where the axon of one neuron ends upon another. There is reason to believe that the nearly infinite array of neuronal connections is always in a potential state of flux and that the stability of this array is maintained only by constant chemical interchange between connected neurons.

The second great requirement for metabolic energy arises because of the enormous surface area of the neuron relative to its volume. The surface, which is under constant assault from the extracellular environment, "leaks." Each leak must be repaired and the intruding materials ejected to maintain the delicate chemical equilibrium of the neuron—all of which takes energy.

The large surface area of neurons is intrinsic to their function as analytical elements. In many neurons the dendrites, which constitute up to 95% of the receptive area of the cell, are covered with tiny spines. Each spine is in contact with the axon of at least one other neuron. These points of contact, which are called synapses, occur upon the body of the cell as well as upon dendrites with and without spines.

The transmission of a nerve impulse

To understand what a synapse does, it must be realized that each neuron maintains a powerful electrochemical potential across its surface. The interior of the cell is approximately 70 millivolts negative with respect to the outside (−70 mv). If this electrical potential (i.e., the negativity) is diminished by only approximately 10 mv (i.e., goes to −60 mv) for about one millisecond (msec) or less, an explosive change occurs which sweeps over the cell and down its axon at velocities up to 200 mph (320 km/hr). Thus, within a very few thousandths of a second, an event occurring in the cell body is transmitted to the end of the axon. This swiftly running signal, the action potential or nerve impulse, can occur several hundred times per second, although rates of 10–30 per second are much more common.

The monkey shown on page 36 is attempting to catch a "butterfly," which it hallucinates as a consequence of electrical stimulation of its visual association cortex. The cable is attached to 34 electrodes in the monkey's brain. These cause no ill effects or discomfort and are, in fact, sometimes used in human patients. The top picture was taken about one second after the onset of stimulation by electrodes in the visual association area. The monkey looks intently at something close in front of him and the eyes begin a downward tracking movement. In the middle picture, about two seconds after the onset of stimulation, the monkey makes a swift catching movement with his right fist and, at the bottom, carefully examines his hand, a bit disgusted perhaps that he missed whatever it was he was trying to catch. The flying object that he "missed" was created by the electrical stimulation acting on the neurons in this part of the monkey's brain. It is called a "butterfly" because a human patient, similarly stimulated, saw a butterfly and likewise attempted to catch it.

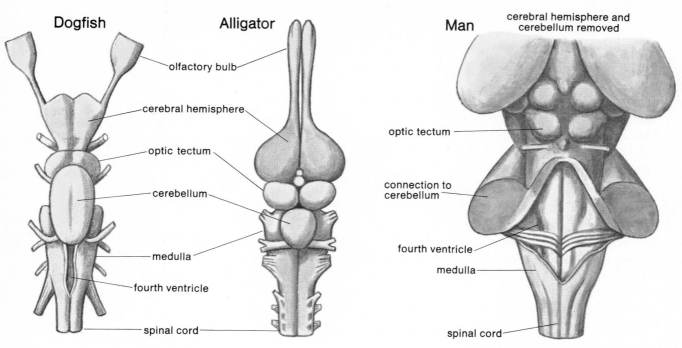

Dogfish   **Alligator**   **Man** — cerebral hemisphere and cerebellum removed

olfactory bulb

cerebral hemisphere

optic tectum

optic tectum

cerebellum

connection to cerebellum

medulla

fourth ventricle

fourth ventricle

medulla

spinal cord

spinal cord

The brains of a dogfish and an alligator are compared with the brain stem of man. The same major components are present in each. In mammals, however, and particularly in man, there has been a great proportionate increase in the cerebral hemispheres (here cut away).

When the impulse arrives at the axon terminal, minute amounts of a chemical transmitter are released, altering the electrical potential of the recipient cell. The direction of electrical change is dependent upon the properties of the receiving cell and the type of chemical released. Changes which decrease the potential of the recipient neuron and thus move it toward the threshold level for initiating an impulse are excitatory and termed excitatory postsynaptic potentials (EPSPs). Those changes which increase the surface potential of the recipient neuron, making it less likely to fire an impulse, are called inhibitory postsynaptic potentials (IPSPs).

Whether or not a neuron discharges an impulse is thus dependent from moment to moment upon the net effect of the EPSPs and IPSPs resulting from the synaptic bombardment to which the neuron is subjected. In this way each neuron integrates the influences from many others and transmits its own signal whenever the majority of influences rule in favor of excitation. The picture one thus gains of the operation of the brain is the ceaseless shuttling of tiny explosions along hundreds of millions of elements arising and dissolving in infinitely varied patterns.

On the opposite page, a large neuron in the cerebral hemisphere of a lizard is compared to its counterpart in man. Each neuron intertwines its branches with hundreds or thousands of others. The axon of each neuron conveys electrical and chemical messages to other neurons near and far. The dendrites receive these messages from many other neurons. In mammals this type of cell sends its axon into the spinal cord to control the movement of muscles.

Sensory systems

It is astonishing to realize that all knowledge of the world comes into the brain in the form of nerve impulses. As we survey the sunset, read a printed page, or behold the majesty of the Milky Way, we are not aware that the perception of what we see is based upon pulses traversing the million nerve fibers from each eye. Nor is there any hint that our visual world is split precisely down the middle so that the right half of each eye projects exclusively to the left half of the brain,

38

and the left to the right. Only after many relays and neural transformations are these two halves of the visual world finally put together. The myriad details in operation of the other sensory systems are equally unobtrusive.

The "recognition" of the world is undoubtedly evolved primarily in the cerebral cortex, the contorted sheet composed chiefly of neurons that forms the surface of the brain. Major functional subdivisions of the cortex can be denoted according to the origin of the axons entering it and the destination of those leaving it. Axons coming from the eye, for example, synapse massively on neurons in the lateral geniculate nucleus of the thalamus, which is the part of the brain that serves as a relay center for sensory impulses en route to the cerebral cortex. Axons of these neurons, in turn, pass directly to the visual cortex. Similar arrangements hold for the other sensory systems, where thalamic "relay" neurons convey the information to the cortex.

Even though essentially all of the cortex is supplied by neurons located in the thalamus, the functional classification of cortical areas other than those directly related to sensation or movement becomes quite complicated. These other regions in the cortex, which are referred to as association areas, occupy an increasingly larger proportion of the total cortical surface in evolving from lower mammals to man. But the farther an association area is from the boundaries of the sensory and motor areas, the more difficult it becomes to determine its function.

The cortex, which is about one-tenth of an inch (2 mm) thick, is so densely packed with cells that about 50,000 of them lie within a column the diameter of a pencil lead. On their way to the surface of the cortex, the major dendrites of each of these neurons pass through a field of about 4,000 neighbors. Despite this dense interweaving of dendrites and axons, each neuron performs as an individual, normally responding only to the chemical messages it alone receives rather than to any massed electrical field of its neighbors. Thus, because of the chemical step in synaptic transmission, huge numbers of neurons can be packed into a small volume and still retain their individual functions.

The cortex is organized into columns of cells having related functions. In the visual cortex, for example, columns are found in which each neuron is activated by stimuli falling upon nearly the same point in the eye and moving in a certain direction. In the somesthetic cortex, columns are found in which all cells are stimulated by the touching of a particular area of skin or by the movement of a particular joint of a limb. These cellular columns apparently analyze various features of the information relayed to them. For the visual system they might extract from incoming impulses various qualities of spatial pattern, direction and velocity of movement, or brightness. The processes and purpose of these neuronal columns, however, are still not fully understood.

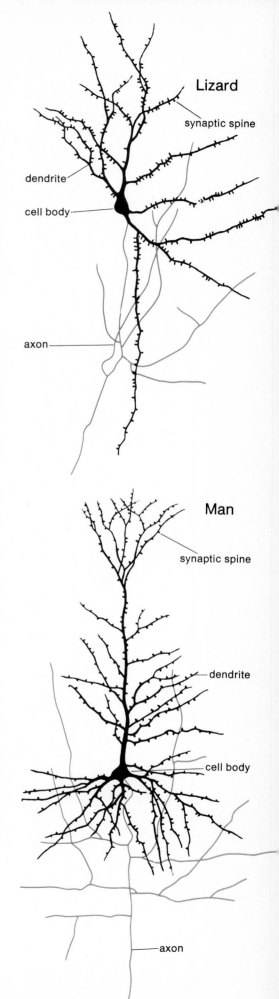

Movement

All bodily movement originates as impulses in the motor neurons of the spinal cord. The axons of these neurons leave the central nervous system and terminate in muscle fibers. A twitch of each muscle fiber occurs with each nerve impulse. The finesse of a movement is controlled by the frequency of discharge of the motor neurons (from 2 to 50 per second) and the number of motor neurons firing at any given instant. There are about 200,000 motor neurons in the human spinal cord, many of which can be individually controlled.

A simple demonstration of motor neuron firing is often performed in neurophysiology laboratory exercises for medical students. A student carefully inserts a needle into one of his muscles in such a way that its exposed tip can register the electrical change set up by each nerve impulse. The electrical change is then amplified and converted

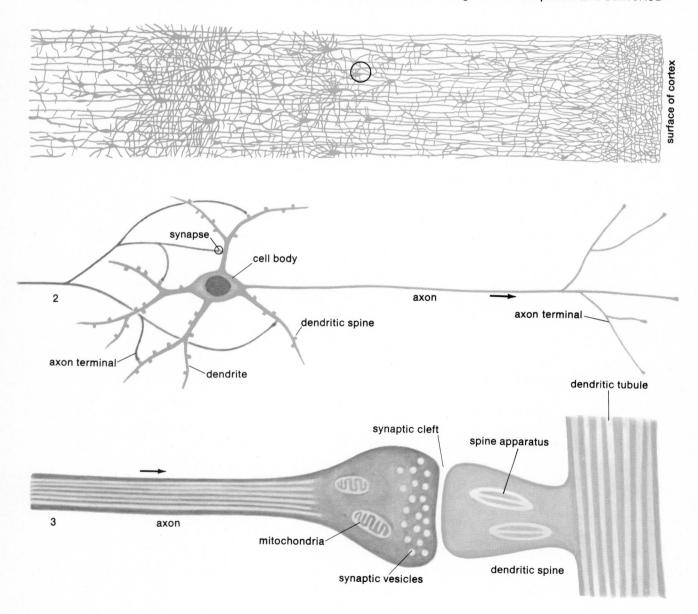

surface of cortex

2

synapse

cell body

axon

axon terminal

dendritic spine

axon terminal

dendrite

dendritic tubule

synaptic cleft

spine apparatus

3

axon

mitochondria

synaptic vesicles

dendritic spine

into a sound signal so that each discharge of a motor neuron can be heard as an abrupt, popping sound. By varying the degree and manner of his movement, the student is able to regulate the sound frequency from a single pulse up to a staccato.

The neural circuitry which enables the student to exert this degree of selection and control over a single motor neuron among his 200,000 on the basis of what he hears is of the highest intricacy. It is this quality of control, however, which distinguishes the capabilities of the human brain from that of other animals. The dog, for instance, has the same number of motor neurons (about 14,000) to control its tongue as does man, yet man can talk and the dog cannot. The difference lies in the neural systems which man can use to regulate the discharge of his motor neurons.

A major center of this control is in the motor cortex. About one million of the hundreds of millions of cells in this area send their

The electrical potentials of a neuron are diagramed below. The interior of the cell "at rest" is 70 mv negative with respect to the outside. However, it is under constant bombardment from synaptic action which creates EPSPs (excitatory postsynaptic potentials) and IPSPs (inhibitory postsynaptic potentials). If the threshold is reached by several EPSPs occurring concurrently, the neuron discharges and a nerve impulse travels down the axon.

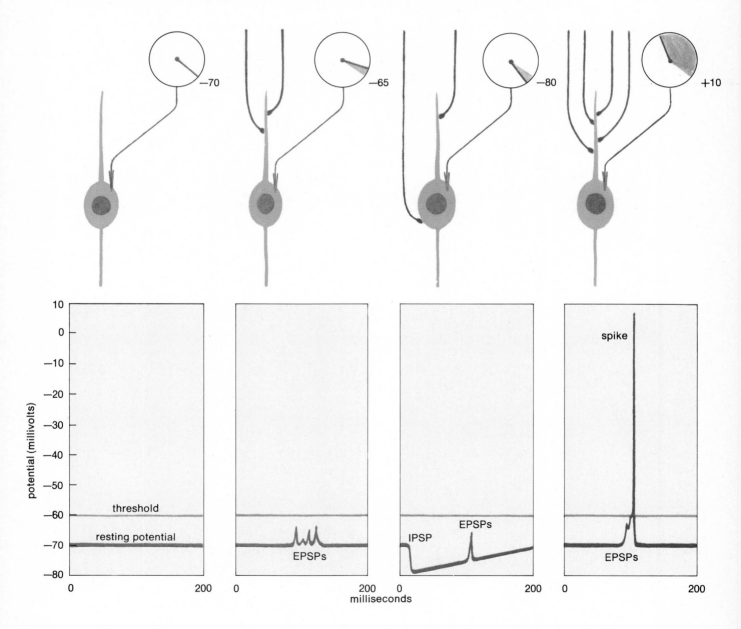

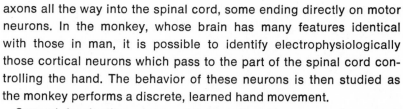

axons all the way into the spinal cord, some ending directly on motor neurons. In the monkey, whose brain has many features identical with those in man, it is possible to identify electrophysiologically those cortical neurons which pass to the part of the spinal cord controlling the hand. The behavior of these neurons is then studied as the monkey performs a discrete, learned hand movement.

Several fascinating pieces of information have come from such studies with monkeys. First, the discharge pattern of the cortical neurons is predetermined to a large degree, as indicated by their beginning to fire about 100 msec before the movement occurs, and their frequency of discharge is related to the force of the movement. Second, by measuring the time between the application of an electrical stimulus to the monkey's visual cortex (as a signal for him to begin the movement) and the onset of firing in neurons of the motor cortex, the "decision time" can be determined. This time, during which the monkey somehow initiates the predetermined firing of the cortical cells projecting upon his motor neurons, is approximately 70 msec, a relatively long time in neurophysiology. Someday the nature and location of the decision process may be identified, together with the nature of the system which programs the firing pattern of the controlling cells in the motor cortex.

Centrencephalic system

Movement of a hair on the back of the hand by about 5° can be detected, yet such movement sets off but a single nerve impulse probably in only a single nerve fiber terminating at the base of the hair.

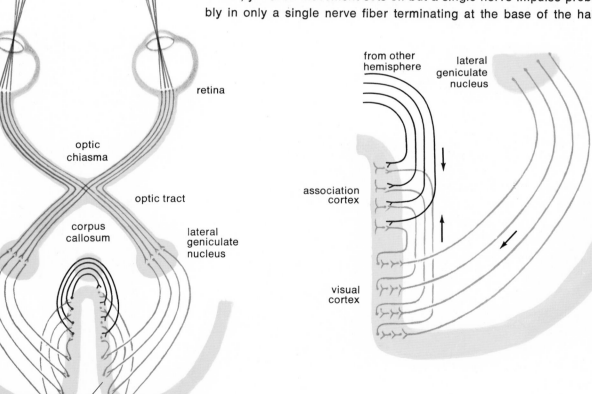

Similar sensitivity is present in the eye. It can thus be concluded that a single nerve impulse can be augmented into a conscious experience by sensory systems of the brain. In view of this extraordinary sensitivity, how is it that tens of thousands of impulses each second impinge upon the brain without effect? Saliva in the mouth, passage of air through the nose, pressure from clothing, and major portions of the auditory and visual environment continually fail to register their presence, yet can be instantly perceived when attention is directed toward them.

It is apparent from these facts that a major function of the brain must be the selection and channeling or "gating" of sensory input. When a monkey becomes drowsy, for example, a volley of impulses synapsing in the lateral geniculate nucleus of the thalamus fails to excite the cells and almost nothing is relayed to the visual cortex. Then, when the monkey is suddenly alerted, transmission at the lateral geniculate nucleus "opens up," and even more cells are excited by the input volley than during the relative inattention of normal wakefulness. Thus, information coming from the eye is subject to powerful modulation at the thalamic "relay" nucleus. The source of this modulation is the centrencephalic system.

Not all portions of this system can be identified with equal clarity, and the mechanisms or even the nature of their functions are often uncertain. Nevertheless, a system of neurons can be defined—most of them probably of a reticular (netlike) type—occupying midline positions throughout the brainstem (hence "centrencephalic") whose function is to control sensorial input and analysis. (The brainstem is an enlargement at the base of the brain where it connects with the spinal cord.) These neurons are responsible for the phenomena of attention, awareness, sleep, and perhaps, to some degree, the transmutation of neural activity into the unity of consciousness.

The singular importance of the centrencephalic system is sometimes illustrated by destruction of a small but critical portion of it. Such injured patients may survive for years, yet remain unconscious, from a brainstem lesion not much larger than a cherry pit that leaves the great mass of the brain and all its major sensory and motor paths intact. From this and other evidence it is sometimes proposed that the centrencephalic system is the primary locus of consciousness and that it unifies the countless disparate actions concurrent in the two halves of the brain. This is probably not entirely true. Although the centrencephalic system occupies a key position in this regard, it is, to a large degree, the slave of the cerebral cortex. If the cerebral cortex is anesthetized, consciousness is lost in man even when the drug does not reach those portions of the centrencephalic system where lesions produce unconsciousness. Perhaps even more significant is the fact that consciousness apparently becomes double following disconnection of the two cerebral cortices.

A great mass of 200 million axons, the corpus callosum, connects the left and right cortex. Thus at least 2% of the neurons in the cor-

Represented on the opposite page are the anatomical connections of the visual system. The one million axons from one eye enter the brain as the optic nerve (left). About two-thirds of the axons cross to the other side in the optic chiasma and continue as the optic tract, joined by the noncrossing axons, to synapse in the lateral geniculate nucleus. Axons from these neurons then convey the excitation via the optic pathways to the visual cortex. On the right is an illustration of how the visual system puts together the divided visual field by relays passing through the corpus callosum. The lens system of the eye inverts and reverses the image, half of which is sent to each half of the brain. The corresponding halves from each eye occupy separate cell columns in the visual cortex. Information from these columns is then sent to columns in the visual association cortex, and these columns send their analysis to appropriately related columns in the visual association cortex of the other side of the brain.

The future of brain research

Available tools and techniques inevitably shape the scientific concepts of a particular era. In the late 1940s the development of microelectrodes that could be placed inside living, functioning nerve cells revolutionized understanding of basic neural processes. Since then highly sophisticated surgical, electronic, behavioral, and microchemical techniques have been developed that should effect equally revolutionary advances in understanding perception, sleep, emotions, and memory or learning. The practical ramifications of such knowledge are immeasurable.

One of the fascinating results of the microminiaturization of electronic components (see *1969 Britannica Yearbook of Science and the Future,* Feature Article: MICROELECTRONICS—THE CHALLENGE OF THE CHIP) will be the opportunity this gives for precise electrical stimulation of the brain at many loci concurrently for very long periods of time. It is too early to say whether exploitation of such procedures will be therapeutically rewarding. There are, however, enough encouraging data at hand to urge that the possibility be vigorously explored. The greatest immediate need is a power system which can utilize the body's own chemistry and thus permit the permanent implantation of electronic units. Experiments are already under way on monkeys to determine whether, as seems likely from earlier work, certain types of epilepsy might be controlled by using microelectronic devices to provide repeated stimulation of the affected neurons, keeping them sufficiently active so that they are incapable of convulsive discharge.

Another possibility involving microelectronics, but one that is exceedingly more difficult conceptually and technically, is the development of a prosthesis for those who are blind or deaf from loss of their peripheral sense organs or nerves. While it is certain that normal sight or hearing never could be produced by such a device, no

tex are devoted to coordinating the activity in the "two brains" that exist within one head. When these connections are severed in animals, or sometimes in man for relief from epileptic convulsions, a situation is created in which two separate minds exist concurrently within one individual. Because each half of the brain apparently acts independently, a monkey with such a "split brain" can process twice as much visual information as can a normal animal.

The independence of right and left brain can, indeed, be directly demonstrated. By an ingenious optical arrangement it is possible for each brain simultaneously to learn tasks that are contradictory to each other. For example, the right brain can be taught to choose a triangle instead of a circle at the same time that the left brain is being taught to choose the circle rather than the triangle. Similar demonstrations can be achieved in human split-brain subjects, but because

44

matter how sophisticated, there is a distinct possibility that some useful sensation could be developed. A monkey is able to tell which of two electrodes in its visual cortex is stimulated even when they are only 0.04 in. (1 mm) apart. Thus the brain can process these highly abnormal inputs with a rather surprising degree of precision. But no one yet knows whether it can process such information from more than one point at a time. Unless it can, all ideas of usefully connecting a television scanner to an array of brain electrodes in the blind are impractical. Obviously the feasibility will be tested.

Perhaps more difficult still is the possibility of modifying the course of psychotic reactions or even endocrinological disturbances by electrical stimulation of the limbic system. There are already some modest instances of success in this regard. Most psychiatrists and surgeons, however, understandably will insist on waiting for much more knowledge about the physiology of the limbic system and the nature of psychoses before committing their patients to the uncertainties of such therapy. Yet it is also legitimate to ask whether localized electrical stimulation of the brain bears more risk or has less scientific justification than the commonly used treatment of electroconvulsive shock.

There is, of course, a great effort under way to identify neurochemical abnormalities related to psychoses, and to develop drugs to ameliorate them. Within the past decade treatment with drugs has had remarkable success and, with fuller understanding of the underlying chemistry, such success will undoubtedly be extended. It is perhaps also not too much to hope that with further knowledge a pill might be developed that would in large measure accomplish quickly the same neurochemical changes as occur in sleep, thereby adding years to the effective life of each of us!

Yet even these far-ranging prospects for the future only skirt the true fascination of the brain, the tantalizing fact that within its adroitly tangled web is bound the ultimate mystery of man's being.

man's right brain has no speech function such demonstrations must employ procedures similar to those used with animals to communicate with this part of the human brain. In right-handed human subjects essentially all language functions are performed by the left brain. In the split-brain condition the "talking" left brain has no access to the experiences of the right brain, nor can the right brain, by the movements it controls, signal knowledge of any events to the left brain. Yet communication can be established with each brain independently to demonstrate that each has its own life experiences.

In such a situation it is apparent that the centrencephalic system by itself is not capable of coordinating consciousness in the two halves of the brain. Yet much remains puzzling since, for instance, the centrencephalic system in such split-brain individuals continues to exert its usual bilaterally symmetrical control over the background electrical activity of the brain, recorded as the electroencephalogram (EEG). The EEG activity, which can be recorded through the scalp, arises from continuous flux of EPSPs and IPSPs in cortical neurons. The degree of synchrony in the play of these potentials is controlled primarily by the centrencephalic system and in gross measure reflects the functional state of the brain at the time of recording. Thus, when the subject changes from a state of relaxed wakefulness to one of attentiveness, the EEG abruptly alters from slow, relatively large amplitude waves to low-voltage, fast activity. When the subject falls asleep the EEG becomes characterized by still different patterns. These changes all remain concurrent in each half of the brain in split-brain subjects. (*See* Feature Article: SLEEP AND DREAMS.)

Limbic system

The limbic system is an extensive, though not particularly large, group of intricately interconnected neural structures surrounding the midline surfaces of the cerebral hemispheres and passing into the brainstem. In evolution it has been closely associated with the olfactory system at the base of the brain, but its ramifications considerably exceed those portions of the brain thought to be devoted to the analysis of odors.

The functions of the limbic system are probably best summarized by stating that they are concerned with preservation of the self and of the species. In achieving these ends, activity of the limbic system is naturally integrated with that of the great sensory and motor systems of the brain, yet the limbic system remains to a considerable degree a distinguishable entity. It is characterized by an extraordinary anatomical complexity and, like the centrencephalic system, it exerts a compelling control over human behavior far out of proportion to its size.

The importance of the limbic system in health and disease can scarcely be overestimated inasmuch as it regulates the entire body economy and, in addition, gives rise to our emotional life. It exerts control over the anterior pituitary gland (hypophysis), the secretions of which, in turn, act upon other endocrine glands. Through this means the nervous system enters into the regulation of blood salts and sugar, urine formation, growth, basal metabolism, sexual cycles and characteristics, and resistance to infection. Through more direct neural mediation the limbic system affects blood pressure, digestion, and temperature regulation. It also organizes such complex instinctual behaviors as hunting, feeding, mating, and fleeing or fighting. These behavioral actions all have powerful emotional concomitants which have proven to be accessible by electrical stimulation of the limbic system in both animals and man. Such stimulation, as is the natural stimulation producing these behaviors, is either strongly sought or avoided.

It seems likely that the limbic system provides a motivational evalu-

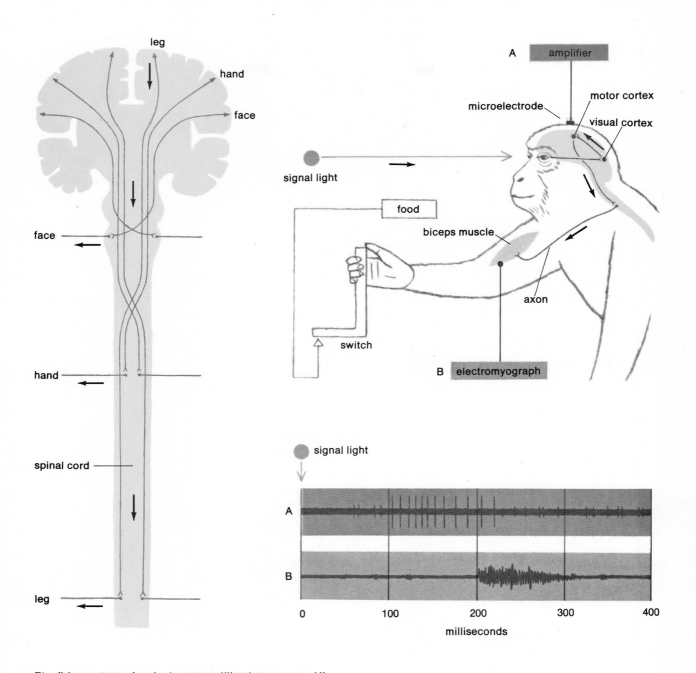

The firing pattern of a single neuron (like that on page 41)
projecting into the spinal cord from the motor cortex
of a trained monkey is recorded as the animal sees the "go" light
and pulls the lever. The neuron begins to discharge
about 70 milliseconds after the signal from the eye begins
to move toward the visual cortex of the brain (electromyogram A).
The muscles begin to fire sometime later (electromyogram B),
and physical movement does not begin until about 100 milliseconds
after the start of the discharge in the motor cortex.
At the left is the general scheme for control of movement
by cortical neurons.

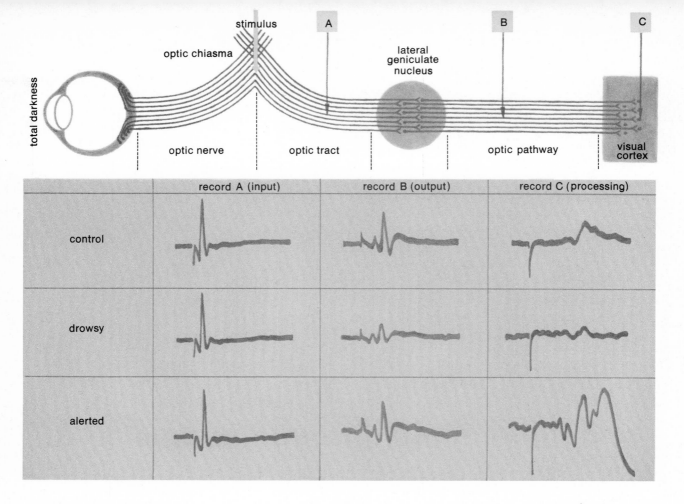

The diagram shows the visual pathway from the eye through the optic nerve, optic chiasma, optic tract, lateral geniculate nucleus, optic pathway, to the visual cortex. Recording points A, B, and C are marked, with a "stimulus" applied near the optic chiasma, and "total darkness" at the eye.

	record A (input)	record B (output)	record C (processing)
control			
drowsy			
alerted			

The "relay" nucleus in the thalamus controls transmission of nerve impulses in the visual system, as can be shown by applying an electrical stimulus every three seconds to the optic tract of a monkey sitting in total darkness (top diagram). In the record of the system's electrical responses (bottom), column A, which traces the impulses entering the lateral geniculate nucleus, does not change. Column B records the synaptically relayed impulses between the nucleus and the visual cortex, where impulse processing occurs (column C). The peaks in B and C are caused by the different conduction velocities in the nuclear neurons, which are of two sizes. When the animal is aroused suddenly, transmission increases beyond normal levels.

ation of all sensory input in terms of approach or avoidance, and also originates the "drive" to seek particular forms of stimulation. Electrical stimulation in certain areas of the limbic system, for example, produces feeding behavior, driving animals to seek food and ravenously consume large quantities, even though they have been fed to satiety just prior to onset of the stimulation. Following destruction of these areas animals sometimes never again eat voluntarily, although their behavior remains normal in other respects. Similarly, absence of fear and aggressive behavior occurs after loss of other limbic areas (the amygdala), an effect particularly striking in such ferocious animals as the lynx or wild rat, which become docile after these lesions. On the other hand, savageness or intense fear can be produced by localized electrical stimulation of the limbic system in tame, domestic animals.

The "basic personality" of the individual is thus a manifestation of the organization and activity of the limbic system. Further evidence of this appears from experiments on two distinct types of domestic cats, those that attack when handled and those that purr and stretch when petted. Following surgical removal of all the cerebral cortex but leaving most of the limbic system untouched, these characteristics in each animal remain exactly as they were preoperatively. Even more striking is the production of a "split personality" in the split-brain monkey. When the animal uses the eye connected to the "in-

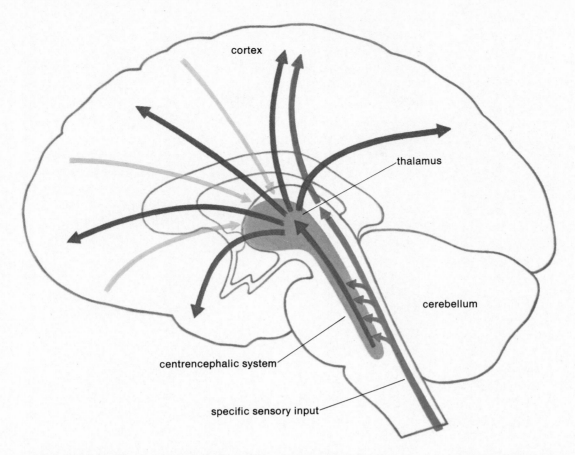

cortex

thalamus

cerebellum

centrencephalic system

specific sensory input

tact'' half-brain, it is normally fearful and aggressive toward man; but when it can see only with the eye connected to the half-brain lacking the amygdala, it is unafraid and readily accepts food from the experimenter without threatening or attacking him. The personality of the ''same'' monkey thus depends upon the condition of the limbic system in the brain with which he views the world.

The relevance of such observations to human emotional problems is immediately apparent. Abnormalities of sensory or motor systems can produce loss or confusion of sensation, convulsions, paralysis, or incessant purposeless movement; but similar abnormalities in the limbic system can distort one's appraisal of the world or unleash irrelevant storms of emotion. Hundreds of thousands of people suffer this horror of chaotic emotion; they experience sorrow, rage, fear, or ecstasy garbled as to context, devoid of reality. They are the insane, and the evidence accumulates insistently that the source of their affliction is to be sought in disorders of the limbic system.

This diagram of the centrencephalic system shows its diffuse projection into the cerebral cortex, and the controlling input which this system receives from the cortex. Also diagrammed are the collateral connections given off by the specific sensory systems (auditory, tactile, etc.) as they pass the centrencephalic system. Powerful centrencephalic control of thalamic relay nuclei are not shown.

Memory

The precise nature of memory is unknown, yet it is one of the most important immediate problems confronting the neuroscientist. The solution is rendered particularly difficult, first, because there are undoubtedly several types of memory and, second, because the

49

mnemonic (memory) processes—unlike those discussed previously for motivation, attention, sensorial analysis, and movement—are not unique to any particular system of the brain but are, instead, general properties of neuronal systems.

It seems inescapable that a permanent memory must require some permanent alteration in the structure of the brain, that is, in the connections of neurons. This raises a perplexing question: What is the present status or functional role of those neurons which in a 20-year-old man will store his next 50 years of memories? No one can even guess the answer to such a question until it is clear what changes occur in the memory process. It is equally difficult to speculate what practical consequences the solution of the problem will have, but it seems likely it might revolutionize educational procedures, possibly allow the right half-brain to acquire some language functions, and point the way to erasing or replacing pathological memory features in neuroses or psychoses.

At present, memories can be effectively erased only if attacked immediately after they start to form. For instance, if a cat receives unexpected punishment while eating, it will show great hesitation about returning to that feeding place the next day. If immediately after the punishment, however, intense electrical stimulation is applied to that portion of the limbic system mediating fear behavior (the

Tracts
olfactory tract — 1
mammillary thalamic — 2
stria medullaris — 3
habenullo peduncular tract — 4
stria terminalis — 5

Nuclei
septal area — SA
anterior thalamus nucleus — ATN
mammillary — M
habenula — H
interpeduncular — IP
limbic midbrain — LM
amygdala — AMYG

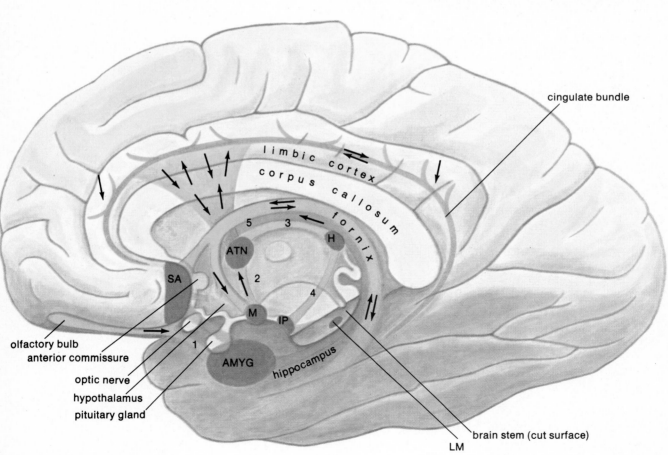

50

amygdala), the punishment produces no effect upon subsequent behavior. Stimulation elsewhere in the brain or in the amygdala several
hours after the experience does not produce such erasure. Thus it
seems that normal activity of the amygdala is required to record an
aversive experience immediately after its occurrence. By further
combination of such electrophysiological and behavioral techniques
it should be possible to isolate selectively a neural system in which
mnemonic events are occurring, and then to analyze the nature of
these events.

There is a peculiarity of associative memory processes which is
often overlooked, yet which probably provides an extremely important
clue as to their nature. This is the temporal paradox of associative
learning. The paradox occurs in terms of neural events because it is
always a subsequent event which changes the response to an antecedent stimulus. Thus, in the example above, it is the punishment, which
occurred after the cat's response to the stimulus of the feeding place,
that somehow worked back upon the neurons responding to this
stimulus. When the neural system was again activated by the same
stimulus, the normal system produced an entirely different response
(avoidance rather than approach) because the antecedently active
system had been drastically modified by the subsequent event.

In thinking of the world and the nervous system in terms of causal-
ity, the natural expectation is that antecedent events should modify
those occurring subsequently, and indeed such has been the consistent observation in thousands of neurophysiological experiments.
Recently, however, in an oceanic relative of the snail special neurons
have been found in which the capability of a weak synaptic system is
enhanced for a long time if its initial action is briefly and immediately
followed by excitation in a more powerful synaptic system. This is
exactly the paradigm required for associative memory, and further
study of this simple nervous system may provide fundamental insight
into mnemonic mechanisms.

The explanation of the foregoing effect most probably lies in an
interchange of chemical agents among the participating neurons, the
direction of the interchange being dependent upon the timing of the
events. Few would deny the likelihood that memory will prove to be
linked to neurochemistry, and there are already several experiments
showing enhancement or suppression of mnemonic processes by
various drugs. It is, however, another step entirely to think that a
specific memory could be chemically extracted from one brain and
effectively transferred to another. This idea has received such great
publicity that some prediction here of what the future probably does
not hold seems appropriate.

The concept of interindividual memory transfer assumes: (1) that
the experimenter with no knowledge whatever of the chemical events
of memory will be able to isolate from the thousands of memory
states of an animal just those chemical memory traces he is seeking,
free of any interfering trace; (2) that the chemical basis of memory

*Illustrated on page 50
are some components of the limbic
system. Not indicated are areas
in the frontal and temporal lobes,
besides the midline limbic cortex,
that have rich interconnections
with the limbic system.
It has been stated
that these regions of the cortex
mediate between the internal world
of the body, represented
in the limbic system,
and the external world,
represented in most of the cerebral
cortex. Some portions of the limbic
system have developed in close
association with the olfactory
system, as the connections indicate.
The hypothalamus is particularly
important in regulating body
hormones via the pituitary gland.*

51

has no subtlety which could be undone by chemical extraction, no precise configuration as part of a neuron; (3) that the chemical agent is so simple as to pass unhindered by the blood-brain barrier which screens most large molecules from the brain to protect it from infection; (4) that the chemical substance constituting the memory trace would be appropriately incorporated into just those neurons among millions that would control the behavioral expression of the transferred memory; and (5) that the vast complexities of temporal and spatial sequence and of motivation are either irrelevant (no experiment yet suggests that they are) or are all transferred in toto via the extracted chemical essence of memory. In the opinion of the author, such expectations are clearly irrational and have been satirized recently by the proposal that one might transfer a picture from one television set to another by infiltrating the recipient set with a chemical extract from the donor set.

Brain transplants

Another currently popular but naïve speculation is the proposal, following the remarkable endeavors with transplantation of human hearts and other organs, that someday the human brain will be transplanted. Were such a procedure possible, the "body" would be the transplant, and the brain, inasmuch as it is the conscious person, would be the recipient. The surgical problem is several orders of magnitude more difficult than cardiac transplantation because, to be effective, the entire nervous system (spinal cord, eyes, inner ear, etc.) would have to remain intact. Orderly growth of nerve fibers out into the new body might fail and, in any event, would require many weeks even before a breath could occur (provided the proper motor neurons became connected to the proper muscles), let alone swallowing or speech. There is definitely no prospect for success with such procedures in the foreseeable future.

Should the time ever arrive, however, use might be made of the remarkable and unexpected results of Japanese scientists who have succeeded in freezing a cat brain, keeping it in the frozen state for months and then, upon careful warming, obtaining surprisingly normal electrical activity from it. Such experiments encourage the belief that ultimately it may be possible to freeze and thaw a brain without serious damage. Whether this could also be done for the eye, and whether suspended animation could be achieved without intolerable injury, is, of course, still highly problematical.

Philosophical implications

Study of the brain is unique in its direct relation to the nature of human experience. Nuclear physicists and cosmologists probe the universe for meaning, but the constructs which they achieve can never extend beyond those possible in the processes intrinsic to the brain. In this respect study of the brain is the ultimate science.

For centuries the relation of brain to mind remained too vague to penetrate the extensive speculations of theology. With the Darwinian revolution, in which man's direct lineage from other forms of life became unequivocally apparent, and with the presently occurring revolution in which the working of the brain is coming to be understood in intimate detail, man stands ready to answer the ultimate question of his identity: Is he a being or a machine?

If there is an answer to such questions, study of the brain at present seems the most likely course to reveal it. Since most cultures and ethical systems have evolved around the belief that the mind is a metaphysical agent, a conclusive demonstration that it is not would change the course of human history far more drastically than has Marxist materialism. On the other hand, what more momentous discovery than proof of a metaphysical correlate to brain activity!

Here, then, is the most important scientific question which can be asked, but one which may prove to be unanswerable. It may be that as the mechanisms of consciousness are analyzed, the phenomenon itself will recede—as cloud becomes fog—the entity indiscernible in its parts. Furthermore, there are no means to observe consciousness; it can only be experienced directly within the entity producing it. Thus, a nonbiological computer sufficiently complex to compose poetry or philosophical essays might declare itself to be conscious and respond to all queries as though it were. Proof that such a mechanism was not conscious in the same sense that man is conscious might be impossible! But is this any more of a dilemma than the probability that within a century or two a human being may be manufactured from artificially synthesized nucleic acids, nurtured in plastic flasks, to gradually develop body and brain in human form which, upon maturity, will declare itself conscious and ponder its destiny?

FOR ADDITIONAL READING:

Doty, Robert W., "Philosophy and the Brain," *Perspectives in Biology and Medicine,* pp. 23–24 (Autumn 1965).

Gregory, R. L., *Eye and Brain: The Psychology of Seeing* (McGraw-Hill, 1966).

"The Human Brain," British *Science Journal* (May 1967).

Katz, Bernhard, *Nerve, Muscle, and Synapse* (McGraw-Hill, 1966).

Wooldridge, Dean E., *The Machinery of the Brain* (McGraw-Hill, 1963).

AUDIOVISUAL MATERIALS FROM ENCYCLOPÆDIA
BRITANNICA EDUCATIONAL CORPORATION:

Films: *Fundamentals of the Nervous System; Frontiers of the Mind.*

Filmstrip: *The Nervous System.*

Transparencies: *The Human Head.*

Game Theory: Strategies for Resolving Conflict
by Anatol Rapoport

**Mathematical research often reveals similarities
in concepts that may seem widely unrelated. In recent years,
studies in game theory have demonstrated that such games of strategy
as chess, bridge, and tic-tac-toe are related to concepts in
marketing, political science, and even automated warfare.**

Game theory, which derives its name from the so-called games of strategy (chess, bridge, etc.), deals in general with the problems posed by rationally conducted conflict. In a game of strategy each of two or more players has at his disposal a number of plans of action (strategies) from which he can choose one that leads to a certain outcome. But because the players prefer different outcomes, their interests are in conflict. Thus, the problem faced by each player is to choose a strategy that, in conjunction with the strategies chosen by others, will lead to the best outcome he can achieve. In the meantime, of course, each of the other players is attempting to do the same.

A simple two-person game

The properties of a simple game can be demonstrated by a zero-sum game, one in which the gains of one player are always equal to the losses of the other. Usually in such a game a "rational" player is one who attempts to maximize his gain (or at least to minimize his loss) and thereby minimize his opponent's gain (or maximize his loss).

Simple situations of this sort can be represented by a game matrix, as shown in Game 1. Let one player, Castor, have a choice among three strategies (C_1, C_2, C_3), which are represented by the horizontal rows of the game matrix. The other player, Pollux, has a similar choice of three strategies (P_1, P_2, P_3) among the three vertical columns. When both players have chosen a strategy (each in ignorance of the other's choice), an outcome, which is represented by one of the boxes of the matrix, is determined. For example, if Castor chooses C_1 and Pollux chooses P_3, the outcome is in the upper right-hand corner. The numbers in the box are the "payoffs" to the players, Castor's being the bottom number and Pollux' the top. In this case,

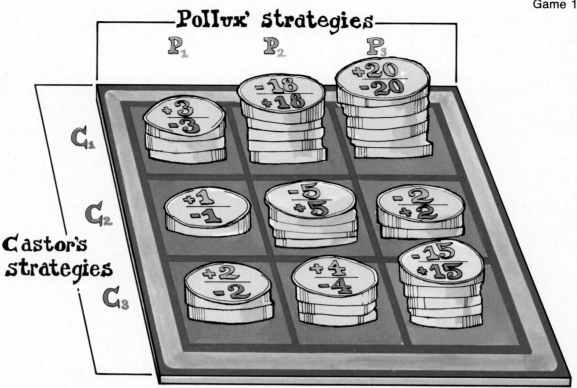

Castor has lost 20 and Pollux has won 20. (The payoff numbers in Game 1 have been chosen arbitrarily for the sake of illustration.)

A prescription of a choice of strategy to each of two rational players is called a "solution" of the game; the corresponding payoff is called the "value" of the game to the player who gets it. In the solution of Game 1, Castor should choose C_2 and Pollux P_1. If Pollux chooses P_1, where he is sure of a gain, Castor cannot do better than choose C_2. Similarly, if Castor chooses C_2, Pollux cannot do better than choose P_1. If two "rational" players play Game 1, the outcome will always be the same: Castor will lose one unit to Pollux.

Games of this sort, which include chess, checkers, go, and tic-tac-toe, are called games of pure strategy. Among the available strategies in such games there is always a best one for each player, which guarantees the best possible outcome against a player who likewise uses his best strategy. This is easily seen in the case of tic-tac-toe, which always ends in a draw if played by competent (*i.e.,* rational) players. If chess were played perfectly, the outcome of every game would also be the same, although it is not known whether it would be a win for White, a win for Black, or a draw. The reason this does not happen (and so interest in the game continues) is because the "best" chess strategies are not known; the game is too complex to be "solved."

The situation described for Game 1 is typical of game theoretic analysis. Game theory, however, is not usually concerned with solving particular games. For this reason it is futile to look to game theory for guidance in acquiring strategic expertise in games or in real-life conflicts. The main concern of game theory is to analyze different types of games in order to provide a clear perspective on the sort of problems that are involved in solving them. One of the insights acquired through game theory is that the notion of "solution" must be assigned different meanings in different types of games.

A game with a mixed strategy solution

To see how the concept of "solution" must be modified, consider Game 2. Let Castor be a military commander, faced with the choice of attacking Sector 1 or Sector 2. Pollux, the opposing commander, must choose between reinforcing Sector 1 or Sector 2. As in Game 1, the numbers in the game matrix have been assigned arbitrarily to represent the payoffs, or "worths," to the two commanders of the various outcomes. For example, if Castor attacks Sector 2 while Pollux defends Sector 1, Castor breaks through Sector 2 and gains 8 points while Pollux loses 8. A breakthrough in Sector 1, on the other hand, is worth only 5 points to Castor. If Pollux has reinforced the sector attacked, the attack is repelled. The respective costs of defeat in the two sectors are represented as a loss of 10 and a loss of 2 points to Castor.

Game 2

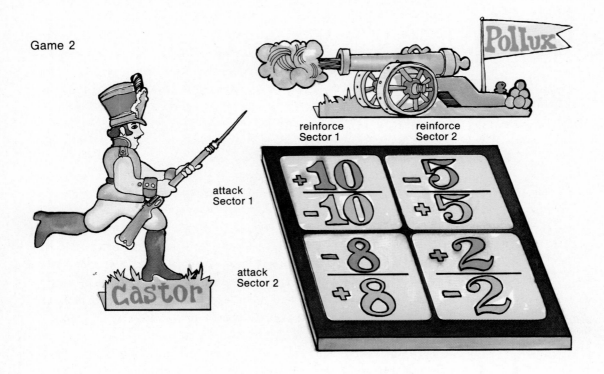

Because there is no pair of strategies, each of which is best against the other, an attempt to solve this game in the same manner as the previous one leads to an impasse. If the outcome is, say, the lower right-hand corner (assuming that Castor was cautious and Pollux has guessed that he would be), Castor could have done better by attacking Sector 1. If, on the other hand, the outcome is the upper right-hand corner, Pollux could have done better by defending Sector 1. Here the players are trying to outguess each other, but because both are rational, we cannot assume that one is better at outguessing than the other.

Game 2 is an example of a game without best pure strategies. Each player, however, can choose a so-called mixed strategy, which is best in the sense of giving him the largest possible expected payoff from a statistical point of view. A mixed strategy is chosen by casting lots in such a way that each strategy has a certain prescribed probability of being chosen. Assuming that this same game is to be played over and over, Castor's best mixed strategy is to attack Sector 1 40% of the time (or Sector 2 60% of the time). Pollux' best mix is to defend Sector 1 28% of the time (or Sector 2 72% of the time). Castor can expect an average payoff of 4/5 of one point per game, while Pollux loses 4/5 of one point per game. It can be shown that neither commander can improve his expected payoff by altering this strategy.

While making military decisions by casting lots may seem bizarre, the procedure appears more natural in parlor games. A well-known example of a parlor game requiring mixed strategies is poker, in which strategies involve betting (or calling) depending on the hand one holds. A rational player must mix his strategies; that is, he must sometimes (not always) bet high on a weak hand and low on a strong one. Otherwise, he will give information about his hand by the size of his bet, and will not be called when he has a strong hand. A complete analysis, which would be too complex to be carried out, would prescribe a best mixed strategy for every possible hand—that is, the frequency with which one should bluff, call, raise, or fold.

Game theory reveals some interesting differences in the two types of games described so far. In games of pure strategy, for example, secrecy is irrelevant if the players are rational. Each can deduce the other's best strategy, and an attempt to deceive the opponent by using some other strategy can only harm the would-be deceiver. In games of mixed strategy, on the other hand, secrecy is absolutely necessary in any particular play of the game. But secrecy is irrelevant with regard to the probabilities assigned to the best mixed strategy. Each player can deduce the other's best strategy mixture, and a deviation from this mixture cannot improve one's expected payoff. Indeed, such a deviation may impair the expected payoff.

These conclusions do not apply if there is reason to suppose that the opponent is not "rational." Fleecing an incompetent poker player or outsmarting an incompetent commander is usually accomplished by noting the weaknesses, ignorance, or compulsive predilections of the opponent rather than by the use of best strategy mixtures. Because this kind of psychological analysis is based on the use of intuitive knowledge, it cannot, as a rule, be systematized or made explicit. Thus, it is important to keep in mind that advantages that depend on the psychological evaluation of the opponent fall completely outside the scope of game theory.

The Minimax Theorem

We have seen that in Game 1 there is a best pure strategy for each player and in Game 2 a best mixed strategy. This is in accordance with the Minimax Theorem, which was proved in 1928 by John Von Neumann, the undisputed founder of game theory, and which states that in every two-person zero-sum game there is either a best pure or a best mixed strategy for each player. Methods for finding these best strategies have also been developed. Accordingly, a hope was expressed in some quarters that game theory eventually might stand in the same relation to strategic decisions in business, politics, diplomacy, and war as probability theory has stood in relation to risky decisions in gambling, actuarial work, investment, and medical diagnosis. Actual developments in "applied game theory," however, have been, for the most part, quite limited. While it is true that some problems of military tactics or of competitive strategy in business can be formulated as games, these models usually serve only to illustrate and clarify the problems rather than to reveal "best strategies" in real conflicts. This is because the complexities and the ambiguities of real-life situations usually are too difficult to capture adequately in such models.

There are, however, a few outstanding exceptions to this situation. Among them are problems known as games of pursuit and evasion. For example, a missile designed to intercept an enemy missile has a built-in "strategy"; *i.e.,* it is guided by automated decisions that depend on the position, direction, and velocity of the missile to be intercepted. Similarly, an evasive strategy can be built into the attacking missile. Thus, the two missiles are actually engaged in a two-person zero-sum game. The payoffs can be clearly defined in terms of the probability of penetration or of the distance of the interception from the target (to be maximized by one "player" and minimized by the other). With the increasing automation of warfare, it is reasonable to expect that those concerned with war technology will pay increasing attention to problems of this sort.

Mixed motive games

In the author's opinion, the most serious objection to the view that game theory can serve as a foundation of a science of rationally conducted conflict derives from the limited applicability of Von Neu-

59

mann's Minimax Theorem. On reflection, it is clear that real-life conflicts, in contrast to games of strategy like chess, are rarely analogous to zero-sum games. Typically, the interests of conflicting parties are partly opposed and partly coincident. A strike, for example, may be damaging to both the employer and his employees; severe competition may hurt both (or all) the competitors; a diplomatic impasse may lead to a war that nobody wanted; a war may cripple both (or all) belligerents. In other words, the losses of some of the conflicting parties are not necessarily balanced by the gains of others. (This violates a fundamental assumption of the Minimax Theorem.) Game models of such situations are called nonzero-sum or mixed-motive games.

As a simple example of a mixed motive game consider Game 3,

Game 3

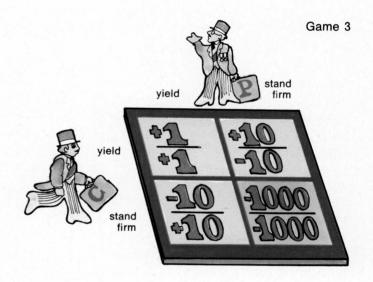

nicknamed "Chicken." Each of two nations negotiating an issue has a choice of yielding or of standing firm. If both yield, a compromise results with a moderate payoff, say one point, to each. If, however, one nation yields, the other gains an advantage of 10 points while the yielding nation suffers a 10-point loss. If both stand firm, a confrontation results, say a nuclear war, in which both nations lose heavily; *i.e.,* 1,000 points. In view of these possible outcomes, which strategy should be adopted by each nation—yield or stand firm? If it is rational to yield, and one expects the other to be rational, then it would be safe to stand firm. But, then, if it is safe to stand firm and if the other is rational, he too may stand firm. The result is disaster.

In Game 4 the dilemma is even more prominent. Assume that the strategies represent decisions by two competing manufacturers to sell their products at a high price or at a low price. The matrix of possible outcomes shows that if both sell at a high price, both make a moderate profit, which may be represented as one point. If both sell at a low price, both suffer a moderate loss of one point. If one

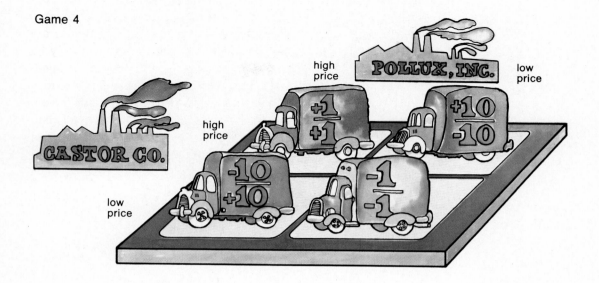

firm sells at a low price while the other sells at a high price, the price cutter captures the whole market of 10 points while the other goes bankrupt by losing 10 points. Here, the conclusion is inescapable: each manufacturer should sell at a low price, regardless of what the other does. For if the other keeps the high price, the market will be captured by underselling. If the other cuts the price, one must do likewise in self-defense. Yet if both act "rationally" by selling at a low price, both suffer a loss. If, however, each acts "irrationally" by selling at a high price, each makes a profit!

Games 3 and 4 illustrate situations where the very notion of "rational choice" is ambiguous. A choice that appears rational from the point of view of each player may lead to an outcome detrimental to both. Such results are observed in panics, where each seeks his own safety and, in so doing, contributes to a disaster affecting all, including himself.

The power of coalitions

Game theory has been extended to the analysis of situations where the interests of the players are partly opposed and partly in agreement. These situations give rise to problems different from those that characterize zero-sum games. In so-called cooperative games, players have the opportunity to coordinate their strategy choices so as to achieve outcomes that both (or all) may prefer to some other outcomes. To this extent the players cooperate. Their preferences among these unanimously preferred outcomes differ, however, and so their interests clash. In this context game theory becomes a theory of bargaining. The bargaining leverage of each player is embodied partly in the "threat strategies" available to him and partly in the payoff that he would get if he played against a coalition of all the

61

other players. This payoff, which is called the player's "security level," is analogous to value in the two-person zero-sum game.

Of special interest are games with more than two players in which there is a single prize that can be captured by some of the coalitions, called "winning coalitions," but not by others. Coalitions that cannot capture the prize but can prevent others from capturing it are called "blocking coalitions." Suppose the "prize" is the power to act. The actions of committees, juries, legislatures, and shareholder meetings are clearly examples of such games. The winning and blocking coalitions are determined by the voting rules, the number of votes held by each player or bloc, by whether anyone has veto power, etc. In an American jury, for example, only the coalition of all the "players" is a winning coalition, and every player constitutes a blocking coalition.

In the United Nations Security Council, the winning coalitions are those that include all five permanent members and at least three others. Coalitions that include at least eight of the nonpermanent members or at least one of the Big Five are blocking coalitions. All other coalitions are without power. Note that the Security Council's power to act would remain exactly as it is under the present rules if each of the Big Five were given 8 votes, each of the other members 1 vote, and if 43 votes were required to take action. This sort of analysis reveals the relative "power" of individual members and blocs of members. Game theory is not concerned with the power derived from personal influence, but with that power which accrues to individuals from the "rules of the game."

As a simple example of how coalitions form, consider a game with three players in which the object is to divide $1 among the three by a majority vote. Since any two of the players constitute a majority, the dollar represents the security level of every coalition of two players. Obviously, all three players cannot obtain their security level. It follows, then, that no apportionment of the dollar can be "stable," since there will always be a pair of players who will get jointly less than they *can* get ($1). Therefore, they need not accept the "settlement." But if they form a coalition and claim their dollar, each can be tempted to leave the coalition by the odd man, in whose interest it is to offer the tempted player a larger share of the dollar and to take the rest (rather than nothing). Although in this game no coalition can be "stable," in some games stable apportionments are possible. Such games, which are said to possess a "core," have found some applications in theoretical economics, particularly in market theory.

A science of strategy or of conflict resolution?

It is noteworthy that the problems arising in coalition games are far removed from the original problem posed in game theory: How should a game of strategy be played by a rational player? It is evident that once the area of investigation transcends the simple two-person zero-sum game, the very notion of being rational becomes ambiguous. One must first of all distinguish between individual and collective rationality, as is seen in the dilemmas generated by non-zero-sum games. When the number of players exceeds two, the "player" may be a coalition, in which case the interests of all of the players cannot be brought either into concordance or into strict opposition with each other, because potential coalitions have overlapping memberships. A concentration of attention on the interests of a particular player, which is what a decision-maker might expect from a practical application of game theory to his problems, fails to capture the entire logical structure of the conflict and often leads to a strategy that gives far from optimal results. On the other hand, when all of the interplays of interests are taken into account, game theory becomes more properly a theory of "conflict resolution" rather than a "science of strategy."

Nevertheless, the expectation persists that a scientific approach to rationally conducted conflict can be built on the foundations laid by game theory. Some consequences of this expectation are unfortunate. Because the concept of "the best strategy," for example, is most clearly defined in the context of the zero-sum game, there is a tendency on the part of those concerned with strategic decisions to conceptualize conflicts as clashes of diametrically opposed interests. Applications of game theory in these contexts may increase the sophistication of strategic calculations, but since the techniques are available to everyone, no one can ultimately expect to gain an advantage. The "best" evasive strategy built into an attacking missile is sure to be matched by a "best" intercepting strategy of the anti-missile missile, and vice versa. It is difficult, therefore, to see what benefits are to be expected, besides those that accrue to people with a vested interest in the military profession or its adjuncts, from the general growth and refinement of military technology and of "strategic science."

The greatest promise of game theory, on the other hand, may well lie in the insights imparted by "higher" game theory, that concerned with the analysis of nonzero-sum and multiperson games. The main relevance of these insights is not to a "science of strategy" but to a general theory of conflict, in particular to a theory of conflict resolution. In this respect the impact of game theory is already being felt in economics, sociology, psychology, and political science.

FOR ADDITIONAL READING:

Hurwicz, Leonid, "Game Theory and Decisions," *Scientific American* (February 1955).

Rapoport, Anatol, "The Use and Misuse of Game Theory," *Scientific American* (December 1962).

Shubik, Martin (ed.), *Game Theory and Related Approaches to Social Behavior* (John Wiley & Sons, 1964).

Williams, J. D., *The Compleat Strategyst* (McGraw-Hill, 1954).

Man in America:
The Calico Mountains Excavations by Louis S. B. Leakey, Ruth DeEtte Simpson and Thomas Clements

Stone Age man in America?
A famous archaeologist and his colleagues describe their
attempts to find proof that man lived in the United States
as long as 50,000 years ago, and possibly even earlier. A geologist,
however, disagrees with their interpretation of the evidence.

A cold wind drove rain and sleet into the face of the white-haired craftsman as he knelt among broken chalcedony cobbles on the rock-mantled alluvial fan east of California's Calico Mountains. Eager men and women pressed close to watch and learn how Stone Age man fashioned his tools by banging one stone against another.

Except for a background of trailers and the distant rumble of Las Vegas-bound traffic, this might have been a scene viewed 50,000 to 100,000 years ago. It was, in fact, March 12, 1965, and the craftsman was Louis S. B. Leakey, who had come to examine the archaeological excavation and artifacts at the Calico site in the Mojave Desert of California. Those who watched were his crew. They were learning the mechanics of creating artifacts like the ones being recovered from the excavation. It was the discovery of these artifacts that had brought Leakey to the Mojave Desert.

For Leakey and his crew this was a rewarding day, the culmination of a long cold winter of exploratory excavation in a pioneer archaeological project. Resolutely the crew of seven had dug as Leakey stipulated—with dental picks, sculptors' tools, brushes, and other small tools. They viewed each bit of loosened soil with the hope it would supply some clue to the question that had brought them into the desert in the first place: Had man been here when the alluvial fan was accumulating during the Ice Age, which began approximately 1,000,000 years ago and ended about 15,000 years ago?

Now, with knowledge of the problems encountered at other excavations of possible Pleistocene archaeological sites, and with Leakey's orders for a tightly controlled excavation to guide them, the Calico

General view of the main excavation area at Calico Mountains. The original excavation is in the background; the second pit is in the foreground.

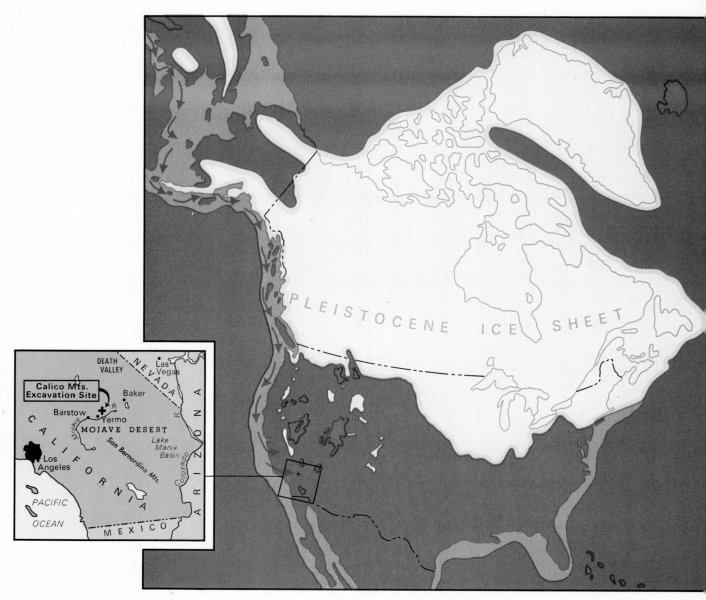

North America during the Ice Ages

LEGEND FOR LARGE MAP

	Modern shoreline
	Ancient shoreline
	Probable migration route
	Extent of glaciation
	Mountain glaciers
	Pleistocene lakes

Small map shows the Calico Mountains excavation site and the surrounding terrain

crew was in hopes of recovering stone tools that would prove man had inhabited this area as long as 50,000 years ago.

Leakey considers the problem

How long has man occupied the American continent? This question has perplexed archaeologists and anthropologists for many years. During the last century a number of stone "spearheads" and "arrowheads" were reported in association with long-extinct animals such as the American mastodon. This evidence led to the postulation that man's arrival in the United States might date nearly as far back as his presence, side by side with the woolly mammoth, in France and southwest Europe generally, which was from about 35,000 to 15,000 years ago.

Gradually, however, thinking shifted away from the idea of such an early arrival of man in America until, by the end of World War II, the generally held view was that man appeared in America no earlier than a few thousand years B.C. Any evidence that seemed to provide an age greater than 5000 B.C. was commonly discarded as unreliable. But then the discovery of two early Paleo-Indian cultural complexes at Folsom and Clovis in New Mexico, as well as the gradual development of the use of carbon-14 dating techniques, began to yield clear evidence that man's history in North America dated back to at least 10,000 B.C., while for some sites an age of nearly 20,000 years began to be discussed. (Traces of carbon-14, a radioactive substance, are found in all organic materials. Because carbon-14 decays—changes to carbon-12—at a constant rate, the amount of carbon-14 remaining in an archaeological specimen is indicative of the specimen's age. Radiocarbon dating techniques are considered reliable, however, only for specimens less than 45,000 years old.)

Theoretically, however, even an age of 20,000 years would appear to be much too recent for the first arrival of man in America. A wide variety of indirect lines of evidence seems to point quite strongly to a considerably earlier date. In the first place, the nature and extent of the human population occupying the Americas at the time of the arrival of the first European explorers has to be considered. From Alaska in the north to Cape Horn in the extreme south, there were numerous tribes of men, each speaking a different language, each exhibiting a different physical appearance, and each responsible for a different type of culture. There were also traces of at least two major civilizations, the Aztec and the Mayan. Taken together, these facts suggest that a time span of only 20,000 years was much too brief to account for these differences. Moreover, the earliest recognized stone-tool culture—namely, the various manifestations of projectile points—was so widespread in what is now the United States that a long period prior to its development, differentiation, and dispersal had to be postulated.

Another factor suggesting that man may have arrived in the Americas much earlier than 20,000 B.C. is the geological and geographical evidence which indicates that there was once a very wide land bridge linking Asia with North America in the area of the Bering Strait. As our knowledge of the distribution of man in the Old World increased, it became apparent that early man had penetrated into Asia more than 400,000 years ago. It is likely, therefore, that some representative of man would have crossed the land bridge while hunting animals. After all, this bridge was crossed by some of the major animals of America, such as the bison, the mountain sheep, and the mountain goat, which are relatively recent arrivals from Asia, where they evolved earlier. Moreover, at a fairly late time in the Pleistocene a true elephant, distinct from the American mastodon, had crossed the bridge from Asia and had become widespread in North America.

67

Migration route proposed by Leakey

With all this evidence pointing so strongly to an early arrival of man in America, it is somewhat surprising, then, that there has not been a more intensive search for artifacts. Some efforts, of course, have been made, but mostly in the wrong places—at least in my opinion.

Clearly, if man first crossed into the Americas at the time when there was a wide land bridge in the Bering Strait region, it follows that the relative land and sea levels at that time must have been very different from those of today. The sea level must have been appreciably lower because of the vast quantities of water locked in the ice sheets. Furthermore, there is every reason to believe that the land bridge would have persisted as such well into the succeeding warmer climatic phase, when the huge ice sheets melted, because a change to a warmer climatic condition is always accompanied by a much slower adjustment of the relative land and sea levels.

It can be postulated, then, that if early Stone Age hunters did cross from Asia into America in the wake of herds of animals, they must have done so at a time when most of the North American seashore was a good many miles out to sea rather than where it is today. The present existence of a shallow submarine shelf along this coastline is evidence for this view.

With all of these points in mind, I asked myself, "What route would I have taken in exploring new country if I had been in the 'shoes' of the Stone Age hunters at that time?" At any point in his development man must have an adequate supply of drinking water, especially if he is at a cultural stage where he cannot carry or store it. I surmised, therefore, that in his case I would have followed routes where I would most likely find drinkable water.

Undoubtedly, early man was already a hunter but not a very skilled one. He had to rely, to some extent, on foods other than the flesh of animals he killed. Under such conditions I further surmised that, in his shoes, I would have chosen a route where I could be reasonably certain of finding food if my hunting was unsuccessful.

All of these factors seemed to indicate the same answer: "Follow the shoreline southward." Along the seashore it is hard to go many miles without finding at least a trickle of fresh drinkable water, because all water from the interior has to find its way, ultimately, down to the sea. Furthermore, no matter what other sources of food may or may not be available, along a shoreline one can always find shellfish exposed by the receding tides, stranded fish in pools, a variety of crabs and other crustaceans, an occasional dead seabird, and possibly edible seaweeds.

A shoreline route, therefore, would provide water and a quantity of food, with occasional forays into the interior for game animals. Such a sea-level route also tends to be warmer than one at higher altitudes, and there are usually sheltering cliffs with rock shelters to provide protection against the worst effects of weather.

Eventually, there must have come a time when these early Stone Age invaders had traveled far enough south to reach a point where the ancient shoreline and the modern one more or less coincided. By this time they would be well away from the worst effects of the northern cold. Their numbers, too, might be expected to have increased, and as they became more accustomed to the new country, they would tend to begin exploring deeper into the interior in their search for food.

Leakey begins his search for evidence

Because the shoreline over which Stone Age man traveled now lies mainly beneath the ocean, I believe that the evidence concerning the earliest migration of man into the Americas will be discovered only when we are able to conduct undersea exploration and excavation more successfully than at present. Other early important sites will doubtless also be found, as, for example, on places like Santa Rosa Island, which is off the coast of Santa Barbara, Calif. At the time of the land bridge this island must have been a hilly zone, rising from the coastal plain with the sea not too far distant to the west of it. But even though it may be difficult to locate evidence of the earliest arrival of man, there is still a good chance of finding evidence of subsequent stages prior to 20,000 years ago, which is now the usually accepted date for man's arrival in America.

An aerial view of the eroded remnant of the alluvial fan in which the Calico Mountains archaeological site is located.

Dan Morrill © EB Inc.

At this point we must consider what requirements were essential before Stone Age man could occupy a region. These included: (1) the presence of drinkable water; (2) the presence, not too far away from the water, of types of stone suitable for making stone tools; and (3) conditions that would provide good opportunities for successful hunting.

The Calico Mountains site, which I visited for the first time with Ruth DeEtte (Dee) Simpson in May 1963, provided all of these facilities. There was a great alluvial fan in an area that is now almost desert. Its presence indicated an abundance of water at some remote geological period. Around the base of the mountains there was good exposure of chalcedony as well as some other suitable rocks for making stone tools. Beyond the front of the fan, in the area that later became Lake Manix, there was a large, flat location that at one time must have been swampy and highly suitable for the hunting of animals.

While examining an undisturbed deposit of the fan with Dee Simpson and her colleagues, I found traces of what seemed to me to be human artifacts in situ. I immediately decided that the site was suitable for exploration by excavation, which started in 1964. So far as I am concerned, the results have been conclusive: *this area of California was occupied by man more than 50,000 years ago.*

Geological history of the Calico site

The archaeological site is situated near the east end of the Calico Mountains, approximately 15 mi E of Barstow, Calif It is in the drainage basin of the Mojave River, which rises in the San Bernardino Mountains, in California, and flows north and northeast through the Mojave Desert, ending in Lake Mojave near the town of Baker, Calif.

During the Pleistocene, or Great Ice Age, the Mojave River filled various basins, creating sizable freshwater lakes that extended as far north as Death Valley, Calif. The Lake Manix Basin, southeast of the Calico Mountains, is one of those that was filled repeatedly by the Mojave River during the Wisconsin or Late Ice Age, and possibly even earlier. In the drier interglacial ages and subages, the ancestral Mojave River followed much the same course as the modern river.

Desert mountains are frequently surrounded by accumulations of alluvium (rock fragments, gravel, sand, and silt) that are transported from mountain canyons by intermittent floods and deposited at the foot of the mountain. Because these deposits are quite often fan-shaped, they are called alluvial fans. The archaeological site at the foot of the Calico Mountains lies on and within a deeply eroded remnant of such an alluvial fan. Since its formation in the Lake Manix Basin during one of the drier interglacial ages or subages of the Great Ice Age, erosion and other geological changes have reduced the fan to a series of low hills. It has also been cut off from the mountain canyon that provided the alluvial debris. Today, the fan is inactive, exhibiting its distinctive shape only when viewed from the air.

The alluvial materials in and on the fan can be traced directly to their sources in the Calico Mountains, where they are exposed today in Mule Canyon and its tributaries. These materials include chalcedony, jasper, petrified wood, limestone, volcanic tuff, rhyolite, andesite, and dacite. The chalcedony and jasper on the fan afforded essential high-grade tool-making material to early human hunters as they followed camels, horses, elephants, and other Pleistocene animals along the course of the ancestral Mojave River. Since the artifacts testifying to man's presence are found deep within the fan, it is evident that man must have made tools there while the fan was forming.

Geomorphic evidence observed so far indicates that the fan was subjected to three stages of erosion. If these three stages correspond to the three subages of Wisconsin glaciation that occurred in the Sierra Nevada, then the fan must have been formed during the pre-Wisconsin interglacial age. (The Wisconsin glacial period, which consisted of several glacial advances and retreats, was the last of the four major glacial periods during the Pleistocene. The date at which it began is not yet known, having been estimated at from 50,000 to 120,000 years ago but most probably somewhere between 80,000 and 100,000 years ago. In Europe, the Wisconsin is equivalent to the Würm glacial period.) On the basis of this possible correspondence and the artifacts collected at the Calico site, it is the opinion of Thomas Clements, the project geologist, that the fan was formed from 50,000 to possibly 100,000 years ago, and that man's presence in the area must date from that time.

How the Calico project began

In 1948, Ritner Sayles, a veteran amateur archaeologist, took Gerald Smith and Dee Simpson to a row of hills east of the Calico Mountains in the Mojave Desert near Barstow. Smith was compiling records of archaeological sites for the San Bernardino County Museum, Bloomington, Calif.; Dee Simpson was at that time a staff member at the Southwest Museum in Los Angeles. Strewn about the hills, which rose above the shorelines of Pleistocene Lake Manix, were workshop materials and artifacts unlike anything ever seen before in the known archaeological assemblages from the Mojave River region. ("Workshop materials" are accumulations of flakes, broken stone tools, and other items in places—*i.e.,* workshops—where early man manufactured his stone tools. An "archaeological assemblage" refers to an accumulation of archaeological specimens—pottery, projectile points, grinding tools, etc.)

Six years later, under the auspices of the Southwest Museum and the Archaeological Survey Association of Southern California, Dee Simpson began a survey of the archaeological sites in the Lake Manix

Dan Morrill © EB Inc.

Courtesy, Bob Ashton, Sr.

The excavation has yielded hundreds of artifacts, including tools and flakes of jasper and chalcedony. Two views of a tool fashioned on a cornerstruck flake are shown in the top and bottom photographs; one of several segments of a fossil tusk recovered during the excavation is displayed in the center.

Basin. At 1,780 ft above the highest established shoreline for Lake Manix, the survey, which was designated as Phase I of the Manix Basin Project, recorded sites characterized by tool assemblages that were similar to those reported earlier by Ritner Sayles. A selection of these tools was taken to Europe in 1958 for examination and comparative studies. Among those who saw them was Leakey.

Five years later, when visiting California after his initial dramatic successes at Olduvai Gorge in what is now Tanzania, Leakey remembered the Lake Manix materials and was taken by Dee Simpson to the area where they were found. The region appeared to him as a likely place to look for evidence of man's early occupation of America. Subsequently, a search of the eastern Calico Mountains, northwest of the basin, led to the selection of a high ridge for exploratory excavation. It was here that Leakey stood on a hot day in May 1963 and said, "Dee, dig here." Grabbing large cobbles, he quickly built four rock cairns to mark the location of a square area, 25 ft on each side. Thus was born Master Pit I.

From the project's interpretive program comes this portrayal of the major soil changes in a section of the north wall in Master Pit I. The slope at the top reflects the slope of the ground surface; irregularities at the bottom indicate the unfinished floor of the pit.

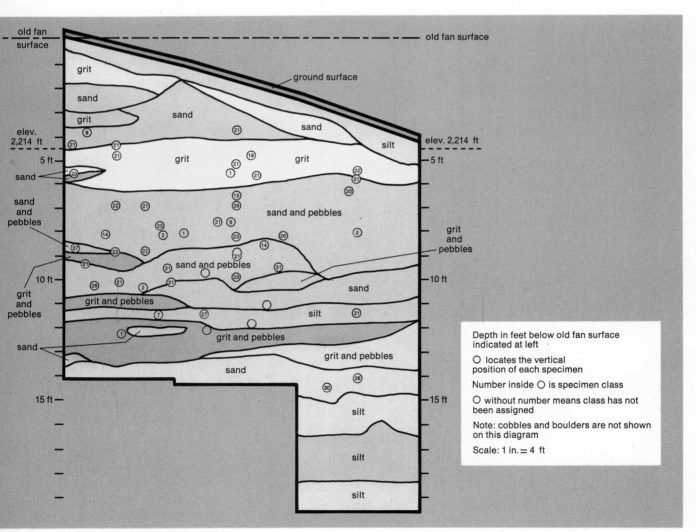

Exploration of the site

Following Leakey's visit in May 1963, he presented the data and potential of the Calico site to the National Geographic Society, which agreed to support an exploratory excavation. Leakey would direct the project, which would be administered by Gerald Smith and the San Bernardino County Museum. The fieldwork would be supervised by Dee Simpson, who is now the San Bernardino County archaeologist; the geologist would be Thomas Clements, formerly chairman of the department of geology at the University of Southern California.

Excavation began on Nov. 1, 1964. As each worker in the crew of seven began removing the earth from Master Pit I, every fragment of soil and rock was examined with painstaking care. Three or four feet below the surface and a month after work began, an undisturbed primary alluvial fan of Pleistocene age was encountered. Beneath the surface of this old fan, which was delineated by a conspicuous

An eastward view across Master Pit I. The floor levels indicate the progress of work in five-foot squares. The underlying Miocene has been reached in the northeast corner (upper left).

Dan Morrill © EB Inc.

73

boulder line in the pit walls, there was a marked increase in cementation of the deposit. Ripping tools were used to loosen the debris in this stage of the excavation. Since late in 1964 it has been the coarse sands and grits below the boulder-strewn surface of the old fan from which the uniquely different artifacts that provide the crucial archaeological evidence have been recovered. It was the discovery of these artifacts that brought Leakey back to the site in March 1965 with Matthew Stirling, an authority on American archaeology who is associated with the Smithsonian Institution in Washington, D.C.

Leakey says "yes"

On the morning of March 11, 1965, Leakey and Stirling stepped onto the visitors' platform high above the southwest corner of Master Pit I. After Leakey had greeted the crew, moments of quiet followed while he began his examination of the artifacts. Then Leakey's soft but excited voice was heard explaining the importance of one piece after another to Stirling. Slowly the crew began to realize what was happening: Leakey was accepting as man-made some of the materials in the pit!

By the end of the day Leakey had selected more than 25 specimens that he declared to be unquestionably fashioned by man. Stirling, though more reserved than Leakey, said he was "about 85% convinced." It appeared that the door to a whole new era of American archaeology had swung open. Both men agreed that the work must continue for a second season.

A new season, a new perspective: Phase II of the project

By October 1965 the pioneering aspect of the Calico project had essentially ended. As the second season began, there was one major objective: to expand Master Pit I and to deepen and extend related test pits and trenches in order to accumulate a sizable number of artifacts. As the digging progressed, an interpretive program was begun. Plastic casts and drawings were made of key specimens; soil profiles and distribution charts were developed. Meanwhile, a comprehensive photographic program continued in the pits and field laboratory.

In March 1966 another major plateau was reached in the progression of events at the Calico site. A symposium of nine scientists was convened to determine if enough had been learned or if more data were needed. The members of the symposium asked that another pit be dug so that its story could be compared with that of Master Pit I.

The walls in the southwest corner of Master Pit II (below) show both water-laid and mudflow deposits. The study collection of jasper samples (bottom right) and the stockpile of siliceous materials in the screening area (bottom center) were extracted from the pit.

Dan Morrill © EB Inc.

They maintained that *if* the "tools" had been fashioned by nature, any pit dug in the same rocky deposit of the fan would yield comparable materials. To support a third season of work devoted to opening this pit and carrying it down to at least 20 ft, another grant was obtained from the National Geographic Society.

Dee Simpson and Leakey examine new specimens from the excavation and select those that are most significant.

Subsequent work, different objectives

The third season was dominated by the excavation of control pits and the refinement of the interpretive program. In a very real sense, the emphasis had left Phase II (exploration and the accumulation of specimens) and was centered on the development of special objectives (Phase III).

Control Pit I, situated about one-quarter mile northwest of Master Pit I, was opened in November 1966. Within its boundaries of 15 × 10 ft, 6 diggers worked while 12 helpers screened and sorted materials at the screening platforms. Four months later and 28 ft beneath the surface—after examining 11,961 pieces of siliceous rock (chalcedony and jasper) and discarding thousands of volcanic cobbles and boulders—it was agreed that no man-made artifacts had been recovered and that work should stop in Control Pit I. During the next two months a smaller Control Pit II was excavated with the same results.

With additional funds from the National Geographic Society for a fourth season, work continued during the winter of 1967–68. It was apparent, however, that excavation in Master Pit I was nearing completion. The fourth-season yield from the pit was small, but even below 13 ft some outstanding pieces were recovered. The discovery of artifacts at this depth added to the significance of the finds.

At Leakey's request Master Pit II was opened 40 ft northwest of Master Pit I. Ultimately the excavation reached the same fan struc-

continued on page 78

A scientist disagrees . . .

Doubt about the presence of man in the New World before the end of the last glaciation was dispelled in 1926, when scientists excavated skeletons of a large and extinct form of bison near the little town of Folsom, N.M., and found a number of flint spearpoints among the bones. This discovery proved that ancient man had hunted an extinct form of bison in America between 10,000 and 11,000 years ago. Since the Folsom discovery over 100 sites of early man have been found in America and have been dated between 8,000 and 12,000 years ago by radiocarbon methods.

It is for the millennia before 12,000 years ago that we have only disputable or indefinite evidence for the presence of man in the New World. There are six or more locations in the United States, Mexico, and Venezuela where there are archaeological sites that are either in excess of 12,000 years old or contain the remains of extinct big-game animals, but in each case either the association with artifacts or the correlation to dated sequences is in dispute. Nevertheless, it appears likely that some demonstrable proof for the existence of man in the New World between 12,000 and 30,000 years ago will be found in the near future.

It is beyond 30,000 years ago that the evidence for New World man is extremely tenuous. Here the evidence offered is much the same as it was during the 19th century. The reported Calico Mountains site in California is in this category because the flints there occur in an alluvial-fan deposit that contains a significant percentage of flint. It is possible, therefore, that the "artifacts" were actually flaked by natural processes and not by man.

Alluvial-fan deposits form by a combination of geologic processes known as mass wasting and fluvial transport. In mass wasting, rocks derived from outcrops by natural splitting roll down slopes and into drainages where they are subsequently moved by streams. If some of the outcrops are chert or flint, as they are at the Calico site, then fragments of this readily flakable material can become chipped and battered as they fall from outcrops and roll down slopes against other rocks. In being moved out of mountain valleys by streams, the flints are further subjected to percussion by stream processes or mudflows. As the streams spread over alluvial fans along the mountain front, the coarser particles are eventually buried as the fan builds up. Pressure increases as the thickness of the deposits increases, and pressure-retouch type of flaking will occur.

Moreover, streams may entrench themselves into the fan and, in so doing, move sediments that had remained static for thousands of years. Under these conditions a flint cobble or large spall may be retouched again by percussion, thus producing a second generation of flaking. Also, granitic rocks can become so weathered that they disintegrate when moved a second time; this allows the more resistant flints to become concentrated.

When all of these processes are considered, it is clear that there are innumerable possibilities for flakes and flake scars to be produced that are indistinguishable from those produced by primitive man. It is conceivable, therefore, that even crude bifacially worked flints could be produced by natural processes during the deposition of flint-bearing gravels, and this may be the problem at the Calico site. The critical question is not how old the deposit is or what the plants and animals were at the time of deposition but whether any of the flints buried in the deposits actually are the work of man. Unfortunately, we may never know. For every potential artifact there are literally thousands of natural pieces of flint of equal size. Therefore, for every 1,000 fragments of flint in a natural deposit, some pseudo-artifacts can be expected to occur.

Another problem with the Calico Mountains and similar sites is that even the experts disagree as to what constitutes an artifact. Ten different authorities would likely select ten different assemblages of possible artifacts from a given sample of a thousand or so pieces. These problems have plagued archaeologists since long before the term "eolith," or dawn stone, was first proposed for flints from the Crag deposits of East Anglia, Eng., in the 1890s. It has long been recognized that at a point in human evolution there must have been a time when primitive man used only slightly modified stones as tools; without other substantiating evidence, these would be indistinguishable from natural stones. Such is especially the case in flint-bearing gravels.

In archaeological sites, concentration of flints anomalous to a deposit and in association with fossil bones, fire hearth, or other indisputable cultural evidence in stratigraphic context is sufficient evidence to support the interpretation that man was indeed present. If such corroborative evidence were to be demonstrated at the Calico site, it might revolutionize prevailing theory on human occupation and peopling of the New World; the intensive degree of weathering and strong soil development displayed by the alluvial-fan deposits at the Calico site indicate a mid-Pleistocene or older age for the deposits. Such an age for artifacts in the New World would suggest the presence of pre *Homo sapiens*. Yet, all evidence after more than a century of investigation indicates there has been no human evolution in the New World and that man reached the Western Hemisphere in late Pleistocene time, after achieving a fully modern stage elsewhere.

—C. Vance Haynes, Jr.
Department of Geology
Southern Methodist University

. . . and Dr. Leakey replies

Vance Haynes writes, "the flints there [at the Calico Mountains site] occur in an alluvial-fan deposit that contains a significant percentage of flint. It is possible, therefore, that the 'artifacts' were actually flaked by natural processes and not by man." (The material he refers to as flint is not, I think, flint, but chert.) This criticism is, in essence, that which has been made by all those who are unwilling to accept our conclusions as to the man-made nature of the specimens that we consider to be "artifacts" at the Calico Mountains excavations. Haynes himself voiced this opinion to us during his visit to the site several years ago. On that occasion he maintained that—in his view —if we were to make a "random excavation" of similar size and to a similar depth *anywhere into this particular fan,* we would, inevitably, discover an equally large number of specimens that simulated man's workmanship. These specimens would be similar to those we were finding in the site I had selected two years previously.

In consequence of his claim and to test his theory, we expended considerable money and much effort to carry out his suggestion. This random test excavation yielded tens of thousands of pieces of chert (some large broken lumps, some smaller broken fragments of material), but there was not one single specimen that I, personally, would have classified as an "unquestionably humanly made artifact." But there were three specimens which a less critical person thought might be classified as artifacts.

Another factor against Haynes's hypothesis that nature made what we call artifacts at Calico is that the vast majority of the irregular pieces of naturally broken chert and blocks within the fan matrix are of very poor quality material, full of holes and irregularities. The specimens that exhibit evidences of human workmanship, on the other hand, are, almost without exception, made from carefully selected material. Nature, so far as I know, has no means of such selectivity! If nature had been the cause of the many large flakes

we have found, then a high proportion of them should, I believe, have been cortex flakes of poor quality chert, which is not the case.

Haynes raises the question of "eoliths," and cites in particular those of the Crag deposits in East Anglia, Eng. Let me assure him that, having studied the problem of pseudo-artifacts at intervals since 1926 from such sites as the Crag deposits, Gray's Inn (London), and Chard, Eng., I naturally took into full account the possibility that nature was the maker of the specimens I was classifying as artifacts at Calico. I satisfied myself entirely, however, that such an explanation had to be ruled out in the case of our Calico site.

There is yet another factor that must be considered. I know from my experiences at the English sites mentioned above that, where nature knocks off flakes that simulate the work of man, the majority are not transported very far from where they were detached. Again and again, at Chard and in the Crag deposits, one finds the flake that was knocked off lying in the deposit not far from the lump of stone from which it was detached. At Calico, although we have numerous flakes of medium to large sizes from a very small area of excavation, we have only a very limited number of cores, or lumps, showing negative flake scars of a size comparable to the flakes found. This suggests to me that the flakes that we have found, as well as the other artifacts, were made at some other point, not as yet located, and that they were carried by human agency to the very limited area where we found them.

Moreover, we now have in the collection numerous examples of "duplication," which is a thing nature seldom does. For example, we have about 30 typical concavo-convex flakes, any one of which would be difficult for nature to make. In fact, I have never seen such a flake at a site where nature's handiwork is proven.

Naturally, we expect skepticism about the Calico finds, particularly because there is very strong feeling against the presence of man in America as early as the Middle Pleistocene. (Incidentally, I agree with Haynes that the site is probably of Middle Pleistocene age.) It would, perhaps, be salutary to remember that although the first *Australopithecus* skull was discovered by Raymond Dart as long ago as 1924, and although many subsequent finds were made by him and by Robert Broom in the years that followed, it was not until 23 years later—1947—that there was general acceptance that the australopithecines were Hominidae and not Pongidae.

—Louis S. B. Leakey
National Centre of Pre-History and Palaeontology
Nairobi, Kenya

An artist prepares molds for casts of the artifacts while new information is added to the statistical records. The laboratory technician (right) is applying permanent labels to the specimens.

continued from page 75

ture and surface marked by massive boulders as those encountered in Master Pit I. Had nature been fashioning the "tools," most certainly some would have been found in the boulder level, yet there were none. After passing through the boulder level, however, good man-made artifacts were recovered from Master Pit II.

Interpreting the evidence

The authors believe that a sizable enough collection of man-made artifacts has been recovered from the Calico site to substantiate their theory concerning man's early existence in North America. This view is now shared by an increasing number of archaeologists and geologists. Others, however, still find it difficult to accept the specimens as conclusive evidence of human workmanship. (See *A scientist disagrees. . . . and Dr. Leakey replies,* pages 76–77.)

Although Leakey has examined hundreds of specimens recovered from the site, much more detailed analysis and comparison with Asian and other Paleolithic-like assemblages must be accomplished before any effort is made to assign the Calico artifacts to specific typological classifications. It is apparent, nevertheless, that the Calico excavations have yielded man-made stone tools, some of which appear to have been primitive hand axes and scrapers.

During the fifth season at the Calico site, the emphasis has been on processing geomorphological information and increasing the artifact assemblage. At this point in the project, however, it is pertinent to ask ourselves, "What accomplishments do the findings indicate? What new dimensions have been added to the sum total of knowledge with reference to American prehistory?"

First, through a tightly controlled and closely supervised excavation, it has been demonstrated that evidence of Paleolithic-like occupation can be detected and recorded on the American continent.

Second, Leakey's selection of the excavation site on an ancient alluvial fan has introduced an entirely new aspect of American archaeology. It is now evident that major Pleistocene drainage areas must be reexamined far away from shorelines and terraces.

Third, the Calico site has produced an assemblage of lithic (stone) tools and workshop materials significantly and distinctively different from any of those previously seen in America. Detailed analysis of the materials must still be made, however, and the specimens must be compared to Asiatic Paleolithic assemblages before specific tool types can be designated.

Shown above is the stockpile of unmodified siliceous material that was removed from Master Pit II.

Fourth, the several excavations afford the student an opportunity to study a controlled cross section of a Pleistocene alluvial fan, making readily visible features that are difficult to observe in natural exposures or in a limited excavation.

Fifth, the alluvial fan provides a story of geomorphological development and erosion that, at this point in the project, would seem to make mandatory the acceptance of a minimum of approximately 50,000 years as the age of the deposits.

Finally, the project has added a greater dimension to American prehistory. It has opened the door to a new era of research and has brought into the realm of feasibility the concept of a Stone Age man in America and of an American Paleolithic culture.

It will take other similar projects and other similar demonstrations of credibility before the existence of a Stone Age man in America is fully accepted. Calico will not long remain the oldest known site of its kind, but it will stand as the place where a major breakthrough was achieved in discovery, excavation technique, interpretation, and provocative open-minded thinking.

FOR ADDITIONAL READING:

Belden, L. Burr, "50,000 Years Ago," *Desert Magazine,* pp. 8–11 (December 1968).

Leakey, Louis S. B., Simpson, Ruth De Ette, and Clements, Thomas, "Archaeological Excavations in the Calico Mountains, California: Preliminary Report," *Science,* pp. 1022–23 (May 31, 1968).

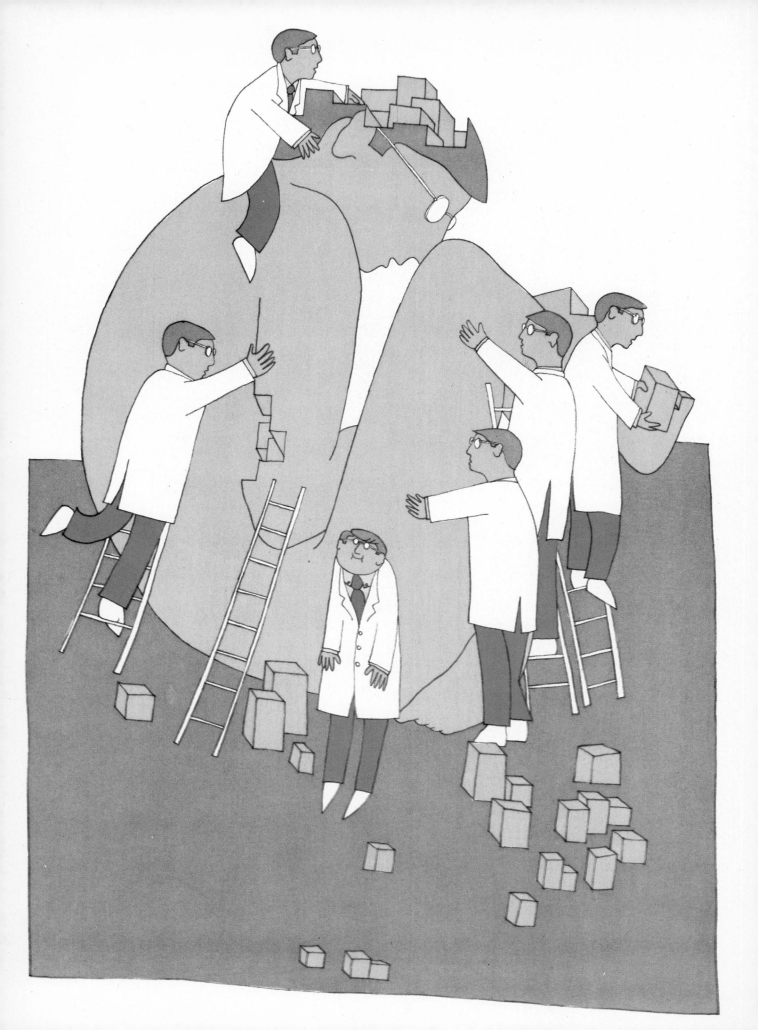

Humanics and Genetic Engineering

by Joshua Lederberg

**A distinguished scientist and Nobel laureate
describes man's attempts to understand and control
his genetic endowments. At the same time, he expresses his hopes
and concerns about the ability of society to apply this awesome
power toward constructive ends for the betterment of all mankind.**

Humanics is defined in the dictionary as the scientific study of human nature. It tells something of our past traditions that the word is an unfamiliar one; but the subject it describes is inevitably caught up in the recent rush of progress in experimental biology. In particular, dramatic advances in our knowledge of the biochemistry of deoxyribonucleic acid (DNA) and of its function as the material basis of heredity have provoked much new speculation about the application of this new knowledge to man and his problems. (See *1969 Britannica Yearbook of Science and the Future,* Feature Article: THE LANGUAGE OF LIFE.) As a result of these advances, we anticipate better tools to mitigate disease, to improve agriculture, and to exploit microorganisms in industry.

We must also visualize, however, the impact of genetic engineering on humanics, which includes the possible modification of human nature toward previously unattainable ideals. Phrases like "genetic programming" or "genetic engineering" may conjure up the Frankensteinian image of a mad scientist or a technocratic dictator pushing the buttons that will control an assembly line of babies produced to order for service as infantrymen or storm troopers or docile subjects. Some may even imagine that their own genes may somehow be subjected to alteration at someone else's command or, alternatively, that they will have unlimited options to create any manner of offspring they wish—perhaps a child who might grow up as an athletic prodigy with an IQ of 350 and a head of hair that automatically shears itself at regular intervals. Actually, our present knowledge of genetic science is not the obvious limiting factor for the furtherance of such aims. Rather, we lack the necessary insight into the essential biochemistry, developmental biology, psychology, and social dynamics of these phenomena. And indeed, were we to gain such insight, genetic engineering would probably be a redundant tool in competition with many other ways of influencing human development and behavior. To avoid the distorted view of genetic engineering that is all too prevalent in contemporary journalism, the topic must be examined within a broader view of man's evolutionary history and of the impact of established institutions on human biology.

Unconscious genetic engineering

Genetic engineering has, nevertheless, been an important element in human cultural progress. The beginnings of agriculture depended on the remarkable insight that the seeds of a given plant would beget others like it. Early agricultural man, in his development of crops like Indian corn and wheat, accomplished technical miracles that have still to be surpassed by contemporary plant science. This kind of "biological engineering"—to produce reliable food crops from wild grasses—achieved a phenomenal result without the benefit of profound insight into the mechanism of heredity or the chemistry of DNA. The prescientific domestication of animals such as the dog likewise speaks for an uncanny shrewdness on the part of early man.

We have no way of knowing whether prehistoric man consciously applied similar principles to guiding his own evolution by selective breeding. In many subhuman primates the social hierarchy does give a dominant male privileged access to receptive females during their intervals of maximum fertility. With the development of democratic ideals, however, the very concept of compulsory selective breeding as a method of engineering human improvement has been discredited as a violation of elementary human rights. Nevertheless, the whole social fabric constitutes a pattern of genetic engineering of human qualities more or less consciously intended to prevent deviance from the established norms of a given community. Racial characteristics may just as likely have been conserved by cultural discrimination against deviants and strangers who displayed differences in these obvious features. Other customs, like monogamy, primogeniture, prohibitions against incest, nationalism, war, and commerce have played their part in the de facto policy of genetic engineering of the human species.

Very few new techniques for genetic engineering have been firmly established, although there are many important innovations in early prospect. Genetic analysis has, however, helped to expose the actual practices just summarized, and to point out that they do constitute a pragmatic social policy of human reproduction, whether or not this was arrived at by conscious legislation.

Genetic diseases

The principal utility of genetics in modern medicine is in diagnosis, now applicable to many specific genetic diseases with great precision, mainly by the use of biochemical and of microscopic methods. It is often possible to counsel the parents in a family where a rare disease has cropped up about the prospects of a similar anomaly occurring again in future children. Since many parents will respond to discouraging advice by not taking chances, this kind of genetic counseling is a de facto form of selective breeding. Its principal benefit, however, is intended to promote the integrity of the family and to prevent the conception of children likely to suffer from a serious defect. A by-product of genetic counseling in this situation is to reduce the frequency of defective genes in the next generation.

Because certain deleterious genes can also be detected in the hybrid carrier state, some individuals may use this information in their selection of mates. As yet, we have no reliable statistical information on the subject, but it is doubtful that any significant number of people take genetic factors into account when they fall in love and marry. From a population-genetic point of view, selective mating does not help to eliminate a deleterious gene from the

Computer techniques allow geneticists to analyze chromosome patterns virtually automatically. A computer scans a photomicrograph of a set of chromosomes and assigns numbers from one to six to the levels of darkness within the picture. A computer printout (right) reproduces the original micrograph. Detail at left reveals the computer's numbering system.

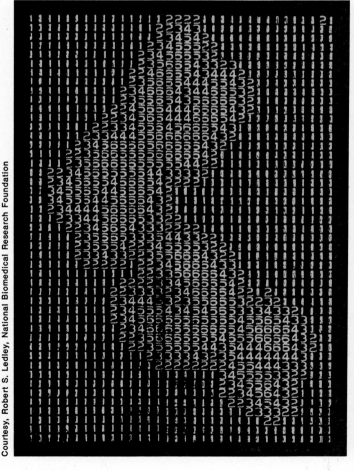

population; it merely postpones the overt occurrence of defective offspring. Since future generations may well be better equipped to repair a genetic defect than we are at the present time, selective mating can hardly be called an imprudent policy.

The genetic diseases to which such considerations apply are each quite rare, but there are enough of them to warrant the spreading practice of genetic diagnosis in order to furnish significant information to a considerable proportion of the population. The average human being carries the equivalent of eight or ten potentially harmful genetic defects, all of which are usually masked in the hybrid condition. Although most of these defects are not now recognizable by biochemical analysis, studies of DNA specificity and of cell fusion are beginning to revolutionize our approach to these problems.

Cell cultures from specimens of blood or from tiny fragments of skin have enhanced the diagnosis of many genetic diseases. More recently, this technique has also been applied to cells obtained from the amniotic fluid that surrounds the developing fetus. By this method the occurrence of a serious genetic disease in a young fetus can be diagnosed and the mother may request a therapeutic abortion so as to avoid bearing a severely crippled or retarded child. (*See* Year in Review: MEDICINE, *Medical Genetics*.)

A number of genetic diseases can now be detected prenatally. Of these cystic fibrosis, a metabolic disorder in children, is undoubtedly the most prevalent and, therefore, statistically the most important. Its incidence, however, is too rare to recommend the routine examination of amniotic fluid in every pregnancy. On the other hand, the carrier state for cystic fibrosis can also be determined in the parents, and fetal examination would be indicated if there is already one chance in four that the fetus may be diseased. While the elimination of fetuses having this serious genetic disease may appear to be a negative approach, this procedure should be weighed against the assurance that can be given parents of being able to nurture a child free from disease on future attempts. Eventually, a better understanding of the biochemistry of cystic fibrosis may lead to methods of treatment so effective that the disease would no longer be the serious burden to the young child that it is today.

In many respects, mongolism, or Down's syndrome, is more serious than cystic fibrosis because of its severe mental retardation. Prenatal examination can reveal the extra chromosome that causes the condition. Down's syndrome occurs in one of about 600 births, but certain individuals have a chromosome pattern that predisposes them to a much higher frequency of afflicted progeny. For such mothers, and mothers with pregnancies at advanced ages, a prenatal examination of fetal cells is especially indicated.

Paradoxically, additional conceptions undertaken to compensate for an eliminated fetus will tend to increase the frequency of the deleterious gene in the population. For example, the child with

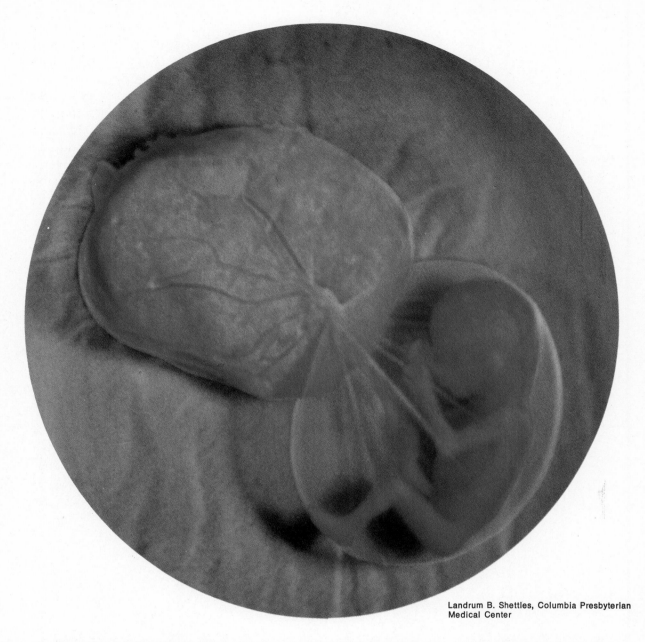

Landrum B. Shettles, Columbia Presbyterian
Medical Center

cystic fibrosis was, until recently, not likely to survive until reproductive age and, therefore, did not contribute to the gene pool of
the following generation. Also, the diseased child tended to displace a potential sibling whose odds are two in three of being a
carrier for the gene and who would eventually contribute to the
gene pool. If, however, our objective in this kind of medicine is to
alleviate unnecessary human distress, then we should focus our
attention on the reduction of the disease, rather than on the elimination of the gene for it. In spite of the obvious natural selection
against it, the gene's very capacity to survive in the human population indicates that it might also carry some still unexplained and
even beneficial function in human fitness.

*The presence of a serious genetic
disease can be detected before birth
by examining cultured cells
obtained from the amniotic fluid
that surrounds a developing fetus.
Above, a ten-week-old fetus
in its amniotic sac can be seen
at the right. Attached to the sac
is the placenta, which provides
the fetus with a source
of nourishment by uniting it
to the mother's uterus.*

Selective breeding

Another characteristic (one hesitates to call it a disease) that can be diagnosed by prenatal examination is the sex of the fetus. Improved determination of fetal sex at an early age, and the development of drugs to induce a voluntary abortion that is essentially indistinguishable from induced menstruation may make individual control of the sex of the offspring technically plausible. The use of abortion for this purpose, however, would probably be repugnant to most people. If there are biases favoring one or the other sex, we should, perhaps, be giving more attention to rectifying a social order that fosters such discrimination.

Germinal choice, which is another approach to selective breeding, has been advocated strongly by Julian Huxley and the late Hermann J. Muller. Their scheme would provide for the banking of sperm from preferred men in cold storage for later voluntary use in artificial insemination. Real problems arise, of course, in the identification of preferred males, even some years posthumously, and in the social environment in which the qualities of one versus another potential sire are publicly touted.

However bizarre these schemes for selective breeding may appear, the present world does exhibit a wide disparity in the number of offspring produced by different parents. In some sense, our other social policies establish the pattern for these discrepancies. Yet, we know too little of human genetics to sustain an informed criticism (or approval!) of that pattern. It is much more difficult not to be alarmed at some examples of negative family planning in relation to parents' ability to provide each child with the parental care that should be his birthright. On the other hand, we have still to devise compulsory schemes that can discourage overbreeding where it de-

Phase contrast microscopy reveals the two distinctive shapes that human sperm can take. Sperm with round "heads" carry the Y, or male, sex chromosome. "Heads" of sperm carrying the X, or female, sex chromosome are characteristically oval in shape. Various schemes for selective breeding are contingent on the ability to detect the genetic traits that a particular sperm is carrying.

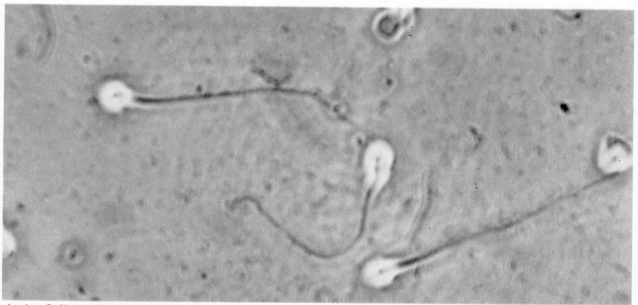

Landrum B. Shettles, Columbia Presbyterian Medical Center

means a child's rights without at the same time creating an unacceptable invasion of the personal freedoms of the parents.

Experiments in genetic intervention

Let us now consider some of the more speculative proposals for genetic intervention that are founded on experiments with laboratory animals and plants. It is not easy, however, to set clear boundaries for the subject of genetic intervention. Since one could postulate that the right set of genes could forestall the possibility of a disease developing in a person, any disease can then be said to have a genetic aspect. Preventive measures, such as the Sabin vaccine for polio, can be regarded as an artificial replacement of the human genes that are unequal to this one of life's challenges. We do not know, however, whether any living human beings already contain genetic factors for resistance to polio virus. If they did, the comparison of resistant and sensitive individuals would put the genetic aspect of this kind of medicine into sharper focus.

The same point can be made even more vividly by considering the global disease called malnutrition, which is usually regarded as a dietary insufficiency stemming from a lack of appropriate amino acids in the available food. But, because no known human beings have the necessary built-in genes to accomplish the internal synthesis of the required amino acids and vitamins, malnutrition can also be regarded as a pan-human genetic defect. By contrast, most plant species and many microorganisms are well endowed with the necessary genes for the biosynthesis of these materials.

It is not inconceivable that some humans already possess those genes needed for effective internal synthesis of amino acids. This idea, in fact, now appears somewhat less fanciful than it did with the recent discovery that, among the world's adult population, probably only Caucasians usually have the genes needed for the formation of lactase, an enzyme for the digestion of milk sugar. On the other hand, many samples of Negroes and of Orientals tested as adults lacked this capacity and tended to be intolerant of milk. (See Year in Review: FOOD AND NUTRITION.)

One conceivable approach to solving the problem of malnutrition would be the attempt to find and selectively breed those individuals whose genetic endowment may possibly enable internal synthesis of amino acids. Or we may solve this genetic deficit by producing proper food and distributing it to those who need it, thus accomplishing the same purposes as selective breeding.

It is clear that the growth of the human brain is retarded by either maternal malnutrition or malnutrition of the newborn, or both (see Feature Article: WHEN YOUNG CHILDREN GO HUNGRY: EFFECTS ON LEARNING AND BEHAVIOR). It is also sad to have to report that malnutrition is practiced on a large scale as a central process in the world political system. One does not have to grow babies in bottles, as Aldous Huxley envisaged in *Brave New World,* in order to achieve a separation of human capacities into alphas and gammas. We can merely contrive to feed some mothers and deny others.

The brain, in its growth, must be subject to some explicit regulation from external stimuli. This is an urgent item on the humanicist's agenda. We need powerful tools to deal, on the one hand, with obvious defects that cry out to be corrected and, on the other, with the possible enhancement of human intellectual ability. The closest parallel to this in present practice is the care that physicians take to be sure that pregnant mothers do not suffer from thyroid deficiency.

Genetics and transplants

Another approach to the modification of an established genetic makeup is the transplantation of the tissue or organ from another individual. When the indication for such a transplant is a failing heart or kidney, obviously the operation is not a compensation for a genetic defect. The message is clearer, however, when the indication is a metabolically insufficient pancreas—say diabetes, though the primary lesion may be elsewhere—or a congenital deficiency in some other endocrine gland.

Tissue transplantation is still seriously impeded by two factors: the phenomenon of tissue rejection based on genetic incompatibility of different individuals, and the serious difficulty of obtaining viable organs for transplant. Fundamental genetic studies on the determination of the protein structure of antibodies and of tissue antigens may be expected to eliminate the first obstacle. As for organ supply, a thorough understanding of tissue rejection may make it possible to use animal organs for transplant purposes. (See *1969 Britannica Yearbook of Science and the Future,* Feature Article: NEW PARTS FOR OLD: THE LATEST MEDICAL ADVENTURE.) One approach that would allow the use of animal organs would be the early inoculation

Hybridization experiments with mouse embryos indicate the feasibility of combining the most desirable characteristics of several different parents into a single offspring. A pair of black mice and a pair of white mice, such as the four pictured at left, were mated. Fertilized embryos were then removed from the two females. The embryo membranes were removed and the cells were allowed to fuse in a culture medium. After two days the fused embryos were implanted in a third recipient female (such as the white mouse in the center), who gave birth to a hybrid mouse (right) with genetic traits from both sets of "parents."

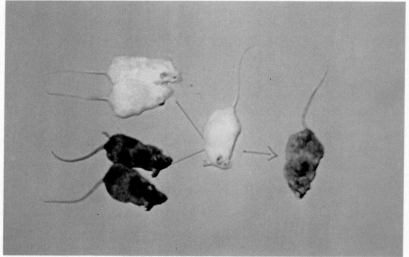

Courtesy, North Carolina State University at Raleigh

of infants with purified pooled antigens representing the tissue specificities of potential future organ donors.

Transplantation, in the sense of mixing cells of different origin into one organism, can be done experimentally at very early stages of embryological development. Already, as many as four different mouse eggs, representing eight different parents, have been fused to form a single embryo that matured into a single adult mouse. This procedure has great theoretical interest because of its potentiality for incorporating complementary advantages from a variety of different parental strains.

Experiments with microorganisms

Except for a calculated choice of parentage, intelligent design plays a limited role in controlling the genetic makeup of an individual. In microorganisms, however, it is now possible to introduce specific new genetic information in a much more controlled fashion. But such experiments still have considerable random components, and usually it is not possible to instruct one particular cell to adopt a specific new genotype. Instead, a large number of cells are exposed to DNA that has been contrived to have the desired characteristics. One out of the many cells may incorporate the foreign DNA and with it some new characteristic. The occasional cell that responds in the appropriate fashion can then be separated from the other cells.

The great force of recent work in molecular biology stems from the use of relatively simple experimental materials, such as viruses and bacteria. The direct manipulation of individual genes within the chromosomes in cells of higher organisms, however, presents formidable and possibly insuperable technical difficulties. Nevertheless, we can foresee the use of viruses to mediate the transmission of specific genetic information. This process of viral transduction was first described in 1951 by Norton D. Zinder and Joshua Lederberg for bacteria of the *Salmonella* group.

Contemporary work with animal viruses by a number of other workers now strongly suggests that these viruses may also be capable of introducing genetic information in the cells that they infect. For example, the SV-40 virus of monkeys, which as far as is known is harmless in man, leaves a number of copies of its DNA sequences in the chromosomes of cells infected in tissue culture. This suggests that viral DNA can be engineered and that synthetic viruses can be used for the modification of genetic defects. For example, it should soon be technically feasible to attach the genetic DNA that codes for the enzyme phenylalanine hydroxylase, which functions in the liver of normal men and animals, to the DNA of SV-40 virus. The inoculation of an infant with such a hybrid virus would be expected to alleviate the disease phenylketonuria.

continued on page 92

Courtesy, North Carolina State University at Raleigh

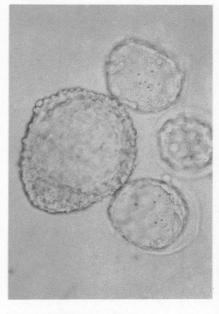

A fused embryo of the type used in the hybrid mouse experiment illustrated on the preceding page is considerably larger and lacks the membrane found on three normal mouse embryos.

In defense of genetic engineering

Humanics, the understanding of human nature, is rightly viewed as the capstone of Western culture. Scientific insight is, however, a challenge to traditional thought and authority in at least two ways. It amplifies the power for good or harm that men can inflict on one another, when we are already on the brink of failure to contain massive aggression. Perhaps even more embarrassingly, it reveals existing flaws in the providence and justice of our social institutions—like the world arrangements that leave so many human beings underfed and uneducated.

Many thoughtful critics have questioned whether we are socially and morally prepared to cope with such newly emerging powers as genetic engineering. Some go so far as to advocate explicit restraints on technological development in this field, a plea that is readily translated into diffidence about financial support for basic biological research. The straw man has even been erected that pictures scientists (but which ones?) as demanding that we put into practice everything that is technologically possible, without regard to the human consequences.

Such absurdities should not require discussion, but insofar as they do, they have a positive answer. The consequences of ignorance are no less frightening, perhaps more unpredictable than those of scientific understanding. When we contemplate large-scale technological applications in any sphere, we need a wide range of scientific knowledge to analyze their consequences. Restraints on research in genetic science might restrain sophisticated genetic engineering, but they will make even more plausible the crude efforts of those who advocate the legalized involuntary sterilization of the "unfit" and deprive us of many urgently needed advances in medicine and in agriculture.

Sharply limited military research would never have uncovered the genetic hazards of radioactive fallout. The euphenic point of view may upset some people who do not know how to handle the responsibility of choice for the quality of their offspring, but our present uninformed choices, like those that lead to global malnutrition and mental retardation for millions of infants, are also a policy. Man may have lived in a paradise of submissive ignorance before he ate from the tree of knowledge, but human civilization began just then and there is no return.

This is not to shrug off the perversion of science. Brute force is the overriding instrument of authority, but the most totalitarian governments will exploit more subtle weapons to secure the peaceful cooperation of their subjects. The "control of the mind" by chemicals is the usual cliché one thinks of here, but Aldous Huxley himself pointed out that the scientific techniques portrayed in *Brave New World* were intended as a parody of existing institutions. Is it less intrusive on a human personality to indoctrinate a child in a given set of religious beliefs than it would be to "program" his genes? (Usually, the answer is "yes"—if the religion is the right one.)

But dictators will not stop at propaganda; they will use genetic engineering too, if they have the wit and if they stay in power long enough. The only answer is to strengthen our democratic institutions, of which public education to make informed critical judgment is the most crucial. We should also minimize the intrusion of government in any aspect of individual reproductive policy. It is incredible to think that, until recently, many states had laws that interfered with the dissemination of information about family planning. It is equally incredible that most states still interfere with the private decision of a mother to abort an unwanted pregnancy.

The self-awareness that characterizes man is part of his unique capacity for cultural evolution. During the past 100,000 years, this has completely overtaken his biological evolution. Biological change during this period is not only much less important than the cultural, but is itself deeply influenced by self-awareness, as illustrated by the rapid differentiation of the races with respect to obvious features as opposed to the deeper elements of humanity. Self-awareness may also impede substantive biological change unless we can learn to assimilate a view of the human future that allows for variety, experimentation, and change. What is quite new is that we are now scientifically aware of evolution and must take on the burden of conscious choice about its future directions.

The most important ethical inference from the fact of human evolution is that we are still perfectible. It is one of the least debatable of human purposes that our posterity should be wiser than we are, and above all for deciding the direction of the species. This principle puts a high premium on preserving the flexibility of decision for future generations, to make the fewest irreversible decisions. It is arguable whether evolutionary commitments are less reversible than cultural ones, but we would still prefer euphenic and somatic modifications to those that committed the whole species to a new genotype. On the other hand, we should not confuse global shifts (for which war is already more pertinent than eugenics) with isolated experiments in genetic engineering, any more than we would confuse global indoctrination with efforts at educational experimentation.

continued from page 89

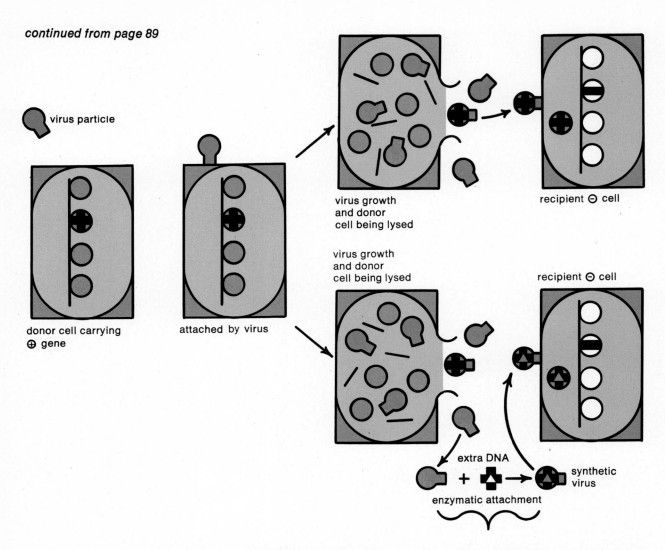

virus particle

donor cell carrying
⊕ gene

attached by virus

virus growth
and donor
cell being lysed

recipient ⊖ cell

virus growth
and donor
cell being lysed

recipient ⊖ cell

extra DNA

synthetic
virus

enzymatic attachment

Man has, in fact, been practicing a similar form of genetic engineering for quite some time. When Edward Jenner discovered the
vaccination against smallpox, he introduced the use of a variant
virus to compensate for a "genetic defect" shared by all mankind;
namely, our inherent sluggishness in producing antibodies against
the smallpox virus. The projected design for the use of more carefully engineered viruses to generate specific enzymes shows an
obvious parallel to this long-established medical procedure.

This approach to genetic engineering also has the advantage
that, in all likelihood, the genetic information carried by such viruses
is not incorporated in the sex cells for transmission to the next generation. This is a purely empirical observation: to be sure of keeping
future options open, this limitation of virogenetic effect to somatic
tissues must be carefully verified in every case. At this writing, only
one important technical difficulty remains, that of attaching specific
segments of DNA from totally unrelated sources. However, enzymes
discovered in 1968 for rejoining DNA molecules broken in just one
strand are already being used as essential reagents in research.

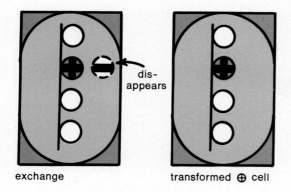

exchange   transformed ⊕ cell

Transduction with Natural and Synthetic Virus

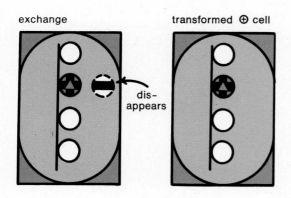

exchange   transformed ⊕ cell

Tailor-made DNA is now a reality. Molecular biologists, following nature's lead, can transplant a segment of DNA into a bacterium and change its genetic constitution. The process of transduction with a natural virus occurs commonly in certain kinds of bacteria. It requires the aid of a bacterial virus, which displaces certain genes in the bacterial DNA (top row). In the laboratory, transduction with a synthetic virus is accomplished by using an enzyme to attach a desired bit of DNA to a special carrier virus. The resulting synthetic virus is then allowed to infect a bacterium, thereby transferring the DNA that was previously incorporated into the virus (bottom row).

The theoretical possibility of virogenic attachment to chromosomes and propagation to further generations cannot be completely determined without empirical study. If we do not keep a vigilant lookout on the effects of viruses—whether used for vaccination against disease, for genetic repair, or as infectious agents in our environment—we may be in for some unpleasant surprises. Because the use of viruses for vaccination purposes has not been generally associated with the alarms of "genetic engineering," these agents do not receive the close attention they deserve in view of their biological potentialities. At the very least, viruses used for vaccination should be chemically purified and identified as having only the one desired species of DNA or RNA (ribonucleic acid). This standard has not yet been adopted by the pharmaceutical industry, nor has it been included in the regulations enforced by governments.

The extraordinary specificity of pairing by the two strands of a DNA molecule has opened the way for studying biological specificity, mainly by molecular hybridization. The specific reagent in these experiments is a solution of DNA single strands prepared from reference material. For some purposes, this DNA may be incorporated into a culture medium of solid agar or attached to the surface of filter membranes. When exactly complementary strands of DNA, or sometimes of RNA, are added, conventional double-stranded DNA structures will be re-formed and can be detected by a variety of different methods. Some of these methods are so sensitive that it may be possible to discern even single nucleotide differences between a reference and an unknown in a sample. These procedures will, undoubtedly, be instrumental for the isolation of specific-gene DNA, an objective which has already been achieved to a limited extent. Molecular hybridization also furnishes a method of distinguishing from each other the messenger-RNAs produced by different cells.

Vegetative propagation

Other advances in cell biology have opened up some additional technical possibilities for the evasion of genetic scrambling that now invariably accompanies sexual reproduction. The propagation of new plants from cuttings is a familiar experience in horticulture. In lower animals such as earthworms, vegetative reproduction is a common occurrence; missing organs can regenerate spontaneously in small fragments cut from the previous individual. One might speculate that deeper insights into the mechanisms of this embryological development could lead to similar phenomena, even in man, but these are remote prospects indeed!

An alternative approach is offered by experiments in frogs, in which the existing nucleus of a fertilized egg was displaced and the egg renucleated with a nucleus from a tissue cell of a mature frog. The purpose of these experiments was to determine whether tissue differentiation was invariably associated with a permanent loss of developmental functions in the cell nucleus. Apparently this is not always true, for some nuclei of adult tissue cells are capable of supporting the total development of a new frog from a renucleated egg. From a genetic point of view, however, the new frog was vegetatively propagated from the mature tissue because it carries exactly the same set of genetic information.

Groups of individuals derived by vegetative propagation and having identical genetic constitutions are called "clones." The prospect of producing genetically homogeneous groups of individuals presents some interesting issues; in addition, it is a way of propagating a genotype already tested in one generation for further trial in a second. We already have a foretaste of the properties of a clone in the behavior of identical twins.

Clonal propagation would afford an otherwise unavailable opportunity for certain humanic experiments, in the same sense that efforts to optimize a child's education are experiments. Without such tests it is unlikely that we will ever be able to know the extent

Clonal reproduction, the vegetative propagation of identical organisms, is a boon to research. By the use of ultraviolet radiation to destroy an existing nucleus, and deft micromanipulation to insert a desired nucleus, laboratories can produce an unending supply of frogs made to order, with identical genetic endowments.

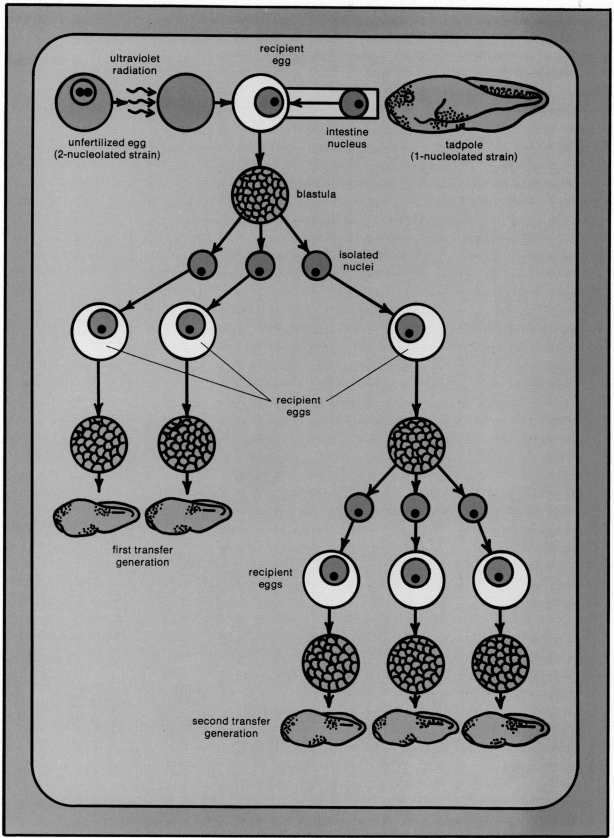

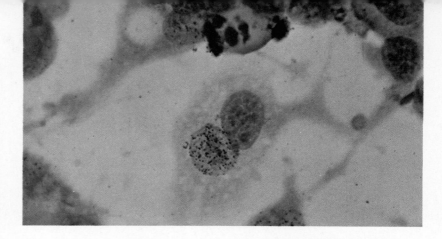

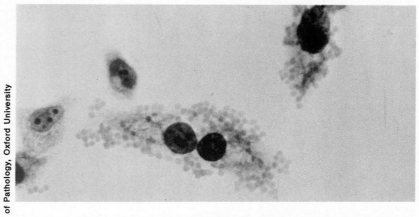

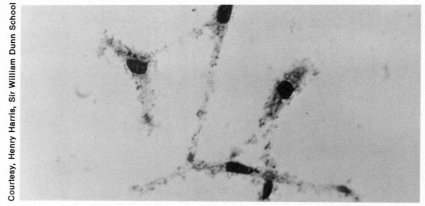

By fusing human cells with cells of other species and testing the ways in which the human cell replaces known defects in the animal cell, it is possible to determine the genetic functions that different human chromosomes carry. In the top picture, a human cell nucleus has fused with a mouse nucleus. The human nucleus has been made radioactive, as seen by the black dots on its surface, so that it can be distinguished from the mouse nucleus. Two hybrid man-mouse cells are visible in the middle picture: one contains two nuclei; in the other, fusion has occurred. Red cells on their surfaces have been attracted by the presence of mouse surface proteins. Because the other cells in the picture do not show up red, they are known to be simple human cells. In the bottom picture, a small colony of growing, single-nucleus man-mouse hybrid cells is identified by its specific adsorption of the red cells.

Courtesy, Henry Harris, Sir William Dunn School of Pathology, Oxford University

to which the performance of acknowledged geniuses or athletic stars are manifestations of unusual genetic endowment.

The technical limitation to human cloning is mainly the much smaller size of mammalian eggs when compared with the egg of a frog, but, almost certainly, this is not an insuperable difficulty. There may be, however, other obstacles based on differences in the biology of the frog egg and that of the human that are not yet known.

Within the last few years, it has been discovered that tissue cells can be made to fuse with one another in the presence of certain virus-derived particles. These cells thus form "vegetative hybrids" that can originate from such widely distinct species as fish and human. The technique has already become quite important in the analysis of the genetic functions carried by different human chromo-

96

somes, which can be tested for their ability to make up for known defects in other animal cells.

Vegetative hybridization and the use of the hybrid cells to re-nucleate an egg open the door to another form of genetic engineering—hybrid plants or animals containing some or many chromosomes from distant species. Crop improvement is the most obvious area for applying this technique. In fact, many Soviet workers have made far-reaching claims for the efficacy of graft-hybridization in plant improvement, but most of these claims defy reproducibility and credibility. Perhaps for this reason the whole subject has been virtually ignored by Western geneticists, who may thereby have missed some kernel of useful innovation.

The future of genetic engineering

When we approach functions as complex as human intelligence and sympathy, we must be quite humble about our capacity to unravel the components of heredity and environment. Certainly, there is no gene that can ensure the ideal development of a child's brain without reference to tender care and inspired teaching. The paths to intelligence can be deviated at many points—for example, the child born deaf was for all practical purposes an idiot until we learned the special techniques needed to teach him. These considerations suggest that the main role of genetic science may be to sharpen perceptions of how to engineer the environment for the optimum development of existing genetic types. When we have reached some mastery of this challenge, we can more reasonably advocate the extension of genetic engineering beyond the repair of the most obvious and urgent forms of genetic defect.

See also Year in Review: MOLECULAR BIOLOGY.

FOR ADDITIONAL READING:

Dobzhansky, T., *Mankind Evolving* (Yale University Press, 1964).

Haynes, R. H., and Hanawalt, P. C. (eds.), "The Molecular Basis of Life," *Readings from the Scientific American* (Freeman, 1968).

Lederberg, Joshua, "Experimental Genetics and Human Evolution," *Beyond Left and Right: Radical Thought for Our Times,* ed. by Richard Kostelanetz (Morrow, 1968).

Lerner, I. M., *Heredity, Evolution and Society* (Freeman, 1968).

Platt, J. R., "The New Biology and the Shaping of the Future," *The Great Ideas Today 1968* (Encyclopædia Britannica, 1968).

Sonneborn, T. M. (ed.), *The Control of Human Heredity and Evolution* (Macmillan, 1965).

Taylor, G. R., *The Biological Time-Bomb* (World, 1968).

AUDIOVISUAL MATERIALS FROM ENCYCLOPÆDIA BRITANNICA EDUCATIONAL CORPORATION:

Films: *DNA: Molecule of Heredity; Gene Action; Laws of Heredity.*

"What's past is prologue."

The Science Year in Review: A Perspective

by Philip Handler

At this juncture in the history of science and technology, there is evidence of a growing preoccupation with problems concerning the interaction of science and society. The scientific leadership in the U.S. is concerned with the slackening of federal support for scientific research, with the effects of the draft, and with the growing disenchantment of some segments of the population (particularly youth) not only with science as a career but also with its stance as a contributor to the enrichment of intellectual life. The political leadership is increasingly alarmed by the more frightening consequences of science and technology, of power exceeding wisdom and understanding, of the increasing mechanization of social relationships. Yet science has never been more vigorous or successful; technology has never been more fruitful.

The successes of science

Today astronomers are pressing forward with their newly acquired ability to observe the heavens over almost the entire electromagnetic spectrum. The incredible pulsars have been discovered in the optical range; astrophysicists have announced the detection of formaldehyde, ammonia, and water vapor in the vast interstellar clouds—discoveries with dramatic implications for cosmological theory.

Exploration of the earth has proved to be as rewarding, if perhaps not yet quite as glamorous, as that of outer space. The new understanding of the mechanism of formation of the Mid-Atlantic Ridge and the demonstration of a multitude of salt domes in the Caribbean, a substantial fraction of which appear to lie above large oil reserves, is surely sufficient reward for one year of oceanography.

Solid-state, medium- and low-energy physics are continuing to advance rapidly, and if high-energy physics has paused briefly while awaiting construction of the 200-Bev accelerator, it can be only a matter of time before new particles are produced for theoretical physicists to fit into an intellectual framework. In chemistry, reaction mechanisms are understood with a sophistication unimaginable two decades ago, and the synthetic arts of the organic chemist provide an ever richer cornucopia of new materials.

Less tidy, perhaps, than the physical sciences, the life sciences are experiencing spectacular and sometimes confusing growth. The first enzymatic production of an infectious, viral DNA; the synthesis of an enzyme by two quite different chemical techniques; and the deciphering of the amino acid chain of gamma globulin were only three of the year's triumphs. The mechanisms of both animal and plant hormones are being revealed; small breaks have appeared in the barrier that separates us from an understanding of the chemical basis of cellular differentiation; a beginning has been made toward understanding how information is encoded in the central nervous system; and the physiological bases of behavior have become increasingly apparent.

Science and man

These are unprecedented achievements, and they constitute only a sampling of the whole. But when we have enumerated them, we still must ask: how do they relate to the immediate, major problems before mankind? How, for example, do they bear on containment of the population explosion, and on the development of an adequate, worldwide agricultural enterprise?

The greatest threat to the future of the human race is man's own ability to procreate. Hunger, pollution, crime, despoliation of natural beauty, extermination of countless species of plants and animals, dirty, overcrowded cities with their paradoxical loneliness, continual erosion of limited natural resources, and the seething unrest that creates political instability and leads to international conflict and war—all derive from the unbridled growth of human populations.

Informed demographers tell us that, regardless of any foreseeable efforts, the population of the planet will somewhat more than double its present size by the century's end. The inescapable conclusion would seem to be that, in the interim, we must use all the technical and social skills at our command to limit this process. Unfortunately, our knowledge of human reproductive physiology is distressingly meager. It must be markedly expanded if we are to acquire the reliable, cheap, innocuous, and reversible contraceptive procedures required to stabilize the world's population at an acceptable level.

A similar problem emerges when we consider the need for enhanced agricultural productivity. The principal barriers to such productivity probably derive not from lack of biological knowledge, but from cultural and economic considerations and the unavailability of adequately trained manpower in the less developed nations. Yet there is also much to be done by way of developing improved strains of crops, upgrading poultry and cattle stocks, and exploiting opportunities for aquaculture.

Tremendous ethical problems also face mankind. Some derive from the possibility of harmful effects on the human gene pool, a result of the coupling of our traditional ethics with the development of medical procedures that lead to the survival of the genetically unfit. Some will become manifest if what has been called genetic engineering becomes a reality. Some will become excruciating when our species contemplates giving positive direction to its own evolution. These will necessarily become issues of public policy far more painful than our current struggles with the ethics involved in transplantation procedures or the distribution of a limited number of dialysis units for the treatment of kidney disease.

Our various technologies have been strained to their limits by the national efforts in defense and space, and by a host of industrial purposes, but we have scarcely begun to apply our technological capabilities to those social problems that most sorely beset us. It is imperative that there be diverse, comprehensive, frequently multidisciplinary approaches to achieve a more sophisticated understanding of the origins of societal problems—an understanding that, it must be hoped, will lead to long-term solutions.

Contents

Agriculture

Some advances were reported in the worldwide war on hunger. For the first time in its history, Kenya produced enough of its primary food staple, corn (maize), to meet its own needs and to provide a modest surplus for export. To achieve this result, Kenya had undertaken an intensive program of agricultural improvement, which included a breeding program that produced hybrids yielding 30–80% more than local varieties; agronomic production research to identify the best growing practices; a network of demonstration plots located within walking distance of most farmers; and establishment of a commercial seed firm that produced and distributed hybrid seed at reasonable prices.

Research on rice and wheat in the Orient (see *1969 Britannica Yearbook of Science and the Future,* Year in Review: AGRICULTURE) was moving in two directions: maintaining yield gains already achieved through the use of improved varieties, and extending the use of those varieties. Scientists were particularly concerned over the possibility that the new strains might be decimated by diseases or insects to which they had no resistance. This had happened when earlier improved varieties of wheat had been introduced in the temperate zones, and the danger in the tropics was even greater. Accordingly, plant pathologists, plant geneticists, and entomologists were making a concerted effort to breed in resistance to such pests.

Since plant protein is cheaper than animal protein, increasing the quality and quantity of protein in crops used for human consumption provides a means of raising the nutritional standards of poor populations at minimum cost. Horticulturists at Purdue University, West Lafayette, Ind., developed strains of potatoes containing 11.7% crude protein, compared with about 3% for most currently grown varieties. Potato pro-

Workers at the International Rice Research Institute, Los Baños, Phil., prepare fields for a test of new rice varieties. High-yield strains developed here are playing an important role in the "green revolution" of rising productivity in the rice-growing regions of South and Southeast Asia.

Courtesy, International Rice Research Institute

tein is more digestible and of higher quality than protein from many other plant sources and, with the development of improved strains, the potato could become an important protein source. Breeding for higher protein content seemed feasible for other crops as well. Scientists in several countries have shown that protein percentages and quality can be increased in sorghums, wheat, oats, pinto and navy beans, and corn.

Forage for man and animal. Forage crops, grasses, and legumes traditionally utilized by livestock were receiving new attention. A process developed at the University of Wisconsin made it possible to separate and refine protein from alfalfa leaves, and further refinements might permit alfalfa protein, which is well balanced in amino acids, to be reduced to a tasteless, odorless, colorless powder for use by humans. In tests conducted at Mysore, India, alfalfa protein had proved to be as good as skimmed milk in promoting the growth of malnourished children. Up to 2,400 lb of crude protein can be produced per acre of alfalfa, compared with 780 lb for corn, 700 lb for soybeans, and 325 lb for wheat.

Two new processes made it possible to predict animal response from small samples of forages with more confidence. One was a two-stage digestibility process, developed in England. The other was a U.S. method that utilized detergents to separate relatively undigestible plant walls from more usable cell contents. By using these methods, plant breeders could evaluate breeding lines and individual plants according to their potential for producing meat or milk.

Can plants do better? The basic food-producing process is photosynthesis, whereby plants manufacture sugar from carbon dioxide and water in the presence of light. Ordinarily, plants utilize only a very small percentage of the available energy from sunshine in carrying on photosynthesis, but British and U.S. scientists earlier found some ryegrass and alfalfa plants with superior efficiency. Using refined techniques, University of Minnesota scientists were screening collections of foodcrop plants from all over the world in an attempt to find varieties with high photosynthetic efficiency and low photorespiration rates. Such plants, used in breeding, could produce high-yield strains. Along similar lines, scientists were finding ways in which plants could utilize higher levels of carbon dioxide, both in greenhouses and in the field.

Plants need up to 700 lb of water to produce a pound of dry matter. Most of the water passes out through thousands of tiny pores called stomates, which also serve to admit carbon dioxide. Scientists at the Connecticut Agricultural Experiment Station identified two chemicals that, in

Courtesy, Connecticut Agricultural Experiment Station

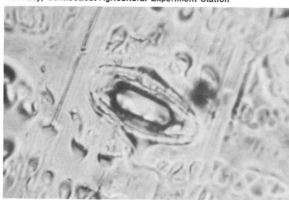

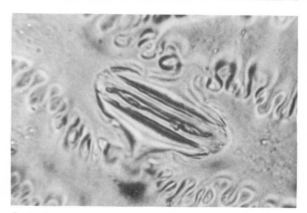

Stomate of a corn plant, normally open (above), can be closed (below) by chemical treatment. Partially closing these tiny plant pores reduces water loss and may help the plant to withstand drought or to survive in semiarid regions.

field tests, significantly reduced water loss by partially closing the stomates but did not interfere with carbon dioxide intake. This raised the possibility that aerial spraying of such chemicals could enable high-value crops to withstand droughts, make possible the extension of farming into semiarid areas, and improve efficiency in the use of irrigation water.

New aids for the farmer. With the ability of instrumented satellites to remotely "sense" conditions on the earth already well established, U.S. scientists were beginning to combine aircraft and satellite data in the service of agriculture. Such data, analyzed by high-speed computers, can reveal the presence of plant diseases, measure crop acreages, map soils, and precisely identify the burning edges of forest fires.

Such techniques should be of particular value in helping less developed countries assess their agricultural problems and potentials. With help from the United States, Mexico and Brazil had already begun to develop their own remote sensing programs.

101

Michigan State University scientists reported the development of an asphalt barrier to the upward percolation of water in soil. The asphalt, in the form of an emulsion, is introduced into the soil about two feet below the surface, where it forms a barrier about one-eighth of an inch thick that holds water near the roots of plants. The method should prove of greatest benefit on highly porous, sandy soils in humid regions. Yields of tomatoes, cucumbers, cabbage, and potatoes were increased as much as 80% through its use.

Canadian researchers proposed use of a protein-base fire-fighting foam to protect low-growing fruits and vegetables against killing frosts, and commercial development of the process was begun. If successfully developed, the process could be used by both home gardeners and farmers and would benefit growers working at high altitudes as well as in high-latitude areas.

—Thomas Ronningen

Archaeology

Near East

Iran. The International Congress of Iranian Art and Archaeology, held in Teheran in April 1968, brought together for the first time the postwar generation of archaeologists who were working not only in Iran but in Lebanon, Turkey, Afghanistan, Pakistan, and the U.S.S.R. One of the most significant trends which became evident at the conference was toward discovery and recognition of the earliest settled communities which prepared the way for the beginning of civilized living in western Asia. For example, Maurits van Loon reported on the site of Tell Mureybit in Syria, a village covering six acres, whose people lived entirely on wild foods about 10,000 years ago, at the end of the Ice Age. Shortly after 8500 B.C. (according to carbon-14 dating) permanent houses were built with stone-paved floors and clay walls on stone foundations. The economy was based upon wild cattle, onagers (a type of wild ass), and gazelles, as well as wild wheat. Another significant discovery by van Loon was that warfare laid Mureybit to waste about 7800 B.C. But what was most surprising was the fact that the beginnings of settled urban living were found to be earlier than the domestication of plants and animals, the manufacture of pottery, and other standard criteria of the Neolithic period.

There was also evidence at Tal-i-Iblis in eastern Iran of an enormous increase in metallurgical activity about 4200–4000 B.C. The site contained hundreds of crucible fragments with copper stain and dross, and there were indications that this was a "cottage industry," or a specialty of the entire settlement, rather than the work of a few professionals.

A long-standing puzzle concerning the culture associated with the Luristan bronzes of Iran was well on the way to a solution in 1969. Typical bronzes of the last phase found at War Kabud were dated to the end of the 8th century and beginning of the 7th century B.C. But at Bani Surmah nearby, seals and socketed bronze axes which appeared to be related to those found at Ur and other Early Dynastic materials from Mesopotamia, were dated many centuries earlier. Other cemeteries of the Kani Chinan region, 12 mi NW of Bani Surmah, produced a typical early Luristan standard in situ.

Turkey. In Turkey, the joint Harvard University–Cornell University excavations at Sardis during 1968 and 1969 revealed significant information

A column fragment found in the synagogue area of Sardis, Turk., has as its two main figures Artemis, goddess of hunting, and Cybele, goddess of the earth. Artemis holds a deer and Cybele a lion, while two worshipers look on. The column dates to the 4th or 5th century B.C.

having to do with techniques in metalworking. Careful excavation revealed many small circular depressions in heavily burned floors around a 6th century B.C. altar, which proved to have been used in metal-extracting operations—perhaps the extracting of gold from its ores under intense heat from a bellows-directed flame. Gold in droplets and leaf form was recovered in this area and also a row of brick furnaces which may have served in a process for parting gold and silver. There were also burned terra-cotta pieces thought to be nozzles of bellows and a possible iron blow-pipe.

Pottery found in this metal workshop dated it between 575–555 B.C., or during the reign of Croesus. Since the Lydians of Sardis are traditionally credited with the invention of true coinage, the discovery of such a workshop was significant in terms of the whole Mediterranean area.

Egypt. During 1968 and 1969 the Ikhnaton Temple computer project, under the direction of Ray Smith, reached fruition. By using a computer to process the enormous amount of statistical data, it was possible to plan the complete reconstruction of the temple—a towering square structure, originally covered with polychrome decorations and dedicated exclusively to Nefertiti. Apparently this was the first Shuweet Re (a shrine dedicated to royal women) which has been recovered, although their existence has been known for some time. Reconstructed scenes of jubilee ceremonies were also unearthed.

This Temple of Ikhnaton at Luxor was destroyed about 3500 years ago, but the building blocks were reused in later temples and then recovered when those later temples were excavated and restored. The sorting and ordering of the photographs of these blocks, eventually about 50,000, was clearly a most dramatic and successful use of a computer in archaeology.

A computer was also essential in an experiment directed by Luis Alvarez in the Khafre pyramid at Giza. In the experiment, a spark chamber placed in the burial chamber of the pyramid recorded cosmic ray muons which were passing through the mass of the pyramid above. If there were another open burial chamber above the known chamber, the muons passing through it would be relatively more frequent and more energetic as recorded in the spark chamber. Because these nuclear particles constantly pass through the stone structure at all angles, it thus became possible to locate and detect voids in the mass. Alvarez observed that the mass of this particular pyramid was ideally suited to his experiment.

The effect of the Hyksos, the 18th century B.C.

UPI Compix

One of the 14 carved limestone reliefs uncovered near the Heliopolis obelisk in the United Arab Republic is carefully washed. Archaeologists believe that the discovery will lead to the unearthing of a second obelisk of the long-sought Middle Kingdom temple of Egypt.

invaders from the East and subsequent rulers of Egypt for two centuries, has been a matter of study and discussion for many years. In 1969 an Austrian expedition excavating at Tell ed Debaa near Quantir in the eastern delta of Egypt turned up a temple and a cemetery in the second known site of Hyksos occupation in that country and also gained some new information about these invaders of Egypt. Skeletons found in the cemetery represent people of large stature and build, unlike the short Mediterranean type of people characteristic of Egyptians and the Semites of Palestine and Syria. Also, the pottery and grave goods were non-Egyptian, but instead were iden-

Many of the more than 300 amphorae discovered by Michael Katzev still lie on the ocean floor near Kyrenia, Cyprus. These jars were among the deck cargo of a 4th century B.C. Greek shipwreck.

tical to those representing the material culture of the Middle Bronze Age in Palestine. Male burials were frequently accompanied by pairs of small equines, either onagers or donkeys. These systematic excavations of a true Hyksos site should eventually clarify a significant period in ancient history.

Europe

The Mediterranean. Just off the harbor at Kyrenia, Cyprus, Michael Katzev and his underwater team from the University of Pennsylvania's University Museum excavated during the summer of 1968 a large part of the first known classical Greek ship. They found a deck cargo of more than 300 amphorae (large Greek jars), most of them made in Rhodes.

Their most significant discovery was a hull sufficiently well preserved to give an idea of Greek ship construction. For example, it was ascertained that the hull was lead-sheathed—a technique known in Roman times but not previously thought to have been familiar to the Greeks. Analysis also showed that planking was attached to ribs with bronze nails and that there was an inner lining of "ceiling planking."

The announcement, in December 1968, of the precise location of archaic Greek Sybaris on the plain of the Crati River in southern Italy created a stir in the world press. From a professional

point of view it was important in demonstrating that a newly developed cesium magnetometer could detect archaeological ruins lying up to six meters beneath the earth's surface and chart the outline of a city lying four to six meters deep. Actually this new tool in archaeology was developed on that site over a period of several years.

In some respects, more impressive experimentation with the instruments was demonstrated at Elis, near Olympia in Greece, in 1968. Within a few weeks, the major part of the ruins of a Greek and Roman city was charted in such detail that the plan of the streets and buildings could be made out. Although these ruins lay much closer to the earth's surface, they had not been destroyed and overbuilt like those of Sybaris. In any case, both surveys showed how highly sensitive magnetometers could be used to map extensive archaeological remains where there was no surface evidence.

On the island of Thera (Santorini), north of Crete, Spyridon Marinatos continued excavation of the Minoan town discovered in 1967 which was hidden beneath the pumice and ash deposited during a volcanic explosion on the island sometime during the 15th century B.C. Pumice, an extraordinary preservative, sealed up the ruins, and the problem was to determine whether the site could be excavated beneath the deep deposit of pumice so that the overburden could remain in place, that is, whether it was possible to do an underground excavation. Marinatos reported that the pumice was standing and that it appeared possible to expose the ruins in underground galleries.

England. A new departure involving archaeology and city planning crystallized in 1968 with the formation of the Winchester Excavations Committee. The aim of this group was to recover the history of Winchester from its founding, about the time of Christ, to the present, and to carry out all archaeological excavations before rebuilding the city. This would require cooperation between the town council and the archaeologists, as well as large-scale excavations comparable to those in the Near East. Moreover, it would require year-round research with a permanent director and staff working on assessment of the finds, publication, and annual excavations. This was probably the first example of an attempt at systematic investigations of a European city and might well set the standards for subsequent rebuilding of cities under the pressures of population expansion and modernization.

North America

The continuing search for the earliest Americans, with all its controversy, turned up two recent discoveries which were significant. In 1968, Richard Daugherty, who in the early 1960s began excavating the Marmes rockshelter on the Snake River in Washington as part of a U.S. National Park Service salvage project, cut a trench on the talus slope and into the valley floor below the rockshelter to uncover a new and much earlier occupation level. Daugherty's most important discovery was the human skeletal remains which he found at this level. With the remains were ash, charcoal, burned animal bones, and bone projectile points, as well as skull fragments, teeth, and long bones. Geological dating placed their age at 11,000 to 12,000 years (near the end of the Ice Age). This appeared to be the earliest known burial site in the Western Hemisphere.

Much more controversial was the excavation of the Calico Mountains site near Yermo in the Mojave Desert of southern California by L. S. B. Leakey and his colleagues. Work had been going on there since 1964, but in 1968 Leakey announced that he had found at least 170 objects at a depth of about 13 ft that were undoubtedly the result of human activity. Geologists and geomorphologists dated this deposit at between 50,000 and 100,000 years old. Moreover, Leakey described a ring of stones in the deposit which had all the appearances of a hearth. The assem-

A 100-room Roman palace was unearthed near Chichester, Sussex, Eng. A large garden, with trenches dug for box hedges (left), was cleared, and remnants of mosaic floors (below) left undisturbed for 17 centuries were meticulously cleaned by archaeologists.

Wide World

Archaeologists work to excavate the earliest known burial site in the Western Hemisphere, near Washtucna, Wash. These remains have been estimated to be approximately 12,000 years old, corresponding to the end of the Ice Age.

blage of stone implements was, however, very primitive, and debate continued as to whether they were actually manmade. (See Feature Article: MAN IN AMERICA: THE CALICO MOUNTAINS EXCAVATIONS.)

New devices for remote sensing from aircraft were expected to become important new tools for archaeological surveying. Joseph M. Prochaska, of the University of Tennessee, reported an accidental discovery 20 mi W of Knoxville, Tenn., which was illustrative of the potential of these devices. An aerial survey, utilizing color infrared film, spotted a noticeable rectangle of about 120 ft on each side near Tellico Dam in the area of the village of Chote, which was part of a settlement in the Tellico Plain area known to be occupied by Cherokee Indians about 200 years ago. Color infrared picks up, among other things,

differences in soil moisture and in chlorophyll content in plants as affected by subsurface deposits. Ordinary air photos could not have detected this site.

Archaeology branched off into many new directions because of the new tools and techniques for uncovering the past. One example, reported by the U.S. National Park Service, was the excavation of a Missouri River steamboat, the "Bertrand," which hit a snag and sank on April 1, 1865, in what is now Nebraska. The Missouri River changed its course, and the "Bertrand" was buried under 20 ft of sand and silt about 8 ft below the water table.

Excavation beneath sand and water began in January 1968, and it seemed certain that preservation was excellent. The main deck and hull were intact, and inside there were intact cases of Piper Rheims champagne, canned peaches, tomatoes, gunpowder, blacksmith tools, and many other trade items. The preservation of the boat itself provided a unique opportunity to study the construction of such river craft.

Middle America

Traditionally, the great stone structures in Mexico and Central America have been referred to as "ceremonial centers" rather than as truly urban residential areas. But Rene Millon reported that Teotihuacán in central Mexico was an urban center, with sections of the city occupied by specialized workers such as craftsmen working in shell, stone, and pottery. Moreover, Millon identified many hearths, or cooking areas, simply as dirt floors within plaster-floored buildings, indicating definite residential areas. Thus, the concept of the nature and structure of these ancient civilizations has been altered by more extensive and systematic research in this part of the world.

Further evidence of this change in concept came from David Pendergast's work at Altun ha, a site near the coast in British Honduras. This excavation turned out to be a Mayan trading center, rich in materials from other areas—for example, obsidian from the Valley of Mexico—and sea shells, which presumably were traded to inland sites like Tikal.

East Africa

F. C. Howell reported an additional discovery, in 1968, at the Omo River basin site in the Lake Rudolf Rift, Ethiopia. Another jawbone and several teeth from two types of Australopithecus (robustus and gracilis) were found. But the most significant development there was the dating of these remains at approximately 3.5 million years ago. There was also some indication that *Homo habilis* may be a descendant of the *gracilis* type of these *Australopithecines.* (*See* Year in Review: BEHAVIORAL SCIENCES, *Breakthrough in Anthropolgy.*)

Elwyn Simons referred to a complete lower jaw with teeth intact, found in 1968 in northern India, which may be that of an advanced hominoid. It shared with *Australopithecus* a number of features not shared with most apes. This "near-man" was classified as a new genus, *Gigantopithecus.* It was predicted to have lived from five to ten million years ago.

Most researchers working on these early hominoid forms tended to agree that the divergence in the evolution of apes and men took place much earlier than was supposed a few years ago—perhaps as early as the Miocene (began 27 million years ago) and even the Oligocene (38 million years ago) periods. The number of sites with evidence of primate evolution which were reported in Africa, Egypt, and India should certainly focus attention during the 1970s on these earliest stages in man's development.

Future trends in archaeology

It seems reasonable to expect a pronounced expansion in conservation and salvage archaeology during the 1970s. In the areas of advanced culture, where ancient art objects are found, looting of sites has reached devastating proportions, primarily because deep plowing and construction of various kinds are rapidly exposing rich sites, and because prices paid by private collectors are very high. It has become obvious that an increase in systematic excavation is the only safe way to save much of our cultural heritage. Search techniques, such as magnetometer surveys and improved aerial surveys, as well as undersea search techniques, should help the professionals in their race with the looters.

In the 1960s most archaeologists came to recognize a need for the assistance of professionals in other fields, such as paleobotanists, metallurgists, geologists, zoologists, chemists, and physicists. This meant that each site required more time, more systematic digging, and more complicated interpretation, which inevitably reduced the amount of excavation carried out in any given period. The combination of these two pressures upon archaeological field workers necessitated the expansion of field staffs, more expensive operations, and the development of new equipment and techniques. Fortunately, a great general interest in archaeology has grown,

and this in turn has made available more men, money, and equipment.

In more specific terms, current interests indicate that the 1970s will see more discoveries having to do with early man in Africa and India, more intensive work on all phases of cultural history in the Near and Middle East, further discoveries of early man in America, and additional development of archaeological methods, as well as an expansion of systematic research in Africa and the Pacific islands. In techniques, 1970 should see the more general use of the thermoluminescence method of dating fired clays, since two laboratories (University of Pennsylvania in 1965, and Oxford University in 1968) have announced the successful application of this method.

—Froelich Rainey

Astronautics and space exploration

Manned space exploration

Project Apollo, the United States program to land explorers on the moon and bring them safely back to earth, reached a successful climax in 1968–69 with the flights of Apollos 7–11. The program, first proposed in 1961 by U.S. Pres.

"But we've GOT to go back after 10 days . . ."—Jones, Toronto Telegram, *Canada.*

A training vehicle for the lunar module crashes on its 14th test flight in December 1968.
The pilot, Joseph Algranti, encountered a large lateral oscillation in the craft that caused him to lose
control of it. Algranti, a veteran of the program, landed safely by parachute.

John F. Kennedy, represented the most complex and largest single scientific exploration ever undertaken by man. During its peak activity more than 350,000 people and 20,000 business firms participated in it.

Apollo 7. The first manned orbital flight test of the Apollo command and service modules began on Oct. 11, 1968, when a Saturn IB launch vehicle placed the Apollo 7 command module into a near-earth orbital flight which lasted 10.8 days. The crew members were Walter Schirra, commander; Donn Eisele, command module pilot; and Walter Cunningham, lunar module pilot. Following a normal launch the spacecraft and upper stage of the Saturn were placed into an earth orbit ranging in altitude from 142 to 177 mi. Prior to separation of the command and service modules from the upper rocket stage, the crew manually flew the spacecraft/rocket stage combination. The spacecraft was then separated from the upper stage, and a simulated docking maneuver between the two was completed. This maneuver simulated the operation required during a lunar mission to couple the command module with the lunar module and to separate the lunar module from the upper rocket stage. Later in the mission the Apollo 7 crew successfully maneuvered the spacecraft for a re-rendezvous with the rocket stage.

During the 10.8-day mission eight planned maneuvers were successfully completed, using the service module propulsion system. In general, all spacecraft subsystem performance was excellent. Live television pictures were transmitted by the crewmen to earth. These pictures showed operations within the spacecraft and views of the earth. One of the most significant findings of the flight was associated with habitability, or the ability of the crew to live and operate within the spacecraft. It was found that the size of the command module in the weightless environment was quite adequate for a three-man crew. Compared to the experiences in the Gemini spacecraft, the crew was able to live and operate in relative comfort. Also, for the first time, U.S. astronauts did not wear spacesuits for reentry into the earth's atmosphere.

The flight of Apollo 7 ended in the Atlantic Ocean 260 hr and 9 min after its launch from Cape Kennedy, Fla. The successful flight represented a major milestone in the U.S. manned space flight program, and it restored some of the confidence lost following the Apollo 204 tragedy in 1967 which took the lives of astronauts Virgil Grissom, Edward White, and Roger Chaffee.

Apollo 8. Man's first lunar orbital flight mission, Apollo 8 was made possible by the successes of Apollo 7 and earlier unmanned flights. Frank

Borman was the commander; James Lovell, Jr., the command module pilot; and William Anders, the lunar module pilot. The three-stage Saturn V launch vehicle placed the command and service modules along with its own third stage (Saturn IVB) in earth orbit on Dec. 21, 1968. The crew checked out the spacecraft, and after approximately three hours the Saturn IVB engine was burned for roughly five minutes to accelerate Apollo 8 to escape velocity, 25,000 mph. The Saturn IVB stage was separated, and the spacecraft started its 230,000-mi journey to the moon. During this part of the flight the crew transmitted live television pictures of the spacecraft interior and of the earth.

As the spacecraft neared the moon, it accelerated due to the lunar gravitational pull. The service module propulsion system, thus, had to be fired to slow the Apollo to 3,750 mph and thereby place it in lunar orbit. The spacecraft achieved lunar orbit on Christmas Eve. Lunar operations lasted for ten orbits, which were flown at an altitude of 60 mi above the lunar surface. The crew transmitted television pictures of the lunar surface, studied possible Apollo landing sites, and took excellent photographs of the lunar surface. After approximately 20 hr of flying in lunar orbit, the crew fired the service module propulsion system engines for 3 min to accelerate the spacecraft to a velocity great enough to escape from the moon's gravitational force. The return trip lasted for approximately 63 hr before the spacecraft landed safely in the Pacific Ocean.

With only minor discrepancies, the spacecraft and systems functioned with precision throughout the mission. The crew performance was excellent, despite some illness early in the mission. All mission objectives were met. Apollo 8 qualified the launch vehicle and spacecraft for lunar flight. The crew provided valuable information on the lunar surface through their visual descriptions and the photographs they took. The crew also demonstrated the ability to recognize lunar surface features required for the lunar landing navigation tasks. The flight was heralded throughout the world as an odyssey without precedent in man's history.

Apollo 9. The first manned flight with the lunar module and the first with two manned spacecraft, Apollo 9 had for its crew James McDivitt, commander; David Scott, command module pilot; and Russell Schweickart, lunar module pilot. The objectives of this mission were to evaluate the lunar module under space flight conditions, to perform an extravehicular transfer from the lunar module to the command module, and to demonstrate the capability to fly the two spacecraft on lunar-landing trajectories to achieve rendezvous and docking.

The spacecraft was launched by a Saturn V on March 3, 1969, and placed in a near-earth orbit. The attached command and service modules were separated from the Saturn IVB stage, which contained the lunar module. The command and service modules were turned around and, for the first time, docked with the lunar module. The two spacecraft then separated from the Saturn IVB stage. For the next several days in the mission, combined spacecraft operations were conducted, and Schweickart carried out a brief extravehicular mission. On the fifth day McDivitt and Schweickart separated the lunar module from the command and service modules and, using both the descent and ascent propulsion systems, flew a simulated lunar landing and ascent pattern. The lunar module was separated for approximately 4 hr at a distance as far as 190 nautical mi. The two spacecraft then rendezvoused and docked as planned. For the balance of the ten-day mission the crew performed tracking and photographic tasks.

The performance of both spacecraft and sub-

A trampolinist demonstrates "Jones motion,"
a maneuver that allows a man to rotate his entire body
by moving only his arms. Such maneuvers are expected
to aid astronauts in weightless environments.

Ralph Crane, LIFE Magazine © Time Inc.

Apollo 8, the first manned spacecraft to travel to the moon, breaks out of earth orbit and begins its lunar voyage.

systems was almost flawless, and all mission objectives were met. The crew performance was considered excellent, despite some illness early in the flight. The Apollo 9 mission qualified the launch vehicle, the complete lunar landing spacecraft, the extravehicular-mobility unit (spacesuit and portable life-support system), and the flight-control techniques for manned lunar flights.

Apollo 10. A lunar orbital flight with the complete Apollo spacecraft was the mission of Apollo 10. The crew members were Thomas Stafford, commander; John Young, command module pilot; and Eugene Cernan, lunar module pilot. This flight was a final dress rehearsal for a manned lunar landing. The spacecraft was launched on May 18, 1969, by a Saturn V. After 2½ hr in earth orbit, the Saturn IVB propelled the spacecraft to escape velocity and placed it on a path to the moon. The Apollo crewmen separated the command module from the Saturn IVB and then turned 180° and docked with the lunar module, which was still attached to the Saturn IVB. The lunar module was then extracted from the Saturn IVB. Color television was used by the crew for the first time to show people on earth how the docking was accomplished. The docked spacecraft then continued their journey and eventually went into lunar orbit ranging from about 63 to 75 mi above the moon's surface. On the fourth day of the mission Stafford and Cernan entered the lunar module and separated it from the command module, where Young remained.

In the lunar module the descent stage pro-

pulsion system was ignited to slow the spacecraft so that it could start a descent to the lunar surface. Stafford and Cernan then flew the lunar module into an elliptical orbit ranging from about 9.4 to 220 mi above the lunar surface. After making two such orbits, the astronauts fired the ascent engines to place the lunar module into a path so that it would rendezvous and dock with the command module, which had continued in the original lunar orbit. After docking, Stafford and Cernan moved back into the command module, which made the return trip to earth alone. The lunar module was abandoned and went into solar orbit.

The Apollo 10 crew carried out all mission tasks short of an actual landing. Valuable photographs and observations of the Apollo landing sites were made, although some of the still photographs from the lunar module were unsuccessful. The Apollo 10 crew established a work-rest cycle which was to be used by the lunar landing crews. The mission demonstrated that ground-control techniques required for spacecraft tracking and guidance were adequate for a lunar landing. The spacecraft and all subsystems functioned well throughout the mission, except for a brief period when the lunar module gyrated unexpectedly on its ascent to rejoin the command module. The cause of this trouble remained uncertain. Flight crew performance was outstanding, and all crewmen remained in excellent health throughout the mission.

Apollo 11. "That's one small step for a man, one giant leap for mankind."

With those words U.S. astronaut Neil Armstrong announced the climactic moment of the Apollo program as, on July 20, 1969, he became the first human being to set foot on the moon. He was followed several minutes later by Edwin ("Buzz") Aldrin, and the two then walked on the lunar surface for more than two hours.

Apollo 11, manned by Armstrong, Aldrin, and Michael Collins, began its mission with a perfect launch by a Saturn V rocket on July 16 from Cape Kennedy, Fla. The spacecraft was first placed in orbit around the earth; then the third stage of the Saturn fired and thrust Apollo on its path toward the moon.

The spacecraft arrived at the moon on July 19 and went into lunar orbit. The next day Armstrong and Aldrin entered the lunar module and separated it from the command module, which, with Collins at the controls, continued on its path around the moon. Armstrong and Aldrin orbited the moon in their craft and then began a powered descent that brought them safely to the lunar surface on the afternoon of July 20 (U.S. time).

After remaining in the spacecraft several hours, they descended a ladder to the moon's surface and performed a number of experiments, including gathering rock samples and installing a laser beam reflector and seismic detectors. The two then returned to their craft and on July 21 fired its ascent stage and rejoined the command module in lunar orbit. Later that day the astronauts jettisoned the lunar module and fired the command ship's main rocket to begin the journey back to earth. The almost flawless historic mission ended with a splashdown in the Pacific Ocean on July 24.

Apollo Applications Program. The fourth manned spaceflight program to be conducted by the United States, the Apollo Applications Program (AAP) had flights scheduled for 1971–72. The objectives of the AAP missions are to achieve long-duration flights in order to study man in the weightless environment. Detailed medical and habitability studies will be conducted in flights which will last as long as 56 days. This type of medical information is required for the development of spacecraft and systems for long-term and planetary flights. Other studies will be conducted to study the earth and its resources, and scientific studies in the space environment will also be made.

Basic Apollo spacecraft and equipment were expected to be utilized for the AAP missions. The Apollo command module would be used as a crew transport and command center. The Apollo Saturn IVB launch vehicle stage, 54 ft long and 22 ft in diameter, was expected to be deactivated in flight and converted into a habitable orbiting spacecraft workshop. It would be equipped with floors and wall partitions to form crew quarters. Spacecraft systems and scientific experimental equipment would be carried into it and assembled by flight crewmen. This orbital workshop would have an airlock and a docking adapter attached to one end to permit the command module to dock with it and to allow crewmen to accomplish extravehicular tasks.

The first AAP mission was planned to be accomplished by a dual Saturn IB launch. The first launch, the unmanned AAP-2, would place a Saturn IVB orbital workshop, airlock, and multiple docking adapter into a near-earth orbit. One day later the manned AAP-1 command and service modules would be placed in earth orbit to rendezvous and dock with the AAP-2 orbital workshop. Crewmen would then leave the command module and enter the orbital workshop to use it as living quarters and a scientific laboratory. This first mission is scheduled to last 28 days.

AAP-3 was scheduled to be a manned revisit to the AAP-2 orbital workshop. A command and

The locations of the five lunar landing sites proposed for Apollo 11 are shown at the left. Landing site 2 (below, upper left) was photographed from the Apollo 11 lunar module while in orbit. The module actually landed somewhat beyond this site.

1 through 5
Proposed Apollo landing sites

*Apollo 11 landing site

Courtesy, Yerkes Observatory

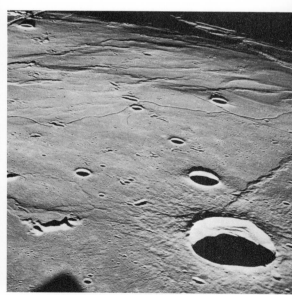

Courtesy, National Aeronautics and Space Administration

service module would be launched into earth orbit to rendezvous and dock with the orbital workshop. This mission would last for 56 days. Medical studies would then be made to increase man's knowledge of the physiological effects of long-term weightless flight. A fourth launch, AAP-4, was designed to carry a solar observatory into earth orbit to rendezvous and dock with the AAP-2 and 3 spacecraft. From this orbiting platform the crew would then conduct solar observations which could not be obtained from the earth.

Soviet manned space flight. The Soyuz is a third-generation U.S.S.R. manned spacecraft (following the Vostok and Voskhod) that has been flown unmanned and with crews of one, two, and three. The spacecraft is estimated to be 33 ft long and 10 ft in diameter, and is made up of three sections: a work-rest section, a flight-crew command section, and an equipment section. The work-rest section contains the living quarters of the spacecraft and also serves as an airlock for extravehicular operations. The crew command section houses the crew for launch and reentry and contains flight controls and displays. The equipment section contains a propulsion system, consumable supplies, and deployable solar electrical power panels. Propulsion and maneuvering systems give the Soyuz spacecraft rendezvous and docking capabilities. U.S. engineers have speculated that the Soyuz has a lift capability which would improve reentry guidance and landing accuracy over previous Soviet spacecraft.

The first manned Soyuz flight was launched on April 23, 1967, into earth orbit. The pilot was Vladimir Komarov, a veteran cosmonaut who earlier had flown a Voskhod flight. The spacecraft apparently experienced attitude control problems, and on the eighteenth orbit it reentered the earth's atmosphere. The parachute recovery system malfunctioned, and the spacecraft crashed, killing Komarov.

The unmanned Soyuz 2 spacecraft was launched into earth orbit as a target vehicle on Oct. 25, 1968. Soyuz 3 was launched the following day, Oct. 26, 1968, with one cosmonaut, Georgi Beregovoi. During the first orbit Soyuz 3 was automatically flown to within 650 ft of Soyuz 2, at which time the cosmonaut took over manual control and brought the two spacecraft closer together. During the second day another rendezvous maneuver was performed. Live television pictures were transmitted from the spacecraft to earth for live broadcast. Soyuz 2 reentered and landed on Oct. 28, 1968, and Soyuz 3 landed on Oct. 30, 1968.

Soyuz 4, manned by Vladimir A. Shatalov, was launched into earth orbit on Jan. 14, 1969, and was followed the next day by Soyuz 5 with a three-man crew: spacecraft commander Boris Volynov and crewmen Alexei Yeliseyev and Yevgeni Khrunov. During the first three days of the flight, the orbital paths of the spacecraft were automatically maneuvered to within 330 ft, where the Soyuz 4 pilot took over manual control for the final docking maneuver. Docking was completed on the thirty-fourth orbit. On the Soyuz 4 thirty-fifth orbit, Soyuz 5 cosmonauts Yeliseyev and Khrunov donned space suits and life-support systems, and made an extravehicular transfer to Soyuz 4. The spacecraft remained docked for approximately four hours. Soyuz 4, with its three-man crew, landed on Jan. 17, 1969, followed the next day by Soyuz 5.

—Richard S. Johnston

See also Feature Article: TOWARD A LANDFALL IN SPACE.

Space-oriented satellites

Among the year's space research programs was one in which scientists focused ultraviolet-sensing satellite telescopes on our galaxy (the Milky Way) and probed deeply into cosmological problems with infrared and X-ray telescopes carried aloft on rockets. Radio scientists listened to strange hisses of low-frequency noise from the earth's polar regions, from streamers of solar plasma, and from distant reaches of the galaxy. Patterns of the magnetic lines of force of the earth's magnetosphere were delineated by spectacularly colored tracer clouds released tens of thousands of miles above the ground. In the Crab Nebula the fastest pulsating radio source (pulsar) known to date was found to emit bursts of X rays 30 times per second. And a balloon-borne experiment discovered a transuranium (heavier than uranium) nucleus in the cosmic rays.

The Orbiting Solar Observatories 3, 4, and 5 of the U.S. National Aeronautics and Space Administration (NASA) and the Naval Research Laboratory's SOLRAD 9 produced great yields of data on the ultraviolet and X-ray radiation from the sun. The European Space Research Organization (ESRO) satellites ESRO 1 and ESRO 2B fulfilled their missions of atmospheric-physics studies and measurements of solar and cosmic radiations. The Soviet Union's Cosmos 215 was reported to have carried a payload of stellar ultraviolet and X-ray detectors which mapped the galaxy.

Orbiting telescopes. The Orbiting Astronomical Observatory (OAO) was NASA's most complex unmanned scientific satellite. A first attempt to use an OAO, in April 1966, was an immediate failure, but spectacular success was achieved with

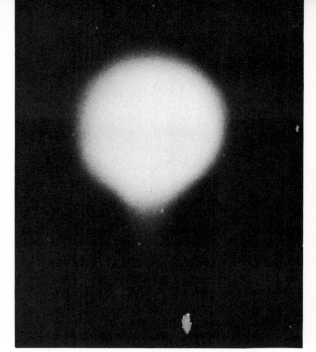

A cloud of barium vapor released by the satellite HEOS 1 demonstrates the effects of ionization and magnetic lines of force in space. The barium first forms a spherical, green-colored cloud (above). Within ten seconds solar photons ionize the barium, causing it to become progressively elongated (right and below) and also changing its color to a shade of purple.

Courtesy, Max Planck Institute for Extra Terrestrial Physics, Garsching, Munich

the second try. An Atlas-Centaur rocket launched the 4,400-lb spacecraft into a nearly circular orbit at an altitude of about 480 mi on Dec. 7, 1968. Two principal experiments on the spacecraft involved the following equipment: (1) the Celescope, which was designed by astronomers of the Smithsonian Astrophysical Observatory, Cambridge, Mass., to photograph ultraviolet star fields by means of an array of four ultraviolet television-type cameras (Uvicons); (2) instrumentation devised at the University of Wisconsin which utilized one 16-in. and four 8-in. telescopes to measure the ultraviolet brightness of individual stars and two spectrometers to analyze their spectra.

By mid-1969 the Celescope cameras had transmitted more than 1,000 star-field images, containing more than 6,000 blue stars of the Milky Way. The University of Wisconsin telescopes had carefully measured approximately 200 stars and a number of galaxies. Among the surprises revealed by the experiments were the presence of intense ultraviolet emission from the nuclei of otherwise normal spiral galaxies and the absence of such emission from some of the more powerful radio galaxies. Having solved the engineering problems of precise stabilization and accurate stellar pointing upon command from the ground, the NASA OAO program was expected to proceed to even more sophisticated operations in the second

113

launching of a spacecraft, scheduled for late 1969 or early 1970.

Radio astronomy. Radio broadcasting around the world is made possible by the ionosphere, a sheath of highly ionized gas which envelops the earth at heights above 50 mi. Radio signals, which are beamed upward from the ground, are mirrored back to earth by the ionosphere; repeated bounces between the ground and the ionosphere channel the radio waves around the curved surface of the earth. Conversely, because the ionosphere reflects cosmic radio waves of low frequencies back into outer space, such waves can be detected only with rocket- or satellite-borne detectors carried high above the ionosphere.

F. T. Haddock and T. E. Graedel of the University of Michigan used a receiver aboard the Orbiting Geophysical Observatory 5 (OGO-5) to record solar-radio-noise bursts at frequencies of 3.5 to 0.05 MHz (megahertz), wavelengths from 85 m to 6 km, which could not penetrate the ionosphere. By tracing the frequency drifts of the bursts the observers concluded that 0.20-MHz signals originate at a distance from the sun of about 33 solar radii and 0.10-MHz signals at about 75 solar radii (almost as far out as the orbit of Mercury). Furthermore, the high temperatures of the solar corona, about 2,000,000° C, appeared to fall rapidly to about 400,000° C at 5 solar radii and to about 25,000° C at 6 solar radii and beyond.

For efficient reception at long wavelengths (low frequencies), the length of the receiving antenna should approximately match the wavelength. Explorer 38, which was prepared under the scientific direction of R. G. Stone at the Goddard Space Flight Center, Greenbelt, Md., was launched on July 4, 1968, and carried two pairs of antennae which, measured from tip to tip, exceeded the height of the Empire State Building in New York City. During the launch phase the antennae were stowed in four spools of pretensioned steel ribbon. Once the spacecraft was in orbit each ribbon was played out and curled into a tubular rod stretching 750 ft from the body of the satellite. Each time the satellite passed over the earth's poles, it received bursts of radio waves that resembled the peculiar transmissions that have long been recorded from Jupiter by ground-based radio telescopes. The bursts, which lasted from seconds to minutes and spread in frequency across the broadcast band, presumably are associated with auroral processes. Explorer 38 also detected solar-radio-noise bursts at great distances from the sun, and radio signals that appeared to originate deep within the galaxy.

X-ray pulsar. History will identify 1968 as the "year of the pulsar." As of mid-1969 approximately 40 of these sources of pulsating radio waves had been discovered, their periods ranging from as long as 3 sec to as short as 33 msec. In January 1969 observers at the Kitt Peak National Observatory in Arizona discovered that a 16th-magnitude star at the center of the Crab Nebula flashed on and off visibly with the same period as a previously detected pulsar there; in March 1969 X-ray pulsations at the same frequency as the radio and light flashes were detected at the same location by an Aerobee rocket. The X-ray power was 10,000 times as great as the radio power and 100 times as great as the optical power. Scientists determined that the pulsar was slowing down at a rate which converts 10^{28} kw of rotational power into radiation. This is sufficient to account for all the electromagnetic power produced by the Crab Nebula, about 10,000 times the power output of our sun.

Electric and magnetic fields in space. Highly Eccentric Orbit Satellite 1 (HEOS 1) was prepared by ESRO and launched from Cape Kennedy, Fla., on Dec. 5, 1968. Its orbit ranged from an altitude of 274 mi to one of 138,000 mi. Included in the payload was a collection of instruments designed by Belgian, French, Italian, British, and West German scientists to measure magnetic fields, cosmic radiation, and the solar wind.

A particularly novel and spectacular mission of HEOS 1 involved the release of a cloud of barium vapor 44,000 mi above the earth. The technique of releasing visible clouds of barium vapor from rockets and satellites was developed by scientists of the Max Planck Institute for Physics and Astrophysics in Munich, W.Ger. Electrically charged plasma particles spiral around magnetic lines of force and, when electric and magnetic fields are crossed at right angles, the plasma drifts at right angles to both fields. Once released the barium gas is ionized by solar ultraviolet photons and then resonates in visible light. The neutral gas cloud is green and spreads out spherically, unconstrained by electric or magnetic fields. Within approximately ten seconds it becomes almost fully ionized, changes its color to purple, and spreads, cigar-shaped, along magnetic field lines.

In March HEOS 1 released approximately five pounds of barium. The gas was quickly ionized, and the purple cloud spread through the magnetosphere for 2,000 mi. It was visible to the naked eye for 22 minutes against the dark sky of North and South America. Finely detailed forms, tracing the magnetic and electric fields, were photographed with powerful telescopes at Kitt Peak

 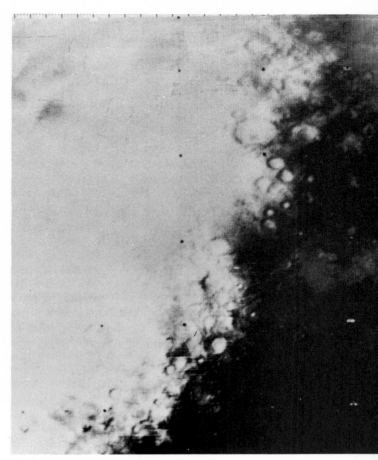

The many small, deep craters seen in the picture taken by Mariner 6 (left) indicate that the Martian surface closely resembles that of the moon. The south pole of Mars, as photographed by Mariner 7 (right), is covered by a white deposit that may be either a layer of frozen carbon dioxide ice or water ice. Southward-facing slopes of craters on the edge of the cap are covered by the ice; northward-facing slopes are bare.

National Observatory and at La Serena in Chile. Much information about the shape of the magnetosphere and the strength of its electric fields was expected to be derived from these photographs. In planned future experiments barium vapor will be released far outside the magnetosphere, in the solar wind, thus creating an artificial comet tail.

Cosmic rays. Cosmic rays were discovered in 1911, but as late as the mid-1940s it was believed that they consisted exclusively of hydrogen and helium nuclei. In 1948 heavier nuclei—lithium, beryllium, boron—and soon afterward nuclei as heavy as iron were discovered by balloon experimenters. In 1966 electronic counters aboard a Soviet satellite found nuclei heavier than those of iron.

Although the light elements—lithium, beryllium, and boron—are rare in the cosmos, they are abundant in cosmic rays. This anomaly is attributed to collisions of cosmic ray protons with heavier nuclei in the interstellar gas, resulting in spallation (fragmentation into smaller and lighter nuclei). From the abundance of lithium, beryllium, and boron, it has been inferred that the primary cosmic rays circulate in the galaxy for perhaps two million years, during which time they make the requisite number of collisions with the nuclei of heavier elements.

In 1968 P. H. Fowler of the University of Bristol, Eng., succeeded in obtaining a picture of the track of a transuranium nucleus which passed through a balloon-borne photographic emulsion. The kinetic energy of this particle was about 300 Bev (billion electron volts). Because the transuranium elements are unstable and short-lived, it would be surprising if they could survive millions of years in space. Their existence in cosmic rays may imply a nearby source, perhaps a supernova.

The planets. On their way to a rendezvous with

Mars were Mariners 6 and 7, launched by the U.S. in February and March 1969. Their trajectories were engineered to carry them within 2,000 mi of the planet. Mariner 6 was to pass over the equatorial zone, and Mariner 7 over the south polar region. At the closest approach a high-resolution camera was to provide pictures with a definition of about 900 ft compared to the 2 mi achieved by Mariner 4. The finest detail seen from earth has a scale of 100 mi. Infrared sensors on the spacecraft were designed to search for water vapor, carbon dioxide, methane, acetylene, and ethylene. When Mariner 7's radiometer looks at the polar cap temperature, it should provide the information necessary to distinguish frozen water from solid carbon dioxide.

The Soviet Union in January 1969 launched two spacecraft toward Venus. Both were designed to make soft landings on that planet, one on its sunny side and one on the dark side. The probes arrived at Venus in May and deployed instrument capsules to the planet's surface. Both capsules transmitted data for about 50 minutes but did not achieve their goal of an intact landing. Among the most striking findings of the probes, according to Soviet scientists, were altitude differences of more than 50,000 ft on the surface terrain of Venus.

—Herbert Friedman

See also Year in Review: ASTRONOMY.

See in ENCYCLOPÆDIA BRITANNICA (1969): SPACE EXPLORATION.

Earth-oriented satellites

The search for scientific knowledge, exploring the unknown, and the establishment of man's capability in space remained the primary goals of most space programs. Increasingly, however, earth-oriented satellites of direct economic benefit to man were being placed in operation.

There are three general classifications of such satellites: communications, earth survey, and navigation. Coincidentally, the first of each of these three kinds of satellites was launched in 1960: Echo 1, a passive, communications-reflector satellite, on August 12; Transit 1-B, a U.S. Navy navigational satellite, on April 13; and Tiros 1, a weather observation satellite, on April 1. In 1968–69 all classes of these satellites advanced in the accuracy and complexity of their performance. Moreover, the momentum and success of existing programs increased, and a broad range of future activity seemed assured.

About 2,400 years ago Socrates stated that, "We who inhabit the Earth dwell like frogs at the bottom of a pool. Only if man could rise above the summit of the air could he behold the true Earth, the world in which we live." By the use of earth-oriented satellites man has raised remote sensors above the atmosphere and is now observing this planet from that vantage point.

Communications satellites. In December 1968 and February 1969 the Communications Satellite Corporation (Comsat) placed two Intelsat 3 satellites in synchronous orbit. Whereas the Early Bird and Intelsat 2 communications satellites could handle 240 two-way telephone circuits each, the Intelsat 3s each provided 1,200 telephone circuits. Two more Intelsat 3 satellites were scheduled to be launched in 1969.

A satellite in a synchronous orbit at an altitude of 22,300 mi has an orbital velocity equal to the rotational speed of the earth. Thus, a satellite in such an orbit remains apparently fixed in space over one point on the earth. The four Intelsat 3 satellites were to be distributed so that one was over the Pacific Ocean, two over the Atlantic, and one over the Indian Ocean. From those points in space, a truly global communication satellite system was expected to be achieved for the first time.

Transmission and receiver terminals provided the ground links for the satellites. In 1968 there were terminals in five European nations, four in Latin America, six in the United States, and one in Canada. During 1969 ten additional terminals began operation—two in Latin America, three in the Asian Pacific, four in the Middle East, and one in Morocco, the first on the African continent.

The commercial service of Comsat grew substantially in 1968. By the end of the year, 941 satellite telephone circuits were being leased commercially on a full-time basis compared with 717 at the end of 1967 and 73 at the end of 1966. Events such as the Apollo space flights and the Olympic Games were transmitted throughout the world for commercial television broadcasts. Approximately 666 hr of such broadcasts were transmitted in 1968 compared with 225 hr in 1967 and 78 hr in 1966.

During 1970–71 it was expected that Intelsat 4 satellites, each having a capacity of 5,000 telephone circuits, would replace the Intelsat 3s. Twenty-one new ground stations were scheduled to start operations by 1971: six in Africa, seven in the Asian Pacific, four in Latin America, three in the Middle East, and one in Greece.

The U.S. Department of Defense strengthened its communications satellite systems. These military spacecraft used both synchronous and lower altitude orbits. During 1970–71 military communications satellites similar to Intelsat 4 were to be placed in synchronous orbit. Transmissions would be made either to large (85-ft diameter) fixed ground stations or to small, quickly deployable, ground terminals for tactical situations.

The Soviet Union placed ten Molniya communications satellites in highly elliptical, 12-hr orbits ranging in altitude from 300 to 24,750 mi. These satellites formed the basis of the Orbita television network across the Soviet Union. Some Cosmos spacecraft in similar orbits were believed to be Soviet military communications satellites.

In Europe a consortium of France, West Germany, and Belgium was proceeding with a plan to launch two satellites, each with the approximate capacity of an Intelsat 3. This program, known as Symphonie, was not expected to achieve operation before 1972. The European Space Research Organization (ESRO) began studying the design feasibility of a system which could meet requirements for European regional television broadcasting.

Earth-survey satellites. This broad category of satellites continued its development from initial relatively simple photography to many forms of observation of the earth for a wide variety of purposes. The first of such satellites, Tiros 1, transmitted cloud-cover pictures enabling meteorologists to track, forecast, and analyze storms. Many additional weather satellites have since been launched, and the U.S. program has made meteorological data available to countries throughout the world. More than 400 Automatic Picture Transmission (APT) stations at meteorological offices obtain facsimile-printed cloud pictures in about three minutes from Environmental Science Services Administration (ESSA) satellites. Each of these pictures, taken from an altitude of about 900 mi, covers approximately 1,700 sq mi. Some satellites are equipped to send a daily readout of global cloud cover from a video tape storage system. In 1969 the first of an advanced Tiros M series of weather watchers was equipped with an optical scanning radiometer.

The mouth of the Colorado River as it flows into the Gulf of California was photographed by Apollo 9 astronauts from an altitude of 130 nautical mi. Arid sandy area is at right.

Courtesy, National Aeronautics and Space Administration

This sensor measured variations in infrared radiation from the earth and thus provided nighttime cloud photographs.

The U.S. National Aeronautics and Space Administration (NASA) was developing sophisticated Nimbus satellites. The Nimbus B series was designed to obtain temperatures at various altitudes in the atmosphere. These would enable meteorologists to draw accurate vertical temperature and humidity profiles, and it was hoped that these data would make possible accurate weather forecasts a week in advance. Future satellites would be designed to measure the rates of change and movement of these profiles, which should result in even longer range forecasts.

The U.S.S.R. in 1968 launched two spacecraft in the Cosmos series believed to be meteorological satellites. Their probable purpose was to obtain cloud data in preparation for the launching of military reconnaissance satellites.

A GEOS satellite, launched in 1968, was engaged in providing data on the exact locations of the continental masses. An accuracy of ten meters was expected. Additional tasks for such geodetic satellites in the next few years are expected to include measuring continental drift and the tidal movement of land masses, and predicting earthquakes.

In addition to weather watching and mapping, many other uses of earth-survey satellites are feasible or appear possible. The remarkable orbital photographs made by U.S. astronauts in the Gemini flights and during Apollo 7 and 9 are yielding new understanding of the physical features of the earth's surface. For the first time man has viewed the folds and fractures (faults) in the earth's crust. Geologists and mineralogists have found such photographic data immensely valuable in identifying likely sites for the prospecting of oil and minerals.

Satellites have identified and evaluated water resources by mapping the location and size of watershed areas, the movement of glaciers, and snow cover. In the search for fresh water, color photography from satellites allows identifications of biological, chemical, and industrial pollutants in water. Similarly, infrared photography along ocean coast lines has located fresh water escaping into the ocean. Once such escape areas are found, consideration can be given to saving this water by drilling suitable wells inland.

By similar techniques and the use of cameras equipped with optical filters to define narrow wavelengths, the motion and temperatures of ocean currents, such as the Gulf Stream, can be plotted. Because there is a close relationship between fishery production and the thermal char-acteristics of the ocean, fishing fleets that possess such temperature data can improve their efficiency. The possibility exists for the eventual spotting of schools of fish by such techniques.

Observations from survey satellites also might assist in mapping navigation routes in coastal and shoal-water areas and in helping control silting in major harbors and navigable rivers. Surveys from space are expected to produce data that would not be feasible by measuring techniques at the earth's surface. Another important use of photographic imagery involves the help that it can give to farmers. Satellite photography can identify arable land as well as soil which is not suitable for agriculture because of unfavorable salinity. Infrared photography can identify the existence and spread of insect pests and blights by means of noting minor variations of color undetectable close at hand. (*See* Year in Review: AGRICULTURE.)

These and other civilian applications of survey satellites are being proved feasible by such spacecraft as NASA's Applications Technology Satellite (ATS) series and Nimbus. In the U.S. there was increasing interest in and support for developing an operational earth resources satellite program at an early date. Within the U.S. government the departments of Agriculture and Interior and the U.S. Naval Oceanographic Office were particularly interested in such a program. It seemed probable that in 1971 or 1972 an earth resources satellite will be launched. Equipment on such a spacecraft would include a spectrometer that would scan wavelengths to help determine soil and crop classifications; a three-color, high-resolution television camera; and an interrogation system for ocean buoys and remote stream gauges. Buoys, water gauges, strain gauges, and other surface instruments, strategically placed in remote areas, would, upon satellite command, transmit data for relay to data-handling stations.

The military forces of both the U.S. and U.S.S.R. were actively engaged in the surveillance of the earth from space. Such programs are, of course, not publicized for reasons of security. It is known, however, that extreme-resolution photographs are made of subjects of military interest, such as ballistic missile launch sites. In the immediate future it appears likely that the military will use narrow bands in the electromagnetic spectrum for the detection and tracking of ships and military movements.

Navigation satellites. This specialized class of earth-oriented satellites, first launched by the U.S. Navy in 1960, originally was launched without public announcement for reasons of military security. The prime purpose of the Transit series of satellites was to enable nuclear submarines to fix their positions accurately under all-weather surface conditions. Thus, star-sighting became unnecessary. Operating essentially as a beacon in the sky, the Transit system was removed from its secret status in 1967. Three Transit satellites were launched in 1967 and another in 1968. Wide use of this navigation system by the U.S. Merchant Marine was expected in the next few years. In the 1969–73 period approximately 11 more Transit satellites are expected to be launched.

The U.S.S.R. launched six navigation satellites in the Cosmos series during 1968. Presumably, these were for use by Soviet nuclear-missile submarines as well as surface ships.

Conclusion. Earth-oriented satellites are serving the needs of man in ways which could not have been predicted a decade ago. Clearly these remote tools in space can perform many tasks that are not possible or feasible from the earth. With the exception of photography by astronauts all of the tasks have been performed by unmanned spacecraft. With the probability of semipermanent earth-orbiting space stations by the mid-1970s, however, it may be expected that man will monitor and maintain many of the surveillance operations of both civilian and military nature.

—F. C. Durant, III

Astronomy

The sun

Investigation of the sun and its changes is the main work of a large number of the world's astronomers and space scientists. At hundreds of observing stations in many countries, such solar phenomena as sunspots, prominences, flares, the corona, and solar radio noise are being monitored daily. A rapidly increasing variety of observational techniques is being applied to the sun. Instruments aboard artificial satellites are widely used to study solar radiations at wavelengths that cannot penetrate the earth's atmosphere; these devices reveal intensely bright patches of X-ray emission on the sun's surface, as well as great bursts of very low-frequency radio noise that happen far out in the corona. By 1969 advancing technology permitted measurements of the sun's infrared radiation to wavelengths as great as 400 μ (one micron = 0.000039 in.).

Umbral flashes. Apart from this extension of solar observing to new spectral regions, much progress resulted from the ingenious combina-

tion of standard techniques to gain improved efficiency. In particular, it proved rewarding to take large-scale motion pictures of the sun's disk in monochromatic light. For example, Sacramento Peak Observatory, N.M., was engaged in an extensive program of lapse-rate photography of sunspots in ionized-calcium light. The exposures were taken with a long-focus telescope through a filter transmitting only a range of wavelengths 0.3Å (angstrom) broad, centered on the strong 3934-Å spectral line of calcium (one angstrom = 0.00000001 cm). These film strips revealed an unsuspected phenomenon: compact bright flashes occurring within the dark central regions (umbrae) of sunspots. A typical umbral flash is roughly 1,500 mi in diameter and lasts about 50 sec. During its brief life the flash travels a short distance upward and outward from the center of the umbra. Several minutes

"I don't know about you, but I'm sick and tired of working nights."—James Weaver, © 1969 Saturday Review Inc.

after one umbral flash has faded out, another is likely to appear nearby.

Umbral flashes are by no means rare; at any moment, a fair-sized sunspot will contain several. They are, however, visible only in ionized-calcium light, which is why they were not discovered previously by visual or ordinary photographic observations. Umbral flashes added a new complication to the already intricate theoretical problems of sunspots.

Temperatures in the sun's atmosphere. In studying the sun astronomers noted that its temperature decreases from about 15,000,000° K (0° K = −273° C) at its center to several thousand degrees at the sun's apparent surface (photosphere). But because the sun's outer envelope (corona) has a temperature of 1,000,000° K or more, there is evidently an intermediate level, somewhat above the photosphere, at which the temperature reaches a minimum.

Owen Gingerich of the Smithsonian Astrophysical Observatory, Cambridge, Mass., analyzed recent measurements of ultraviolet solar radiation with instruments aboard rockets and spacecraft, and measurements of infrared radiation studied from high aircraft and balloons. In this way he redetermined the vertical temperature profile of the sun's atmosphere and found that a minimum temperature of 4,200° K is reached about 370 mi above the photosphere. Below this level the temperature increases gradually; above it, the increase is rapid. Until Gingerich announced these findings in 1969, the minimum temperature was thought to be as great as 4,600° K.

Solar magnetic fields. Lockheed Solar Observatory, near Los Angeles, was one of several stations where the ever-changing magnetic field of the sun was being mapped by various techniques. Scientists there successfully developed a relatively simple photographic method, in which motion pictures are taken of the sun through a filter that admits only the 5324-Å line of iron. At places on the sun's disk where a strong magnetic field exists, this particular radiation becomes polarized (Zeeman effect). By taking the motion pictures through a polarizing sheet behind a rotating quarter-wave plate, magnetic areas on the sun appeared to "blink" when the projected film was viewed.

This technique provided a simple way of charting localized magnetic disturbances on the sun. Such disturbed areas often become the site of sunspot regions and of solar flares that can adversely affect shortwave radio communications on earth.

The moon

The inside of the moon. The U.S. spacecraft Lunar Orbiter 5 provided important information about the subsurface of the moon. P. M. Muller and W. L. Sjogren of the California Institute of Technology (Caltech) discovered small irregularities in the orbital motion of the spacecraft which demonstrated that the moon's gravitational field is not quite symmetrical. These scientists found six localized regions on the moon of higher-than-average gravity. As Lunar Orbiter 5 passed over these regions, it speeded up temporarily. These areas range up to 125 mi in diameter.

Muller and Sjogren interpreted these gravity irregularities as caused by concentrations of dense material lying below the lunar surface, like raisins in a pudding. The two men named these concentrations "mascons." Their depths remained uncertain but were roughly estimated as 30 mi.

The most remarkable property of the mascons is that the five most pronounced examples coincide with circular lunar seas, such as Mare Imbrium; none lies under the large, irregular maria. This fact supports the hypothesis, favored by some, that the circular maria are the impact scars made by high-density bodies of asteroidal dimensions which collided with the moon.

In April 1969 the Caltech scientists announced the discovery of six additional mascons from their continuing analysis of Lunar Orbiter 5 data, with supporting evidence from Lunar Orbiters 3 and 4. This brought to 12 the number of mascons now known on the nearer side of the moon.

Lunar riverbeds. Most of the thousands of long, narrow, flat-bottomed lunar valleys (rilles) are nearly straight, but about 30 are known that meander in a way suggestive of rivers on the earth. The typical meandering rille begins at a small crater on high ground and winds its way for many miles before ending on lower ground. Some examples even show oxbows. Until 1968 most astronomers denied that these winding rilles could be the dried-up beds of ancient lunar rivers. They argued that in the absence of any appreciable atmosphere liquid water could not persist on the moon's surface. Lunar water was conceivable only in the form of a hypothetical permafrost, many yards below the surface.

During recent months, however, the puzzle was solved by Stanton J. Peale and his colleagues at the University of California at Los Angeles. They determined that if the permafrost layer should be breached by the impact of a large meteorite, water would froth up to the surface. But, contrary to usual belief, water exposed to a vacuum does not simply explode into vapor; instead, it quickly forms a protective layer of ice. Thus, the released lunar water could flow to lower ground as a stream under a continually growing canopy of ice that prevents evaporation. Numerical calculations showed that a winding rille of typical size could be produced by such a lunar river in less than 1,000 years. Eventually, the ice would vaporize to leave the dried-up bed.

Small-scale experiments in laboratory vacuum chambers were performed by U.S. Air Force scientists in an effort to confirm the possibility of the formation of such ice canopies and the preservation of water flowing under them. Because there was no alternative theory that satisfactorily explained the detailed structure of the meandering rilles, these features were regarded as good evidence that some liquid water has existed on the moon.

Planets

Icarus. On June 14, 1968, the fast-moving asteroid Icarus passed within 4,000,000 mi of the earth, as had been predicted. For several nights this minor planet was close enough for detailed observations with large telescopes by many astronomers in the U.S., the Soviet Union, and France.

Photoelectric photometry by U.S. astronomers revealed that the brightness of Icarus varied rhythmically, indicating that this asteroid completed one rotation each 2 hours and 16 minutes. Its light was slightly polarized, to an extent that

suggested that the asteroid reflects about 26% of the sunlight striking it.

Icarus was the first asteroid from which radar echoes were obtained. This difficult observation —a triumph of electronics technology—was made by teams at the Jet Propulsion Laboratory (JPL) in Pasadena, Calif., and at the Massachusetts Institute of Technology's Lincoln Laboratory. In the JPL experiment, 450,000 w of continuous-wave power were beamed toward Icarus; the returning signal was so weak that it had to be accumulated for three or four hours to be clearly recognized. This work suggested that the surface of Icarus is jagged and that it reflects microwaves as does an iron meteorite.

Mass of Pluto. In late 1968 astronomers at the

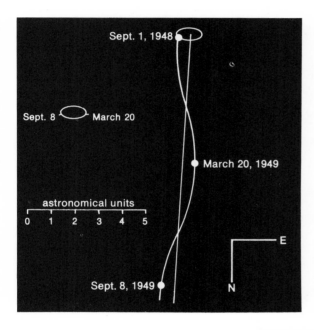

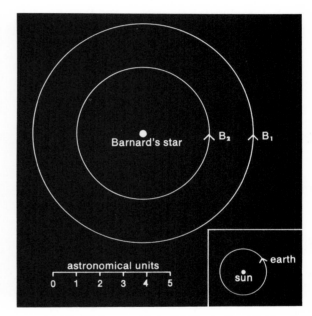

Barnard's star demonstrates the presence of a companion planet in the composite of three photographs, taken at 6-month intervals, at the right. The three dots at the lower left show the proper motion and parallactic shift of Barnard's star during this period. These motions, also shown diagrammatically (above), show irregularities caused by at least one planet orbiting the star. The theoretical positions of two companion planets in relation to the star are compared with the earth's orbit around the sun (above right).

Courtesy, Peter van de Kamp, Sproul Observatory

121

U.S. Naval Observatory, Washington, D.C., completed the most comprehensive analysis of the observed motion of the planet Neptune since its optical discovery in 1846. After evaluating the perturbations of Neptune caused by the attraction of the outermost planet, Pluto, these scientists calculated the first reliable determination of the mass of Pluto as only 0.18 the earth's mass.

This mass determination resolved a dilemma that had perplexed astronomers ever since the discovery of Pluto in 1930. Percival Lowell, in predicting a planet beyond Neptune, had expected a 12th-magnitude planet with 6⅔ times the earth's mass. Because the actual Pluto was as faint as magnitude 15, either it was a body of much smaller mass than anticipated or else it was a massive body with either improbably high density or improbably low light reflectivity. With Pluto definitely established as a body of slight mass, it became clear that Lowell's prediction was a lucky accident and that the discovery of Pluto was really due only to the thoroughness and wide extent of the photographic search for it at Lowell Observatory, Flagstaff, Ariz. (For additional information on planets, *see* Year in Review: ASTRONAUTICS AND SPACE EXPLORATION, *Space-oriented Satellites*.)

Stars

Another planetary system? The second closest star to the sun is Barnard's star, 5.9 light-years away; only the triple system Alpha Centauri is nearer. Barnard's "runaway star," a 9th-magnitude dwarf in the constellation Ophiuchus, travels across the sky at the rate of one degree in three and a half centuries—the largest motion yet discovered for any star.

In 1968 Peter Van de Kamp announced the results of his refined measurements on more than 3,000 photographs of Barnard's star. He proved that its motion across the sky departed very slightly in a periodic fashion from uniform straight-line travel. This implied that the visible star was being attracted by a small unseen companion. This companion, revolving around the primary star once every 25 years, seemed likely to be a very small body, with only about 1.7 times the mass of the planet Jupiter.

But in April 1969 van de Kamp pointed out an alternative explanation for the disturbances of the visible star's motion. The observed effects he said, could be equally well explained by the hypothesis of *two* unseen companions, moving in circular orbits with periods of 26 and 12 years and with respective masses of 1.1 and 0.8 times the mass of Jupiter.

Even though it is not yet possible to decide whether the one-companion or two-companion hypothesis is correct, it already appears that Barnard's star is the "sun" of another system of one or more planets. The fact that the second closest stellar neighbor to our sun also has a planetary system is a strong indication that such retinues must be of frequent occurrence among the stars of our galaxy (the Milky Way).

Birth of a planetary nebula. In the Milky Way slightly over 1,000 planetary nebulae have been discovered. These are vast, slowly expanding bubbles of rarefied gas, each excited to shine by a very hot central star. The known nebulae form a sequence ranging from small, very bright, quasistellar types to large, very faint ones that are almost indistinguishable against the sky. It has been estimated that a planetary nebula takes about 30,000 years to evolve along this sequence. According to current theories of stellar evolution, a planetary nebula is produced from a giant star; the star explodes and its atmosphere is expelled catastrophically, while the star core collapses to form a white dwarf which then becomes the nebula's central star.

An extraordinary variable star in the constellation Sagitta was pointed out in mid-1968 by G. H. Herbig of the Lick Observatory on Mt. Hamilton, Calif., and by the Soviet astronomer A. A. Boyarchuk as probably a planetary nebula in the process of formation. This object, known as FG Sagittae, has been brightening steadily from about magnitude 15 in the year 1895 to 9 at present. Herbig's detailed spectroscopic study indicated that the light of FG Sagittae comes from a compact shell of luminous gas, expanding at about 45 mi/sec as material flows out from a central star it masks. The radius of this nebular shell had grown to about 26 times the star's radius by 1965. The increase in luminosity of FG Sagittae has been due primarily to the growth in surface area of this shell, which, however, is still so compact that it appears starlike in even the largest telescopes. In recent years the temperature and, hence, the surface of the shell have diminished slightly.

Circumstellar envelopes of silicate grains. Recent improvements in the sensitivity of infrared detectors were quickly applied by astronomers to study stellar spectra to wavelengths as great as 14 μ. The pioneer in this work was F. J. Low of Rice University, Houston, Tex. Those stars observable in the micron range are primarily very red, cool giants and supergiants.

In 1969 N. J. Woolf and E. P. Ney of the University of Minnesota obtained a new measurement which showed that the infrared spectra of the

Courtesy, Lick Observatory

stars Mira Ceti, Chi Cygni, Betelgeuse, and Mu Cephei deviated markedly from black body spectra (a black body is a theoretical substance that is a perfect absorber and emitter of radiation). These stars appeared abnormally bright at wavelengths between 9.5 and 14 μ; Mu Cephei, for example, was five times brighter than expected in this interval.

The Minnesota astronomers argued that this excess emission could not originate in the star itself but was, instead, radiation from a cloud of solid particles surrounding the star. Analysis of the radiation indicated that the particles consisted of such silicate minerals as pyroxene ($MgSiO_3$) and olivine (($Mg,Fe)_2SiO_4$). Theoretically, condensation of solid grains can be expected in the outer atmosphere of red giant stars.

At Lick Observatory the infrared spectrum of the cool supergiant star 119 Tauri was studied in considerable detail over the wavelength range 2.9 to 12 μ. Three absorption bands were detected, one near 8.2 μ that was attributed to silicon monoxide (SiO) and conspicuous bands at 9.7 and 10.6 μ that are probably due to pyroxene. This discovery pointed to the existence of silicate grains in interstellar space, in the general vicinity of cool stars but at greater distances than the circumstellar emission reported by the Minnesota investigators.

The galaxy

Magnetic field of the galaxy. Indirect evidence for the existence of extensive, weak magnetic fields in the Milky Way first appeared in the 1940s, when the light of many distant stars was discovered to be partially polarized. This polarization was attributed to elongated dust grains in interstellar space, which were aligned by an interstellar magnetic field so that they were more or less parallel. More recently, the observed polarization of galactic radio noise provided additional indications of such large-scale magnetic fields.

Direct measurement of an interstellar field was reported in mid-1968 by G. L. Verschuur at the U.S. National Radio Astronomy Observatory, Green Bank, W.Va. His observations with the 140-ft radio telescope at Green Bank revealed that the interstellar hydrogen line of 21-cm wave-

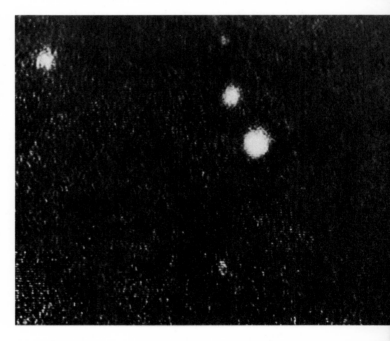

The Crab nebula (top), the remnant of a supernova, is the site of a pulsar that has been detected optically. Two views of the central portion of the nebula (center and bottom) show the effect of the flickering light of the pulsar; the large bright star in the middle of the center picture has virtually disappeared below.

123

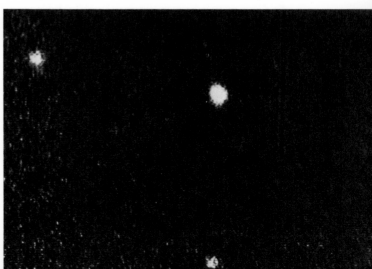

length shows clearly the splitting (Zeeman effect) characteristic of this line when it originates in a magnetic field. The spacing of the Zeeman pattern indicated an interstellar magnetic field strength of about 2×10^{-5} gauss.

The absorption in question originates within hydrogen clouds that lie in the so-called Perseus spiral arm of our galaxy, about 6,000 to 10,000 light-years distant from the sun. Similar observations for several other nearer hydrogen clouds in different parts of the Milky Way showed either weaker magnetic fields or none at all.

Interstellar molecules. About 1920 optical observations began to accumulate that established the presence of clouds of interstellar dust that dimmed and reddened the light of background stars, and also of the existence in interstellar space of a rarefied medium of calcium and sodium atoms. In the 1950s radio astronomers proved that neutral hydrogen was an abundant constituent of the interstellar medium, since its microwave emission line of 21-cm wavelength could be detected in all parts of the sky. Then, in 1963, interstellar clouds of hydroxyl (OH) ions were discovered at many places in the Milky Way.

During late 1968 and early 1969 radio astronomers were successful in their searches for three additional kinds of molecules in interstellar space. In each case laboratory studies of the microwave spectrum of the compound had been made so that the wavelength of the most promising line was known in advance.

The discovery of interstellar ammonia gas (NH_3) was announced by a University of California team in December 1968. Their observations were made with a new 20-ft-diameter radio telescope, tuned to the 1.2652-cm microwave line of ammonia. Several hours of tracking a dense cloud of dust and gas in the direction of the center of our galaxy revealed the presence of this microwave line in emission. Evidence was also found for another, weaker ammonia line at the 1.2637-cm wavelength.

The ammonia radiation originated in a cloud about three minutes of arc in diameter in which strong OH absorption had already been detected. The California scientists calculated the temperature of the ammonia as about −248° C and estimated that the cloud contains one molecule of this gas per liter. Subsequently, these researchers detected the 1.2652-cm radiation of ammonia from several other dust clouds in Sagittarius. This compound, thus, appears to be widespread in the galaxy.

In February 1969 the same University of California team discovered the 1.35-cm emission line of water vapor in the microwave spectrum of the Orion nebula. The line was double-peaked, indicating that the molecules are concentrated in two clouds, one of which is approaching the observer at about 18.5 mi/sec and the other cloud receding at half this rate. These large velocities rule out any possibility that the observations refer to water vapor in the earth's atmosphere. Soon afterward a U.S. Naval Research Laboratory (Washington, D.C.) group used an 85-ft radio telescope at the Maryland Point Observatory to detect seven other compact cosmic sources of the water vapor emission line. All are small nebulae that also radiate OH emission.

In March 1969 interstellar formaldehyde (H_2CO) was recognized by its characteristic absorption line at 6.21-cm wavelength, superimposed on the microwave continuous spectra of two OH clouds. This remarkable discovery was made at the U.S. National Radio Astronomy Observatory. Within a few days this same absorption feature was observed in 15 of 23 radio sources examined. Formaldehyde is the first organic polyatomic molecule to be detected in the interstellar gas. It tends to occur in the same regions of space as OH, in comparable abundance.

Taken together, these discoveries of widespread ammonia, water vapor, and formaldehyde in our galaxy suggest a well-advanced chemical evolution in interstellar space. Other, more complex organic molecules may well exist there; if such are found, conceivably life could originate in the gas from which stars and planets form.

Crab nebula pulsar. The rapidly pulsating cosmic radio sources known as pulsars continued to stimulate lively interest among astronomers. By Feb. 24, 1969, the first anniversary of the announcement of pulsars, about three dozen of these enigmatic radio sources had been discovered, and more than 200 technical papers had been published on the subject.

A major breakthrough began to materialize on Oct. 20, 1968, with the discovery at the U.S. National Radio Astronomy Observatory of a pulsar, NP 0532, that more or less coincided in position with the Crab nebula. This source pulsated at the remarkably short radio period of 0.033 sec, the shortest yet found for any pulsar.

The Crab nebula is believed by astronomers to be the expanding gases from a supernova explosion in 1054 A.D. The latest study of the expansion of the nebula was made in 1968 by Virginia Trimble at the Mount Wilson and Palomar Observatories, Calif. Her painstaking measurements of some 200 knots of nebulosity on photographs taken from 1939 to 1966 verified that the expansion had begun nearly 1,000 years ago. The outward motions, if extrapolated backward in time, tended to diverge from very near a faint double star at the center of the nebula. In fact, R. Minkowski and W. Baade had suspected in 1942 that the southwestern component of the double star was the stellar remnant of the supernova.

These facts made possible the identification of the optical counterpart of the NP 0532 pulsar. On Jan. 15 and 16, 1969, astronomers using the 36-in. reflector at Steward Observatory, Kitt Peak, Ariz., searched the central part of the Crab nebula with a photoelectric photometer and appropriate electronic equipment for detecting any 30-Hz (Hertz) light variation. They were rewarded by finding a 0.033095-sec optical flicker that originated from the vicinity of the southwest member of the central double star.

This discovery was fully confirmed on Jan. 19 and 20 at the McDonald Observatory, Mt. Locke, Tex., with the 82-in. reflector there. By placing a pinhole in their optical system, the Texas astronomers demonstrated that the flashing object was essentially a point source. Within a few days, the optical pulsations of NP 0532 were also observed photoelectrically at Kitt Peak National Observatory, Ariz., and at C. E. Kenneth Mees Observatory, Rochester, N.Y.

In March 1969 the variations of NP 0532 were measured at X-ray wavelengths, independently by groups at Columbia University and the U.S. Naval Research Laboratory. In both experiments, detectors were flown above most of the earth's atmosphere in Aerobee rockets. (*See* Year in Review: ASTRONAUTICS AND SPACE EXPLORATION, *Space-oriented Satellites*.)

The Vela pulsar. NP 0532 is not the only pulsar known to be associated with an old supernova. In the southern constellation Vela the pulsar PSR 0833–45 was announced by Australian radio astronomers in October 1968. Like the Crab Nebula pulsar, it had an exceptionally rapid pulsation rate, in this case every 0.089 sec. Moreover, PSR 0833–45 lies near the center of a vast wreath of nebulosity known as Vela X, which is considered to be the debris from an unrecorded supernova explosion several thousand years ago.

The optical object corresponding to the Vela pulsar was believed to have been identified in April 1969. Long-exposure photographs taken at the Inter-American Observatory (Cerro Tololo, Chile) revealed a peculiar 19th-magnitude star exactly at the position the Australians had determined for the pulsar. This star had the excess ultraviolet radiation characteristic of old novae, and its photographic image appeared nebulous. Astronomers are continuing to observe the star in an attempt to determine if it emits optical flashes in an 0.089-sec period.

The rate of pulsation of the Vela pulsar is very gradually lengthening, a property shared with other well-observed pulsars, including NP 0532. But in April 1969 Jet Propulsion Laboratory scientists announced that their recent measurements of the Vela pulsar revealed superimposed irregularities. In late February, for example, the period suddenly shortened and then, after a few weeks, was again lengthening. Such behavior indicated that pulsars could not safely be used as precise timekeepers to test certain relativistic effects.

Future astronomical events

The first total eclipse of the sun since 1961 to be visible from somewhere in the United States will occur on March 7, 1970. The narrow track of totality will begin southeast of Hawaii, cross southern Mexico and the Gulf of Mexico, cut through northern Florida, and extend along the Atlantic Coast to North Carolina; it will then continue over the Atlantic to Nantucket Island (Mass.), Nova Scotia, and Newfoundland. The maximum duration of the total phase will be nearly three and a half minutes in Mexico.

Much of the scientific study of this eclipse will be conducted from high-altitude aircraft, as was done during other recent total eclipses, thus avoiding the risk of clouds hampering observations. One proposal for the 1970 eclipse was to carry instruments aboard a large supersonic aircraft which, by careful navigation, could keep up with the moon's fast-moving shadow and thus stretch out the duration of totality to one and a half hours.

On May 9, 1970, the first transit of Mercury across the face of the sun in a decade will occur. For nearly eight hours the planet will be visible in small telescopes as a tiny black dot as it moves eastward across the sun's disk. The entire event will be visible from central and eastern Europe; in the U.S. (except along the Pacific Coast), part of the transit will be observable after sunrise.

The latest scientific use for transits of Mercury is the precise determination of the planet's diameter by E. Hertzsprung's technique. In principle, a photoelectric photometer compares the light from two equal, adjacent small areas on the solar disk, one of those areas containing Mercury. The planet's angular size can be deduced from the proportion of sunlight cut off by the planet, whose disk is perfectly black. Observations of this kind are planned for the 1970 transit.

—Joseph Ashbrook

See also A Gateway to the Future: THE MOUNT WILSON AND PALOMAR OBSERVATORIES: TWO ROOMS WITH A VIEW.

Atmospheric sciences

As man has gained more knowledge of the earth's atmosphere and the factors that determine its behavior, and as he has also learned to release and harness more powerful sources of energy, he has entered an era when he can have an effect on both the weather and the climate. But because the effects produced by human activities usually are not planned, they are often quite undesirable. Atmospheric scientists have been acutely aware of this situation and have taken steps toward improving ways of observing the atmosphere, especially on a global scale, of understanding its behavior, and of predicting its future patterns.

The WWW and GARP

The international World Weather Watch (WWW) and the Global Atmospheric Research Program (GARP) continued their efforts to improve global observations of the weather and to develop the communications and tools for analyzing those observations with large computers. The ultimate objective of both projects has been to extend the range of useful weather predictions from the present limit of a few days to the approximately one-week limit of our present technology.

The basic technique for observing the atmosphere in depth has been the rawinsonde, a balloon-borne radio transmitter that sends back temperature and pressure (and usually humidity) readings as it rises, and also, by means of its motion, gives a measure of the wind at each level. The WWW has been primarily interested in a program to establish more rawinsonde stations in places where there are large gaps in the global network for collecting weather information. In 1967 the congress of the World Meteorological Organization approved detailed WWW plans for improving the weather-watch network and for establishing three main world meteorological centers, in Washington, D.C., Moscow, and Melbourne, Austr.

At its meeting in Princeton, N.J., in January 1969, the international Joint Organizing Committee reviewed the plans for the GARP, which had been formulated the preceding year by a number of working groups. The main features of this ambitious program were: the utilization of high-speed computers; a satellite weather-observation network; and the analysis of tropical atmospheric behavior.

One of the main reasons for instituting the GARP was a recent demonstration showing that high-speed computers could be used to calculate how the atmosphere ought to behave globally.

Such a use of computers has been referred to as "making numerical models of the general circulation of the atmosphere." A major effort of the GARP has been to develop better models of this type, taking advantage of the best available computers in the U.S., U.K., West Germany, the Soviet Union, and Japan. Computer experimentation would be necessary for those who are trying to develop better observing systems; and the modelers, in turn, would have to learn how to use these new kinds of observations.

Another major objective of the GARP that took shape in 1969 was the development of a system for observing the atmosphere from spacecraft; it would supplement (but not replace) the surface and rawinsonde networks. The first complete test of this system, however, probably cannot be made until about 1975.

The many pictures of clouds obtained by U.S. and Soviet weather satellites since 1960 are well known. But not so well known is the fact that, by the use of infrared techniques, U.S. and Soviet satellites have calculated cloud-top and sea-surface temperatures as well as the temperature distribution in the stratosphere at about 20 km (12.5 mi). The U.S. meteorological satellite, Nimbus 3, launched on April 14, 1969, has been testing these techniques, and future meteorological satellites will also try systems that measure atmospheric and surface emissions at radio frequencies (millimeter and centimeter wavelengths).

To measure winds in the atmosphere from satellites, U.S. meteorologists have observed cloud drifts from satellites that remain over the same area on the Equator. But such wind determinations are incomplete because the height of the moving cloud cannot be measured. Systems for measuring winds by tracking constant-level balloons from satellites have been developed and tested in the U.S. and France; these promise to give accurate calculations of winds as well as air temperature. The system of the future, reported by the International Committee for Space Research (COSPAR), envisaged thousands of such balloons, each built to last for more than six months and so light and fragile that they would be no hazard to aircraft. A U.S. system was tested by two short balloon flights conducted by the National Center for Atmospheric Research (NCAR) from Palestine, Tex., in August 1968 and February 1969. Each balloon carried a package designed by the U.S. National Aeronautics and Space Administration (NASA) which could "talk" by radio to the satellite ATS-1 stationed over the Equator, 22,000 mi above South America. The location of each drifting balloon was continuously determined to an accuracy of about one mile; as the

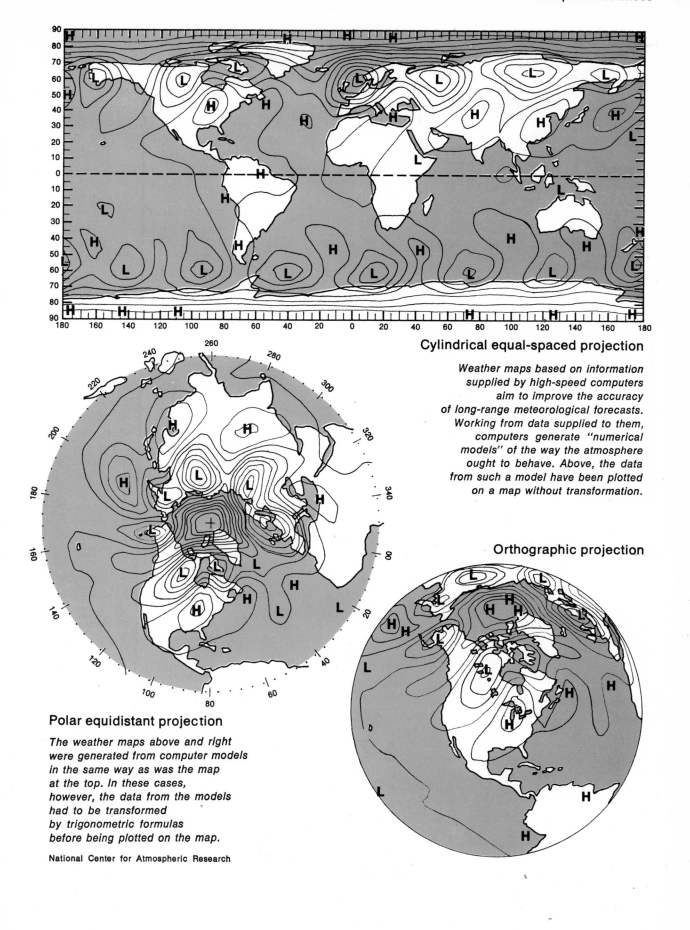

Cylindrical equal-spaced projection

*Weather maps based on information
supplied by high-speed computers
aim to improve the accuracy
of long-range meteorological forecasts.
Working from data supplied to them,
computers generate "numerical
models" of the way the atmosphere
ought to behave. Above, the data
from such a model have been plotted
on a map without transformation.*

Orthographic projection

Polar equidistant projection

*The weather maps above and right
were generated from computer models
in the same way as was the map
at the top. In these cases,
however, the data from the models
had to be transformed
by trigonometric formulas
before being plotted on the map.*

National Center for Atmospheric Research

balloons observed such phenomena as air temperature, they transmitted this information to the satellite, which, in turn, relayed it to a receiving station in Virginia. This test marked a step toward the future development of a global atmospheric observing system in which buoys, remote weather stations, and ships at sea, as well as balloons, would all send their positions and messages via satellites to a central location.

Another aspect of the GARP which received special attention was the problem of how the atmosphere in the tropics behaves. In particular, GARP has been trying to understand and predict the atmospheric motions caused by the tropical "heat engine" which provides most of the heat for the rest of the atmosphere. The atmosphere picks up energy at the surface, mostly from the tropical oceans, in the form of heat and water vapor. This thermal energy is then carried into the higher layers of the atmosphere by cumulus clouds, and from there to each of the poles. The patterns of cumulus convection in the tropics are complex and were largely unpredictable in 1969. To remedy this, a number of expeditions were sent by the U.S. to the tropics to make careful observations in those regions where few weather stations exist.

In 1969 plans were made for the first international test of some of the GARP concepts and observing systems in 1973; and 1976 was tentatively set as the year for the first major global experiment in which atmospheric observations by every means available would be collected and applied to the numerical models of the general circulation that were expected to have been perfected by then. It was hoped that, given an accurate description of the real atmosphere for a period of time, it would be possible to make useful predictions for periods of a week or more. Meteorologists were confident that this combination of WWW and GARP would culminate in a leap forward in the science of weather forecasting and would also permit new conclusions to be drawn about man's ability to change the weather and climate.

Unintended changes in the atmospheric environment

Urban air pollution. All of the major cities of the world, without exception, have been plagued with an increasing load of pollutants in their air. In the industrialized and motorized cities such as New York, Chicago, Los Angeles, London, and Tokyo, the air quality has become seriously affected by smoke from burning solid fuels and trash, carbon monoxide and hydrocarbons from motor vehicles, and oxides of nitrogen and sulfur

from a variety of sources. All of these are harmful to some extent.

Techniques have been developed to reduce the pollution emitted from automobiles and factories, and these have been vigorously applied in a number of cities, of which Los Angeles is perhaps a prime example. In the U.S. about 100 million tons of pollutants (carbon monoxide being the major one) were added to the atmosphere in 1968. The 1968 report of the U.S. Department of Health, Education, and Welfare (HEW) predicted that the combination of governmental controls over pollution from all sources, especially automobiles, would result in a gradual decrease in air pollution in most of the major U.S. cities, but that

if more stringent national control is not imposed after 1970, vehicular pollution levels will reach a minimum during the late 1970's and then begin to rise in response to the ever-expanding numbers of motor vehicles. . . . Consequently, [HEW] has under way an active research and development program to seek out new control approaches and to help industry continue its aggressive role in developing improved control technology.

To carry out these objectives, HEW has, among other things, set standards for certain kinds of pollutants (sulfur oxides and solid-fuel smoke in particular) and for control of motor vehicle exhaust. The department has also assisted the states in developing suitable inspection programs. Other countries, notably Japan and those in Western Europe, have also taken somewhat similar steps to enforce pollution abatement programs.

Global changes in air quality. Quite another aspect of air pollution has been the long-term effect on the climate of the world resulting from changes in atmospheric composition. Carbon dioxide, a major product of the combustion of fuels such as coal and petroleum products, has been gradually increasing as a constituent of the earth's atmosphere since about 1920. Currently about 10^{10} tons of carbon dioxide are added to the atmosphere each year (there are about 2.35×10^{12} tons in the atmosphere already). Part of this addition stays in the atmosphere, part goes into the oceans, and part is incorporated into living organisms. The net result has been a rise of about 0.2% per year in atmospheric carbon dioxide. Theoretically, this increase in carbon dioxide should cause a small rise in the mean surface temperature of the earth over a period of decades, but scientists have not determined exactly how much.

The mean temperature of the world did rise by about half a degree centigrade between 1880 and 1940, but since that time it has decreased slightly. This reversal might have been due to an increase in the mean amount of smoke and haze produced by man, but this hypothesis has not yet been proved. A great need has thus arisen for monitoring the composition of the atmosphere at several stations suitably located throughout the world. If man is indeed changing the atmosphere of his planet and the environment in which he must live, it is important that he discover how he is doing it and what the consequences might be.

—William W. Kellogg

See also Feature Article: NATURE ON THE RAMPAGE; Year in Review: ENVIRONMENTAL SCIENCES.

Behavioral sciences

Anthropology

Anthropology looks at the species *Homo sapiens* (man) from its dim prehistoric origins to its present worldwide complexities. At the earliest level, the year brought forth a major discovery of new fossils in East Africa which once again pushed back man's origin in time (see *Breakthrough in Anthropology*). It also saw publication of a major work, *Man the Hunter* (University of Chicago symposium), which discusses a series of new studies of surviving societies of hunters, in the light of our rapidly growing knowledge of the social behavior of primates in the wild, and the archaeological and fossil record.

Only in the last 10,000 years of man's long career, when technological competition became adaptive, has he been a changer of nature. His character was formed in the hundreds of thousands of years when social harmony was valuable. Through that period, cooperation within and between hunting-gathering bands was more critical than the competitive innovation that divides and isolates. The record thus minimizes the importance of intraspecies aggression and competition in the formative million years of the human career, bringing into question such recent popular works as Konrad Lorenz's *On Aggression* and Robert Ardrey's *Territorial Imperative.*

The anthropologist comes home. Despite the importance of such studies of man's origins and evolution, most anthropologists depend for their understanding of the species on meticulous comparison of the human condition as found in historic and living societies. Of particular significance in this regard was the growing emphasis on "urban" anthropology. In the late 1960s the work of anthropologists in urban heartlands constituted a movement corresponding in importance to the "community study" approach to peasant society a generation earlier.

Urbanization had become the most conspicuous of worldwide phenomena, bringing with it a trend toward modernization that rode roughshod over traditional cultures and, at the same time, a widespread expression of the need for "humanization" —for the meaningful participation of individuals in society. In this period of revolutionary change, anthropological understanding of complex societies was a necessity. Discussion of how general anthropological theory can take account of such complexity was opened during the year by Marvin Harris in *The Rise of Anthropological Theory.*

Meanwhile, specific new contributions to theory included (1) Chie Nakane's reinterpretation of the Japanese social system in such a way as to make possible structural comparisons with other national societies; (2) McKim Marriott's discovery of a multilateral system of transactions lying behind what previously had been a rather muddled

continued on page 131

Norwegian explorer Thor Heyerdahl's papyrus boat "Ra" sets out from Safi, Morocco, on May 25, 1969. Heyerdahl, who crossed the Pacific in the raft "Kon Tiki" in 1947, hoped to prove ancient Egyptians could have sailed across the Atlantic to America. Storm damage to the "Ra," however, forced him to abandon the vessel on July 18.

UPI Compix

129

Breakthrough in anthropology

New discoveries in East Africa. During the summer of 1968 an expedition led by University of Chicago anthropologist F. Clark Howell found, in southern Ethiopia, manlike teeth and jaws that almost double the history of man's ancestors in East Africa to nearly four million years ago. The expedition, supported by grants from the U.S. National Science Foundation and the Wenner-Gren Foundation, was part of the International Omo Research Expedition, authorized in 1966 by Emperor Haile Selassie of Ethiopia to work in the lower Omo Valley. The expedition spent the summers of 1967 and 1968 there, and worked there again in 1969.

The team, led by Howell, included colleagues from Chicago and the University of California at Berkeley and the University of Ghent in Belgium, and six graduate students from several U.S. universities. Another contingent, made up of French scientists under the direction of C. Arambourg and Y. Coppens of the National Museum of Natural History in Paris, also worked for two seasons in the field in another sector of the Omo Basin.

Howell's contingent of the expedition found 40 hominid (manlike) teeth and 2 lower jaws in a series of old swamp and deltaic deposits in the basin of the lower Omo River in the Eastern Rift Valley north of Lake Rudolf. The French contingent found two lower jaws and a number of isolated teeth. At least two different species of manlike creatures are represented; one, known from two lower jaws and several isolated teeth, was substantially more robust and massive in tooth and jaw structure than the other. This more massive form doubtless is related to the very robust form of australopith, or man-ape, already known from geologically younger deposits in South Africa and Tanzania. The evidence now demonstrates a substantially longer evolutionary history for this distinctive creature than was previously suspected.

Most of the teeth found by Howell's group seem to represent another prehuman species. Insufficient fossil material was found to identify it precisely, but what was found suggests that this species is probably allied in some way with the primitive and small form of australopith from South Africa, *Australopithecus africanus.* If this is the case, its age can be determined more accurately than ever before, and there is now evidence that both forms of australopith coexisted over a very substantial period of time.

The potassium-argon dating method was used by one member of Howell's team to determine the isotopic age of the minerals in volcanic ashes or tuffs that occur throughout the Omo Beds. The method showed the age of the fossiliferous Omo Beds to range from rather more than four million years ago to somewhat less than two million years ago.

One important question remains to be answered: Were these creatures more like men or more like apes? One criterion for stating that early hominids were like men is the finding of stone tools associated with them. No definite proof of stone tool-making has as yet been found with these creatures. Of course, this might merely be related to the environment under which the deposits were accumulated. If these creatures were really tool-makers, however, there should also be stone artifacts. If future work confirms this absence, some substantial modifications will be required in certain theories of hominid origins, which have tended to stress capabilities for tool-making behavior as being critical in the success of the earliest adaptation of Hominidae to life in open-country environments.

The expedition also recovered exceptional quantities of fossil mammals and other vertebrates throughout the Omo Beds. These large collections of fossils promise to throw much new light on the origins and evolution of the distinctive African fauna.

The most important fossil mammals were: (1) three kinds of elephants, as well as the extinct *Dinotherium;* (2) both black and white species of rhinoceroses; (3) three-toed as well as true equids; (4) three species of hippopotamuses; (5) six genera with eight species of pigs; (6) two species of giraffe as well as the okapi and the extinct antlered giraffid *Libytherium;* (7) a primitive camel; (8) at least ten major groups of antelopes totaling some 20 species; and (9) diverse varieties of carnivores, including two types of hyenas, some canids and felids, and a giant extinct form of civet. The Omo Beds also revealed the first and oldest documented occurrence in East Africa of the camel, a species that appears at a broadly comparable time in Asia and Eastern Europe. Other fossils show that true horses first appeared in East Africa about two million years ago.

Previous paleontological collecting in the area had revealed about two dozen species of mammals in the Omo Beds. The new work of the Omo Research Expedition clarified their identity and nearly tripled the total number of mammals known, most of which are extinct species. This indicates that the diversity of mammals in eastern Africa several million years ago was even greater than it is now.

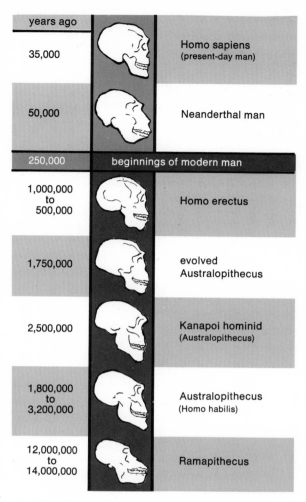

years ago		
35,000		Homo sapiens (present-day man)
50,000		Neanderthal man
250,000		beginnings of modern man
1,000,000 to 500,000		Homo erectus
1,750,000		evolved Australopithecus
2,500,000		Kanapoi hominid (Australopithecus)
1,800,000 to 3,200,000		Australopithecus (Homo habilis)
12,000,000 to 14,000,000		Ramapithecus

Revised time chart for man and his ancestors.

continued from page 129
set of ideas about caste rank, which will permit systematic description and comparison of "caste systems"; (3) David Schneider's radical reformulation of the kinship system in the United States, which suggests new ways of regarding "culture" that will make comparative study possible; and (4) Claude Lévi-Strauss's continued unfolding of the character of human thought in the third volume of his *Mythologiques.* In comparison with such contributions, local "urban anthropology" was only in its primitive beginnings. A first general discussion was provided during the year by Oscar Lewis (*A Study of Slum Culture*) and Charles Valentine (*Culture and Poverty*). (*See* Feature Article: URBAN SOCIETY: A BLUEPRINT FOR THE CITY OF TOMORROW.)

The new urgency. That anthropologists were preparing themselves for the major task of studying the complex problems of the human species as it is now developing was best seen in two

interrelated events of the past year: (1) the organization of anthropology for research in "urgent" problems; and (2) the internationalization of the discipline, as evidenced by events at the ninth International Congress of Anthropological and Ethnological Sciences, held in Tokyo in September 1968, and by the founding of an international Center for the Study of Man under the auspices of the Smithsonian Institution.

"Urgent anthropology" has been defined over the years as the need to salvage data that is about to disappear. Thus, programs of "salvage archaeology" have studied data threatened by highway construction or about to be inundated as a result of the damming of rivers. Salvage ethnology, similarly, studies languages, songs, social systems, and other aspects of culture before they are overwhelmed by the onrush of modernization. At the ninth International Congress, however, it became clear that these problems—which seem most "urgent" to European scientists—compete in the new nations with the urgent social problems associated with planning, modernization, industrialization, population growth, and the like. Still a third problem was outlined in a resolution asking nations to respect the existence of all peoples and cultures.

After the discussions in Tokyo, the most urgent problems in anthropology could be summarized as follows: Scholars of the Western "scientific" tradition cannot build the human sciences by themselves; these require the complementary views and techniques of all the major cultural traditions and as many as possible of the surviving minor cultural traditions. What is needed, therefore, is the development in every corner of the world of a growing and changing anthropology. Many people assume that numerically weak peoples must be destroyed in order to advance the interests of nations. Not only does such destruction violate the Universal Declaration of Human Rights; it is also unnecessary. It seems to some people necessary to destroy humanity in order to advance civilization only because the human sciences have not been brought sufficiently into relationship with the technical sciences. Such a relationship requires the education of all to the importance of the human sciences and the development of the human sciences themselves—as pure sciences and as their findings bear upon world problems.

Thus, three equally urgent tasks for world anthropology emerge. The first is mitigation of the human problems of forced acculturation and of the physical destruction of peoples who appear to stand in the way of the interests of stronger peoples. The second is analysis of the scientific problems resulting from the rapid change of traditional forms; whether such changes come about because of force or because the changes are desired, they destroy data that would help in understanding the historical variety of human cultures and thus might help us to understand ourselves and to guide our future. The third involves the speedy education of people of all nations, including statesmen, scientists, planners, and engineers, in the anthropological points of view that are needed both to formulate more effective programs of modernization and to ameliorate their negative human consequences.

The Center for the Study of Man. Some mechanisms already existed for mobilizing the experience and resources of anthropology. *Current Anthropology,* sponsored by the Wenner-Gren Foundation for Anthropological Research, provided a means of communication among the anthropologists of the world. The International Union of Anthropological and Ethnological Sciences was establishing an autonomous and self-perpetuating committee to help set standards and develop rules for international cooperation. However, neither *Current Anthropology* nor the union (or its research committee) were operating agencies. Thus the initiative of the Smithsonian Institution in developing the first research center that could operate positively to coordinate research initiatives in all nations was critically important.

During the year the center decided to "tool up" at once, first by establishing a computerized overall data bank of research—wanted, planned, in progress, and completed—and of the individuals and institutions with competence to discuss the results; and second, by discovering the points of convergence between existing and potential anthropological knowledge and such species-wide problems as nuclear war, racism and colonialism, population, and pollution.

—Sol Tax

See also Feature Article: MAN IN AMERICA: THE CALICO MOUNTAINS EXCAVATIONS; Year in Review: ARCHAEOLOGY.

Psychology

The past year witnessed a continuing increase in concern and involvement on the part of psychologists in social issues and social action. In part, this reflected an expansion and alteration of the psychoanalytically derived therapeutic tradition of working with individuals on an intensive one-to-one basis, examining the thoughts, feelings, and subjective inner experience presumed to lie behind outward expressions. As social issues loomed larger, however, and as it was recognized that a community's growing mental health needs could not be met by lengthy, costly work with individuals, increased attention was directed to newer approaches. One new focus was the attempt to alter social institutions in such a way as to make them more conducive to mental health. Another was the exploration of quicker, less expensive forms of therapy that attack symptoms directly and can be more relevant for poverty groups. Still another involved the training of nonprofessionals for a variety of tasks hitherto restricted by professional boundaries.

Behavioral modifications. A series of techniques subsumed under the broad term "behavior therapies" has had an increasing effect on the therapeutic scene over the past decade. These techniques hold the promise of being shorter and more effective than the usual procedures; they can more readily be learned and employed by nonprofessional workers, teachers, parents, and possibly even by individuals on themselves. Often they can be used effectively with relatively nonverbal persons.

The most prominent of these techniques—"systematic desensitization"—involves a long-recognized psychological principle called reciprocal inhibition. According to this principle, it is possible to reduce responses of fear to specific situations by creating incompatible responses of a more positive nature. The classical example of this principle stems from research first published in the 1920s, which showed that a child's fear of a rabbit could be eliminated if the rabbit was gradually brought nearer to the child while the child was engaging in the pleasurable activity of eating. Present methods for behavior therapy involve a twofold procedure: at first training the client in relaxation techniques and afterward, while he is relaxing (*i.e.,* making a positive response), having him imagine a sequence of scenes of fearful situations, starting with those that are least anxiety provoking. Supplementary procedures involve training in self-assertion given by the therapist, with encouragement as to how to perform between the training sessions, as well as role playing and indoctrination into the principles that underlie the procedures.

At first this type of therapy was limited to simple phobias (for example, a fear of snakes) or to simple anxieties, such as that aroused by the prospect of speaking in public. On the basis of its reported success, however, increasingly complex and more disturbed cases have been treated by this method, apparently with some—but less spectacular—positive results.

Another behavior therapy approach, chiefly derived from experimentation with animals, is based

Gertrude Samuels, "The New York Times"

Workers from the Maimonides Mental Health Center in Brooklyn talk to a neighborhood resident (above) as part of the center's continuing effort to reach out into the community and inform the disadvantaged of its resources and programs. Right, art therapy techniques, such as painting and woodworking, are used at the center to assist patients in working through their problems.

on reinforcement techniques. Changes have been demonstrated in the behavior of retarded children, juvenile delinquents, and disruptive students in a classroom situation through the reinforcement of desirable behavior by praise or concrete reward and by ignoring deviant or undesirable behavior.

One current line of investigation which also shows promise for the future involves self-desensitization procedures. In some cases, the initial procedures are established with the assistance of a therapist, but the bulk of the therapeutic work is conducted at home, usually with a tape recorder. A more recent study, however, shows that under certain circumstances it may be possible for a subject to define his own problem, teach himself the relevant procedures of muscle relaxation and building a hierarchy of situations, and then conduct the therapy on his own. Moreover, although some of this research has been done with college students in a classroom situation rather than in a clinical setting, the findings may ultimately shed additional light on the most complex question confronting research in psychotherapy: which patient and which therapy are best suited to each other. For example, there are indications that certain types of persons who are not likely to be well motivated for conventional psychothera-

pies may be able to profit from self-desensitization procedures.

The self-fulfilling prophecy. Understanding of the factors involved in the education of ghetto children was enlarged in 1968 by the publication of *Pygmalion in the Classroom,* a study by Robert Rosenthal and Lenore Jacobsen about the effects of teachers' attitudes on pupils' school performance. The basis for the research reported in the book was the phenomenon of the self-fulfilling prophecy, the tendency for one's expectations of others to be confirmed not because the others are as we imagine them to be but because one's expectations are communicated in subtle, unnoticed ways and influence the subsequent behavior of the others. The important question posed by this study was whether the generally poorer intellectual performance of ghetto children is a function of their teachers' expectations, rather than solely a result of deficiencies in the child and in his environment. By and large most programs funded by the U.S. government have taken the latter view and have concentrated on improving the child himself by means of remedial instruction and cultural enrichment. Considerably less attention has been given to the role played by the schools and especially by the teachers' attitudes.

The study was conducted at an elementary school with pupils from predominantly lower-class, low-income families. The researchers led the teachers to believe that a test administered to all the students in the school could identify those children with a latent but as yet unrealized potential for academic excellence. After the testing the researchers casually indicated to the teachers which of their students had been found to possess this potential. In actuality, however,

The rapidly growing sensitivity training movement, designed to overcome dehumanizing barriers and to bring about greater openness between persons, uses a variety of group techniques that deliberately break down inhibitions and encourage free expression, including physical contact and nudity.

the researchers had selected five pupils in each class at random and passed off these students as the potential "late bloomers." Thus, the expectation that some of their students could make substantial academic gains was instilled in the teachers, although these students were really no different from the others.

The intriguing results of the study were that, at the end of the academic year, the children whom the teachers expected to make significant intellectual gains did, in fact, make such gains— especially children in the first and second grades. Moreover, when the teachers were asked to describe their students' classroom behavior over the year, it was found that these same children

were described as being happier, as having a better chance of future success, as more interesting and more curious; to some extent, they were also described as more affectionate and more independent. Investigation showed that the teachers had not spent more class time with these students, but rather suggested that the teachers' expectations were communicated in more subtle ways. It was also discovered that children who were not expected to make gains but who did, in fact, do so were rated less favorably in regard to their behavior, in inverse proportion to their academic improvement. A further way in which teachers' ratings of their students reflected their own expectations was the tendency for ratings to mirror the "track," or grouping according to ability, in which the child had been placed at the beginning of the year. Even those students whom the teachers expected would improve were rated less favorably if they were in slower "tracks."

The overall implications of this important research touch on the need to consider the role of the teacher's expectations in influencing the level of performance of the students. Its broader significance concerns the role of the self-fulfilling prophecy itself: how it operates in a variety of human endeavors and how unanticipated human potentials can be recognized and encouraged in part by rising levels of expectations. In other words, can a variety of past failures with poverty groups be seen as attributable to limited expectations? Future research will serve to clarify the more specific processes by which the self-fulfilling prophecy acts as a crucial mediator of such failures.

The ancient nature-versus-nurture controversy, exacerbated by the racial crisis in the U.S., flared up again in 1969 following publication in the *Harvard Educational Review* of an article on intellectual potential by University of California psychologist Arthur R. Jensen. Some of Jensen's conclusions—for example, that not all children are born with the same intellectual endowment and that schools err when they try to force all children into the same mold—were not widely disputed, and were even welcomed by many as a corrective to excessive emphasis on environmental influences. What did provoke violent reaction was his suggestion, based on analysis of IQ test results, that Negroes as a group are deficient in the cognitive and problem-solving aspects of intelligence, and that compensatory education programs for them are, therefore, doomed to failure.

Reactions from Jensen's colleagues were largely critical. His static conception of intelligence was disputed, as was his reliance on the IQ test as a measure of intelligence. It was also claimed that he failed to consider evidence for a high degree of plasticity in the rate of behavioral development, the interaction between environmental and biological factors, and—especially—the effect of early experience and differences in child-rearing practices on both physical and mental development. One finding of particular relevance was the demonstration in rats that the complexity of the environment has a direct effect on the amount of cortical tissue.

In an article written for the *Washington Post,* geneticist Joshua Lederberg agreed with much of what Jensen had to say concerning the importance of heredity, although he felt that Jensen had oversimplified the problem. However, he strongly opposed Jensen's conclusions on racial difference, pointing out that there simply is not sufficient evidence one way or the other. Only when allowance has been made for every possible environmental influence—which in the present state of society is probably impossible—can valid findings on genetic differences be made. (*See* Feature Article: A SCIENTIFIC VIEW OF RACE.)

—Joel Allison

See also Feature articles: FREUD'S PLACE IN MODERN PSYCHIATRY; SLEEP AND DREAMS; Year in Review: MEDICINE, *Psychiatry.*

Botany

The year under review did not see the development of any significant major advances in botany. Several trends, however, were beginning to emerge as important ones, especially those concerned with the classification of plants (taxonomy and biosystematics), plant environment (ecology), the effects of radiation on plants, and the functions of growth-regulating hormones.

Taxonomy and biosystematics

In 1969 there were about 350,000 known types of plants and, undoubtedly, an equal number that were still unclassified. Several years of cooperative work, however, had allowed botanists, computer specialists, and mathematicians to develop programs for making point-by-point comparisons of hundreds of plant characteristics. It was now possible for the botanist not only to establish categories for previously unclassified plants but also to compare, contrast, and relate the characteristics of major taxonomic groups of plants.

This information was of value to scientists interested in evolution, geology, and genetics. If, for example, in a limited area plants of the same species were found, it would be usual for them to show a certain amount of variation, a great part of which is known to be due to the selection and recombination of genetic characteristics. A computer could evaluate the direction of this genetic alteration, its speed, and its effects on the individual plant and the total population.

Plant ecology

Particular attention was being paid in recent months to environmental factors such as fog, which had hitherto been assumed to be of little importance in determining the ability of a plant to maintain itself in a particular environment. The west coast of the U.S., eastern Europe, and the mountainous areas of all continents—regions that are frequently enclosed in clouds and fog for long periods of time—were shown to have distinctly different types of plants than similar areas lacking extensive cloud cover. Work in the mountains of France, on the west coast of the U.S., and in the Green Mountains of Vermont demonstrated that clouds play a significant role in providing water to the plants. The needle foliage of several evergreen plants appeared to act as effective mechanical collectors of wind-driven water droplets. H. W. Vogelmann and colleagues at the University of Vermont found that the amount of water made available for plant growth by interception of water from clouds might be more than 50% of the total water available during the growing season. Not only would this additional water affect the quality and quantity of growth of the plants but it also might have an important bearing on the amount of ground water that descends to lower elevations.

Studies on the speed and effectiveness with which abandoned, marginally effective farmland is returned to the natural state were also of interest to ecologists, physiologists, soils specialists, and foresters. The area proved to be an important one for botanical research not only because it could answer the theoretical questions of what plants move into an area first and why but also because it might be possible, with adequate information, for biologists to speed up the process whereby old, worn-out farms can be turned over to new uses. Work on this subject by Elroy Rice and his associates at the University of Oklahoma provided some surprising information. Apparently, some plants that invade abandoned fields are producers of chemicals that may actually prevent the invasion of other plants that might be useful in providing cover. There had been, in past years, a scattered amount of information on this phenomenon; black walnut leaves release chemicals that prevent the seeding-in of other trees, and some desert plants produce chemicals in their roots that prevent growth of other plants. Yet, the relationship of this phenomenon to the succession of introductions of plant species was a recent, and potentially important, correlation.

A third area of increasing interest is the study of the quantity and quality of sunlight impinging on plants. The plants growing in a forest receive a much different balance of radiation from the sun than do those in a field or even on the periphery of the forest. This is clearly reflected in the species found in these different habitats. Research done in Scandinavia and in the U.S. was concerned with the ecological and physiological basis for these differences. For reasons not clearly understood some species of plants are classifiable as shade plants, either because they can tolerate shaded conditions or are not capable of growing in direct sunlight. Other plants, sometimes of the same or related species, are not shade-tolerant and require direct radiation from the sun for growth. No firm answers to the questions concerning the effects of radiation were yet available, but it was discovered that shade or sun requirements affect many aspects of plant growth. The capacity to produce sugar in the presence of light (photosynthesis), the ability to manage available water efficiently, and enzyme activity of the plant in relation to radiation, temperature, and humidity are all involved.

Plant physiology

Long-term research was dealing with these and related problems. Studies either in the planning stage or in progress were assessing various kinds of land erosion, the ecological effects of sunlight, and the genetics of slow-growing plants such as trees. At the same time, however, much of the research being done in plant physiology was concerned with the effects that various kinds of radiation have on the internal growth and development of individual plants.

Effects of visible radiation on plants. The discovery more than ten years ago of the morphogenetic pigment, phytochrome, revolutionized the thinking on the role of specific wavelengths of visible radiation in controlling plant growth and development. Phytochrome is a molecule in the leaves of plants that is known to become biologically active, presumably as an enzyme that stimulates structural and anatomical development (morphogenesis), under certain light-dark conditions. Too much or too little light prevents proper plant growth. Within recent months several important new discoveries were made that extended the knowledge of the pigment's role but also

Certain plants appear to produce chemicals that prevent other plants from growing in the same area. In a grove of sycamore trees (top), a variety of grasses grow in abundance only at some distance from the trees. Close to the trees, the land is relatively barren. Other tests showed the effects of the sunflower's chemical inhibitors. The two stunted coneflower plants above were grown for two weeks in a nutrient solution that was recycled over living sunflower roots. Control plants (left) show normal growth in the same solution recycled over living coneflower roots.

made interpretation of the entire system more difficult. In darkness, all of the pigment is in one chemical form, but when red light having a spectral range of about 5,000–7,000 Å (angstrom units) is absorbed by the pigment, it is shifted into another form that apparently triggers many different metabolic processes. If the active pigment is again irradiated, but this time with red light of about 7,350 Å, the triggering action is stopped and the pigment reverts to the inactive form.

Several basic questions about this process remained unanswered. Prominent among them was just how the presence of a pigment in a particular molecular form can trigger profound alterations in growth patterns. These growth effects include such varied responses as activation of chlorophyll and chloroplast synthesis, control of seed germination, unfolding of leaves by a combination of cell enlargement and cell division, initiation of flowering, activation of enzymes controlling nitrate reduction to ammonium ions, changes in the form of leaves, and at the latest count, more than 20 other specific changes in plants. It was necessary, therefore, to assume that there is either some master reaction triggered by the shift in the phytochrome molecule or that the pigment shift triggers some generalized set of changes, which in turn provide chemical or physical signals that are interpreted by the cells in different ways. Although these possibilities, and others that can be considered, are not mutually exclusive, attempts to differentiate between them have been difficult.

Complicating the problem were recent discoveries by groups of scientists at Columbia, Harvard, and other universities, and at the Brookhaven (Long Island) National Laboratory of the U.S. Atomic Energy Commission. These groups found that the active form of phytochrome is relatively unstable; some of it reverts to the nonactive form but most of it disappears. The losses in total pigment as determined by the various physical procedures used by these researchers did not fit with the long-established biological evidence that the supply of convertible pigment is fairly constant throughout repeated switching from inactive to active form.

An additional complication, and one that bore directly on the various theories regarding the mode of action of phytochrome, was the fact that the pigment is known to be localized within the plant cell. Recent research indicated that the pigment is attached to specific proteins and is organized in some yet undetermined three-dimensional shape. This organization within the cell would have important bearing on the molecule's ability to perceive red and far-red radiation. Knowledge of a specific spatial and form organization in phytochrome would also have great importance in assessing the still unanswered question of how the radiation signal is transferred from the pigment molecule to other molecules within the cell that are on the direct line to the growth, developmental, and biochemical changes that finally occur.

Near-ultraviolet radiation. The phytochrome molecule was probably the best known of the radiation systems, independent of photosynthesis,

that occur in plants. As the techniques for generating, controlling, and measuring small irradiances of specific wavelengths became more refined, however, photobiologists were able to investigate the possible roles of wavelengths that had previously not been suspected of having morphogenetic properties. Many of these new discoveries were discussed at the Fifth International Photobiology Congress held at Dartmouth College, Hanover, N.H., in August 1968.

Several reports from laboratories in the U.S., Europe, and Japan indicated that near-ultraviolet radiation, just below the limits of human vision, profoundly affects plants and animals, apparently in similar if not identical ways. Although the pigments that detect this radiation and the intermediary steps in the utilization by the plant were still poorly understood, it was established that near-ultraviolet radiation can, depending on its wavelength and intensity, serve to activate or to repress cellular and subcellular processes. Activations include the triggering of the reproductive response in several fungi and algae and the synthesis of the red pigment, anthocyanin, in cells of many different higher plants. Repressions due to near-ultraviolet radiation include alterations in the rate of cell division in a variety of plants and animals, reductions in the respiratory intensity of bacteria, and alterations in the ability of plants to elongate.

Not only does this type of radiation affect laboratory test systems, but studies reported in

Radiation-induced mutations in geraniums (below) manifest themselves in the petals, which are smaller than normal and partly changed from red to white. An irradiated pink chrysanthemum (right) produced a half-yellow, half-bronze mutant flower.

Courtesy, Brookhaven National Laboratory

the journal *Ecological Monographs* showed that the form and distribution of alpine plants also are altered as a result of the increased level of near-ultraviolet radiation in the clear air of the higher mountains. The relationship of these findings to artificial irradiation with fluorescent lamps, where near-ultraviolet wavelengths are emitted in significant amounts, was being assessed by several laboratories in the U.S. and the U.K.

Growth-regulating compounds. Since the first growth-regulating compound, auxin, was isolated in 1935, reports on this class of morphogenetic compounds have continued to increase rapidly. Although no new natural regulator was discovered in the past year, attention did focus on the aspects of growth-regulator action in which these components, or hormones, were known to be involved.

Extensive studies showed that any given, measurable plant response is modulated by the interaction of two or more of the compounds; in several instances, three, four, or even five chemically unrelated growth-regulating compounds were known to be involved. The importance of any single compound in this causal complex was being studied, and it seemed possible that the auxins might be the primary regulatory compound with the others serving to modify auxin action.

Five distinct groups of growth-regulating compounds had been established: auxins and gibberellins, which were known to be involved mainly in extending plant growth; and cytokinins, abscisic acid, and ethylene, which seemed to act primarily as inhibitors. Whether one compound aided or inhibited the action of another now appeared to depend as much on the genetic makeup of the species as on the concentration levels of the compounds present in any given system or at any given site in a system.

The complexity of this hormone function was evident in the most recently reported experiments, which had aimed at determining the nature of abscisic acid. In many plants phytochrome activity appeared to cause the production of gibberellins during long periods of light (photoperiods) and of abscisic acid during short photoperiods. It was suggested from this that abscisic acid acts as an inhibitor of gibberellin activity and prevents such inappropriate reactions as flowering during the wrong season.

Frequently, however, increased concentrations of gibberellins were found to be able to overcome the effects of abscisic acid. In other plant systems, the inhibitory effects of abscisic acid were countered only by the introduction of cytokinins, which had no effect on the gibberellin. In other studies, when abscisic acid inhibited auxin activity, it was counteracted by gibberellin.

Over the years investigations such as these have been done by setting up experimental situations in which the amounts of compounds present, formed, or moving through the plant are determined. Within the past year in reports from East Germany, however, E. Libbert and his students at the University of Rostock showed that much of the auxin involved in isolated test systems may not be produced by the plant at all, but rather by the action of bacteria that are contaminants of the test system. There did not seem to be any doubt that Libbert's work was correct, and the impact of his conclusions on auxin theory and experimental practice might prove to be profound.

—Richard M. Klein

Chemistry

Inorganic chemistry

Metal cluster compounds. The study of crystals by X-ray diffraction has proved an effective method for determining the structures of solid compounds and thus has played an important part in the development of modern inorganic chemistry. Among the many fascinating types of compounds whose structures have been determined by X-ray diffraction in recent years are those containing bonds between metal atoms. These compounds have ranged from fairly simple molecules containing just one metal–metal bond, as found in the manganese compound $Mn_2(CO)_{10}$, to those containing large clusters of metal atoms, as found in the molybdenum complex $Mo_6Cl_8^{4+}$.

A group of Italian and British chemists recently prepared and determined the structure of an unusual compound containing a cluster of gold atoms. This compound, which has the formula $Au_{11}[P(C_6H_5)_3]_7(SCN)_3$, is remarkable for the fact that it contains a larger cluster of metal atoms than has previously been identified in a single molecule. Eleven gold atoms are clustered together at the center of the molecule; the seven $P(C_6H_5)_3$ groups and the three SCN^- ions are located on the periphery of the metal atom cluster. One of the 11 gold atoms is located at the center of the cluster and is surrounded by the other 10 gold atoms. Four of these outer gold atoms lie at the corners of a square on one side of the central atom. Another five outer gold atoms lie at the corners of a pentagon which is parallel to the square and on the other side of the central atom. The tenth outer gold atom is positioned on the axis of the molecule (formed by the central atom and the centers of the square and pentagon) beyond the pentagonal group of atoms.

Chemists do not yet have a consistent theory for rationalizing, much less predicting, the bonding in structures of this kind. Perhaps when a wider variety of such compounds has been discovered and studied, systematic features of their structures will become obvious, and it will be possible to devise a theory of bonding that will encompass all such metal-metal compounds.

Uranocene. A new type of "sandwich" compound was prepared and characterized during the last year by chemists in Berkeley, Calif. (A "sandwich" compound is one in which a metal atom is situated between two flat groups of atoms.) In this case the metal atom was a uranium atom, U, and the flat groups were the ring-shaped cyclooctatetraenyls, C_8H_8. The resulting compound, $U(C_8H_8)_2$, was given the name "uranocene," an analogy to the first identified sandwich compound, ferrocene (in which an iron atom lies between two C_5H_5 rings). In uranocene the uranium atom lies midway between the two parallel C_8H_8 rings. The compound is a green solid which inflames spontaneously upon exposure to air.

Although many sandwich compounds are known, uranocene is of particular significance for two reasons. First, it is the only known example of a complex involving flat eight-membered rings. Second, uranium is one of a group of metals which can use in its bonding a little-understood class of electrons called f electrons. Indeed, the structure and properties of uranocene were predicted from a consideration of the nature of these f electrons. Undoubtedly the next few years will see the preparation of many more examples of sandwich compounds of other "f-electron" metals.

Nitrogen fixation. In the *1969 Britannica Year-book of Science and the Future,* reference was made to recent work aimed at the "fixation" of nitrogen, that is, the incorporation of elemental nitrogen (N_2) into useful chemicals such as ammonia (NH_3). At that time, chemists had succeeded in preparing a number of metal-nitrogen compounds from elemental nitrogen, but nobody had yet succeeded in converting such a compound into ammonia under mild conditions. This last step was, however, recently accomplished by a group of chemists at Stanford University, Stanford, Calif.

The process began with the reaction of nitrogen with a low-valent titanium compound, $Ti(OR)_2$, to form a titanium-nitrogen complex, $[Ti(OR)_2N_2]_n$. This complex then underwent reaction with sodium (complexed with naphthalene) to form an unidentified nitride, which, in turn, reacted with an alcohol to form ammonia and a high-valent titanium compound, $Ti(OR)_4$. The latter compound was reduced to $Ti(OR)_2$ with sodium, completing the catalytic cycle. It should be noted that this cyclic process is a crude analogue of the biological fixation process which occurs in the roots of certain plants such as legumes. In this sense chemists have come one step closer to duplicating the natural process, and, possibly, to the point where they can "teach" this process to plants which now do not know how to fix nitrogen.

Perbromate synthesis. Preconceived notions, unsupported by sound theory, have often deterred progress in science. In recent years, however, chemists have been ignoring such notions and have occasionally made spectacular discoveries that have opened up new fields of study. In 1962, for example, chemists showed that the so-called inert gases such as xenon and krypton, which most chemists previously believed to be incapable of forming ordinary compounds, could be induced to form a whole series of compounds.

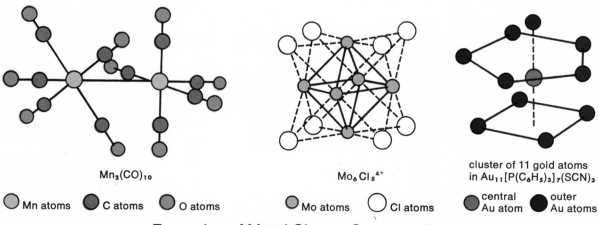

$Mn_2(CO)_{10}$ $Mo_6Cl_8^{4+}$ cluster of 11 gold atoms in $Au_{11}[P(C_6H_5)_3]_7(SCN)_3$

Mn atoms   C atoms   O atoms   Mo atoms   Cl atoms   central Au atom   outer Au atoms

Examples of Metal Cluster Compounds

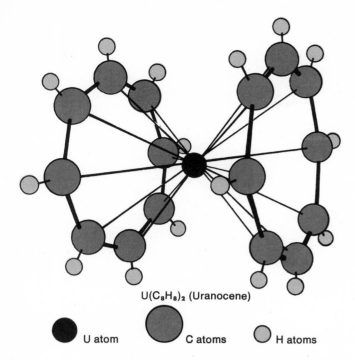

U(C₈H₈)₂ (Uranocene)

U atom   C atoms   H atoms

More recently, another false notion has been shattered. The elements chlorine, bromine, and iodine appear next to one another, in that order, in the periodic table of the elements. Consequently, one would expect that the chemical behavior of these elements would vary in some gradual way. Therefore, for many years chemists have been intrigued by the fact that, although chlorine forms perchlorates (containing ClO_4^- ions) and iodine forms periodates (containing IO_4^- ions), nobody had ever succeeded in isolating (or even detecting) an analogous perbromate, containing BrO_4^- ions. It should be noted that this failure was not for lack of trying.

Thus, most chemists concluded that the synthesis of a perbromate was a hopeless cause and proposed various theories to explain its nonexistence. Recently, however, Evan Appelman of the Argonne National Laboratory, Argonne, Ill., discovered a convenient method for synthesizing perbromates on a large scale by using molecular fluorine to oxidize readily available bromates in alkaline solution. Preliminary studies showed that the perbromate ion has physical and chemical properties between those of the perchlorate and periodate ions. Indeed, it was not at all clear why perbromates had not been prepared previously. Perhaps the stumbling block had been an extremely difficult to form and unstable intermediate species which must be made on the route to perbromate.

Reactions of atoms with molecules. A promising technique for the synthesis of new compounds underwent extensive development during the last year by British and U.S. chemists. The technique

consisted of rapidly condensing together unstable gaseous atoms (formed at high temperatures) with compounds at low temperatures (such as the temperature of boiling liquid nitrogen, −196° C). Many new compounds were synthesized by such atom-molecule reactions. For example, boron atoms (emitted from a boron rod heated to 2,500–2,800° C) react with boron trifluoride, BF_3, to form a polymer of composition $(BF)_x$ and with carbon dioxide, CO_2, to form a polymer of composition $(BO)_x$. Copper atoms (vaporized at 1,400°C) react with boron trichloride, BCl_3, to form molecules of B_2Cl_4; iron atoms react with phosphorus trifluoride, PF_3, to form the remarkable compound $(PF_3)_3Fe(PF_2)_2Fe(PF_3)_3$. Particularly intriguing is the reaction of iron atoms with benzene molecules. They form a solid product which explodes when it is warmed to −40° C and which reacts at lower temperatures with hydrogen to form cyclohexane (an organic ring compound) and with cyclopentadiene (C_5H_6) to form ferrocene. Carbon vapor (emitted by a carbon arc) reacts with boron trichloride (BCl_3) to form $ClC(BCl_2)_3$, $Cl_2C(BCl_2)_2$, and $Cl(Cl_2B)C=C(BCl_2)Cl$. Further studies of this type were expected to yield more new compounds which cannot easily be made by more conventional techniques.

Chemists in St. Louis, Mo., used a rather ingenious technique for following the course of room-temperature reactions of gaseous atoms with molecules. In a typical experiment gaseous germanium atoms were produced by bombarding gaseous germane, GeH_4, with a stream of fast neutrons. This bombardment caused the germanium atoms in some of the GeH_4 molecules to undergo the following nuclear reaction (n = one neutron):

$$^{76}Ge + n \longrightarrow {}^{75}Ge + 2n$$

The ^{75}Ge atoms produced during the neutron

This catalytic cycle yields ammonia (NH_3) from a metal-nitrogen compound.

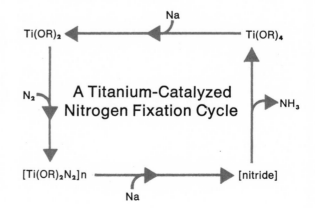

bombardment were ejected from the molecules as neutral atoms (atoms that have no electrical charge) because of the recoil energy associated with the emission of neutrons from the germanium nuclei. These unattached germanium atoms then underwent reaction with other germane molecules in the gas and ended up in products such as $H_3{}^{75}GeGeH_3$ and $^{75}GeH_4$. Because ^{75}Ge is radioactive, the $H_3{}^{75}GeGeH_3$ and $^{75}GeH_4$ molecules were effectively "tagged," and the small amounts of these products which were formed could be determined by separating them and measuring the intensity of their radioactivity. Studies of this general type were expected to be useful for investigating the ways in which atoms react with other molecules.

—William L. Jolly

Organic chemistry

A frequent occurrence in science is the rapid development of a field of endeavor that has lain dormant or received scant attention for a relatively prolonged period of time. In organic chemistry this was particularly evident in 1968–69 for the fields of optical rotatory dispersion, Raman spectroscopy, photochemistry, mass spectroscopy, free radical chemistry, and the mechanism of cyclization reactions. Often reemergence of neglected fields awaited the development of suitable instrumentation or experimental techniques, the formulation of important theoretical principles of special relevance, or the performance of a singularly crucial experiment.

Another general trend that recently has become more apparent involves the fusion of two or more of the traditional subdivisions of chemistry. Many of the elements of the periodic table, such as boron, iron, zinc, and nickel, which formerly were restricted to the province of inorganic chemistry, are becoming increasingly common as atoms bonded to the carbon atoms that are the essential features of organic chemistry. Also, the theories of structure and mechanisms of organic chemistry are being applied successfully to the myriad life processes found in biological chemistry and to the problems of rational drug design associated with medicinal chemistry.

Photochemical reactions. The reactions usually encountered in organic chemistry involve the collision or interaction of molecules that lie in the ground state, that is, the state in which bonding and nonbonding electrons occupy the lowest energy levels. Reactions occur by means of a successful thermal collision of the reacting components or by transforming a ground state molecule into a reactive ground state intermediate,

such as a carbonium ion, a carbanion, a carbene, or a free radical. The pathways taken in such processes have been subjected to considerable investigation by experimental means and theoretical considerations.

By contrast, photochemical reactions are unique in that the initiating step involves the absorption of a quantum of light by the electron of a ground state molecule, which is then transformed into an excited state of higher energy. Because photochemically excited molecules undergo reactions by pathways that are different from those observed for ground state molecules, the ensuing chemical and physical changes frequently result in a product whose structure is quite bizarre. The significance of the bizarre structures does not lie in their strangeness but, rather, in understanding and codifying the complex reactions that are brought about by the absorption of light. In this context, photochemical reactions undoubtedly have a great relevance to those reactions of life processes that are initiated by light, such as photosynthesis, photosensitization, and photobiology, and also, possibly, to the origin of life itself.

In recent months several groups of scientists reexamined the photochemistry of camphor (1), the reactions of which illustrate the unusual structures that can be encountered in photochemical processes. In 1910 Giacomo Ciamcian at the University of Bologna identified (2) as a primary product of camphor; it has now been shown that (3) is formed as well, and that (4) is obtained when the reaction is conducted in ethyl alcohol. Compounds (2) and (3) are isomers of camphor, and their formation illustrates the deep-seated structural changes brought about by light without the usual intervention of chemical reagents. (Isomers are compounds containing the same number and type of atoms but in which the atoms are arranged differently.) Absorption of light by the ketone group ($\mathrm{>C{=}O}$) of camphor creates an excited state that undergoes cleavage at bond "a." The intermediate that is produced, (5), stabilizes itself by the migration of hydrogen atoms to provide a cleavage of product (2) or to recyclize at oxygen to give (3).

During recent years the photochemical isomerization of benzene, thiophene, and other aromatic compounds was being investigated. Recently, Eugene E. van Tamelen and Thomas H. Whitesides at Stanford University, Stanford, Calif., reported the analogous isomerization of 2,5-di-t-butylfuran (6) to the 3,5-derivative (7). In this case an intermediate, (8), was isolated as well. Similar intermediates had been postulated by other scientists, but proved to be too elusive.

It was noted above that photochemical reactions frequently differ from thermal processes. A subtle difference was reported by John E. Baldwin and M. C. McDaniel at the University of Illinois. The substituted cyclobutenone (9) was irradiated in methanol solution and (10) was obtained; when the reactant was heated in methanol in the absence of light, the isomer (11) was produced. This difference in reaction can be even more profound. Harold Hart and R. K. Murray at Michigan State University found that compound (12) underwent decomposition involving loss of dimethylketene when it was irradiated, whereas, when the compound was heated in the absence of light, it proved to be unusually stable.

Carbonium ion chemistry. Carbonium ion reactions deal with processes involving the intermediate formation of structures bearing a positive charge on a carbon atom. In the usual case this deficiency of electric charge is characterized by a tricovalent (capable of sharing three pairs of electrons) carbon atom having a sextet of electrons in its valence shell (outer ring of electrons), as in the methyl carbonium ion $+CH_3$. George A. Olah and his co-workers at Case Western Reserve University exploited the application of powerful acids for the generation and detection of stable carbonium ions, and a considerable number of substrates (materials on which organic catalysts act) of various types were examined by these scientists.

One of the acids used by Olah is a mixture of fluorosulfuric acid and antimony pentafluoride ($FSO_3H:SbF_5$). This mixture has been called "magic acid" because of the incredible reactions that take place within it. Perhaps the most unusual reaction occurs with alkanes that abstract a hydrogen ion from $FSO_3H:SbF_5$ to form a positively charged ion that is quite different from the methyl carbonium ion. Thus, the alkane methane (CH_4) yields the $+CH_5$ ion.

The significance of these experiments lies not only in the chemistry of such intermediates but also in the theoretical interpretation of their structure. In this regard the question arises as to the nature of the chemical bonds in such pentavalent compounds as $+CH_5$. The fate of this compound is extraordinary. Upon heating the reaction mixture, hydrogen gas (H_2) is liberated, and the methyl carbonium ion ($+CH_3$) that is produced attacks a second molecule of methane to yield an ethane molecule ($+C_2H_7$) with an additional proton. The processes are repeated until the most stable cation (ion with a positive charge), trimethyl carbonium ion, $(CH_3)_3C^+$, is obtained.

Substantial support was finally realized for one of the more elusive carbonium ions, the vinyl cation ($R\overset{+}{C}=CR_2$). For the past several decades vinyl cations had become increasingly accepted as possible intermediates in certain chemical reactions. Scientists at the California Institute of Technology recently presented evidence that cyclopropyliodoethene (13, Z=I) underwent ionization to the carbonium ion (14) when it was treated with silver acetate ($AgOCOCH_3$) in acetic acid. The reaction was instantaneous at 25° C, and the acetate (13, Z=$OCOCH_3$) was produced in high yield.

A striking feature of the report was the utter lack of reactivity of a similarly constituted precursor (15) that did not react at all at 25° C and underwent only slight reaction under brutal conditions by heating the reaction mixture for 36 hours in a sealed tube at 150° C. These extremes in reactivity served to emphasize the extraordinary ability of the cyclopropyl group to stabilize carbonium ions. Similar results were reported by another group of chemists at the University of Tübingen who examined the reaction between the chloro compound (13, Z=Cl) and sodium acetate in acetic acid. These investigations destroyed the long-established rule that halogen groups, such as Cl or I, attached to a carbon–carbon double bond are exceedingly unreactive.

Low-temperature chemistry. The ability of a compound to exist long enough to be isolated and have its structure characterized depends on the temperature at which the isolation is conducted. Most organic compounds are stable at room temperature but are generally not stable at temperatures in excess of 500° C, where they undergo profound decomposition. As noted above, thermal collisions are responsible for many organic reactions, and high temperatures increase both the frequency and the energy of these collisions.

There are, however, many compounds that have defied isolation because they are thermally unstable, even at room temperature. Interest in the isolation of these substances increased in recent years owing to the use of low temperatures to achieve isolation. By operating at temperatures as low as −200° C, it became possible to prepare samples of previously unknown compounds and to demonstrate their existence, because at that temperature the thermal energy is insufficient to cause these molecules to decompose or undergo reaction.

In addition to the challenge of preparing unknown and elusive compounds, the significance of this work lies in the ability to produce samples of molecules that were presumed to be transient intermediates in chemical reactions and to obtain evidence for their existence. A case in point is cyclobutadiene (16). For almost 40 years many attempts were made to prepare this substance; all ended in failure because either decomposition to acetylene ($HC \equiv CH$) occurred or the compound underwent a further reaction to form C_8H_8. Finally, Henry A. McGee, Jr., of the Georgia Institute of Technology liberated cyclobutadiene, cooled it extremely rapidly to −196° C, and thus isolated it. The heart of his method was a specially designed mass spectrometer operated at very low temperatures that detected and identified the isolated substance.

Similarly, the reaction between diazomethane (CH_2N_2) and ketene ($CH_2=C=O$) was examined at −150° C; cyclopropanone (17) had been postulated as an intermediate in this reaction but it had not been isolated or characterized. Mass spectrometry at low temperatures, however, confirmed its preparation.

Free radicals are frequently implicated as intermediates in chemical reactions, but they could not be isolated because they are much too reactive. By operating at low temperatures, Brynmor Mile of Shell Research in Chester, Eng., was able to devise a technique whereby free radicals could be generated and detected, and their chemical reactions studied. A halocompound (RX) was frozen on a surface of liquid nitrogen at −196° C, and a beam of vaporized alkali metal was deposited on the surface. A reaction occurred that produced organic free radicals: RX + M· → MX + R·. The presence of these free radicals was demonstrated by measuring their ultraviolet, infrared, and electron spin resonance spectra and by their reaction with alkanes, alkenes, and oxygen.

—Ralph Daniels

Physical and synthetic chemistry

Chemistry as the study of the structure, properties, and transformation of matter clearly has significance which transcends its classic boundaries. Modern chemical research blends with physics, astronomy, and oceanography on the one hand; on the other, a chemical approach to living matter is at the heart of the recent exciting advances in molecular biology, such as clarification of the genetic role of deoxyribonucleic acid (DNA). Chemical research has also been characterized by the vigorous development and application of theory and of powerful new experimental methods. As a result, by 1969 there has been much more intimate knowledge of molecular structure and of how chemical reactions occur than was available a decade ago.

These characteristics stood out clearly in the significant developments made in physical chemistry during the last year. Using an electron microscope, the double helix of the genetic material, DNA, was apparently photographed for the first time. This event raised hopes that electron microscopy might become a standard method for the determination of the structure of large molecules. Ion cyclotron resonance, a comparatively new technique, corrected some long-standing misconceptions of chemists. In this technique ions are made to move in circular orbits by the stimulus of a magnetic field that is perpendicular to them. Under these conditions the orbital frequency of an ion provides information about its mass. Ions absorb energy and move in larger circles when irradiated with an alternating electric field of frequency ω. In pulsed double resonance experiments ions of mass a only are excited by irradiation at frequency ω_a, while the change in concentration of a chemically related species of mass b is determined by monitoring the absorption of electromagnetic energy at its characteristic frequency ω_b. A group at Stanford University, Stanford, Calif., used this technique to determine relative acidities (tendency to lose H+) of compounds in the gas phase. Their findings showed that alkyl groups, structures containing carbon and hydrogen, stabilize negative ions and that stabilization increases with the size of the alkyl group.

Nuclear magnetic resonance. The study of the interaction of magnetic atomic nuclei with an external magnetic field, nuclear magnetic resonance, was employed particularly by groups in the U.S. to detect what is called chemically induced dynamic nuclear polarization. The detection process worked as follows. If in the course of a chemical reaction an intermediate stage with an odd electron (a radical) intervenes, the nuclear magnetic moments (magnetic forces associated with spin and orbital motion) of atoms like hydrogen become aligned (polarized) with the larger magnetic moment of the odd electron, like a compass needle in a magnetic field. Because the subsequent depolarization is a slow process, it persists in the products of the reaction and can be detected by spectroscopy. In this fashion radical intermediates have been detected in several chemical reactions.

One of the serious limitations of nuclear magnetic resonance was being attacked by chemists at the Massachusetts Institute of Technology. Previously, insoluble substances could not be studied at high resolution because samples had to be in solution. By proper orientation and movement of a solid sample, however, the chemists obtained high-resolution spectra in which chemically different hydrogen atoms could be distinguished.

Theory-experiment interaction. Modern chemistry has benefited from a fruitful interaction between theory and experiment. A previous theoretical prediction was confirmed when it was shown, by using oriented beams of methyl iodide (CH_3-I), that the reaction between CH_3I and rubidium (Rb) atoms proceeds more easily when CH_3I is oriented as shown in equation 1 rather than as shown in equation 2.

$$(1) \quad Rb \quad I\text{-}CH_3 \longrightarrow Rb\text{-}I \quad \cdot CH_3$$
$$(2) \quad Rb \quad CH_3\text{-}I \longrightarrow Rb\text{-}I \quad \cdot CH_3$$

Experimentation with biological implications occurred at the University of California at Los Angeles. Chemists there demonstrated that one of the important biological functions of β-carotene, an orange plant pigment closely related to vitamin D, might be to quench (deactivate) singlet oxygen, a highly energetic form of oxygen which would otherwise severely damage plant tissues.

Compound syntheses. Chemical synthesis, in addition to affording chemists with a rich store of reactions and other data, has provided man with drugs, building materials, plastics, and synthetic fibers which do not occur in nature. Specialized synthetic methods have direct significance to the chemist alone, but many eventually make indispensable contributions to work of great human importance. Advances in synthetic applications of organoboron compounds were mainly accomplished at Purdue University, Lafayette, Ind., while new synthetic applications of organo-transition metal compounds (contain bonds from carbon to metals such as iron and nickel) was the result of an international effort. Synthesis of sodium hydride (NaH) was accomplished under very mild conditions, and organocopper reagents, chemicals used to react with other substances, such as $(CH_3)_2CuLi$ became versatile reagents for forming carbon–carbon bonds.

The significance of some syntheses lies in their implications rather than in their immediate practical applications. Such a synthesis was the reduction (fixation) of molecular nitrogen to ammonia by Stanford University chemists (see *Inorganic Chemistry,* above).

A number of compounds which occupy significant places in the theory of chemical bonding have been reported for the first time. The ion CH_5^+ and some related compounds were shown to form in so-called superacids by Dutch and U.S. chemists, and the existence of norbornadienone (18) was demonstrated for the first time, though none of these compounds had, to date, been isolated. Uranocene was the first compound that used the little-understood f electrons for metal carbon bonding (see *Inorganic Chemistry,* above).

Many other compounds were prepared for the first time. New polyhedral boron compounds were reported, among them (19), and biologically active compounds such as prostaglandin-E_1 (20) and oxytetrocycline (21) were synthesized. Several syntheses of tetrahydrocannabinol, the active principle of marijuana, were also reported.

The failure of pesticides such as DDT to control insect populations and the ominous pollution problems resulting from their continued heavy use received considerable publicity. One answer to the pesticide dilemma might be to attack insects with compounds specific to undesirable species. Several new syntheses of the juvenal hormone (22) of the giant silkworm moth pointed in that direction. Minute amounts of the hormone arrested the development of the silkworm and other insects in the pupa stage. Four simple compounds, one of them (23), which serve as the sex attractant of the male boll weevil, were synthesized by the U.S. Department of Agriculture. They might be used to lure female boll weevils into traps or to confuse their attempts to pair with males.

Synthesis of the sex hormone, antheridiol (24), of *Achlya bisexualis,* an aquatic fungus, at the Syntex Co. in Mexico confirmed the structure proposed for the hormone earlier in 1968. Secreted by the female plant, it stimulates growth of the male plant's reproductive cells in concentrations of 0.00000002 grams per liter of water.

Though many of the above syntheses are formidable pieces of work, the most outstanding achievement in the past year was the first synthesis of an active enzyme, that of ribonuclease, by independent teams at Merck & Co., Inc., of Rahway, N.J., and at Rockefeller University in New York City. Ribonuclease, though it is one of the smallest enzymes known, contains 124 amino acids and 1,876 atoms. For a full discussion of the synthesis of an enzyme, *see* Year in Review: MOLECULAR BIOLOGY, *Biochemistry.*

Future outlook. Progress in physical and synthetic chemistry this past year, while exciting, could be outdone in the next. Proposals have been made to extend the periodic table of the elements beyond the present 103 to element 168. Stable atomic nuclei at atomic numbers 114 and 168 were predicted. Thus, more new elements seem to be in the offing. The total synthesis of vitamin B_{12} also seems to be imminent, the two halves of this complex molecule having already been constructed.

A physical technique which is rapidly assuming importance is photoelectron spectroscopy, in which electrons are ejected from atoms and molecules by means of high-energy radiation. It is, in effect, a probe with which one can go deep into the electronic structure of atoms and molecules. Finally, the coming year will almost certainly see a continued integration of the subdisciplines within chemistry and a further erosion of the now indistinct boundary between chemistry and biology.

—C. Peter Lillya

Communications

The high-speed network of communications lines developed by U.S. telephone companies, which reached into most of the nation's homes and businesses, had by 1969 become the medium for more than 100 billion conversations per year. In addition, these lines were used for many other types

Courtesy, CBS Laboratories

A portable color television camera is carried into the infield of a racetrack to photograph the horses. The camera's design permits remote control of focusing, centering, and color registration.

of information exchange, such as facsimile transmission and closed-circuit television. In 1968 a leader of the industry coined the term "Information Utility" to describe the future role of the telephone company.

Telephone companies were offering some new services, such as teletypewriter switching and mobile radio. In accordance with a 1968 ruling of the U.S. Federal Communications Commission (FCC), they were also making their network facilities available to others; thus, the telephone network seemed almost certain to become increasingly important to the country's communications system.

Also of special interest were recent developments in community antenna television (CATV). In 1968 the U.S. Supreme Court ruled that the FCC had the power to regulate CATV and to limit the geographical expansion of any system. At the end of the year, the FCC announced proposed regulations, many of which were being opposed by the industry.

Telephones

The nationwide network of telephone companies in the U.S. comprised more than 109 million telephones (nearly half the last known world total of 222 million). Through this network's international connections its customers could call 96% of the world's telephones.

New telephone equipment. Most existing U.S. telephone exchanges were dial-controlled, using electromechanical switching equipment (the number of manual exchanges is negligible). Future exchanges, however, were already being designed to be operated electronically. Electromechanical exchanges would probably continue in use throughout the 20th century but would increasingly employ electronic devices for ringing, tone generation, and power supply. In the meantime, to accommodate the tremendous increase in long-distance traffic, electronic routing systems were being developed to be installed in switching centers. These systems would be used to switch interoffice trunk lines only, and would not apply to subscriber lines. An electronic translator, first installed in 1969, located the best route for each long-distance call and then routed the call accordingly.

"Dial-in-handset" instruments, in which the dial was located in the receiver, were introduced by several manufacturers during the past year. They involved extensive innovation in components in order to fit into the limited space available. Even the dial, which for 60 years had been three inches in diameter, was reduced to two and a half inches.

Pushbutton calling, originally planned for use in electronic exchanges, was being adopted widely for use with existing exchange equipment. After the two tone signals associated with each pressed digit are received and identified in the exchange, they are then stored and fed to the switching equipment as required to complete the desired connection. The tones are generated electronically within the pushbutton calling unit.

During the year Bell Telephone Laboratories, Inc., Murray Hill, N.J., announced the development of an experimental "electronic telephone" that uses a lightweight electromagnetic microphone, a hybrid integrated circuit providing amplification, an electronic tone ringer, and an automatic volume control. It was expected that some or all of these new components would be used in the next generation of telephones.

The United Kingdom, which placed Europe's first operational electronic telephone exchange in service in December 1966, opened many new electronic exchanges in recent months. Data-transmission on telephone lines was also expanding in the U.K.

In a new switching system introduced in France an automatic line concentrator installed at an outlying point concentrates onto 11 two-wire channels the calls from 60 subscribers, thus permitting large savings on cable costs. When a station initiates a call, it is connected through one of those lines to the central office. It remains connected to that line until the line is needed by another station (that is, when all other lines are in use); thus, there is little switching because usually a relatively small number of the customers makes most of the calls.

To meet customer demands for "antique" telephones, the various companies announced that such telephones may be used on their lines, provided they are first fitted by the company with modern transmission components. This represented a revision of the companies' "foreign attachments" rule, which had previously prohibited the attachment of any device or equipment not supplied by the company. The rule was further modified by the telephone companies to permit the interconnection of data equipment through the network. For this service, the company provides "data sets" that act as intermediaries between the customer's data equipment and the telephone circuits. These sets protect the telephone system against nonstandard operation of the customer's equipment.

Innovations in telephone service. To speed communications in emergencies, telephone companies began to adopt "911" as a universal emergency number in some communities, providing immediate access to all public safety agencies. In New York City emergency calls increased by 50%—from 12,000 per day with the former number (440-1234) to 18,000 with "911."

Telephones and wiring in apartment houses were being used to provide another new service, the Enterphone or Apartment House Door-Answering Service. Through a handset in the lobby of the building, a visitor could talk with the tenant, who could control the door-opener by dialing a number on his phone. If the tenant was using the phone when the visitor called, the tenant received a special signal and could place the outside line on "hold" while talking to the visitor. He would then be reconnected to the outside line when he dialed to permit (or deny) entrance to the visitor.

A one-way (listen only) network which transmitted precautionary messages concerning shoplifters, check-passers, etc., to subscribing businesses was established during the year in Lincoln, Neb. The Lincoln Police Department recorded any warnings it might have on an electronic unit and then signaled all subscribers on the network.

Through the telephone lines, gas, water, and electric meters now can be automatically read, usually during periods of light telephone traffic. When a customer's number is dialed, a device attached to the telephone at the customer's home returns signals that identify the meter and give its present reading. Bills may then be automatically printed from the recorded data.

In the Los Angeles area, 13 school districts established a program of telephone classes for children ill at home. Each pupil had a standard telephone and a Speakerphone (or a headset) which freed his hands. Each teacher at a special "education service center" was equipped with a 30-button telephone and a Speakerphone, and an automatic dialing device for calling the students to "class."

Business telephone services were being expanded by the widespread application of Centrex systems, which permitted dialing of incoming calls directly to the called stations and also provided a variety of interior telephone, conference-call, and other services like those offered by separate customer-owned systems.

Other service improvements in progress included the "upgrading" of multiparty lines by the reduction of the number of parties—to one, in many cases. Subscriber carrier systems that provided private-line service to up to six subscribers on one line were being introduced. Because of the scarcity and high cost of copper wire, manufacturers began turning to aluminum for their cable lines; by 1969 Western Electric Co., Inc., New York City, was making 100 million conductor-feet of aluminum cable per year.

A new 50,000 bit-per-second switched-message service was added by the Bell System to its "low-speed" data-transmission services on certain routes. With this new service, called Data-Phone® 50, a caller may dial a connection as usual and, by conversation with the distant party, arrange for data transmission over the established connection. The new service, to be offered between Chicago, Los Angeles, New York City, and Washington, D.C., was designed to be 25 times as fast as other data-phone services.

Telephones and computers. A new data retrieval telephone, providing both a dial and a touch calling unit, permits a user to have access to a computer by dialing the machine's assigned "telephone number." The user then queries the computer by pushing the touch calling buttons. In a few seconds the computer replies with a voice message automatically created from 32 prerecorded words in its "vocabulary." A typical transaction can be completed in about 30 seconds; in that time the computer might report "credit okay," the amount in a customer's account, or other such information.

In New York City approximately 2,400 students have access to a computer center that will ask a question, record the answer if it is the correct one, and then ask another question. Each student has

A two-way closed circuit television system links the Nebraska Psychiatric Institute in Omaha with an affiliated state hospital 112 mi away. The system is available to both staffs on a 24-hr basis, allowing for a much greater exchange of information and resources.

a specially equipped Touch-Tone (pushbutton-calling) telephone through which he transmits his answers.

Transoceanic telephone service. Although communication satellites captured public interest, cable-laying ships remained busy. A $33-million cable from the continental U.S. to Puerto Rico and the Virgin Islands was placed in service in August 1968. It was capable of carrying 720 telephone, data, and facsimile messages. The American Telephone and Telegraph Co. (AT&T) began using undersea cable between Tel Aviv, Israel, and Marseilles, France, a route formerly served by microwave. AT&T was also laying a similar cable between Green Hill, R.I., and San Fernando, Spain, with links to Portugal and Italy. This would be the fifth telephone cable between the U.S. and Europe; the first was laid in 1956.

During 1967 more than 12 million calls from the U.S. to points overseas were handled—a fivefold increase in ten years. Operator dialing of such overseas calls was extended to 18 countries; 4 more were added in 1969 and an additional 13 were scheduled for 1970. Limited subscriber dialing of such calls began in January 1969 on station-to-station calls to the United Kingdom from New York City; plans for the extension of such service were under way.

Other communications systems

Telegraph service. Transfer of the Bell System TWX (Teletypewriter Exchange) operations to Western Union Telegraph Co. was agreed to in principle by the boards of directors of both companies. Western Union was also making similar agreements with the other telephone companies that operated TWX equipment. Following FCC approval of these negotiations, the merger of TWX with Western Union's Telex system was planned. The telephone companies expected to continue their other activities in the area of data communications, including Data-Phone and private-line facilities that served more than 100,000 teletypewriters.

Mobile radio systems. Continued demand for mobile radio facilities was placing constant pressure on the broadcast frequencies available. The crowding of the radio spectrum (the wavelengths available for broadcasting) limited the FCC in its issuing of licenses, so that even the police did not receive sufficient frequencies. A group of public officials, testifying before the U.S. House of Representatives' Small Business Subcommittee of the Banking and Currency Committee, charged that the FCC, by its "public-safety frequency starvation," was responsible for the 1967 summer riots in Newark, N.J.

In July 1968, the FCC proposed that the frequency shortage be relieved, in 25 major urban areas, by sharing the lower seven ultra-high-frequency (UHF) television channels with land mobile radio services in those areas where they were not assigned for broadcasting. At the suggestion of the FCC and of Telecommunications Management, a Joint Technical Advisory Committee began making a study to aid in setting a national policy for use of the radio spectrum.

For conversation between network telephones and airplanes in flight, the FCC recently doubled channels available (from 6 to 12), and extended the service area (formerly limited to the northeastern U.S.) so that it spanned the continental U.S. The Bell System planned to develop this service in order to permit passengers on planes in flight to talk with their homes or offices.

Plans for revitalizing railroad passenger service included provision for en-route telephone communications. Passengers on the new Washington–Philadelphia–New York Metroliner would be able to initiate (or receive) calls from any point along the 225-mi route to any point across the U.S. and around the world.

Community antenna television (CATV). Originally developed to bring down into low-lying towns the commercial television programs that were passing over them, CATV is now widely used in large cities that are within easy reach of broadcasting towers. Employing coaxial cables for transmission directly to TV receivers, CATV permits a clear picture, unaffected by nearby buildings or atmospheric or other disturbances that would disrupt a broadcast signal. Besides carrying commercial broadcast programs, many CATV operators are originating programs of local news, weather forecasts, and the like.

The U.S. Supreme Court ruled that the FCC has power to regulate CATV and to limit territorial expansion of a system. The FCC announced in December 1968 its proposed rules for the CATV industry; during 1969 it held hearings preparatory to formulating rules that will have the force of law.

CATV operators have commonly arranged to use telephone companies' pole lines and underground cable ducts to carry their coaxial cables to CATV subscribers. In these cases the CATV company sometimes performs its own construction and maintenance work, or the telephone company may build the facilities for CATV transmission and then lease them.

Coaxial cable may be supplemented by microwave radio for CATV transmission. The FCC approved the experimental commerical use of microwave channels in New York City, in Oregon, and in New Mexico. The proposed system, called amplitude modulation link, will use the 18-GHz (gigahertz) band to send signals on 12 channels for a distance of several miles, to antennas atop high buildings, and thence by coaxial cable to the apartments below.

—Walter Axelsen

For a discussion of communications satellites, *see also* Year in Review: ASTRONAUTICS AND SPACE EXPLORATION, *Earth-Oriented Satellites.*

Computers

Though still in its infancy, the computer and information processing industry continued to grow rapidly and extensively, and the outlook for progress in the future was one of unparalleled promise. The past year, however, brought few dramatic technical breakthroughs or inventions; rather, there was steady innovation in applying computer technology to such areas as the arts, business, education, and government.

In all areas the trend continued to make computers even more ubiquitous by making them smaller, less expensive, and more accessible. The technique of "time-sharing," for example, allowed many inexpensive typewriter terminals

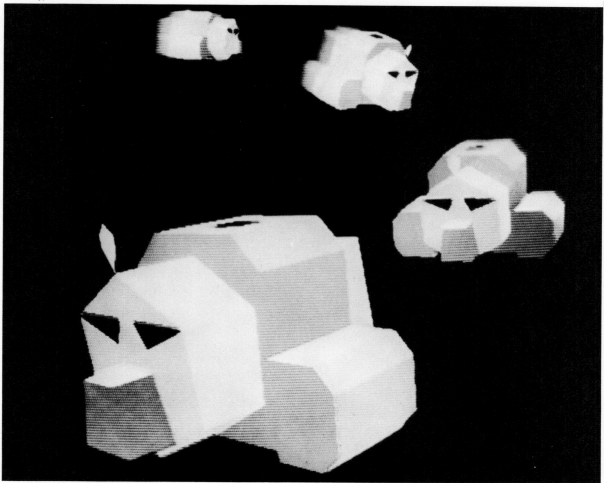

A computer visualizes in rapid succession its conception of the U.S. lunar module.
Many geometric forms can be created by this computer, which allows such shapes to be viewed
from any angle and changes the images many times per second.

(such as airline reservation consoles) to share the resources of a large, powerful computer at the same time. Also, individual, small computers could be obtained for approximately $5,000, in contrast with large-scale computers which can cost several million dollars.

This progress, however, was not without drawbacks. As it continued to cause profound changes in our society, the computer seemed to evoke almost as much fear as praise. The areas in which new applications and controversies occurred during the past year are discussed below.

Art and design

Efforts have been made in recent years, especially in the past year, to bring together science and art. Several exhibitions that attempted to demonstrate this relationship were given in various countries. "Cybernetic Serendipity," open to the general public and technical people alike, was an international exhibition given in London from Aug. 2 to Oct. 10, 1968, that explored and demonstrated some of the relationships between technology and creativity. Its aim was to present activities in which artists and scientists interacted. Some of the projects on display were computer-animated films, music composed and instrumented by computers, computer-produced poems and texts, and computer paintings and computer graphics.

A similar attempt to demonstrate the connection between technology and art was the textile design and weaving exhibit at the 1968 HemisFair in San Antonio, Tex. The process of weaving was actually first mechanized as long ago as the early 1800s by the Frenchman Joseph Jacquard, whose looms were operated by punched cards. The notion of mechanizing complicated operations by the use of punched-card equipment in turn led the Englishman Charles Babbage to design forerunners of our modern-day electronic computers.

In 1830 Babbage and, until recently, all of his successors saw the computer as a "number cruncher"; finally, however, the use of computers for nonnumerical purposes was starting to become more widespread. At the HemisFair a computer and a display terminal were used to direct the weaving process. An electronic "lightpen" was employed to draw a design on the screen of the display terminal. The design was then translated automatically into instructions for a Jacquard loom, which, in less than ten minutes, wove a three-inch swatch of cloth in the given design.

Social implications of computers

Among the issues raised by the increasing use of computers were those of job displacement because of automation and the invasion of privacy. The first of these was probably the most controversial. Although there were those who argued that computers created many more jobs than they displaced, others claimed that the job toll, particularly among unskilled blue-collar workers and even among low-level white-collar workers, was high and would continue to climb. Facts and figures establishing which side was correct were not available.

On the positive side were programs for ghetto youth. Districts such as Watts in Los Angeles utilized the increasing need for computer personnel to encourage the disadvantaged to return to school and obtain training. Subjects included computer operating, keypunching, and programming. Also, a computer-based job-bank system was established in some neighborhood antipoverty centers in order to speed up matching of unemployed individuals with jobs. The computer system was also expected to help centralize and unify the operations of the patchwork of welfare and antipoverty centers now in existence.

The second issue, that of potential (and actual) computer invasion of privacy, was one which was finally being aired publicly and, consequently, had a good chance of being settled productively. The main issue was whether or not the accumulation of personal or statistical information in centralized private or governmental data banks could be justified. The idea of a government-controlled compendium of psychological tests, school transcripts, credit information, medical records, social security and income tax information, etc., filled most people with visions of "Big Brother" materialized.

The proponents of a government-directed national data center insisted that they did not want

"Oscillating Wastebasket" is an example of computer art. A programmer supplies a large-scale computer with mathematical formulas to produce the desired designs. After many calculations the computer sends the drawing instructions to a mechanical arm.

to collect individual records but only statistical profiles in order to help government do a better job of research, planning, and decision making. Access would be strictly regulated and limited, and safeguards against unauthorized usage would be installed. Nonetheless, many opponents believed that such a center would be only the beginning and that soon enough more personal information would be collected. Although there was much argument about the technical problem of safeguarding information, the fundamental debate concerned the rights of an individual to privacy in relationship to recorded information about him. In the U.S. the debate was complicated by the fact that the federal Constitution did not spell out those rights explicitly.

Thinking and creativity

There are several controversial applications of computer technology which are still in their infancy but which are potentially enormous in their implications. One of these potential applications is that of "augmenting human intellect," which Douglas Engelbart of the Stanford Research Institute, Menlo Park, Calif., has defined as the use of a sophisticated computer system to aid people in the intellectual tasks of conceptualizing, visualizing, and organizing problems and solutions. While most people take such computer capabilities for granted, programs for this type of freeform communication are so difficult to construct that computers are still used almost exclusively for mechanical calculations and for regurgitation of previously stored information.

Engelbart's system of time-shared display consoles located in individual offices allowed researchers to compose, store, and manipulate all their working materials. These included specifications, plans, designs, memos, reference notes, reports, and bibliographies. Scratch work, designing, revising, and even a good deal of intercommunication could be done via such consoles. The emphasis was on treating the console as a piece of office furniture, available at all times, and combining the best features of the typewriter, pencil and paper, file cabinet, desk calculator, picture phone, etc., with unusual power and flexibility.

Time-shared display consoles are based on television technology. By using split-screen techniques, the screen is divided for providing separate working areas or for superimposing the face of a collaborator. Thus, several persons may work on a document together without being in the same office. Engelbart's researchers held "on-line" (computer-linked) conferences in which they worked together on a number of interconnected consoles, selecting materials from the file, browsing through them with real flexibility, and revising them. Part of the aim of this group was to see how habits and techniques for creative work change to accommodate this new instrument. It was already clear that both the quality and quantity of work produced were substantially enhanced by this system.

The creation of a hypertext. At Brown University, Providence, R.I., work was progressing along similar lines. The aim there was to build systems which serve two purposes: (1) to store, manipulate, and print conventional text such as this article; and (2) to experiment with collections of nonordered text fragments, taking advantage of electronics. Theodor Nelson, an author and inventor, coined the term "hypertext" to denote "the combination of natural language text with the computer's capacities for interactive, branching, or dynamic display . . . a nonlinear text . . . which cannot be printed conveniently . . . on a conventional page. . . ."

As a concrete example of a simple hypertext, one can visualize the *Encyclopædia Britannica* stored in a computer, any entry being immediately accessible via a display console. Furthermore, one may point (with a "lightpen" or some other device) at any cross reference in the text in order to jump from that segment of text to the referenced entry in the encyclopedia (an instant "see also"). The reference could also be to an article or book other than the encyclopedia. Pushing a RETURN button on the console, the user may immediately go back to his previous place in the text.

Another example of a hypertext involves the set of raw materials which were forged into this article: the collection of the authors' thoughts and notes, articles, and annotations which were typed into the system in virtually random order. Once in the computer a first draft was composed on the display console from the individual fragments. This draft was subsequently edited through several more drafts, all with the aid of a lightpen. Note that hypertext is both text without order and text with many possible arrangements, choices, and orders not presentable together in conventional writing.

Computers in education

One of the most rapidly advancing uses of the computer was in the field of education. In addi-

A computer displays the letter "B" as part of a program to train people unfamiliar with the machines to use them effectively. Achieving such graphic designs is a first step in this project.

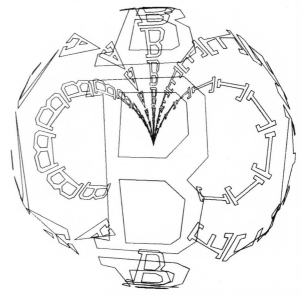

tion to the rather conventional applications of computers to payroll computation, class scheduling, attendance keeping, and grade reporting, computers were beginning to be used for vocational guidance and instruction. For instance, students in high school may specify their criteria for a college they wish to attend and then obtain a list of appropriate schools. Another system, a job data bank, assists students in selecting their careers.

Computer-assisted instruction. A most exciting area of development was that of computer-assisted instruction (CAI), which had evolved from simple rote drills into full-scale teaching programs. One of the most fully researched and usable systems for CAI began in 1960 at the University of Illinois under the direction of Donald Bitzer and his colleagues. An automatic, individualized instructional system for large numbers of students, PLATO (Programmed Logic for Automatic Teaching Operations) provided courses of study in engineering, mathematics, foreign languages, clinical nursing, library training, computer programming, research (learning theory experiments, psychological studies, etc.), and simulation. The system provided for communication in two directions to 20 student stations.

A student using this CAI system had two sources of information: (1) the "electronic book" (slides stored in a computer-controlled selector available to all student stations simultaneously), containing material usually found in textbooks or class notes; and (2) the "electronic blackboard" (a computer-controlled display screen for each student station), allowing diagrams, symbols, and words to be plotted on the student's console. Both slides and computer-generated information could be superimposed on the screen. An electronic keyset (resembling a typewriter) enabled the student to communicate with the computer.

The basic set of rules governing the teaching process in a CAI system was referred to as a "teaching logic." The two different types used were the "tutorial logic" and the "inquiry logic." The tutorial logic was planned to guide a student through an established set of topics, and also provided for branching to specialized text segments. This logic presented the basic information, figures, and examples on the material to be covered, and then asked questions of the student. The student composed his answer and then asked the computer for a judgment on his response. A student could tackle easier or more challenging problems as he progressed, while the teacher could review the student's progress and subsequently direct him.

The other type of logic, the inquiry logic, gave a student the problem to be solved and allowed him to follow any sequence of steps to reach a solution. In this method the student asked questions of the computer in order to obtain facts and figures to solve the problem. The student's response was judged by the computer.

The results of various studies of the PLATO system showed that its greatest advantage was the significant saving in time spent on the lesson material. Student response to the use of the computer as an instructor was favorable.

An interesting and successful use of computers in education was the time-sharing system at Dartmouth College, Hanover, N.H. Not only did 70% of the undergraduates at Dartmouth learn to use the system, but secondary school students began using it as well.

In mid-1969 about 18 secondary schools in a six-state area (New York, Maine, Massachusetts, Vermont, Connecticut, and New Hampshire) were tied into the Dartmouth time-sharing system via teletypewriter terminals connected over long-distance telephone lines. The computer was used both inside and outside of classrooms for assigned computer work, homework projects, and for fun. Teachers used it as an aid to classroom teaching and to write programs themselves.

One advantage of CAI over traditional drill and practice sessions was that each student need not be given the same problem. Tasks of various degrees of difficulty, based on evaluation of past performance (also provided by the computer), were available to fit individual abilities. Another advantage was the immediate reinforcement of learning. The computer judged a student's response at once and, in addition, provided a printed evaluation of the student's performance. This allowed an instructor to determine whether a student should go on to more challenging problems or do remedial work.

CAI, however, was not free of problems. One of the biggest difficulties was that of obtaining suitable lesson material. If such material was to be beneficial to students, programs must be planned by academically oriented individuals rather than just by computer programmers. Yet, at the same time, the programs must be adaptable to the requirements of the computer. The shortage of skilled individuals in all aspects of the production of CAI course materials was a serious problem. Other difficulties not yet dealt with included evaluating and grading lengthy papers (such as those for an English course), and the evaluation of bodily gestures and vocal intonation in student responses.

The cost of CAI, once extremely large, was reduced to a feasible level. The cost to a secondary school of the Dartmouth time-sharing system, for instance, ranged from $4,500 to $12,000 per year, depending on the number of terminals used, hours of use, distance from Dartmouth, and whether the schools were public or private. Bitzer of the PLATO project optimistically predicted that, in a few years, with 4,000 student terminals in use, an individual console will sell for less than $2,000 and the cost per student contact hour could be reduced to less than 40 cents.

—Andries van Dam, Patricia Mitchell
See also Year in Review: ELECTRONICS, *Electronic Memory Systems.*

Dentistry

As dentistry approaches the 1970s, exciting new developments loom on the horizons of research. In the United States leading dental scientists expressed optimism that dental caries (tooth decay) may be completely preventable within the next decade. Other major research efforts were concentrating on the prevention of periodontal (gum) disease, which accounts for the largest percentage of tooth loss in adults.

The steady progress in dentistry's battle with tooth decay was acknowledged in recent months when the National Institute of Dental Research (NIDR) appointed a special investigating group.

Several techniques were under extensive investigation, including the use of antibiotics, immunization with a vaccine, and the application of enzyme therapy. The prospects for developing an effective vaccine against tooth decay were reinforced by the findings of a microbiologist from Northwestern University, reported at a meeting of the International Association for Dental Research in Houston, Tex., in March. He cited experiments in which caries was inhibited in white rats after they were immunized against an enzyme called dextran sucrase, which is produced by streptococci bacteria. The relatively insoluble dextran tenaciously adheres to the tooth surface as well as to adjacent microorganisms that attack the tooth structure. Because the dextran sucrase enzyme is a "foreign" protein not produced by the body itself, rats and humans may be able to develop antibodies against it and reject it.

Another promising discovery was a harmless chemical or enzyme called dextranase, which prevented the formation of plaque (a film of mucus containing bacteria on a tooth) in hamsters and thus resulted in a reduced decay rate. Dextranase was also expected to play a role in curbing periodontal disease, since plaque formation is a principal contributing cause to that disorder. A mouthwash containing the enzyme was being used on an experimental basis by human subjects in Maryland, Alabama, and Massachusetts.

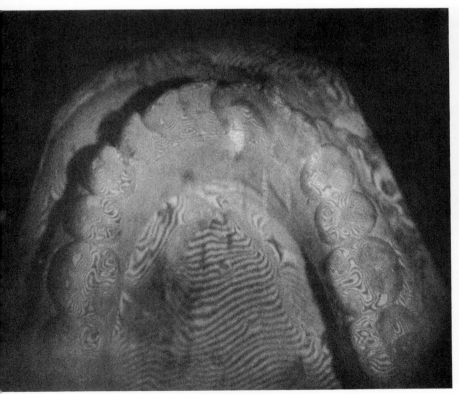

Courtesy, Jerry R. Varner, University of Michigan

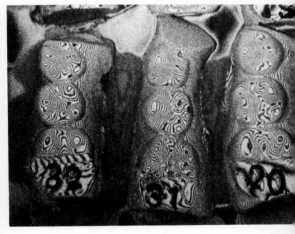

Human teeth are revealed in great detail by the recently developed photographic process of holography. Such detailed pictures may eventually be used to identify people in the same way as fingerprints; for example, the slightly varying sets of teeth at the left and center (above) belong to identical twins. At the left is a depth contour hologram of lower teeth.

Fluoridation. Water fluoridation continued to be the dental profession's most effective, economical, and safe procedure in reducing tooth decay; in children it often resulted in reductions of up to 60%. The first country to use fluoridation was the U.S., which introduced it in the mid-1940s. Meanwhile, the roster of other nations initiating fluoridation steadily increased. By 1969 the countries leading in fluoridation progress were Australia, Ireland, Canada, the Netherlands, and Chile. In the U.S., with the backing of all competent health-oriented organizations, including the American Dental Association, an effort was launched to obtain statewide fluoridation legislation in all states. Currently about 83 million Americans live in communities serviced by communal water supplies containing the optimum amount of fluorides.

In areas without water fluoridation many dentists gave their patients fluoride treatments, which resulted in decay reductions of approximately 40%. In order to facilitate mass treatment, a procedure of self-application of a fluoride was tested with school children in Indiana. The children brushed their teeth with a special stannous fluoride paste under the supervision of dentists or dental hygienists.

A dental scientist found graphic evidence that fluorides can reverse the decay process and can even heal incipient cavities. Photographs taken with a scanning electron miscroscope confirmed the concept that fluorides could "halt and heal" early enamel (outer layer of tooth structure) cavities. The researcher removed samples of enamel from extracted third molars or wisdom teeth and placed them in acid solutions similar to those causing decay. Some of these samples had been pretreated with stannous fluoride. In contrast, one sample was first exposed to the acid and then treated with the fluoride solution. After 24 hours in acid the sample not treated with fluoride showed a widespread loss of enamel substance, while the one treated with fluoride displayed excellent resistance to the acid.

Supplementary methods to prevent tooth decay for persons living in a fluoridated area were being studied. A Canadian dental research scientist achieved a 30% decrease in the tooth decay rate of children three years after the biting surfaces of their first molars were painted with a plastic coating. Reporting on the findings in November 1968, he said that the study involved 130 children and that the coating was applied only to decay-free teeth. The sealant consisted of a mixture of base polymers and methyl methacrylate. The experiment showed that the sealant did not prevent progress of already existing cavities and that re-coating once a year would lead to a higher decay prevention rate.

Periodontal disease research. Some products from food proteins may occasionally contribute to the development of periodontal disease, according to a University of Tennessee dental researcher. He found in animal experiments that food proteins, when repeatedly consumed, can enter the gum through tiny abrasions or scratches and gradually produce "sensitized" areas. These areas then may cause chronic inflammations, which could contribute to periodontal disease in humans as they did in animals.

NIDR scientists began probing the possibility that bacterial endotoxins (poisons released by bacteria) may play a role in the progression of periodontal disease. Animal experiments revealed that once periodontal tissues are damaged by cuts or scratches, small concentrations of endotoxin can cause serious and sustained inflammation, like that of periodontal disease.

Smoking was also recently linked to the development of periodontal disease. This was indicated by a study of 7,000 patients at Roswell Park Memorial Institute in Buffalo, N.Y., which revealed that the poor periodontal condition of smokers was comparable to that of nonsmokers 15 years their seniors.

Oral cancer and smoking. Oral cancer and its prevention continued to be of major concern to the dental profession in the U.S., where 16,000 new cases are reported annually and 6,000 deaths per year are attributed to this disease. A study of 191 patients at Philadelphia General Hospital indicated that persons under 45 years of age who drink and smoke and are also suffering from diabetes, tuberculosis, cirrhosis of the liver, or anemia may face a greater risk of developing oral cancer than older individuals under similar conditions. Researchers in California also found that tongue cancer has been strongly associated with cigarette smoking and a smoker's risk of death from tongue cancer is higher than from mouth cancer generally. Annual incidence rates for cancers of the oral cavity show cancer of the tongue to be more than twice as common as cancer of the floor of the mouth and the number of deaths from tongue cancer to be twice as high as for the latter variety. A number of studies have also indicated that smokers face a greater risk of developing mouth cancer than cancer of the pharynx.

Other dental research. Highlights of other important dental research activities in recent months included marrow transplants in dogs to restore deteriorated bone structures in the mouth. This experiment could prove helpful to human dental patients who are unable to retain dentures

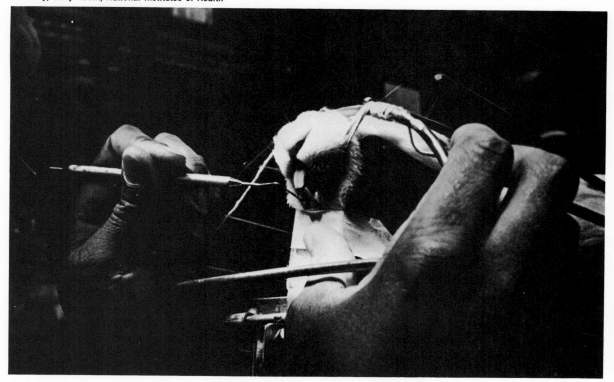

The gum tissue of a rabbit is inspected to determine the effects of various substances and their relationship to periodontal disease.

because their jawbones do not provide sufficient ridges for holding dentures.

Experiments at NIDR revealed that a group of chemicals given to rats at specific times during pregnancy caused cleft palate in many of their offspring. These findings were expected to aid cleft palate studies with humans. In other research a simple one-minute blood glucose test that can help a dentist screen patients for possible diabetes in undiagnosed cases was developed in recent months.

Research aimed at discovering a way of reducing the discomfort of tooth extractions indicated that potassium hydroxide might be helpful in this regard. The chemical was successfully tested in monkeys. Also tested on monkeys was an enzyme technique which might slow down the rejection of tooth transplants long enough—from six to eight years—to make such transplantation a useful procedure.

Dental education and manpower. Dental education in the U.S. for some time has been troubled by a lack of adequate financing, which, among other things, resulted in the closing of St. Louis University School of Dentistry. The money shortage was particularly severe for the privately supported schools, which constituted half of the 52 dental schools in the nation. American Dental Association (ADA) officials repeatedly pointed out that the closing of any dental school would be a crippling blow to the objective of increasing dental manpower in the future. Moreover, a 30-year effort by the ADA, which in 1967 resulted in a proposed national children's dental health program, was seriously retarded when the U.S. Congress eliminated entirely for fiscal 1969 a program of pilot dental health projects for financially needy children. The ADA urged Congress to appropriate at least $5 million to start the program. The ADA warned that such financial crises would seriously impede the profession's efforts to cope with the mounting manpower problem in dentistry.

Increased demands for dental services—spurred by the population explosion—a rising awareness by the public of the need for regular dental care, the availability of prepayment programs (currently covering 5 million Americans and expected to cover 50 million by 1975), and the broadening of public health programs to include dental care were all expected to place a strenuous burden on the dental manpower capacity. Among moves to increase the dental work force were efforts by the ADA to encourage expanded use of dental auxiliary personnel.

—Lou Joseph

Earth sciences

Geology and geochemistry

In August 1968 the world community of geologists held the quadrennial meeting of the International Geologic Congress in Prague, Czech. The 4,000 scientists from 66 countries focused their attention on geologic problems of world significance. Many developing nations had available, for the first time, detailed geologic maps and information essential for answering such global questions as the cause of continental drift. The collection of maps displayed at Prague was the most comprehensive accumulation of geologic work ever assembled.

Environmental geology. Because urbanization pressures forced the utilization of nearly every square foot of space both in cities and in the areas immediately surrounding cities, geologic hazards were too often ignored. Several alternatives were available to urban planners, however: government controls could exclude certain types of land usage which are geologically unsafe; geological engineers could help design structures which would resist the hazards present; or regional planners could strive for maximum use of the geologic environment and minimize its geologic handicaps.

The disastrous mudflows and landslides in the Los Angeles area in January 1969 resulted from heavy rains percolating into soft sedimentary rock. Entire hillsides were lubricated and slid into the valleys. In the future, city planners would need help from geologists in designing building codes to protect the populace against such hazards, and insurance planners would need guidance in developing just and realistic insurance programs. (*See* Feature Article: NATURE ON THE RAMPAGE.)

The public continued to become increasingly aware of earthquake hazards. Based on the average frequency of earthquakes, California was long overdue for a major quake. Meanwhile, geologists raced against time to learn if earthquake predictions are possible. Some scientists forecasted quakes in California for April 1969, but nothing serious happened. Mystics and astrologists excited the country with dire predictions that California would fall into the Pacific in April. Most geologists, in fact, did expect a serious earthquake in California sometime in the 1970s. If one should occur during the time of winter rains, landslides could be jarred loose on an unprecedented scale.

In January 1969 the U.S. Coast and Geodetic Survey issued a new map which rated potential earthquake dangers. The last such map was prepared in 1952, and since then much new information has emerged. According to the new data, Los Angeles and San Francisco were in serious danger; and Memphis, Tenn., St. Louis, Mo., Boston, and Charleston, S.C., could also reasonably expect damaging quakes within a century.

The United Nations warned that in the coming

A fossil specimen of a previously unknown species of the lamprey dating from the middle of the Pennsylvanian period 280 million years ago was found with five others in shale deposits in an Illinois mine. This enlargement shows the body outline of the lamprey and some of its internal structures.

Courtesy, David Bardack, University of Illinois at Chicago Circle

decades an earthquake which would kill more than a million people could occur somewhere in the world. As larger portions of the earth become densely urbanized, chances of such a disaster greatly increase. The worst earthquake in history took place in 1556 in China, when 800,000 people perished.

Because of these potential dangers and for a variety of other reasons, urban planning requires detailed geological evaluation. Subsurface water supplies (wells) must be protected from contamination; geologists must aid in selecting waste disposal areas; tunnels and bridges must be solid structures firmly emplaced in bedrock. As an example of such studies, computer analysis of ground water circulation in Nevada allowed regional planning of well water use in areas dependent on ground water.

All of this regional and urban planning required a detailed knowledge of the rocks beneath the soil. Few areas have adequate geologic maps, even the area along the San Andreas fault in California. An augmented geologic mapping program was, therefore, begun and was expected to continue into future years. The city of Columbia, Md., was a good example of planning where geologic factors were considered in order to obtain the best and safest use of the available land.

Continental drift. During its 1968–69 voyages, the research vessel "Glomar Challenger" obtained deep ocean cores on both sides of the Mid-Atlantic Ridge. The sea-floor-spreading concept, postulated by geophysicists, was that the bottommost sediments, immediately overlying basalts under the ocean floor, should be youngest near the ridge and become older as the American and African continents are approached. This interpretation was supported by the results of ten cores taken in the North Atlantic between New York City and Dakar, Senegal, and ten cores in the South Atlantic between Dakar and Rio de Janeiro, Braz. From the South Atlantic data the rate of continental drift was estimated at two inches a year for the last 70 million years (see *Geophysics,* below).

In February 1969, Gilles Allard and Vernon Hurst of the University of Georgia reported a new matching of rock types from eastern Brazil with rocks in Gabon in Africa. The Precambrian Propria geosyncline (a 600 million-year-old geosyncline located in Propria, Braz.) province had been discovered in 1964 trending (having an alignment) perpendicular to the Brazilian coast. The two researchers reported a corresponding structural trend of Precambrian rocks in Gabon; it coincided with the trend projected from Brazil, using the fit of the continents before drifting as

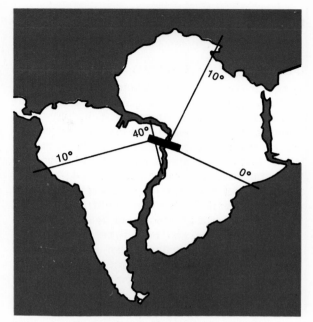

The geophysical similarities between two regions in northeastern Brazil and western Africa have led scientists to postulate that the continents were originally joined.

postulated by Edward C. Bullard in 1965. Similar nonmarine Jurassic (about 160 million years ago) and Early Cretaceous (about 125 million years ago) sediments overlie the Precambrian in Brazil and Gabon. Preserved in the sediments in both places were 30 identical species of fossil ostracods (a type of crustacean), several identical fossil fish species, and similar hydrocarbon deposits. Late Cretaceous (about 75 million years ago) salt on both continents was thought to date back to the birth of the Atlantic Ocean as the continents separated. A matching sequence of Late Cretaceous limestones and clastic (a generic term for rocks like sandstone and shale) sediments was found above the salt in both Gabon and Brazil.

The Propria geosyncline trend projected from Brazil to Gabon indicated where the continents were once joined. This predrift geographic match corresponded well with two previous discoveries: mylonite zones (made of coarse sediment formed by the interaction of rocks during movement on fault surfaces) along ancient faults cutting Brazil and central Cameroon were found to fit well on both sides of the predrift restoration, as did a geochronological border reported in 1967 by P. M. Hurley, separating basement rocks more than two billion years old in Africa and South America from much younger basement rocks.

In related studies Tuzo Wilson of Canada and others proposed that the energy responsible for folding great mountain systems along continental borders may have resulted from the collision of drifting continents far back in Paleozoic (from 225 to 600 million years ago) and earlier times.

Paleontology. The most active area of paleontologic research during 1968 and 1969 was paleoecology (the study of the relation of fossil organisms to their environment). It was found to be possible to identify ancient equivalents of nearly all modern ecologic settings by the analysis of fossils and their associated sediments in rock strata even hundreds of millions of years old. Based on studies of fossils, the water depths of ancient seas which once covered most of the continents could be calculated with a potential error of less than ten feet in some cases. Research groups at Yale and Brown universities had intensive programs in this area of study.

Several unusual fossils were reported in late 1968 and early 1969. The first fossil lamprey (jawless fishes of the class Agnatha, the most primitive group of vertebrates) was reported by David Bardack and Rainer Zangerl. They found six specimens from Illinois in concretions of Pennsylvanian age (260 million to 300 million years ago).

An ancestral eohippus (a type of primitive, four-toed horse) from the Paleocene of Wyoming (about 65 million years ago) enabled scientists to postulate that the horse originated in an epoch earlier than previously known, nearly 60 million years ago.

F. Clark Howell of the University of Chicago led a research team to Ethiopia, where they found the oldest hominid fossils yet discovered. Nearly 40 teeth and two lower jaws occurred in strata four million years old. These manlike fossils were located near remains of giraffes, camels, rhinoceroses, and carnivorous animals. (*See* Year in Review: BEHAVORIAL SCIENCES, *Breakthrough in Anthropology.*)

Geochemistry. Geochemical research continued to emphasize the chemical analysis of rocks to understand their origin. Scientists found that andesite magmas (rocks that developed from a molten state) along continental margins seem to originate chiefly by chemical fractionation of parent basalt magmas. Some geologists favored mixing oceanic basaltic magmas with continental granitic magmas to see if they could produce andesite, but this process was considered unlikely because of two lines of evidence presented at an Oregon research conference. First, trace elements and isotopes of lead and strontium in andesites have the wrong abundance to enable a significant enough assimilation of granitic rocks into basaltic magmas to produce intermediate andesite. Second, the andesites along continental margins are remarkably constant in composition, even though volcanoes pierce different types of basement rocks and crustal structure. The method of producing andesite magmas, therefore, had yet to be discovered.

Gerald Wasserburg of the California Institute of Technology developed an improved mass spectrometer that allowed precise isotopic measurement and radiometric age determination. Precision was improved 10 to 20 times, permitting better measurement of rock ages. As a result, it should be possible to work with many geologic materials that were previously undatable.

—John M. Dennison

Geophysics

Earthquakes threatening to plunge large tracts of land into the ocean, whole continents drifting apart at the rate of several centimeters a year—these were among the more crucial problems that geophysicists studied during 1968 and 1969. Joining with geophysicists to observe and analyze the intricate interactions between earth and water, earth and land, and earth and air were seismologists, oceanographers, geologists, and meteorologists. Their discoveries established the trends that were expected to continue into the 1970s.

New advances in geophysics were the result of the development of more sophisticated investigative instruments and the increased availability of computers to organize data and to program statistics of the geological features at the earth's surface. By using computers and new instruments, the international Upper Mantle Project (UMP), which began in 1962, demonstrated that the earth was not simply a radially inhomogeneous sphere in which the structure and composition of each layer was nonuniform, but that each layer was also internally inhomogeneous. It also became clear that the upper parts of the earth were constantly undergoing large-scale motions. Moreover, there seemed to be a definite link between these motions and the internal variations in structure and composition of the upper mantle—each being the mechanism for the other.

Geomagnetism. The reasons were not clear for the dynamic interactions in the interior of the earth that were demonstrated by the two above-mentioned phenomena. It was clear, however, that the earth's crust is highly mobile and that this mobility cannot be attributed to forces originating at or above the surface. The vertical movements of the layers appeared to be caused by the accumulation of sediment within the continental blocks (the land masses) and around their margins (the coasts). The marginal areas were especially inter-

Based on the work by Tom Cardamone for *Fortune*, "Ocean Floor Spreading," based on the work of Walter C. Pitman, Lamont Observatory

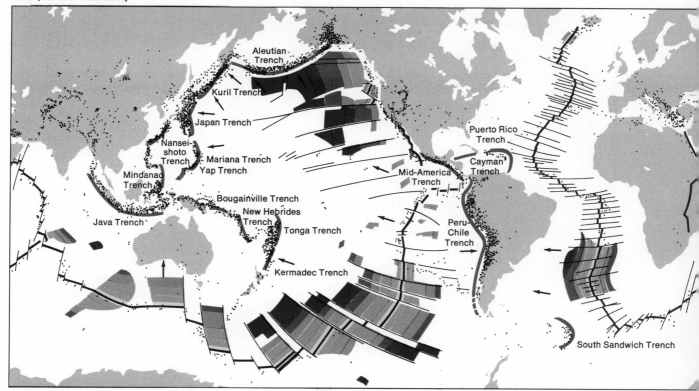

Ocean-floor spreading during geological periods

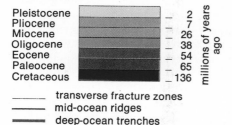

	millions of years ago
Pleistocene	2
Pliocene	7
Miocene	26
Oligocene	38
Eocene	54
Paleocene	65
Cretaceous	136

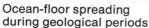

—————— transverse fracture zones
—————— mid-ocean ridges
══════ deep-ocean trenches
⁓⁓⁓⁓ earthquake epicenters 1961–67

New crust, as it arises out of the mid-ocean ridges, forces the old crust outward. By using magnetometers, scientists were able to determine the relative age of the crust according to its distance from the ridge. (Each color band in the chart depicts a geological period.) The deep-ocean trenches (heavy black lines) that lie around the edges of the Pacific Ocean are the sites of the most powerful earthquakes. Smaller earthquakes sometimes erupt at the ocean ridges. Each dot represents an earthquake shock recorded between 1961 and 1967. The floor of the Pacific appears to be the stage for most of the disruptive activity.

esting because the thick sedimentary deposits that accumulated along many of them in the past had been heated and deformed and converted into mountain systems. Because the deformed sediments occupied less surface space than when they were initially deposited, it was first postulated that the earth was shrinking.

In the 1950s, however, a new line of thinking took over. Geophysicists discovered that the mid-ocean ridge system was a continuous tectonic feature (a force that deformed the earth's crust) over 60,000 km long and covering an area equal in size to that of all the continents. The features associated with the ridge and with its landward extensions in Iceland, East Africa, and western North and Central America led to an expanding earth hypothesis. This, of course, was in direct

conflict with the shrinking earth theory, especially since it was necessary that both expanding and contracting forces be called upon simultaneously to explain the same observed features.

In the 1960s a solution to the dilemma was proposed. It had been suggested earlier, on the basis of studies of the magnetism of Icelandic lavas, that the earth's magnetic field had reversed itself periodically over the course of geologic time. In the presence of the earth's magnetic field, the lava stones became magnetized as they cooled from their molten state at the edge of the oceanic ridge and before they were pushed away from the ridge by new lava flowing up through the opening. By using magnetometers to determine whether the magnetization acquired by the minerals within a particular lava bed was in the same

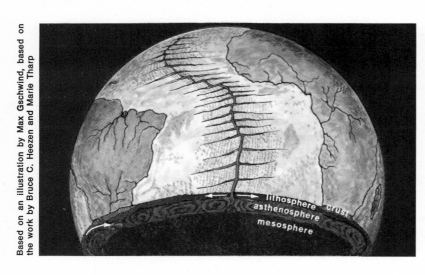

A cross section of a segment of the earth illustrates recent geophysical theories. As hot material rises up from the asthenosphere and passes through the ridge opening in the lithosphere, the lithosphere plates move slowly away from the ridge, causing cracks to appear on the earth's crust. Trenches, like the Peru-Chile Trench (lower left), are formed when a continent is forced back over a lithosphere plate, driving it under the landmass. Scientists believe that this friction has helped to create mountain ranges like the Andes.

direction as the earth's at the time of measurement (a positive reading), or whether it was reversed (a negative reading), Fredrick J. Vine and Drummond H. Matthews discovered many local magnetic variations (anomalies) all over the earth's surface. They hypothesized that the positive and negative magnetic variations might be caused by the particular location of the rocks at the time of their exposure to the earth's magnetic field. If true, this theory would throw some doubt on a previous hypothesis that the composition of a rock, rather than its location, was the cause of its particular magnetic imprint.

It was then found by many investigators that the ocean ridges were marked by a long linear pattern of magnetic anomalies that fanned away from the ridges in a symmetrical manner. By studying young lavas from many parts of the world, Allan V. Cox, Richard Doell, and G. Brent Dalrymple established a time scale for the reversals of the earth's magnetic field during the past four million years, correlating the linear anomaly pattern with their time scale. It was suggested that each positive or negative variation resulted from the exposure of the lava to different magnetic fields, reflecting either the normal or reversed situation of the earth at the time of exposure. Because young lavas are frequently found at the centers of the ridges, it was concluded that the positive magnetic anomaly over the center represented the present epoch of normal magnetization, and the pattern of positive and negative anomalies on the flanks of the ridge represented earlier periods in the history of a reversing magnetic field. Although earthquake activity in this epoch has been confined to the centers of the ridges, the exact link between ridge systems and earthquakes had not been determined.

In any case, the crustal rocks increase in age according to their distance from the center of the ridge. Recent drilling in the deep ocean confirmed this, yielding ages for the crustal rocks that are in remarkable agreement with the ages predicted on the basis of magnetic anomaly analysis (see Year in Review: OCEANOGRAPHY).

The shifting earth. The flow of lava, which creates new crust at the centers of the oceanic ridges, coupled with the lateral movement of the older crust, resulted in a massive space problem. Either the earth had to expand to ease the pressure, or the old crust must disintegrate in some manner. In regard to the Atlantic Ocean the continental drift theory provided an explanation, and it became widely accepted that Europe and Africa were separating from North and South America at the same rate as new crust was forming along the ridge.

In the Pacific, however, such was not the case. Most of the large earthquakes that occur each year are located either along the axes of the ocean ridges or along a belt that extends around the margins of the Pacific and from the Himalayas to the Alps. All of the intermediate and deep-focus earthquakes (earthquakes that break at the fault deeper than 44 mi) occur along the Pacific belt. In their studies of shallow and deep-focus earthquakes along this belt, Jack Oliver, Lynn R. Sykes, and Bryan L. Isacks concluded that the lithosphere (the earth's crust) is being thrust beneath the island arcs and continental margins to depths of about 435 mi. This underthrusting, which seemed to be linked somehow with the earthquake phenomenon, provided the mechanism for disposing of the excess crust created along the ridges. For some yet unknown reason, underthrusting occurs primarily in the regions where active mountain building is taking place.

—Charles L. Drake

See also Feature Article: NATURE ON THE RAMPAGE.

Education, Science

Throughout the past year, the main concerns of science education continued to center on curriculum development, evaluation of student achievement, integration of all the sciences for teaching purposes, training for the teaching of new curriculum projects, and increased cooperation among science educators of all nations. In the U.S., especially, there was emphasis on the special needs of science students in ghetto and poverty areas, the proper education of students about drugs and drug abuse, and the question of how best to provide sex education. The reduction of funds for such financially supportive organizations as the National Science Foundation (NSF) and the U.S. Office of Education threatened to affect science education at all levels. (*See* Year in Review: SCIENCE, GENERAL.)

International activities. The integration of science teaching was a major concern of UNESCO's Division of Science Teaching during the year. An international conference on this topic was held in Varna, Bulg., during September 1968 under the sponsorship of the Commission de l'Enseigne-

ment des Sciences, and a detailed report was to be issued late in 1969.

Harold Foecke, formerly with the U.S. Office of Education, was named as the new director of the Division of Science Teaching. A new position of regional coordinator for Asia was established, with the main office in Bangkok, Thailand. Bangkok was also headquarters for the UNESCO Project on High School Chemistry Teaching, which during the year completed a textbook, a teacher's manual, and a teaching kit. The UNESCO curriculum projects in mathematics and biology also released new materials.

The ferment in science curriculum development during the past few years had resulted in the identification and production of a large amount of inexpensive equipment. Much of this work had been done in the U.S., but it was evident that such equipment would have tremendous value in the less developed nations. Accordingly, the U.S. Agency for International Development was supporting a two-year study at the International Clearinghouse on Science and Mathematics Curricular Development, located at the University of Maryland, to produce a guidebook on improvising

Head of ancient Peking Man forms the cover design of a Biological Sciences Curriculum Study Chinese-language textbook. The Rocky Mountain deer and the plum flower symbolize the American and Chinese cultures, while the three plants represent friendship enduring under difficult conditions.

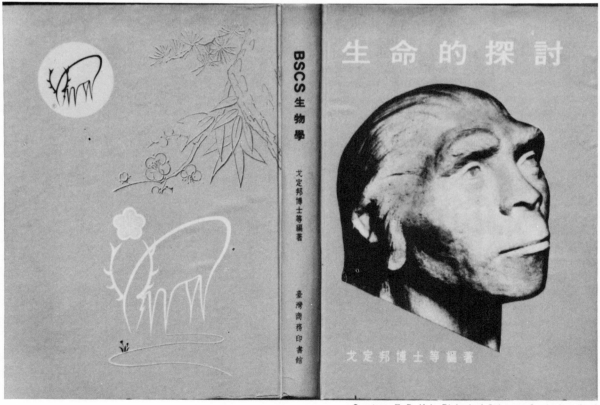

Courtesy, T. P. Koh, Biological Sciences Curriculum Study

Courtesy, Ford Foundation

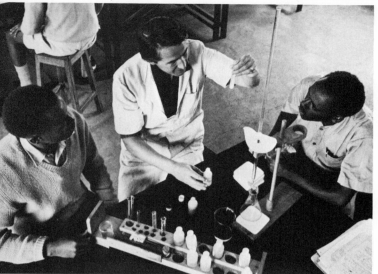

Chemistry students watch a demonstration at Alliance High School, Kikuyu, Kenya's leading secondary school. Science courses at the school were set up with the assistance of the Ford Foundation in a program designed to expand and modernize Kenya's science education facilities at the secondary level.

science equipment for student investigations. When completed, it would be distributed throughout the world. A related document was produced during the year by a Peace Corps group in India.

Curriculum development. The sixth annual report of the International Clearinghouse, released during the summer of 1968, summarized the work of over 100 non-U.S. and 225 U.S. projects in science and mathematics curriculum development. All the U.S. projects had felt the effect of tightened federal budgets, with the most serious cutbacks coming in the vital area of project evaluation.

Almost all the projects used a "package" approach, in which they developed not only text-type materials for students and handbooks for teachers, but also such supplementary materials as films, film loops, and overhead transparencies. In some cases computer-assisted instruction constituted an important facet of the work.

Since the first major attempts at modern science curriculum development had begun in the mid-1950s, many outstanding projects had been initiated. Among the earliest of these was the Physical Science Study Committee, which by the late 1960s had completed a second edition of its text for high school physics students and had turned its attention to advanced high school and college physics, junior high school introductory physical science, and science in the elementary schools. The original text and teacher's manual

by another pioneering project, the Chemical Education Material Study, had been revised by three separate groups. The Biological Sciences Curriculum Study produced second editions of its three high school biology texts.

Following the pattern of these early groups, in which scientists, science educators, and science teachers worked together, were numerous other curriculum development projects on a variety of subjects. At the senior high school level these included, among others, (formerly Harvard) Project Physics (with emphasis on physics for the general student), the Engineering Concepts Curriculum Project, the Anthropology Curriculum Study Project, and the High School Geography Project. At the junior high school level the emphasis was on integration, as in the Introductory Physical Science course, combining physics and chemistry; the Earth Science Curriculum Project; and the Secondary School Science Project, an interdisciplinary physical science course.

There was activity in the lower grades as well. The American Association for the Advancement of Science completed its "Science—A Process Approach," which provided teaching materials for

Elementary school children learn the effects of heating and cooling on various materials as part of the Elementary Science Study program, developed by the Education Development Center, Inc., Newton, Mass. Formed in 1967, the center works closely with schools and colleges in formulating new curricula.

Courtesy, Education Development Center

kindergarten through sixth grade. The Conceptual Orientation Project for Elementary Schools continued to write materials around selected "great ideas" in science, while the Elementary Science Study developed a number of science units with such titles as "Kitchen Physics," "Mystery Powders," and "Microgardening."

Special training programs for classroom teachers were considered essential for new curriculum implementation. The NSF continued to furnish funds to institutions of higher learning for the establishment of institutes and workshops, but it was obvious that not all classroom teachers could be reached with the limited funds available. To fill this gap, conferences for science supervisors were being developed, designed to prepare supervisors to train their staff members locally.

Professional organizations. The year 1969 marked the 25th anniversary of the founding of the National Science Teachers Association (NSTA), the "science arm" of the National Education Association. In addition to its convention in Dallas, Tex., in March, the NSTA held 10 regional conventions and 120 special silver anniversary meetings sponsored by local groups. To complement its publications *Science and Children* for elementary school teachers and *The Science Teacher* for high school faculty, the NSTA planned to sponsor a journal on science teaching for college professors. During the year the NSTA received funds from the National Institute of Mental Health for the purpose of developing teaching materials and workshops on drugs and drug abuse.

The NSF again furnished funds to the National Association of Biology Teachers to hold a number of three-day regional conferences for selected biology instructors. At these sessions, outstanding biologists presented their latest findings at a level that could be interpreted easily by the teachers.

—J(ohn) David Lockard

Electronics

Since the early 1960s the scientific community has been predicting the imminent conclusion of a decade of electronic revolution. This "end" was still being predicted in 1969, and was still just as elusive.

There was, however, ample reason to describe the years 1958 to 1968 as revolutionary. Of the ten fastest growing industries in the U.S. during this period, five were in the electronics field: the computer industry led the list with a phenomenal growth of 511%; close behind it was the cathode-ray tube industry with a 460% growth; and in third

"There's no denying the profound impact all this has on the course of human life, but let's never forget one thing. It's still love that makes the world go round."
—Weber © 1969 the New Yorker Magazine, Inc.

place was the semiconductor industry with a 284% growth.

Semiconductors

During 1968 and 1969 the branch of electronics which experienced the greatest technological advancement was probably the semiconductor industry, although these advancements were evolutionary, rather than revolutionary, in nature.

The evolution began after World War II, when three scientists at the Bell Telephone Laboratories developed the transistor. This device, functionally equivalent to the vacuum tube, had most of the advantages of its predecessor and few of the disadvantages. From the consumer viewpoint, its greatest attribute was its small size. To industry, however, its long life, speed of operation, high reliability, low cost, and ease of packaging were of equal importance. It was paradoxical that those very characteristics which made the transistor superior to the vacuum tube were the same ones that were being further improved upon by the development of integrated circuits (IC's) and large-scale integration systems (LSI's).

IC's. The advent in the early 1960s of the monolithic integrated circuit (a collection of semi-

Electronics

antcOR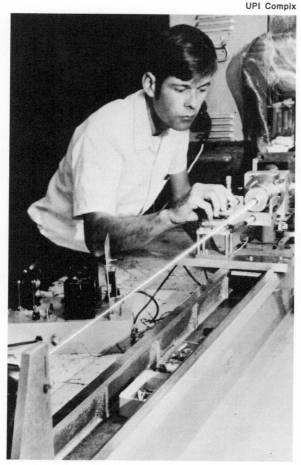

The first device that can generate continuous visible laser beams at varying wavelengths is tested at Stanford University, where it was developed. Light beams are passed from an argon source through a heated lithium niobate crystal by means of a lens and mirror system; changing the temperature of the crystal allows the laser to be "tuned" to any color from infrared to green-blue.

conductor circuitry—resistors, capacitors, diodes, and transistors—manufactured as one circuit in a single-crystal chip of silicon semiconductor) was both an offshoot of the manufacturing techniques used for transistors and an economic necessity. The growing computer industry, made possible by the invention of the transistor, was turning out machines so complex that "the tyranny of numbers" was fast becoming a problem. There were too many wires, too many soldered connections, and too many devices; and each was a potential trouble spot.

International Business Machines (IBM) was one of the first companies to use IC's in quantity in one of their computer systems. However, because monolithic integrated circuits failed to solve completely the problem of circuit element inter-

action, IBM chose to use what was called "hybrid" integrated circuits. In such circuits the components were physically separate, therefore eliminating any circuit element interaction. After portions of the circuits were fabricated, tiny discrete electronic components were then added.

Changes in the methods of making integrated circuits came about primarily in the processes for manufacturing monolithic IC's. Because the construction of these "microchips" was extremely complex, it was much more difficult to eliminate some of the procedural difficulties in the monolithic than in the hybrid IC's. For instance, in the epitaxial growth method (the deposition of one crystal on the surface of another), a slice of substrate (the paper-thin silicon wafer that serves as the base for IC's) goes back and forth between the photoresist room and the diffusion room as many as eight times while various chemical and mechanical operations are performed on it. From the oxidation process (which coats the epitaxial layer to protect it from contamination), the substrate and epitaxial layer are transferred to the photoresist room for another chemical coating, and then to the various etching processes, and back again, over and over until there is a uniform and precise pattern in the base region. The only feature which made this process economically justifiable was the fact that it could be accomplished simultaneously on thousands of identical circuits, each an exact photographic duplicate of the next.

A controversial subject in electronics involved the method by which these individual circuits (each smaller than the letter "o" on this page) were mounted in and connected to the leads of a conventional integrated circuit package. The conventional method for completing these connections (called thermocompression bonding) was to attach a number of wires (normally 14) to pads on the IC, either at high temperature or with ultrasonic energy. Because the wire used was about ⅓ the thickness of a human hair, this entire process had to be accomplished under a microscope; naturally such a process resulted in many rejects. Two processes competing to replace this method were the "flip-chip" technique and the "beam-lead" technique, neither of which required any wires. In the beam-lead technique the separation of the various chips was accomplished by chemical etching, and the chips were fastened to the substrate face up. In the flip-chip technique a diamond scribe was to separate and break the chips, after which they were fastened to the substrate face down.

LSI. The electronics industry had barely become used to the idea of integrated circuits when the concept of large-scale integration (LSI) made its appearance. Although the LSI circuit was hardly more than an extension of the integrated circuit, the difference was great and the problems in its manufacture and use were magnified. An IC is a circuit consisting of up to 20 transistors and diodes on a microscopic chip of silicon, but an LSI is a circuit consisting of literally 1,000 devices, properly combined in a circuit, on a tiny chip of silicon about ⅛ in. square. Many years of research were being committed to the process, and before 1980 the influence of LSI's should be felt in industrial and commercial applications throughout the world.

Other solid-state devices. Although the commercial implications of IC's and LSI's exceeded those of other semiconductor devices, work proceeded in other areas of solid-state research. For instance, the capability of gallium arsenide to generate microwave energy directly was found to have interesting possibilities. Such a device, called the Gunn oscillator after its discoverer, J. B. Gunn, could conceivably be used for personal radar, for communications equipment, and even for burglar alarms. Before gallium arsenide, it had been necessary to use large electron tubes, called klystrons, to generate microwave energy. During 1968 and 1969, however, several scientists from General Electric demonstrated that gallium

arsenide diodes could be effectively linked in series, thereby pushing the system out of the milliwatt range, and perhaps well up into the kilowatt range. (*See* Year in Review: PHYSICS, *Solid-State Physics*.)

Even the traditional silicon-controlled rectifier (SCR) underwent some changes. An SCR capable of operating at a frequency as high as 30 KHz (one Hertz equals one cycle per second), without causing destruction due to high inrush current, was developed recently.

Consumer Electronics. Electronic applications in the home approximately doubled between 1966 and 1969, and sales of electronic appliances reached $6 billion per year. Although there were obvious IC applications in hearing aids, intercoms, and automotive accessories, semiconductor circuits were also used in equipment for which they had never before even been considered. For instance, there was a rush among television manufacturers to use IC's in their sets. The Columbia Broadcasting System developed a portable and wireless television camera capable of transmitting its signal several miles. The entire unit weighed only 32 lb, half of which was the weight of a self-contained battery. One manufacturer of food blenders used IC's to eliminate pushbuttons and switches; a user simply had to touch a small plate in order to change the speed

An engineer stands in front of a device that records television images on a magnetic disk. Flicker-free images can then be transmitted to a user's television set at a rate of 30 frames per second. The disk can store 32 images at one time.

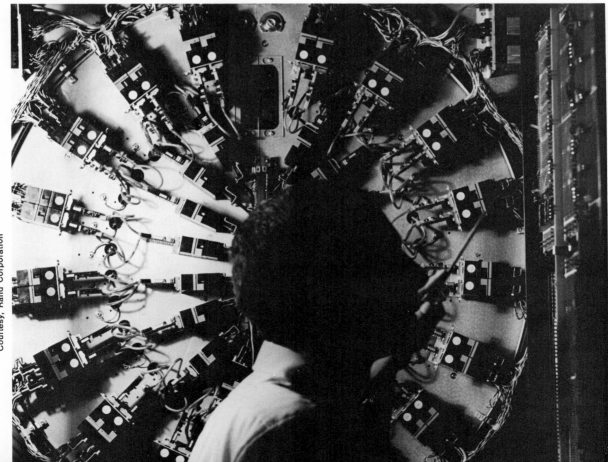

(a practical utilization of body capacitance). The U.S. Post Office Department made a major effort to develop address encoding and reading equipment. This system was expected to reduce significantly the number of times mail is manually sorted.

Many teenagers derived benefits from electronic technology in the form of the multitude of amplifiers associated with their ever-present music. Multiple microphones and speakers, along with the internal microphones on guitars, amplified sound to levels as high as 120 db—a level equivalent to a jet airplane 100 ft away. And not only were electronic devices used to amplify sound, they were also used to "treat" it. For instance, a device which produced an effect called "fuzz tone" would distort a beautifully amplified sine wave (a wave whose displacement is the sine or cosine of an angle proportional to time or distance or both) by deleting every other cycle. This, of course, introduced harmonics which systematically modified the traditional sound.

Electronic memory systems

New techniques were developed which were eventually expected to replace the magnetic ferrite core traditionally used for computer memory systems. These new techniques applied to the static systems used by virtually all computers, and did not involve the electromechanical rotating memories. Drums and discs continued to be used for the latter, and it did not seem likely that they would be replaced or made obsolete for many years. In the area of static—or all-electronic—memories, several potentially feasible techniques were developed. They included thin-film memories, plated wire memories, and semiconductor memories. Each time one of those types was improved and refined, however, a new discovery was made which boosted the speed and performance of magnetic ferrite cores and lowered their cost.

In the early days of computer development, the thousands of doughnut-shaped magnetic cores (literally millions in larger computers) resembled a vast quantity of "Cheerios" breakfast cereal. But this image changed as the size of the cores was reduced. Researchers on high-speed computers began using 22-mil (1 mil = 0.001 in.) cores, and one manufacturer even considered the use of 12-mil cores. The 22-mil core was so small that a piece of table salt could not fit through the hole, yet three and, in some cases, four wires were passed through these cores to form memory systems. With the old 100-mil cores, the switching time was several microseconds (1 μsec = 0.000-001 sec); this was reduced to as little as 140 nsec (1 nsec = 10^{-9} sec) with the smaller cores.

One of the possible successors to the magnetic core was the planar thin-film memory. This method promised more speed and shorter access time than any other technology available. Furthermore, its power consumption was considerably lower than that of many other methods, and was definitely lower than several of the magnetic core memory configurations. But as of 1969, it had not been sufficiently developed to be widely used.

A second contender in the memory field was the plated wire memory. In this system the basic storage element was an extremely thin conductive wire coated with magnetic film. The wire was sandwiched between the surfaces of a printed circuit board and then "stacked" with others to complete a finished memory array. Although the manufacturing of this plated wire was tremendously complex, the finished product was quite simple—only one wire, rather than thousands of magnetic cores, made up a portion of the system. This memory device was better than the magnetic core memory because of its nondestructive readout capabilities. (In magnetic cores the readout process, a pulse applied to the binary memory cells to ascertain which cells contain information units, "destroys" the information stored in the cells, making it necessary to reinstate this information—not an impossible task, but a time-consuming one.)

The greatest limiting factor in the use of plated wire was its high cost. Even the most successful application of plated wire memories resulted in a cost increase for the memory system of at least three times that of magnetic cores. The price differential, however, was reduced somewhat, and the plated wire memory seemed likely to gain wider use.

The development of the semiconductor memory reached a significant point in 1968 and 1969. The advent of LSI's and the improvement of semiconductor technology led some scientists to predict that by 1975 all computers would contain at least one semiconductor memory. Some companies established divisions devoted exclusively to this technology.

Lasers

Throughout 1968 and 1969 there were continued advances in laser (light amplification by the stimulated emission of radiation) technology. Because lasers produce coherent light (the beams are polarized and monochromatic), they have been extremely valuable in industry, measurements, medicine, and, ultimately, communications.

One of the most successful accomplishments of recent laser research was the development of a device which permitted the user to "see" through extreme fog, heavy rain, or blizzards. The primary principle employed in this device was the elimination of backscatter (the reflection of light off the particles between the viewer and the object viewed). It had long been realized that backscatter is instrumental in reducing the ability of the viewer to "see." In the laser radar system, a gating pulse (a pulse which transmits signals in a selected fraction of the principal time interval) is delivered to the apparatus at such a time that the laser light from the object being viewed is expected to be reflected back. Therefore, the light being reflected from undesired particles is not passed on to the viewer. Following the production of a lightweight device of this sort, a much larger equivalent was developed for underwater viewing from submarines. A somewhat similar laser device was used by a few airports. This product made it possible to determine accurately the level of visibility at the runway. This instrument also served as an air pollution monitor by measuring the amount of contaminants in the atmosphere.

The laser also began to be used by surgeons to cut tissue without drawing blood and to "weld" detached retinas in eye surgery; by engineers to vaporize the edges of IC's and to weld the wires within transistors; and by builders to align tunnels and bridges.

Possibly the greatest potential use of lasers is in communications systems that would be able to carry an untold number of telephone conversations, simultaneously, between two points. Several companies, including General Telephone and Bell Telephone, committed large amounts of money for research along these lines. Lockheed Missiles & Space Co. also undertook research in this area, emphasizing, however, satellite communication.

—Robert E. Stoffels

See also Year in Review: COMMUNICATIONS; COMPUTERS.

Engineering

Chemical engineering

The most noteworthy activities in chemical engineering during the past year were those that recognized human needs for pure water, nourishing food, and clean air. There were bioengineering advances in the search for a man-made heart and in the treatment of severe burn and shock patients. In the fields of style and comfort there were glamorous new synthetic fibers and unusual fabrics.

Pure water from seawater. Fresh, pure water, long an elusive goal for much of the world, was closer to becoming a reality for water-starved areas in Texas, southern California, Spain, Mexico, Kuwait, Hong Kong, and Italy. This was a result of important water-desalting projects announced during recent months. Most surprising, however, was a setback, the cancellation of the much-publicized 150-million-gallon-a-day Bolsa Island seawater desalting project planned for a 43-ac man-made Pacific island near Los Angeles. The project, whose nuclear power plant was to generate 1,800 Mw of electricity, succumbed to rising costs. When first proposed several years ago, the project cost was estimated at $444 million, but by 1969 it had risen to $765 million.

Other desalting projects moved ahead, however. The U.S. and Mexico planned a series of huge combination electric-power and water-desalting plants to provide fresh water to the arid southwest U.S. and Mexico. A series of billion-gallon-a-day desalting plants powered by nuclear reactors were to be located along the upper area of the Gulf of California. The first, to cost about $1 billion, was planned for the late 1970s.

At Roswell, N.M., the U.S. Department of the Interior's Office of Saline Water (OSW) planned to build a test-treating unit for brackish (low-salt content) water. An OSW official also anticipated desalting plants for both Kuwait and Hong Kong in the near future. A $7-million, 7.5-million-gallon-a-day desalting facility was under construction near Tijuana, Mex.

Chemical plants, hungry for water that they needed in their manufacturing processes, announced that they were building desalting units. A 2.5-million-gallon-a-day system was to be built in Brindisi, Italy, for Montecatini-Edison's petrochemical plant. Near Brownsville, Tex., Union Carbide Corp. planned to build a 288,000-gallon-a-day desalting unit. In Spain the U.S. was to build a 70,000-gallon-a-day desalting plant at Palomares, the first such unit in that country.

Meanwhile, desalting research continued at a brisk pace. Among the methods creating the most interest were flash distillation and reverse osmosis. The former evaporates water away from its salty contents; the latter depends on the same type of process that controls many body functions—a special membrane through which salt-free water is passed.

Food for the starving. By 1970 more than 70% of the world's population will live in major diet-deficient areas: Central and South America, Africa, Asia, India, and Communist China. Petroleum and chemical companies were among those working to narrow the "protein gap" that will exist in those regions. Proteins from petroleum (petroproteins) are made from gaseous methane (natural gas) or liquid petroleum fractions that are fermented by special microorganisms to form proteins. But, at present, the costs involved in such a process are excessive.

Fish protein concentrate (FPC) is a second approach to feeding the world's hungry populations. FPC is on the verge of worldwide mass production except in the U.S. In Sweden the Astra Corp. was building a 3,000-ton-a-year FPC plant at Bua on the west coast. Oceanic Development Corp. of Houston, Tex., was building a 200-ton-a-day FPC plant in Peru. Other upcoming projects included an FPC plant in Nova Scotia by a Hooker Chemical Corp. affiliate, and an installation on Vancouver Island by Protein Concentrates Ltd. In the U.S., however, Food and Drug Administration (FDA) restrictions blocked wide-scale commercial introduction of FPC.

In other developments concerning food Japanese researchers reported that gamma-ray irradiation had produced a mutated strain of rice with double the normal amount of protein. In the U.S. the Atomic Energy Commission used irradiation to make rice more disease-resistant. On the negative side, the FDA ruled that the U.S. Army could not use radiation-preserved canned ham; tests had revealed that animals fed irradiated pork had fewer offspring. Bacon also joined the prohibited list, leaving only white potatoes, wheat, and wheat flour approved for radiation processing.

The du Pont company found a way to freeze food by direct contact with Freon refrigerant gas. This process maintained a high food quality because of the speed with which the freezing took place—only a few seconds for french fried potatoes. The U.S. Department of Agriculture (USDA) branch in Albany, Calif., was experimenting with a method of preserve-drying foods that did not result in the usual damage to texture, particularly in regard to meat and fish. Loose water was withdrawn by osmosis (*see* above) through edible membranes, but bound water (chemically held) was left in place. Also in Albany, the USDA developed a chemical potato peeler. Potatoes were sprayed with hot lye and then tumbled inside a perforated drum while exposed to infrared heat. The small amount of remaining skin was taken off by rotating rolls and brush-washing.

The quest for clean air. In Los Angeles smog-conscious officials asked for legislation against jet-aircraft smoke plumes. The U.S. Federal Aviation Administration and the Society of Automotive Engineers began a program to measure pollutants in jet-engine exhausts. Across the Pacific worried Japanese officials suggested a slowdown by petroleum refineries, steel plants, and power stations to reduce air pollution.

Reacting to stiff new U.S. air pollution laws aimed at sulfur dioxide emissions by industry, chemical engineers helped develop new flue-gas cleanup processes; at Union Electric's Meramec, Mo., power plant, Combustion Engineering, Inc., put its new process to work in which sulfur-containing stack gases are wet-scrubbed in a slurry of calcined limestone; construction began on a unit to recover sulfur from iron-ore roaster gases at Sudbury, Ont., using an Allied Chemical Corp. process; United International Research Inc. of Long Island City, N.Y., announced a catalytic oxidation process to make weak sulfuric acid from sulfur dioxide fumes; Monsanto Co. unveiled its new "Cat-Ox" process to oxidize sulfur dioxide in power-plant flue gases, after which the resulting sulfur trioxide would be absorbed in water to produce salable sulfuric acid. Meanwhile, the U.S. government sponsored a $443.9-million sulfur oxides research and development program to extend past 1972.

Outside the U.S. antipollution laws were also getting tougher. New sulfur dioxide removal processes were developed, and older ones were honed to greater efficiency. Ten major Japanese companies had sulfur dioxide control processes either operating or under construction. In West Germany there were four such major company projects, and one each in the United Kingdom and France.

Waste disposal dilemma. What to do about the ever-increasing amounts of liquid and solid wastes generated by expanding industry and a growing population was a problem of mounting concern. The Franklin Research Laboratories in Philadelphia proposed a pipeline from Trenton, N.J., to extend 80 mi into the Atlantic Ocean. Industrial plants along the line would feed hard-to-handle liquid wastes into the pipeline, thereby protecting the waters of the Delaware River Basin.

Trouble surfaced in the Soviet Union's Caspian Sea, the world's largest inland body of water. Soviet officials mounted a campaign to stop pollution of the Caspian, with emphasis on nearby oil wells that were spilling into the sea. Oil pollution struck the U.S. too. A gigantic oil slick appeared off the southern California shore when Union Oil Co. drillers were unable to stanch the flow of oil at its offshore drilling site near Santa Barbara. Chemical dispersants and log-boom barriers were among the methods used to try to control the spreading oil. The well was finally blocked by forcing mud into the shaft.

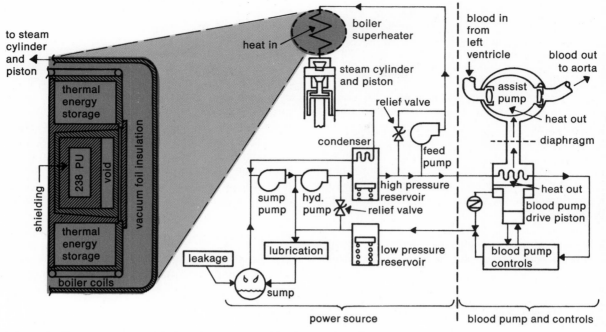

Schematic diagram of proposed plutonium-powered blood pump for a human heart.

A major conflict shaped up between pollution-control advocates and those who used nitrogenous fertilizers (ammonia, ammonium nitrate, urea). Barry Commoner of Washington University, St. Louis, Mo., charged that nitrates from those fertilizers could degrade into nitrites by bacterial or enzymatic action before (or even after) the nitrates enter the human body along with the foods they once fertilized. Such nitrites could destroy the oxygen-carrying power of the blood, causing asphyxiation and possible death by methemoglobinemia. The danger, said Commoner, was particularly great in baby-food spinach, though no cases of methemoglobinemia were reported in the U.S. The USDA, which was monitoring the situation, decided that there was no great threat to health. The Tennessee Valley Authority, however, which was active in fertilizer manufacture and research, began to study the possible danger from nitrates.

Used plastic articles were a worldwide problem. They do not decompose under ordinary conditions, and burning them causes air pollution. In Britain, the Society of Chemical Industry was studying the problem, while in the U.S. the Department of Health, Education, and Welfare awarded a $100,000 contract to TRW Inc. of Redondo Beach, Calif., to develop a chemical method to dispose of plastics—without polluting the air.

Bioengineering and man-made hearts. Cooperation between chemical engineers and medical researchers grew in recent months. The engineering principles used in giant oil refineries and chemical plants were found to apply equally well to artificial heart work. In Houston, Tex., over the 1969 Easter weekend, a mechanical heart with an external power supply kept a male patient alive for 60 hours, while physicians waited for a suitable human heart for transplantation. The patient died 30 hours after the transplant, but the mechanical heart was judged to be a success.

There was much to be done, however, before the cumbersome affair used at Houston could be miniaturized and implanted within a human body. Blood pumps were needed to move blood through the body's arterial and venous systems. At Britain's National Institute for Medical Research, a simple biomedical pump was made out of vibrating plastic pipes. Based on a U.S.-discovered principle, a flexible pipe is connected to a more rigid segment and then vibrated near the junction, thus pumping fluid through the pipe. The pump worked with a gentle push and did not damage blood cells.

To provide the energy needed to power the blood pump, researchers have been considering radioactive plutonium-238. Decaying plutonium generates steam to run a single-cylinder steam engine, which, in turn, operates the blood pump. Sixty grams of plutonium-238 would run the pump for 90 years. The problem with this device is to protect the body from radiation-induced leukemia. Another power source under study is an electricity-generating biological fuel cell, basically the same as the hydrogen-oxygen fuel cells that provide auxiliary power aboard the Apollo space ships. In the body, glucose (sugar) and oxygen from the blood react in a mechanical cell to generate electricity. More research is needed, however, before biological fuel cells are ready for body implantation.

One major unsolved problem was the control system in a mechanical heart. Venous and arterial pressures and blood flow rates must be measured and the signals sent back to a control center that will regulate the speed of pumping. Such an apparatus will be, in essence, a miniature computer. But first, methods for pressure and flow rate measurement must be devised for use within the human body.

Chemical engineering and medicine. Severe burn and shock patients have benefited from a chemical engineer–physician team at the Columbia-Presbyterian Medical Center in New York City. Patients are treated as though they were small-scale chemical plants, complete with raw-material intake, chemical reactors, and product output.

Fifty critically ill patients have already been treated by this team. The hospital personnel carefully prepare and analyze the patients' intake of drugs and food to determine their basic components. Excreta are similarly analyzed and recorded. In addition to the standard blood chemistries, temperature readings, and pulse tests performed by nurses and technicians, the patients' rooms are designed to measure and record heat and weight losses or gains, glucose metabolism, and respiration.

For metabolic studies a patient is injected with carbon-14 (a radioisotope)-tagged glucose. The subject's head is placed inside a transparent plastic canopy into which air of controlled temperature and humidity is blown. Air exhaled by the patient is then caught and analyzed. The measurements, in turn, are sent to a computerized data-processing center, where up-to-the-minute tables and graphs concerning a patient's condition are calculated and then compared with previously established standards.

Man-made fibers. A major segment of the chemical industry for which chemical engineers make important contributions is synthetic fibers. The past year saw a number of developments in both fibers and fabrics—in particular, man-made silks.

Du Pont announced its new synthetic silk fiber, the polyamide-based Qiana. Said to be wrinkle-resistant and light, with durability, crease- and pleat-retention, and dyeability, the fiber was expected to be used first in high-quality women's apparel. Allied Chemical's synthetic silk fiber, a polyamide called Source, was made available for luxury carpets and would soon be found in luxury apparel.

In Japan the Toyobo firm planned to produce a silklike synthetic called K6. It was said to be the first commercial fiber made from a combination of a synthetic material (acrylonitrile) and a natural substance (protein from milk casein). K6 resists acids and alkalies and does not water stain, but it was not considered a wash-and-wear fabric. It was scheduled to be introduced late in 1969 for kimonos and high-quality Western clothing.

—Robert L. Davidson

Civil engineering

Winner of the Outstanding Achievement Award of the American Society of Civil Engineers for 1969 was the Oroville Dam and Edward Hyatt Power Plant, in northern California. Five other major projects won nominations for the award, granted annually by the 117-year-old society. Although several other civil-engineering works made headlines around the world in 1968–69, less conspicuous, but perhaps even more significant, were new developments in low-cost housing technology.

The Oroville Dam. Rising 770 ft above the turbulent Feather River, Oroville was the highest of any dam in the Western Hemisphere and would also be the highest earthfill dam in the world until completion of the Soviet Union's Nurek Dam. Its 80 million cu ft of embankment made Oroville the third largest in the world in volume (behind Fort Peck Dam, Mont., and Oahe Dam, S.D.). Also, owing to the distance of the dam from the area where the materials for its construction were taken, Oroville's engineers achieved the world's record for earth-moving. A 668-ton digging wheel, self-propelled traveling hopper cars, and a 7,000-ft conveyor belt were among the massive tools with which the impervious core material and the earth and rock fill for the dam were dug and delivered from distances ranging from 7 to 13 mi away.

Besides its record for ton-miles of earth-moving, Oroville boasted a number of unique or unusual features, including its provision for control of the temperature of released water, and the reinforced rock arch for its power-plant machine hall. Among contributions to dam engineering developed at Oroville was the determination of stresses in the rock mass at the site of the dam.

Apart from its primary functions to store and conserve water and to generate power, Oroville was designed to serve such important secondary purposes as flood control, the suppression of salinization of water, and the providing of recreational facilities. Lake Oroville's 15,000 ac of water and 165 mi of shoreline, with eight separate shore recreation areas, were expected to accommodate many kinds of water sports.

New Madison Square Garden. New York City's fourth version of the famous Madison Square Garden sports arena is a $130-million complex designed not only for basketball, hockey, track, and other sports but for other forms of entertainment, as well as for convention events and exhibitions. Located on the site of the Pennsylvania Station, the new structure involved demolition of the station and erection of the building while trains of the Penn Central and Long Island railroads were kept running on schedule and related services continued to operate.

A circular structure 425 ft in diameter, the new Garden contains a main arena seating 20,000 spectators, a smaller auditorium which seats 5,000, a 48-lane bowling center, a movie theater, an art museum of sports, and the Garden Hall of Fame. Its cable-supported roof hangs 153 ft above street level, providing a vast column-free space for the arena. Forty-eight cables extending from the exterior ring in the center carry two floors of air-conditioning and other equipment.

Monroe Community College. Opened in the fall of 1968, the new Monroe Community College at Brighton, N.Y., was designed to accommodate 6,000 full-time students on a 3,140-ac campus whose ten main buildings are interconnected in a huge E-shaped configuration. Covered walkways protect students and faculty against rigorous upstate New York winter weather, with the back of the "E" facing against the prevailing winds. A duo-duct system provides heating and ventilation, with air handling decentralized throughout by means of strategically placed towers that hold the mechanical equipment. Reinforced concrete, used extensively throughout, guaranteed durability and reduced maintenance problems.

Poe Lock, Sault Ste. Marie. The growing size of iron-ore freighters necessitated a larger lock connection between Lake Superior and the rest of the Great Lakes at Sault Ste. Marie, Mich. The new Poe Lock, built immediately adjacent to two smaller locks and replacing a predecessor built in 1896, measured 1,200 ft long and 110 ft wide and was capable of accepting ships of 55,000 tons, twice the size accommodated by the older locks.

The problem of constructing the widest possible lock, with adequate length and depth, without disturbing the operation of the other locks on either side required many innovations in engi-

Two new Soviet power-generating projects demonstrate that nation's continuing advances in civil engineering. Above, assembly teams finish putting together the sixth turbine of the Krasnoyarsk hydroelectric power station in Siberia. The station at the right, on the Barents Sea, is the first in the U.S.S.R. to convert the rise and fall of the tides into electrical power.

Novosti from Sovfoto

neering. The lock walls and approaches were designed not only for efficiency but also to blend aesthetically with the rest of the canal grounds. The adjacent park was improved for the benefit of the 800,000 annual visitors, with a long viewing platform provided.

Muddy Run pumped-storage plant. The world's largest pumped-storage installation, the Muddy Run Generating Plant of the Philadelphia Electric Co., generating up to 880,000 kw, went into operation in 1968–69. Located on the banks of the Susquehanna River near Philadelphia, the eight-unit plant was distinguished by the extensive instrumentation of its main dam, which provided an exceptionally complete record of the dam's overall performance.

Pumped storage is an increasingly important element in power production, especially in the U.S. Water pumped uphill to a reservoir during off hours of power consumption provides a reserve of power for peak-load hours. The Muddy Run installation, with its 100-ac reservoir, also provides valuable recreational facilities.

John Day Dam. The nation's largest multi-purpose engineering project, the $448-million John Day Dam on the Columbia River, between Oregon and Washington, contains a 113-ft single-lift navigation lock and a power plant capable of producing 2.7 million kw, largest in the U.S. until the third powerhouse goes into operation in Washington's Grand Coulee Dam. Involved in the construction was the relocation of several towns, complete with utilities, and with full consideration of the attitudes and preferences of the affected people. Interstate and state highways, and 140 mi of main-line railroad, had to be relocated without interference with traffic. Following a study of the effects of the dam on the ecology of the region, two fish hatcheries were provided and a 30,000-ac waterfowl preserve founded. Several recreational parks were established, with other large areas reserved for future industrial and port development. The coordinated efforts of engineers, biologists, architects, and regional planners were necessary for the success of the project.

Soviet dams. Nearing completion at two widely separated points in the U.S.S.R. in 1969 were two record-breaking dams—one the highest masonry arch dam in the world and the other the highest dam of any type, the world's first thousand-footer. Soviet civil engineers have earned a solid reputation for large-scale construction projects. The Aswan Dam on the Nile River in the United Arab Republic is probably their best-advertised creation, but Aswan is dwarfed by the monster Nurek Dam, blocking the Vakhsh River close to the border of the U.S.S.R. and Afghanistan. Nurek

rises 1,040 ft from bedrock, beginning with a 52-ft concrete base beneath its impervious core. Because the Vakhsh River flows in a region subject to earthquakes, the decision was made in favor of an earth-fill dam, which resists seismic forces better than masonry and for which plenty of fill was available nearby. Chief engineer Georgi Abroskyn used 200 tons of explosive charges to do his first major earth-moving, toppling a 535,000-cu yd pile of material into place for the bulk of the upstream cofferdam. When completed, the Nurek Dam will house a nine-unit power plant that is designed to produce 2.7 million kw of electric power before the water flows out to irrigate 1.6 million ac of farmland.

The other new Soviet giant, astride the Ingur River at the foot of the Caucasus Mountains, will rise 886 ft, topped among existing dams only by Switzerland's Grand Dixence (932 ft). To provide the mountain of concrete required for this masonry arch dam, chief engineer Konstantin Dadiany built a continuous-mix plant which turns endless belts of sand and gravel into finished concrete without batching.

The Churchill Falls Project. A thousand feet deep in the granite bed that underlies the Canadian wilderness at Churchill Falls, Nfd., tunneling crews began blasting out the world's largest underground hydroelectric plant, with a planned capacity of 5.2 million kw. The project, which will cost not quite $1 billion, was the largest single current engineering project under way in North America.

Its most unusual aspect was the relationship of the water-storage element to the powerhouse. Normally a huge dam and reservoir dominate the scene of a hydroelectric development, with the power facilities relatively modest in scale; at Churchill Falls, however, no giant dam is required. The Churchill River cascades down 1,000 ft in a space of 20 mi of white water above and below the falls, a natural force that only requires harnessing by dikes and penstocks. The 40 mi of low dikes will create a reservoir one third as large as Lake Ontario but will require only the relatively modest amount of 26 million cu yd of earth fill to do the job. The excavation for the huge powerhouse, on the other hand, necessitated the drilling and blasting of 2.3 million cu yd of solid granitic gneiss. Extensive exploratory drilling revealed almost ideally sound rock throughout, with no underground water. A cross-section of the 1,026-ft-long powerhouse is 81 ft in width by 154 ft in height.

The Snowy Mountains scheme. Another of the century's largest-scale projects continued on schedule in the upper ridges of the Snowy Moun-

Daylight is seen at the end of the first tailrace (a channel for conveying water) to be excavated in Canada's Churchill Falls project, designed as the world's largest underground hydroelectric plant.

tains of Australia, where an army of engineers and workmen from throughout the world were engaged in harnessing the once-wasted waters of the Snowy River. A complex of large dams (highest 520 ft), many smaller dams, almost 100 mi of tunnels, and more than 80 mi of aqueducts were combining to capture the river's waters, which formerly flowed uselessly down the southeastern slopes of the mountains into the Tasman Sea. The river was to be channeled westward to join the Murray and Murrumbidgee rivers, thereby furnishing 1.9 million ac-ft of water for irrigation while producing 4 million kilowatts of power for Sydney and the coastal industrial region.

The scheme consists essentially of 56-sq mi Lake Eucumbene, the central storage reservoir, and two separate systems of dams and tunnels; one leading from the reservoir to the Murray River and the other to the Murrumbidgee. Two long tunnels (total 28 mi) were designed to permit flow in either direction. When the two systems produce an excess runoff of water, the tunnels will be used to feed the central reservoir. When, on the contrary, the systems require water, the tunnel flow is reversed.

Construction during 1968–69 was proceeding on Murray 2 Power Station, scheduled to produce 550,000 kw, and on the pumping station and tunnel at Jindabyne. Blowering Dam was completed in 1968, with its power station scheduled to produce 80,000 kw by late 1969. Jounama Dam, 140

ft high with a 1,400-ft crest, was also nearing completion.

World's largest cofferdam. "A vigorous nation builds for its future," says the motto on the Barrier Dam Monument in the Netherlands. To back it up, Dutch hydraulic engineers, for centuries preeminent in their field, have become engaged in a project which dwarfs even the 18-mi ocean dike with which 40 years ago they converted the Zuider Zee into a freshwater lake, the IJsselmeer. Their present operation involves the construction of complex closures for the mouths of three huge estuaries: the Maas River, the Rhine River, and the East Scheldt River. To transform this entire coastal region into a storm-secure, maximum-yield, agricultural-industrial-recreational complex, the Dutch established a Delta Plan, which called for four major dams and several lesser barriers. To keep the port of Rotterdam open and at the same time desalinate the shoreline, closures would force nearly the whole volume of the Rhine and Maas rivers into Rotterdam's narrow New Waterway.

In 1968–69 work was nearly completed on the Haringvliet Dam, a three-mile-long structure equipped with 17 sluice gates. To make construction feasible in the tidal channel, a mammoth cofferdam, or ring dike, was built in the middle of it, forming a rectangular isle, 1,500 × 600 yd, with rounded corners. A hook on the sheltered side provided a harbor for construction vessels. An embankment causeway was built from the north shore to the ring dike; on the south side a lock would provide for local shipping and fishermen. Within the ring dike hydraulically operated sluice gates were built.

Experiments in mass-produced housing. Because not only low-income U.S. families but also those with median incomes often find it impossible to afford traditional individually built-on-site houses and apartments, an effort has been made to develop technology for mass-produced housing of many types. Engineers and builders have concentrated mainly on two methods, prefabrication and the systems approach.

Prefabrication is nothing new. Edmond Coignet pioneered it in building a gambling casino in France in 1861, using reinforced concrete. In the 1870s settlers bound for the American West took along prefabricated wood houses, the pieces numbered for assembly. Nearly all low-cost single-family dwelling units have been partly prefabricated for some time.

The Soviet Union pioneered the precast utility core, incorporating bathroom and kitchen, and also made entire precast rooms. The early Soviet ventures ran into some troubles, with certain apartment houses requiring nets hung over the sidewalks to catch falling pieces of facade. The joints between prefabricated panels were the

Sacks of dry cement are stacked to form the walls of a home in an effort to cut down construction costs of low-priced housing. The stacks are reinforced with metal rods and soaked with water; they are then sprayed with a finish to give an adobe-like appearance.

Courtesy, Dicker Stack-Sack International

Achilles heel of the system, which, however, has been much improved.

A shortage of labor rather than cost problems dictated the widespread adoption of prefabricated housing in postwar Europe, and at first prefabrication methods did not always compete with economically conventional construction. Recently, however, prefabrication became competitive in cost in Europe, while in the U.S. it promised spectacular savings.

The systems approach, first developed for military and aerospace programs, was expected to have major applications in construction. It was pioneered with great success by architect-engineer Ezra Ehrenkrantz, whose School Construction Systems Development program in California attracted national attention. Ehrenkrantz used the same set of components for the construction of 13 elementary schools and high schools, thereby achieving a 20% reduction in cost for structural ceiling-lighting components; heating, ventilating, and air-conditioning parts; and partitions, cabinets, and lockers. As a result Ehrenkrantz's firm was involved in several pioneering construction projects in 1968. Among other things he developed a package of new, standardized building components for the University of California's Residential Building Systems project. By using these components he hoped to improve the quality and flexibility of student dormitories at California at no increase in cost. Ehrenkrantz also was planning the Great High Schools project in Pittsburgh, Pa., new buildings for Indiana University, and a school system for Tallahassee, Fla.

Ehrenkrantz's aim was to produce individually designed buildings using a high proportion of systems components. "To handle today's environmental problems," he said, "planning teams should consist of experts in architecture, engineering, manufacturing, economics, management, labor, and the social sciences."

The systems approach was applied to residential construction in Cambridge, Mass., where a truck crane and crew of ironworkers pieced together in less than a month the precast steel framing elements of a seven-story apartment building. This system, called Componoform, was developed by Russian-born Egon Ali-Oglu. A rigid frame eliminates the need for load-bearing walls and permits wide flexibility in interior partitioning. Components include 14 × 14 in. columns with beam sections jutting from the tops, 14 × 21 in. tie beams, and 9-in.-thick hollow-core floor slabs. Ironworkers fasten the beam-column sections in place, join the tie beams between column arms, and weld the steel plates on column and beam endings. All structural elements, stairs, and exterior walls are precast. The Compono-form system was also used on five four-story dormitories at Canada's Acadia University in Wolfville, N.S., and on a Montessori school in Stamford, Conn.

Homes for the poor were displayed in a research project which the U.S. Department of Housing and Urban Development (HUD) carried out in Austin, Tex. In a space of two acres 10 houses were exhibited; each could be bought for as little as $500 cash and monthly mortgage payments averaging $65 (which a HUD interest subsidy would cut to $35). The homes featured much prefabricated construction, and their full prices ranged from $4,975 to $7,000.

—Joseph Gies

Nuclear engineering

In a year-end statement for 1968 Glenn T. Seaborg, chairman of the United States Atomic Energy Commission (AEC), said:

The most dramatic peaceful application of nuclear energy in the United States continued to be the generation of electricity. Fifty-six nuclear power plants are now operating or being built in the U.S., and some 44 more are planned. . . . The AEC estimates that by 1980 the capacity of nuclear generating plants should be 120 to 170 million kilowatts, about 25 per cent of the Nation's total.

Impressive progress was also made during the year in the development of nuclear power for space applications and in the development of nuclear explosives for commercial applications. The past year also witnessed a milestone for the nuclear-powered merchant ship, NS "Savannah." But most important was the increasing recognition of the opportunities, responsibilities, and problems which are presented by the need for and capability of large-scale nuclear generation of electricity.

Generation of electricity. In the U.S. the demand for electric power has grown at an average rate of 7% per year since about 1940, requiring an approximate doubling of electric power generating facilities each decade. The total installed generating capacity in the U.S. in 1969 was approximately 300 million kw. By 1990 it was expected to be approximately 1 billion kw. During the past year the consequences of this tremendous use of energy and its future implications were placed in proper perspective. As a result the future role of nuclear energy emerged more clearly, and the nuclear industry achieved a new maturity and perspective.

The increased recognition of nuclear power potential was reflected in increased estimates of

Courtesy, Kerr-McGee Corporation

Loading a reactor pin into a rotating welding tube is one step in the fabrication of nuclear reactor cores. In this case, uranium oxide pellets, which are the end products of a conversion process from gaseous uranium hexafluoride, are placed inside the tube. The operation takes place in an inert atmosphere.

the rate of growth of nuclear power and of future uranium requirements. In response to these large estimated future requirements U.S. uranium exploration activities increased dramatically in 1968, when the industry drilled an estimated 25 million ft for exploration and development. This contrasted with 10.7 million ft in 1967 and a previous peak in 1957 of 9. 2 million ft.

A second major activity related to the commercial uranium supply involved the enrichment of uranium by the AEC. Effective Jan. 1, 1969, the AEC was permitted by law to begin enriching privately owned uranium. On Sept. 7, 1968, the first domestic contract was executed between the AEC and the Kerr-McGee Corp. for enriching privately owned domestic fuel. In addition, the AEC planned to terminate its guaranteed purchase price for plutonium and to discontinue entering into leasing agreements for power reactor fuel at the end of 1970. The nuclear power industry would thus become a basically commercial enterprise.

continued on page 242

Toward a Landfall in Space

by Jay Holmes

Landing a spacecraft on the moon or a planet by pinpointing targets in the immensity of space requires a wide array of navigation and control equipment. In setting a course to their destination, astronauts use instruments ranging from the age-old sailor's sextant to the most sophisticated of modern computers.

"Zero 1 zero 6 8 niner 2 6 zero," says ground control at Houston, Tex. "Peripieye zeta. Down zero 4 8 left zero 5. The remainder is not applicable. Sirius Rigel set of stars for GDC alliance. Twelve niner 1 5 5 zero 1 zero negative ullage. We'll pass the horizon data later."

"Roger," replies the navigator-astronaut on board the Apollo spacecraft en route to the moon.

So goes the bulk of the communications between ground control and astronauts: a seemingly endless recital of numbers, letters, and names of stars. Though apparently prosaic, the exchanges are a deadly earnest necessity. Their purpose is to assure that the ship is on course for its destination and a safe return to earth, and that there are alternative plans for safe return in case of emergency.

As ships have done for centuries, spacecraft sail by the stars, whose constant locations provide reference points for fixing position in space. But a voyage through the solar winds and the sea of interplanetary space is vastly more perilous than a cruise past Cape Hatteras, North Carolina, a journey around Cape Horn, or Ferdinand Magellan's circumnavigation of the earth. For a landfall in space is an almost infinitely rarer thing than on the oceans of the earth. In the solar system the planets and their moons are only specks of dust in a seemingly endless emptiness surrounding the sun.

A man on the moon, Edwin E. Aldrin, Jr., stands next to a seismic sensor and views the Apollo 11 lunar module in which he and Neil Armstrong landed. In the background are other items deployed by the astronauts.

All photos, courtesy, National Aeronautics and Space Administration

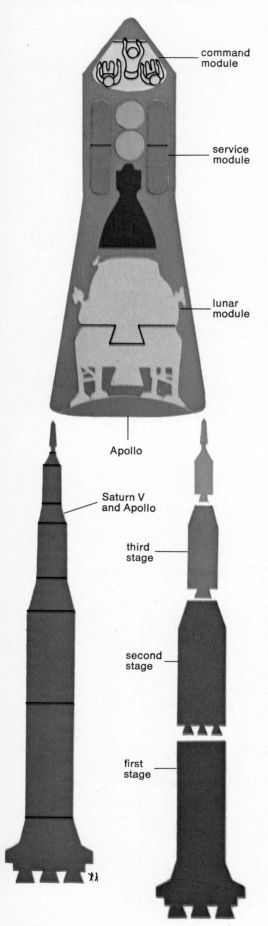

command module

service module

lunar module

Apollo

Saturn V and Apollo

third stage

second stage

first stage

The Apollo spacecraft rests on the tip of the Saturn V booster rocket prior to launch. At the right, the Saturn is shown divided into its three stages. The size of the Saturn V is indicated by the two human figures at the lower left.

Because of the immense distances to be traversed, all present and contemplated space flights follow curved paths, varying only slightly from the earth's normal flight in orbit about the sun and often making use of the motion of the moon in its orbit about the earth. The distances proportionately magnify the effect of the slightest navigation error. A miscalculation of only one degree in the course from the moon back to earth could result in missing the earth by more than 4,000 mi. And unlike sailors of old, modern astronauts could not turn around if they should find themselves so far off course—no spacecraft in existence or planned at present could carry enough rocket fuel for such a maneuver. The laws of motion would carry them inexorably away from the earth and into a separate orbit of the sun—their ship a derelict in interplanetary space.

Thus, we can understand and appreciate the intensity of concentration on providing accurate navigation and control in a space flight. The process includes position checks every few hours, double-checking of calculations on board the spacecraft and on earth, and hairline adjustments of the flight trajectory whenever warranted.

Navigation principles for space flight

In space, navigation is a more difficult task than on the sea. Position and movement must be measured in three dimensions rather than two. But this major difference is offset to some extent by two advantages the astronaut has over the sailor: (1) he can always see the stars in the cloudless expanses of space, and (2) he is supported by a comprehensive system of tracking stations and computers on earth, operating in a fashion similar to that of aviation traffic control.

To assure accurate navigation, space-flight equipment designers have provided for duplicate systems that can operate independently of each other, one on board the spacecraft and one on the ground. On a normal space flight these separate systems are operated concurrently, and the results are checked against one another. But the astronauts can operate the on-board system independently in case of difficulty in communicating with the earth. And the ground system can do the job by itself in the event of a problem on board the spacecraft.

If the results of the two navigation calculations should differ to any important degree, the work would be rechecked to identify the error. In the case of minor disagreement, the astronauts and ground crew can agree to "split the difference." This agreed-upon result then forms the basis of a decision on the operation of the stabilization and control systems, which employ the propulsion engines to change the flight path.

A spacecraft spends most of its time coasting along the path established at the beginning of its flight by the thrust of the powerful rockets of its launch vehicle. Unlike the pilot of a ship or an airplane, the astronaut does not constantly steer his craft. Only a few changes in course are made en route by firing the relatively small spacecraft propulsion engine. On the Apollo 8 flight in December 1968, for example, astronauts Frank Borman, James Lovell, Jr., and William Anders used their main propulsion engine only once, for 2.4 seconds, during the 66-hour flight from earth orbit to a point near the moon. Most of the fuel in the spacecraft propulsion system is reserved for major maneuvers near the destination of the voyage—to descend into orbit, to land, or to launch the craft on the return flight.

A principal goal in designing the Apollo spacecraft was to permit man and automatic machinery to function efficiently together. Nowhere was this more difficult than in guidance and control. Man's presence in space, as contrasted with the automatic operation of unmanned spacecraft, provides the major advantage of his ability to react to unexpected events. He can make adjustments, point and focus viewing devices, change modes, repair or replace parts, modify flight plans, and revise flight activities—if he receives, on time, the information he needs for decision and action.

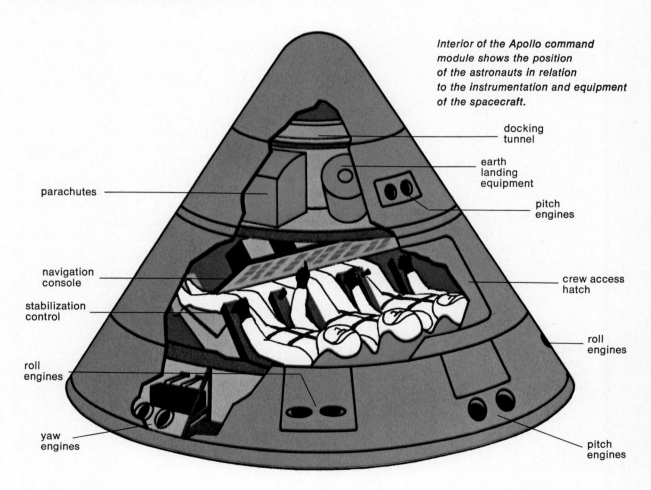

Interior of the Apollo command module shows the position of the astronauts in relation to the instrumentation and equipment of the spacecraft.

docking tunnel

earth landing equipment

pitch engines

parachutes

navigation console

stabilization control

crew access hatch

roll engines

roll engines

yaw engines

pitch engines

181

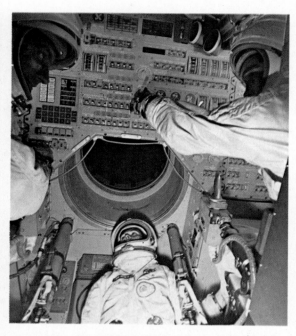

But only computers and other automatic equipment have sufficient ability to measure accurately, remember details, and make the speedy calculations required by the conditions of space flight. The principal problems in designing guidance and control for a manned spacecraft stem from the need to provide sufficient and timely communications between man and his machines.

Navigating with the Apollo spacecraft

Both the command module and the lunar module of the Apollo spacecraft are equipped for navigating in space. The navigator sits between the other two astronauts in the command module, which carries the three from earth into lunar orbit and from lunar orbit back to earth. Soon after the spacecraft is under way, the navigator folds away the center seat, so as to operate the equipment from what would be a standing position if gravity were still present. He must move cautiously at first. On Apollo 8, navigator Lovell learned to his regret that a queasy stomach can result from too-rapid movement

A wide range of sophisticated equipment was necessary for the Apollo lunar flights. Opposite page, left, is the Saturn V rocket that launched Apollo 9, with the spacecraft on top; top right, astronauts check the instrument panel in an Apollo command module; center right, astronauts James McDivitt (foreground) and Russell Schweickart study the instruments in a simulated lunar module; bottom, the Mission Control Center of the Manned Spacecraft Center at Houston, Tex. Below, with the earth in the background David Scott opens the hatch of the Apollo 9 command module to view the just-completed docking with the lunar module.

before one's body becomes accustomed to weightlessness. U.S. astronauts encountered this condition for the first time when they began flights in the relatively spacious interior of the Apollo command module. The smaller size of the earlier Mercury and Gemini spacecraft had precluded such intravehicular activity. Soviet cosmonauts, however, had reported comparable difficulties as early as 1964, beginning with the three-man flight in Voskhod 1.

The guidance and navigation system of the command module is at the navigator's feet as he lies on his back during the lift-off from the earth. This system is an extremely sophisticated array of 40,000 parts measuring four feet high, two feet deep, and two and a half to three feet wide. It consists of a digital computer, a system of gyroscopes and accelerometers, optical viewing devices, supporting electronics, and a display and keyboard, all built into a sheet-aluminum base filled with plastic foam. A second display and keyboard, identical with the first, is on the command pilot's control panel.

The principal viewing device is a sextant, a tool like those used by sailors to measure the angular height of a star above the horizon. In the Apollo guidance and navigation system, the viewer part of the sextant extends through a side of the spacecraft, so that the navigator can use it to take star sights.

Before a space mission starts about three dozen bright stars are selected as reference points throughout the sky. The navigator begins his task by finding one of those reference stars in the field of view of a wide-angle scanning telescope, which also extends through the spacecraft wall. Then he focuses on the selected star in the viewer of the sextant, which magnifies the brightness of the star 28 times. If necessary, he turns the spacecraft into proper position by operating the reaction control system, which fires small rocket engines.

Next, the navigator takes another sight toward a landmark on the earth, the moon, or another star. The sun would not be satisfactory because its blinding light could damage his unprotected eye. With each alignment he presses a button to command the computer to register the angle between the lines of sight to the two points. On a two-dimensional surface, such as the sea, a sailor can measure the angles of two stars and then use those angles to draw two lines on his chart. Their intersection establishes his location. In three-dimensional space, however, navigation requires the measurement of at least three angles, not in the same plane with one another.

Meanwhile, three gyroscopes and three accelerometers have been keeping track of the spacecraft's movements. The gyroscopes and attached electrical devices measure pitch, roll, and yaw motions. The

The Apollo 9 command/service module is viewed from the lunar module prior to docking. Astronauts James McDivitt and Russell Schweickart were in the lunar module, while David Scott remained in the command vehicle. The object extending from the lower left of the spacecraft is a high-gain antenna.

The Apollo 9 lunar module is seen with its three landing gear "foot pads" deployed in this view from the command/service module. Extending from the landing gear are lunar surface probes.

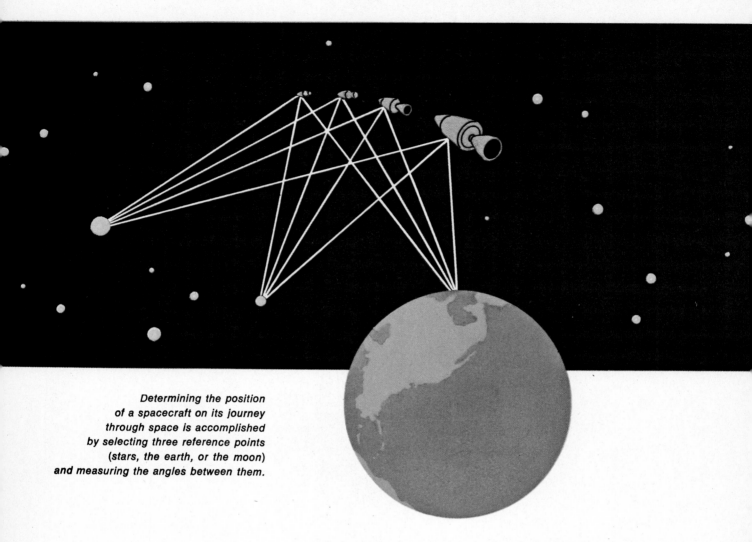

*Determining the position
of a spacecraft on its journey
through space is accomplished
by selecting three reference points
(stars, the earth, or the moon)
and measuring the angles between them.*

accelerometers measure changes in motion along straight-line directions in all three dimensions.

Even when its engines are not operating, the spacecraft is being acted upon by external forces, such as the gravity of the earth, the moon, and the sun, and by minute amounts of friction with atoms, molecules, and occasional dust particles encountered in space. The changes in the spacecraft's motion resulting from these forces are transmitted electronically to the computer, which compares them with the flight plan programmed into its memory bank. If a deviation from the flight plan develops, the computer flashes signals on the command pilot's and navigator's display panels, alerting them to the need to change the flight plan.

On the earth the tracking stations use two tools, radio and radar, to gather information to be fed into computers that calculate the position and motion of the spacecraft. In California, Spain, and Australia steerable antennae 85 ft in diameter that swivel on fixed bases help to pinpoint the direction of the radio signals and make radar measurements of the distance and the speed of the spacecraft.

Tracking from the earth is most accurate when the spacecraft is near the earth. As it ranges outward the angles to be measured grow smaller and the importance of on-board navigation increases. But under normal circumstances, the ground system is more accurate out to the distance of the moon and, therefore, is the primary source of navigation information.

Besides serving as a double check, the on-board navigation system is available when communication is interrupted, either by equipment problems or when the spacecraft passes behind the moon. In addition, experience with on-board navigation helps space-system designers prepare for the time when manned spacecraft will undertake voyages farther from earth than the quarter-million miles to the moon.

Information from the tracking stations and computers on earth is transmitted by the control center at Houston to the navigator in space in the form of a series of numbers and star references. The navigator or the command pilot can relay this information to the computer by pressing the 19 buttons on either of the keyboards. The computer replies by means of a 21-character display.

A steerable antenna swivels on its base to make radar measurements of the position and motion of a spacecraft. As a result of information furnished by the antenna, a spacecraft that has deviated from its course (top two drawings) can be put back on the right track (bottom).

Apollo control system

Probably the most important of the 19 control buttons is the one marked "pro," which stands for "proceed." This button is an on-off switch for the operation of the spacecraft under automatic control. When the automatic control is in operation, pressing this button directs the guidance and control systems to stand by for further instructions. After the instructions have been given, pressing the button again allows the automatic system to proceed.

Other control buttons are marked "verb," "noun," "+," "—," the digits zero to nine, and abbreviations for "clear," "key release," "enter," and "reset." With these, the navigator can change programs, insert ground navigation data, or command the computer to display specific facts from its memory bank.

In addition, the command pilot has two controls similar to the stick of an airplane. One at his left hand moves the spacecraft in straight-line directions in all three dimensions. A rotation control in all three dimensions is at his right hand. Installed with the navigation system is a second rotation control.

Programmed into the computers on the command and lunar modules are the precise mission plan and many plans for alternate missions that provide for foreseeable emergencies. As the time approaches for each major maneuver, a review is made of all aspects of the status of the mission, including the operation of the equipment and the condition of the crew. If all is well, the command pilot presses the "pro" button and the maneuver is carried out. If not, the computer is instructed to switch its program to an alternate mission, such as remaining in orbit about the moon instead of landing.

A Landfall is Reached

Walking on the moon's surface for more than two hours, Apollo 11 astronauts Edwin E. Aldrin, Jr., and Neil Armstrong performed a variety of activities and deployed several packages of scientific instruments. At the left, Aldrin stands on the surface with the moon's horizon behind him; in the glass visor of his helmet can be seen the reflections of the lunar module, several scientific instruments, and Armstrong in the act of taking the photograph. Aldrin climbs down the ladder from the lunar module (above, left) and stands by a device that has been deployed to detect the solar wind (above, right). "That's one small step for a man. . . ." were the opening words of Neil Armstrong as he became the first human being to set foot on the moon; the footprint (below) bears witness to man's presence on the lunar surface. Several additional manned Apollo flights to the moon are scheduled to take place in future months.

Lunar-module navigation

The lunar module, which transports two of the three astronauts from lunar orbit to the landing on the moon and back to rendezvous with the command module, has two stages. Its descent stage includes a rocket engine and other equipment employed for landing on the moon. The main section of the module, the ascent stage, has another rocket engine and uses the descent stage as a launch platform, which it leaves behind on the moon's surface.

In the lunar module the command pilot operates the guidance and control systems, which are similar to those of the command module. In addition, he can control two radars. One is on the descent stage to measure the altitude above the moon's surface and rate of descent toward it. The other is on the ascent stage to measure distance and rate of approach during the rendezvous with the command module on the return flight.

During the final phases of descent toward a landing on the moon and the final approach toward rendezvous and docking of the lunar and command modules in lunar orbit, the lunar module can be controlled manually by either astronaut, watching the radar and the view out of his window, in addition to the other instruments. The navigator on board the command module can also maneuver during rendezvous and docking. But the astronauts can also permit the guidance and navigation system to perform these maneuvers automatically. Propulsion engines containing two liquids that ignite on contact with each other are used to maneuver both the command and lunar modules. The fuel for each module is monomethylhydrazine,

The Apollo lunar module (left) descends to the moon's surface by separating from the command module and continuing downward. When the lunar module ascends from the moon's surface, it leaves behind its bottom section (descent stage) and rejoins the command module, which has continued in lunar orbit.

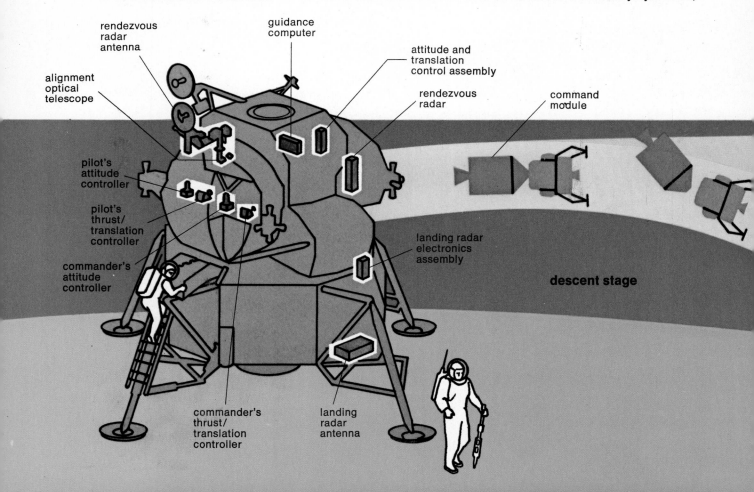

rendezvous radar antenna

guidance computer

alignment optical telescope

attitude and translation control assembly

rendezvous radar

command module

pilot's attitude controller

pilot's thrust/ translation controller

commander's attitude controller

landing radar electronics assembly

descent stage

commander's thrust/ translation controller

landing radar antenna

a petroleum derivative. Oxygen to support combustion is supplied by nitrogen tetroxide, a compound formed by the removal of water from nitric acid. This combination of liquids was selected because its ignition has been demonstrated to be very reliable in several rocket systems. Also, both liquids can be stored without difficulty in closed containers at ordinary temperatures—unlike, for example, liquid oxygen, which must be refrigerated to almost $-300°$ F ($-185°$ C). In addition, by regulating the flow of the liquids into the descent engine of the lunar module, the thrust of the engine can be varied during the approach toward the moon.

Thus, in the Apollo, men have produced a space vehicle that can transport them away from the earth, land on another celestial body, lift off from that body, and return safely to the earth. Other, more complex spacecraft will undoubtedly follow, but the basic principles for navigating through space, as developed for the Apollo, will most certainly serve as valuable lessons for eventual manned space flights ranging deeper into the universe.

FOR ADDITIONAL READING:

Clarke, Arthur C., *The Promise of Space* (Harper and Row, 1968).

Gatland, Kenneth, *Manned Spacecraft* (Macmillan, 1967).

Holmes, Jay, *America on the Moon: The Enterprise of the Sixties* (Lippincott, 1962).

Hymoff, Edward, *Guidance and Control of Spacecraft* (Holt, Rinehart and Winston, 1966).

Ley, Willy, *Rockets, Missiles and Space Travel* (Viking, 1961).

Vertregt, M., *Principles of Astronautics* (Elsevier, 1965).

AUDIOVISUAL MATERIALS FROM ENCYCLOPÆDIA BRITANNICA EDUCATIONAL CORPORATION:

Films: *First Men into Space; Rockets: How They Work.*
Recording: "The Conquest of Space."

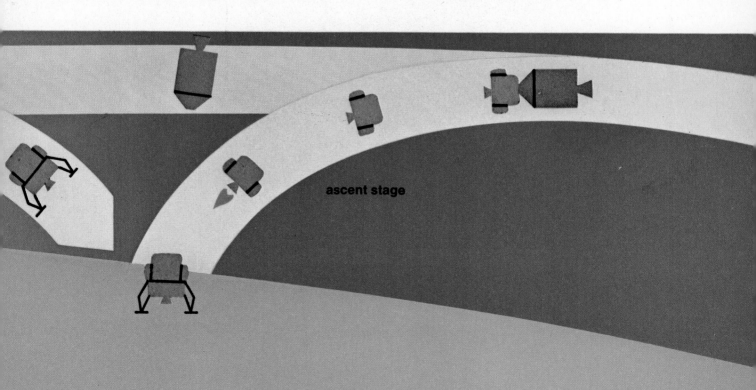
ascent stage

Life Beyond
the Earth
by Norman H. Horowitz

**As man enters the second decade of the
Space Age, exobiology—that branch of planetary science concerned
with the search for extraterrestrial life—will either prove itself or be
forgotten. It will not always be a science in search of a subject.**

For all practical purposes, exobiology is a creation of the Space Age.
To be sure, there were earlier speculations regarding life elsewhere
in the universe, but most of these were fanciful literary exercises
except for a few farsighted prospectuses written by scientists. Before
the advent of interplanetary rockets, any information of biological
significance about the planets was obtained exclusively by astronomical methods. Astronomical observations are still a major source
of important new planetary data, but detailed and conclusive biological explorations of the planets can be performed only by means
of spacecraft.

Up to now, only the moon, Venus, and Mars have been visited by
spacecraft from the earth, but voyages to Mercury, Jupiter, and the
outer planets are, or soon will be, technically feasible. These spacecraft carry automatic instruments that radio their data to the earth.
The capabilities of such instruments, which are really extensions of
man's eyes and hands, are considerable, and there is little doubt that
they will provide some of the answers to the major questions about
the planets with which exobiologists are concerned.

Biological explorations beyond the solar system are presently conceivable only by way of radio communications with intelligent beings
living on planets of other stars. A preliminary search for intelligent
extraterrestrial signals was carried out at the National Radio Astronomy Observatory in Green Bank, W. Va., in 1959, and some theoretical studies of the subject have been made, but there are no
current plans for continuing this project. (See *1969 Britannica Yearbook of Science and the Future,* Feature Article: A SPACE AGE
GOAL: EXPLORING THE SOLAR SYSTEM, *p. 73.*)

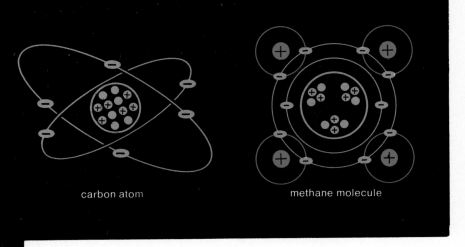

carbon atom

methane molecule

The "Sociable" Carbon Atom

The "sociable" carbon atom (right) combines with hydrogen, oxygen, or nitrogen in a myriad of ways in order to gain the four electrons it needs to attain stability. Among the great number of compounds that result, four of which are shown here, are those required for survival by all living things. Perhaps under different planetary conditions of temperature and pressure other elements could do what carbon does on earth.

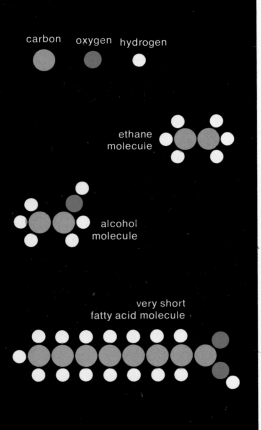

carbon   oxygen   hydrogen

ethane molecule

alcohol molecule

very short fatty acid molecule

Carbon—a vital requirement for life

Life as we know it is based on carbon chemistry. In considering the possibility of life on other planets, we have to ask ourselves: "Will life elsewhere necessarily be carbonaceous?" The answer to this question is almost certainly in the affirmative. There is reason to believe that a necessary attribute of life wherever it occurs is the ability to store and replicate large amounts of information. Such storage and replication require molecular complexity and stability. No other element matches carbon in its ability to form large and complex, yet stable, molecules, nor does any other element form as many different compounds as does carbon. These properties arise from the particular structure of the carbon atom, the outer orbit of which has four electrons. To attain a stable state, the carbon atom requires eight electrons in its outer orbit and can gain them through chemical union with many donor elements, including carbon itself. Other elements—silicon, for example—may resemble carbon in one way or another, but none has the same ability to form four strong bonds with such a variety of elements.

If we assume, then, that life on other worlds would be based on carbon, the upper limit of the biological temperature range is set at 100–150° C because carbon compounds become unstable at higher temperatures. In addition, this assumption poses a significant condition for the origin of life: carbon must be available. Carbon is an abundant element in the sun and in the universe generally, but it is rare in the earth and, presumably, in the other terrestrial planets (Mars, Venus, and Mercury). The relatively high concentration of carbon in the form of carbonates and organic matter that is found at the surface of the earth is the result of the evolution of volatile carbon compounds from the hot interior of our planet over geological time. This outgassing process has concentrated carbon, and also water and nitrogen, from a large volume of the earth into a thin layer at its surface. An equivalent process must occur on any terrestrial planet if it is to support a spontaneous origin of life. For this reason, the atmospheric history of the planets is a matter of great exobiological interest.

Some authors have speculated that, under conditions very different from those on the earth, elements other than carbon might be utilized for constructing living matter. It is not possible to evaluate these suggestions, however, because they have not been developed in detail. For example, a solvent has to be specified for any such noncarbonaceous biochemistry that would have the correct physical and chemical properties under the assumed conditions. Many other questions of a similar nature would have to be answered before any proposal of this kind could be seriously considered.

Mars—the prime target

Of all the extraterrestrial objects within reach of present spacecraft, only Mars is conceivably an abode of life. The surface of the moon, with no atmosphere and subject to unfiltered solar radiation, is too hostile to support living organisms. Conditions on Mercury, which is closer to the sun, are probably more severe than those on the moon. Venus possesses a dense atmosphere, but its average surface temperature of about 400–500° C far exceeds the biological temperature limit of 100–150°C mentioned previously. It has been suggested that buoyant organisms may live in the atmosphere of Venus, high above the hot surface. This is an imaginative but not very credible speculation. Jupiter and the planets beyond are still inaccessible to biological investigation. They are so different from the earth in their physical state and chemical composition that speculation about their biological status seems futile at the present time.

The foregoing remarks are based on the premise that life cannot exist on a planet whose *surface* environment is not compatible with biological requirements. The nature of *subsurface* environments— where temperatures may be more equable, radiation essentially nonexistent, and ice or even liquid water available at sufficient depths— is irrelevant for the purposes of this discussion. Living systems require a constant input of energy, which must come ultimately from the sun. For life to exist on a terrestrial planet, it is necessary that certain organisms collect and fix solar energy. To do so, they must live at the surface in order to absorb sunlight. On the earth, this function is performed primarily by green plants. On a planet like Jupiter, which has an atmosphere rich in hydrogen, methane, and ammonia, organic compounds synthesized by photochemical reactions in the atmosphere might feed organisms living in the lower depths. In this case, biological photosynthesis would not be necessary.

Evidence of life beyond the earth may be demonstrated by the microfossils found in meteorites.
The fossilized ribbonlike tissue (top) suggests life forms on the earth, while the piece of tissue (center) has tubes about 0.0003 inch in diameter with many-sided openings. At the bottom is a greatly enlarged view of the microfossil on the Orgueil meteorite of 1864.

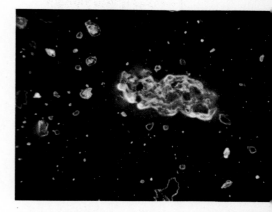

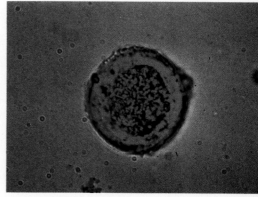

Courtesy, The Lamp, Standard Oil Company (N.J.)

*As the only other planet
in our solar system likely
to support life, Mars has long been
the subject of study
and speculation. The entire planet
(above) is photographed through
a telescope at the Jet Propulsion
Laboratory in California.
A section of the planet's surface
170 mi by 140 mi (opposite page,
top) is revealed in a photograph
taken in 1965 by the spacecraft
Mariner 4. Opposite page, bottom,
is a "map" of Mars as envisioned
by astronomers at Lowell Observatory
in 1905. The shaded areas
were thought to be shallow seas,
while the lines represented canals.*

The Martian environment

Mars is about one-half the diameter and one-tenth the mass of the earth. It has an atmosphere whose pressure at the surface is approximately 1% that of the earth's atmosphere. Carbon dioxide is a major constituent, probably over 50%, of the Martian atmosphere; a small amount of water vapor and carbon monoxide, but no oxygen, has been detected. Temperatures on Mars vary considerably from place to place and from time to time. Ground temperatures as high as 30° C have been reported on the Martian equator at noon. The extreme nighttime temperature has not been measured directly, but it may drop to −80° C or lower. Calculations indicate that the temperature at the poles, in winter, may fall below the freezing point of carbon dioxide (−125° C). If so, the polar caps would contain dry ice, as well as ordinary (water) ice.

Biologically, the Martian environment is severe but probably not incompatible with some form of life. Many species of terrestrial microorganisms live without oxygen, and many could survive Martian temperatures, as proven by laboratory simulation of conditions on Mars. Martian organisms, however, would have to shield themselves against ultraviolet light from the sun by means of pigments or other protective devices. But the most serious limiting factor for a Martian biology is the lack of water. The concentration of water vapor in Mars' atmosphere is extremely low. Liquid water, if it occurs at all, probably exists briefly as moisture in the soil at certain seasons and times of the day. It is possible that ice exists beneath the Martian surface, but this is not directly available to life as we know it.

If there is life on Mars, the best guess is that it is a hardy microbial form that has survived from an earlier epoch, when water was more plentiful, and that it has, by gradual evolution, become adapted to the conditions now found on the planet. Although we have no evidence that Mars ever possessed an ocean, the presence of a large amount of carbon dioxide in the atmosphere suggests that the planet may have outgassed a considerable quantity of water in past ages. If Mars evolved as much water in proportion to carbon as did the earth, then it can be calculated that Mars could have had an ocean three to four meters deep over its entire surface if the outgassed water vapor condensed and remained liquid. It is impossible to assess the reality of such calculations at the present time, but they serve to indicate one of the more optimistic possibilities. Judging from the small sample of Martian terrain photographed by the Mariner 4 spacecraft in 1965, Mars has not had an ocean for at least several hundred million years.

Seasonal changes on Mars

Through the telescope, three general types of surface features are seen on Mars: (1) the white polar ice cap, which waxes and wanes with the seasons; (2) orange-colored expanses, called bright regions or deserts, covering about 60% of the planet; and (3) darker regions, called maria (formerly thought to be oceans), covering about 40% of the surface. Spectral analysis of the light reflected from the planet indicates that the surface is composed of silicate rocks and that the reddish color of Mars is due to a veneer or stain of iron oxide over a basaltic rock. The dark regions may be less oxidized than the bright regions. The mysterious *canali* (mistranslated "canals"), which were discovered by the Italian astronomer Giovanni Schiaparelli in 1877, intrigued the American astronomer Percival Lowell, who was convinced in the early 1900s that life existed on Mars but was being extinguished by climatic changes.

A major Martian mystery, the "wave of darkening," is associated with the change of seasons in the maria. (Because the axis of Mars is tilted to the same extent as the earth's, Mars has seasons like ours, but they are nearly twice as long, owing to Mars' slower revolution around the sun.) A progressive darkening of the maria starts at the edge of the evaporating polar cap in the spring and spreads toward the equator and some 20° beyond it. The effect reaches its maximum at the beginning of summer and then fades out as the seasons advance. A similar wave is propagated from the opposite pole during its springtime. The equatorial maria are thus affected by two waves of darkening annually. Reports that the wave of darkening is accompanied by blue, green, or brown colorations in the maria have never been confirmed photographically and are disputed.

One of the oldest and most persistent theories advanced to explain Mars' seasonal changes is biological: the wave of darkening is caused by the growth of vegetation in the Martian springtime. The direction of movement of the wave, from pole to equator, is explained by the assumption that growth is stimulated by the availability of water vapor as it is being transferred through the atmosphere from one pole to the other. According to another hypothesis, the seasonal changes are due to the reversible uptake and release of water vapor by hygroscopic (water-retaining) salts in the soil of the maria. Other theories invoke physical changes in the soil caused by freezing and thawing, or cycles of deposition and removal of dust or volcanic ash by seasonal winds.

Extraterrestrial space expeditions

Current planning by the U.S. National Aeronautics and Space Administration (NASA) envisages the launching of a progressive series of flyby, orbiter, and lander spacecraft to Mars at approximately 26-month intervals. Soviet plans are not known, but it is generally believed that the Russians may attempt an early unmanned landing on Mars. The following is a summary of the biologically significant aspects of the U.S. program.

Mariner 4, a flyby launched in November 1964, was perhaps the

197

most important interplanetary spacecraft flown up to the end of 1968. It obtained the first close-up pictures of Mars, revealing a cratered surface more moonlike in appearance than earthlike. It showed the absence of a magnetic field and of trapped radiation belts, implying an internal structure of Mars different from that of the earth. It made the first direct measurement of the atmospheric density and surface pressure and found them to be lower than previously predicted. Mariner 4 did not prove the presence or absence of life on Mars, but it showed that the environment is more hostile than had been supposed.

Mariner Mars '69, consisting of two flybys, was launched early in 1969 with a scientific payload weight on each spacecraft twice that of Mariner 4. Some 10–20% of the Martian surface was photographed and an infrared radiometer mapped the surface temperature. Two spectrometers, one operating in the ultraviolet region and the other in the infrared, analyzed the atmosphere. Biologically relevant information sought by Mariner Mars '69 included the following: (1) new data on the topography, structure, and temperature of the maria, deserts, and so-called "canals"; (2) a search for frost deposits and clouds, which would mark underground sources of water; (3) a search for geological evidence, such as ancient ocean beds, which would bear on the question of past oceans; (4) the temperature and composition of the polar caps; (5) the nighttime temperature; and (6) the atmospheric composition and its variability over the planet.

Mariner Mars '71 is to be an orbiter mission with a lifetime of several months in the neighborhood of the planet. The instrumentation will be similar to that of Mariner Mars '69. Major objectives will include observation of the seasonal changes; extended thermal, cloud, and topographic mapping, with particular attention to any areas of special interest revealed by Mariner Mars '69; and the search for potential landing sites for Titan Mars '73 (Viking).

Titan Mars '73 (Viking) is intended to be the first U.S. lander mission on the planet. As such, it will open the possibility for direct biological studies of Mars. Although this mission is still in the planning stage, the following life-seeking experiments are among the candidates for inclusion:

1. Television pictures of the landing area.
2. Direct analysis of the atmosphere by sensitive methods that can, in principle, detect life by observing certain biological products. On the earth, for example, most of the oxygen in the atmosphere is of a biological origin, as are some trace constituents, such as methane. Also due to biological activity on the earth is the diurnal variation in the concentration of carbon dioxide over vegetated areas. In general, the demonstration in a planetary atmosphere of any large departure from the thermodynamically expected state would suggest, but not necessarily prove, the operation of a biological process. In addition, these measurements are expected to yield information on the origin and history of the atmosphere of Mars.
3. Organic analysis of the soil to obtain a general survey of all the major classes of organic compounds present. A soil sample is heated to a high

Infrared Spectrometer

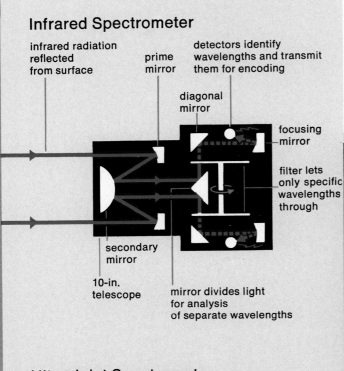

infrared radiation reflected from surface

prime mirror

detectors identify wavelengths and transmit them for encoding

diagonal mirror

focusing mirror

filter lets only specific wavelengths through

secondary mirror

10-in. telescope

mirror divides light for analysis of separate wavelengths

Ultraviolet Spectrometer

ultraviolet light emitted by gases in Mars's upper atmosphere

movable diffraction mirror reflects light in spectrum of separate wavelengths

sensors detect specific wavelengths and transmit them for encoding

mirror focuses separated wavelengths of light on exit slits

exit slit

mirror reflects light

focusing mirror

entrance slit

focusing mirror

The Mariner spacecraft (below) was launched early in 1969 and flew to within 2,000 mi of Mars. Included in the payload of scientific instruments were infrared and ultraviolet spectrometers designed to identify gases in the lower and upper atmospheres of that planet.

The gases in the Martian atmosphere are analyzed by gathering light optically as depicted in the drawings (left). Infrared wavelengths in the lower atmosphere and ultraviolet wavelengths in the upper atmosphere are identified by sensors, and this information is converted into electronic impulse codes for transmission to earth.

Life, or at least many of its basic building blocks, may exist on the planet Jupiter (opposite page). Scientists reached this conclusion by constructing a simulator of Jupiter's atmosphere. By using electrical discharges as an energy source within the simulator (right) the researchers produced many chemical compounds that are forerunners of living systems. A glass-walled chamber (below) shows the effects of an electrical discharge in a simulated atmosphere of Jupiter.

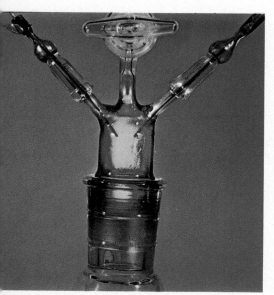

temperature to crack organic materials into volatile fragments that are then separated and identified. Considerable information regarding the original compounds in the soil can be deduced from the data. For example, bio-organic matter in soils is easily distinguished from the organic matter of meteorites.

4. Testing for microbial activity in the soil. If there is life on Mars, it is likely to be microbial. Experiments designed to detect microbial activity in Martian soil include "Gulliver," "Wolf Trap," and the Carbon Dioxide Assimilation Experiment. All three experiments begin by acquiring a sample of soil, which is then treated in different ways to reveal the presence of organisms. In "Gulliver," the soil is used to inoculate a culture medium containing organic compounds labelled with radioactive carbon. Presumably, any microorganisms present will metabolize the labelled compounds and release radioactive carbon dioxide, which is detectable by a Geiger counter. If the organisms multiply in the medium, this will be shown by an exponentially increasing rate of carbon dioxide evolution.

In "Wolf Trap," too, soil is used to inoculate a culture medium. In this case, however, the presence of life will be detected optically by an increase in the turbidity of the medium if multiplication of the organisms occurs.

The Carbon Dioxide Assimilation Experiment will measure the incorporation into organic matter of carbon from carbon dioxide. The wet or dry soil sample will be exposed to radioactive carbon dioxide in sunlight. If living organisms are present, they will convert some of the carbon dioxide into organic matter, either by photosynthesis or by "dark" reactions that occur in all cells. The radioactive organic compounds will then be oxidized to carbon dioxide and detected by a Geiger counter.

The future of exobiology

Biologically, the most interesting object in the solar system after Mars and the earth is probably Jupiter, which is greater in mass than all the other planets combined. The Jovian atmosphere is very deep, the planet is cloud-covered, and the surface has never been seen. Because its atmosphere, which differs radically in composition from those of the terrestrial planets, is composed of hydrogen, helium, methane, and ammonia, it is possible that accumulations of organic compounds similar to those that preceded the origin of life on the earth exist in it. It is conceivable, too, that living organisms inhabit the depths of the atmosphere. It must be understood, however, that these suggestions are entirely speculative at the present time.

The biological exploration of Jupiter presents a formidable problem. For one thing, the planet is so far from the earth that it would take the largest of our present rockets one and a half to two years to reach it. Moreover, Jupiter's powerful gravitational field and the opacity of its atmosphere pose additional difficulties for exploration.

Saturn, which lies beyond Jupiter, is accessible to our biggest rockets, but only at particularly favorable opportunities. Uranus, Neptune, and Pluto, however, are beyond the capability of any present rocket except on those rare occasions when the alignment of the planets is such that the gravitational field of Jupiter can be used to accelerate the spacecraft to one or another of the farther planets. In one such Jupiter-assisted trajectory, called the "grand tour," the spacecraft would swing by Jupiter, Saturn, Uranus, and Neptune in succession. Because the grand tour would take 10–12 years, exploration of the outer planets is clearly a project for the future.

If life is discovered on Mars or on any other planet, it will be an event of major scientific and cultural importance. Its full comprehension, however, will depend on subsequent detailed investigations carried out on the planet itself and, eventually, on samples returned to the earth. If, on the other hand, extraterrestrial life is not found in the solar system, then the interests of exobiology will merge with those of general planetary science, with the common goal of understanding the history of the solar system—a history in which the origin of life on our planet was a particularly notable event.

Courtesy, Kitt Peak National Observatory

FOR ADDITIONAL READING:

Bernal, J. D., *The Origin of Life* (World Publishing Co., 1967).

Horowitz, N. H., "The Search for Extraterrestrial Life," *Science,* pp. 789–792 (Feb. 18, 1966).

Lederberg, Joshua, "Exobiology: Approaches to Life Beyond the Earth," *Science,* pp. 393–400 (Aug. 12, 1960).

Shklovskii, I. S., and Sagan, Carl, *Intelligent Life in the Universe* (Holden-Day, 1966).

Slipher, E. C., *The Photographic Story of Mars* (Sky Publishing Corporation, 1962).

Urban Society: A Blueprint for the City of Tomorrow
by Philip M. Hauser

A city is more than a physical fact. It is also a way of life qualitatively different from what our rural forebears knew. Much of today's crisis, says the author, who is a noted sociologist, stems from our inability to adjust our inherited values and institutions to an increasingly urbanized world. Here he visualizes the city of tomorrow, in which social and political organization will have caught up with technological progress.

That the present and the past are not infallible guides to the future has been amply demonstrated many times by those who have tried to penetrate the mists that obscure what is to come. But Shakespeare, who recognized that "what's past is prologue," had more than the absence of a better alternative as justification for this perceptive insight. There is a continuity in the affairs of men effected by both biological and social forces. The biological fact is that generations of men are in continuous overlap, despite the hue and cry about the "generation gap," and that man's biological heritage as transmitted through the germ plasm reveals no great discontinuities over periods as long as that of recorded history. The social fact is that man's cultures also display remarkable continuity—for man acquires his social characteristics through the continuous process of socialization by which infants are transformed from biological organisms to members of a society. In the process of socialization there is also continuous overlap, so that cultures, their material as well as their nonmaterial components, are transmitted from generation to generation in an almost unbroken stream. To be sure, man's social heritage changes

more rapidly than his biological heritage, but in any society contemporary culture contains many layers that, like geologic strata, have accumulated over time.

Urban societies of the present and the past are the works of man, as the only culture-building animal on the face of the earth. As elements of his social heritage, they are the products of man's ongoing efforts to cope with the physical world in which he lives, to survive, and, increasingly, to improve his lot.

Historical overview

Urban societies are of relatively recent origin. Although man, or a close relative, has been on the earth for at least two million years, he did not achieve fixed settlement until the Neolithic Period, some 10,000 years ago. Prior to that time man lived an essentially nomadic existence, wandering from place to place, largely in quest of food and other essentials for survival. Fixed human settlement, and the subsequent evolution of urban societies, may be viewed as the product of the interrelations of four elements—population, environment, technology, and social organization.

World population in the Neolithic Period approximated some 10 million persons who were beginning to master their own destinies. The river basins, first in Mesopotamia and Egypt and then in Crete and India, provided relatively favorable environments for settlement and growth. But the crucial factors were technology and social organization. Crude as it was, Neolithic technology provided a material basis for settled existence. The great material achievements of the Neolithic revolution—cultivation and the domestication of plants and animals—made it possible for man to abandon his nomadic life and to obtain his sustenance in a peasant-type village. Moreover, the nonmaterial aspects of the cultures that man had developed provided the social organizational potential that made aggregative living possible. These included such elements as stability and order in social relations, family values, respect for the rights of individuals, recognition of "in-group" as opposed to "out-group" interests, and traditionalism—recognition of the value of institutions and processes that had survived and permitted the group to survive.

Although Neolithic technology and social organization made fixed settlements possible, they did not, in general, permit permanent settlement. The typical Neolithic village had to shift perhaps every 20 years because the primitive technology exhausted the resources of the environment. Moreover, as population increased, settlements grew in number rather than in size. The size that a settlement could attain was largely a function of its technology and was governed by such factors as easy walking distance to cultivated land.

The Neolithic village set the stage for the development of the town and the city by producing a surplus. It was a food surplus that made possible the emergence of the first "experts"—artisans, magicians, priests, chiefs, and warriors. The reciprocal development of improved technology, increased division of labor, specialization, interdependence, and more complex social organization permitted even larger human agglomerations. Thus, about 5,000 years ago, towns and cities—agglomerations 10 times and more the size of Neolithic villages—appeared. The first cities and, therefore, the first urban societies emerged in Egypt, Mesopotamia, and the Indus Basin, and they may be regarded as the progenitors of all cities in the Old World. Cities also evolved in Central America three millennia later, probably independently of the Old World developments.

With a few possible exceptions, such as ancient China, man's technological and social organizational development did not permit cities of 100,000 or more until Greco-Roman times. Cities of such size required a relatively sophisticated technology, including well-organized facilities for the circulation of goods and persons, provision for an adequate water supply, a sanitation system, and techniques for greater agricultural and nonagricultural productivity. They also required more complex forms of social organization, manifested in the Greco-Roman forms of government, systems of slavery, concepts of law, social institutions, military establishments, and funds of knowledge, prolegomena to contemporary science and engineering. Not until the 19th century did mankind achieve a level both of technology and of social organization that permitted the proliferation of cities of a million or more, and not until the 20th century were metropolitan areas of many millions possible, together with prospects of megalopolises of tens of millions.

The city, then, is the product of technological and social organizational developments achieved by human populations making use of available environments. The city, in turn, has produced urban societies characterized by the sociologist Louis Wirth's classic phrase, "urbanism as a way of life." The city may be variously viewed as a population agglomeration, as a physical construct, as an economic mechanism, as a form of social organization, and as a political unit. A brief examination of the city from each of these perspectives will serve as a starting point for the discussion of the urban society of the future, for "urban society" encapsulates all of these perspectives.

The city as a population agglomeration

The absence of adequate data prevents a clear tracing of world urbanization before 1800, but it can be reasonably measured from that date. Urbanization refers to the proportion of a population that resides in urban places. The definition of an urban place, however, varies widely from nation to nation, so that the presentation of comparative data for nations or the synthesis of data for the world as a whole involves many technical difficulties. For purposes of international comparability, the United Nations has recommended that an urban place be defined as one having 20,000 or more residents.

World urbanization by the above definition has been traced by the sociologist Kingsley Davis. In 1800 only 2.4% of the world's population was urban. By 1850 the proportion had increased to 4.3%; by 1900, to 9.2%; by 1950, to 20.9%; and, as the United Nations has shown, by 1960, to 30%. Thus, in about one and one-half centuries, urbanization had risen from about one forty-second to almost one-third of the world population.

The dramatic increase in urban population, which may be termed "the population implosion," was of course fed by the great acceleration in the rate of total world population growth, "the population explosion." World population rose by about 29% in the half century from 1800 to 1850, by 57% from 1850 to 1900, and by 49% between 1900 and 1950. In 1800 world population numbered some

900 million. By 1950 the world's peoples had increased to 2.5 billion (by 1960 to 3 billion and by 1968 to 3.5 billion). These large increases, combined with other forces making for urbanization, resulted in urban population growths of 132% between 1800 and 1850, 194% between 1850 and 1900, and 240% between 1900 and 1950.

During the 19th century, urbanization took place mainly in the present economically advanced nations—chiefly in Europe and northern America (north of the Rio Grande). During the 20th century, however, the emphasis has shifted to the less developed nations—in Asia, Latin America, and Africa. For example, in the three half centuries from 1800, urban population in Europe and northern America rose by 184%, 337%, and 160%, respectively. In the same three periods, urban population in Asia increased by 25%, 59%, and 444%. Even with this acceleration, 41% of the population in the more developed nations inhabited places of 20,000 or more in 1960, compared with 22% of the population in the less developed nations.

The category "urban" is generally confined to population clumpings in individual cities or to political entities of a specified size. During the 20th century, however, population agglomerations have spilled over their municipal boundaries into adjoining "suburbia," often including sizable population aggregations that had been independent urban centers themselves. Attempts to measure these population clumpings, ignoring municipal boundary lines, led to development of the "metropolitan area" concept. The metropolitan area is also variously defined in different nations, but comparability has been achieved on a worldwide basis through the efforts of the International Urban Research Center at the University of California, Berkeley. According to its analysis, by 1955 there were 1,107 metropolitan areas in the world with populations of 100,000 or more, and 108 such areas with populations of one million or more. Of the 1,107 metropolitan areas, 341 were in Asia, 279 in Europe, 202 in northern America, 148 in the U.S.S.R., 78 in Latin America, 48 in Africa, and 11 in Oceania. Of the 108 metropolitan areas with one million or more persons, 34 were in Europe, 32 in Asia, 26 in northern America, 8 in Latin America, 3 in the U.S.S.R., 3 in Africa, and 2 in Oceania. It is to be observed that, although Europe and northern America are more highly urbanized, Asia has more metropolitan areas by reason of its much greater total population.

In the United States, "urban" is defined as a place having 2,500 or more inhabitants. According to the U.S. Census of Population, when the first census was taken in 1790 the U.S. urban population included only 5% of a total population of fewer than four million people. By 1850 the urban population was still only 15%; by 1900 it had risen to 40%, and by 1950 to 59% (64% using the "new" definition that includes unincorporated as well as incorporated places of 2,500 or more). By 1960 the urban population of the U.S. had reached 70% (new definition). It was not until 1920 that the United States became an urban nation in the sense that more than half of the population lived in urban places. Hence, only by 1970 will the United States have completed its first half century as an urban nation—a fact that accounts for many contemporary problems and has significant implications for the future.

The city as a physical construct

Archaeological finds reveal many ingenious patterns of construction and design of individual shelters and of urban complexes. The city as a physical construct achieved varying forms for the diverse functions to be performed—habitation, industry, trade, finance, worship, education, administration, security, recreation, and so on. To unite and integrate these structures, well-patterned channels for the circulation of goods and persons were developed, including means of transport and communication. Basic urban amenities were devised, among the more important being systems of water supply, sewerage, and waste disposal.

Lewis Mumford, a lifelong observer of the city and its history, has characterized the evolution of the urban physical plant as the development of ever more complex "containers," of which the urban plant as an entity is the grand container of the other containers. The characteristics of the containers, as well as the size of the urban

plant as a whole, varied with the state of the technology and the limits imposed by the prevailing social organization.

The "preindustrial city" had a definite physical form, as described by Gideon Sjoberg in his book of that name (1965). Within the city wall, a bastion for defense against potential external enemies, the city was subdivided into various sections, often sealed off by moats and walls. Typically, the central area contained the structures housing the key functions of government, religion, and defense, as well as the central market. Close to this central area were located the habitations of the elite, often facing inward for security and privacy and presenting a blank wall to the street. Away from the center of the city, in inverse relation to power and wealth, lived the remainder of the population, with the poorest often residing in the insecure areas beyond the city wall. Within this general framework, the city comprised a congeries of subareas sectioned off on the basis of economic function, social characteristics, ethnicity, or religion. The preindustrial city had relatively primitive infrastructure facilities— transport, water supply, sewerage, waste disposal, recreational space —with concomitant poor sanitation contributing to high levels of mortality.

The Industrial Revolution and the accompanying technological and social innovations transformed the city as a physical construct. Walls disappeared as the population outgrew their confines and as the emergence of national governments decreased the need for local defense. With improved transportation as well as increased security, location near the center of the city lost much of its attractiveness. The 19th-century industrial city was characterized by densely packed populations crowded around factory plants, while the elite tended to move farther and farther from the center. Openness became increasingly attractive to those who could afford it.

In the United States, where cities did not inherit extensive physical plants from the preindustrial era, land-use patterns evolved that turned the preindustrial pattern inside out. It was the working class population that tended to cluster near the center of the city, near industrial plants and jobs, whereas the more affluent population spread out toward the periphery to enjoy openness, low densities, and countryside amenities. In other parts of the world the physical plant assumed various forms combining the pattern inherited from the preindustrial period with the new land-use pattern made possible by industrialization.

Twentieth-century technology, symbolized by electric power, the automotive complex (the auto, the truck, streets and highways), and the telephone, stimulated further decentralization—for industry and business and for the general run of the population as well as for the elite. Industry and business structures as well as dwelling places became more widely distributed, though remaining within the metropolitan area. In Mumford's language, 20th-century technology permitted "the removal of limits." The city as a "container" burst, with "urban sprawl and the emergence of megalopolis"—the coalescence of metropolitan areas.

The 20th century has witnessed a tortuous adaptation of 19th-century urban plant to 20th-century technology, even as ever-developing technology is ushering in 21st-century land-use potentials. Since urban plant is not as mobile as population, and because urban plant involves large capital outlays, it should not be surprising that many problems have afflicted and still afflict the city as a physical construct. Moreover, aggregative living in ever-greater clumpings has generated new collective needs and problems, with which prevailing forms of social organization have not been able to cope. Inner-city blight and slums have developed as the urban plant has aged and been permitted to decay. The "poor," disproportionately including minority groups, have been forced to live in substandard housing because the existing economic and social organization has given them no alternative. The automobile and truck have devoured increasing proportions of the urban plant for movement, parking, and maintenance and have spawned acute traffic congestion. Inadequate social mechanisms have resulted in air, water, and general environmental pollution. Rapid technological advance has hastened the rate of obsolescence of industrial and commercial plant. Rapid population growth has outdistanced the increase in many physical amenities, including water supply, sewerage, mass transit, streets, expressways, and highways. Burgeoning air transportation has outrun the airways and the construction of airports, with near chaotic results.

Although the severity of these physical problems varies among the economically advanced nations, none of them is completely free of such problems. But the physical problems of the developed nations are minor compared with those of the less developed nations. The population agglomerations in Asia, Latin America, and Africa, generated in the main by forces quite different from those operating in the advanced nations, are plagued by completely inadequate physical plant. They are characterized also by huge "squatter" populations living under miserable physical conditions. The horrendous physical problems of cities in the less developed world result not so much from decay as from extreme poverty, which has precluded the construction of even minimal physical amenities.

The city as an economic mechanism

The city, initially made possible by agricultural advances, generated new economic activities that greatly increased nonagricultural productivity. As Adam Smith indicated in the late 18th century, the growth in the size of population clumpings made possible greater division of labor. Specialization, in turn, increased productivity, and such increases were compounded as technology advanced to include the use of nonhuman and eventually nonanimal sources of power—more readily applied to production processes by reason of special-

ization. In this circular process, productivity was further increased by reason of economies of scale, the contribution of mass beltline production; external economies, the advantages of the concentration of similar economic functions; and the minimization of the frictions of space and communication through an improving network of roads and the development of mass communications media.

Urban economic activity created or made more significant a number of concepts and institutions, such as "property," the "wage-worker," "luxury," "poverty," and "economic power." New forms of economic organization and administration emerged, such as gang slavery, the ancient state's system of cultivation and production; the guild system of the preindustrial city; and eventually, in the industrial city, "the factory system," labor unions, organizations of employers, the joint-stock company, and the corporation.

Self-interest became a key economic incentive—not only self-interest in obtaining means of subsistence but also in acquiring as much as possible of the surplus. Self-interest as motivation thrived in the urban setting, where size and density of population operated to devalue personal, family, and community relationships, and inter-personal contacts came to be based on utility rather than on sentiment and emotion. The role of the person in the economy shifted from "status" to "contract," another manifestation of depersonalized relations. In the urban setting, it was easy to accept the dictum that each person "pursuing his own interest as if guided by an invisible hand" (Adam Smith) acted in the collective interest.

Trade expanded with the emergence of nations and national governments, and, with the rise of the industrial city, the "free market" increasingly became the mechanism for the allocation of resources and the regulation of the production and distribution of goods and services. The increased interdependence and, also, the increased vulnerability of the urban economy gave rise to new types of problems—exploitation of child and female labor and other abuses of labor; extremes in the distribution of wealth; great fluctuations in the level of economic activity, with periodic high levels of unemployment; adulteration of products and large-scale fraud; and monopolistic practices. Such abuses and frictions forced government intervention, and the net effect was to increase greatly the public sector of the economy. In its extreme form, government interventionism took the form of socialism, as manifested in the Communist nations.

As in its other aspects, the city as an economic mechanism differs widely between the economically advanced nations and the less developed nations. Urbanization in the developed nations was largely the product of technological and social organizational advance, and was accompanied by increased productivity and higher levels of living. In the less developed countries, cities often were more the product of the economic development of an imperial system than of indigenous economic development. Large cities such as Calcutta,

Jakarta, Saigon, Rangoon, Mexico City, San Juan, and Dakar were developed largely to serve as entrepôts between the mother country and the colony. With the collapse of empires in the post-World War II world, many of these cities lost their economic base. Moreover, in the postwar period these cities often grew not because of their economic pull, as in the West, but because of the in-migration of refugee populations from a troubled countryside and the overpopulation of rural areas as a result of rapidly decreasing mortality.

The city as a social organization

Urbanization has produced a form of social organization quite unlike that which preceded aggregative living in fixed settlements. In the preurban society—the "little community" as designated by the anthropologist Robert Redfield—both potential and actual human contacts were fewer and a different character of society obtained. The little community is characterized by "primary contacts"—face-to-face, intimate contacts across the entire life space of the persons involved—and "primary group" living. Interpersonal relations are based on intimacy, sentiment, and emotion. In urban society—"mass society" as the social theorist Karl Mannheim called it—contacts are "secondary" and occur in "secondary group" living. These contacts are highly segmental, involving interaction only at points where activity is common, as in the relationship of patient and physician, student and teacher, customer and grocer. Under such conditions, interpersonal relations are based on utility rather than on sentiment. People use one another.

Urban society is also characterized by more heterogeneous contacts than is the preurban order. Large population agglomerations bring peoples of diverse backgrounds—differing in culture, religion, language, ethnicity, and race—not only into the same geographic area but also into the same life space—the same social, economic, and political activities. In consequence, frictions and problems arising in interpersonal relations are both more numerous and more intense. Moreover, close contact with diverse values, norms of behavior, and ideas leads to questioning of one's own values, norms of behavior, and ideas, and traditional behavior based on automatic acceptance of one's own social heritage tends to break down. In the mass society behavior becomes increasingly rational rather than traditional, more the result of choice based on consideration of alternatives.

In the little community social control is informal. Constraints on behavior operate through the folkways and mores transmitted as elements of the social heritage. In the mass society social control becomes formal—effected by means of law, administrative fiat, police, courts, and penitentiaries. Formal controls in the urban setting have yet to become as effective in restraining deviant behavior as the informal controls of the little community.

213

The family as the basic social institution has been transformed by urbanization. In the little community it was an integrated and intimate unit, with producing, consuming, educational, religious, protective, and recreational functions. In the mass society many of these functions have disappeared or have become attenuated. In the little community the family was multinuclear or extended in form; in the mass society it is more often nuclear, including only parents and children. In the little community the family was the predominant institution in the socialization of the child; in the mass society it is but one of many, sharing this function with the school, voluntary organizations, and the peer group. Finally, in the little community the family was often under the domination of the male as husband and father; in the mass society the family is increasingly egalitarian and the roles of husband, wife, and children have undergone considerable redefinition.

Bureaucracy is the inevitable by-product of urban society. It is by no means restricted to government—it pervades all aspects of the urban order. The corporation is a bureaucracy. So also are the labor union, the university, the voluntary organization, the church. Bureaucracy is a large-scale organization in the urban setting with a function to be performed. It is characterized by a hierarchy of offices to which duties and obligations are attached; a set of procedures by which its mission is accomplished; selection of personnel on the basis of qualifications rather than kinship and similar considerations; impersonality and criteria of efficiency.

As a form of social organization, the city is dependent on a network of communications through which contact, coordination, integration, and control are achieved. Even the Neolithic village required channels of communication, particularly with respect to the distribution of the surplus. The origin of writing and of arithmetic may be traced to the need for record keeping and communication in urban living. As problems to be resolved grew more complex, mechanisms of communication kept pace; and as the need for knowledge as a basis for policy formation increased, better means of acquiring and utilizing knowledge emerged. It is in this context that the development of mathematics, philosophy, and the sciences can be understood, as well as the utilization of scientific knowledge through various forms of engineering—physical, biological (the physician), and now, increasingly, social (social worker, public administrator).

Contemporary urban society is still in transition from the preurban agrarian order. The various problems that afflict urban societies are to be understood as frictions of the ongoing transition from the little community. This is so whether the problems one is considering be physical (pollution of air, water, and the environment, slums, traffic congestion), personal (delinquency, crime, alcoholism, drug addiction), economic (unemployment, poverty, tax evasion, adulteration of products, monopoly), social (the revolt of youth, ethnic and racial prejudices and discriminatory practices, the black rebellion), or political (chaos in local government function and finance, inadequate public services).

In contrast to the economically advanced nations, in the less developed areas the increased potential for human interaction provided by urban society often is not utilized. In Rangoon, for example, the large population agglomeration comprises a congeries of ethnic, racial, and religious groupings in addition to a Westernized urban center; each of these tends to be self-contained and has relatively little contact with the others. In each of these localized communities, subsistence economies of the cottage-industry type exist, with little or no separation of place of work and place of residence. This operates to maintain an enclave that in most respects remains a "little community." Under these circumstances, large urban agglomerations may not become "mass societies."

The city as a form of governance

In the first fixed forms of human settlement, government was relatively simple in form and function. Early functions involved such elementary operations as control over the distribution of surplus, police and defense functions, and sometimes, as in Egypt where Pharaoh was both king and god, control of religious activities.

The increase in the size and density of population agglomerations, the new dimensions of the urban physical plant requiring huge infrastructure investment, the increased interdependence and vulnerability of the economic order, the rising social costs of frictions in the marketplace, the breakdown of the traditional order, and the growing inability of the social heritage of the past to cope with emergent urban problems have led inexorably to the expansion of governmental functions, functionaries, and powers. This process is by no means universally understood or completed. Moreover, the forms and processes of government have by no means been able to keep pace with urbanization and, in consequence, government itself often exacerbates the problems with which it attempts to deal.

This failure may be demonstrated by using the United States as an example. Political ideology, which has not kept up with the requirements of urban life, has contributed to the lag in governmental effectiveness. For example, the widely held tenet that "that government is best which governs least" made considerable sense in 1790, when 95% of the population lived on farms or in places with fewer than 2,500 inhabitants. Under such circumstances, there was not much for government to do. Similarly, the tenet that "each person pursuing his own interest would automatically act in the interest of the collectivity" also made sense in 1790, when each family head who assumed responsibility for the welfare of his own family was very much contributing to the welfare of the entire nation. But visualize a United States today without a Food and Drug Administration, without a Social Security system, without welfare programs, without a Federal Trade Commission, without a Securities and Exchange Commission, and so on, and one visualizes considerably more chaos than we now experience. These ideological tenets may be regarded as examples of "cultural lag."

Consider another clear-cut example of cultural lag. The U.S. Constitution wisely provided that the citizen had the right to bear arms. In the frontier society of 1790, guns were important means of protecting a family against animals and other hostile forces. They were also an important means of augmenting the food supply. But in this last third of the 20th century, the right to possess guns constitutes a clear anachronism.

Nowhere is this cultural lag more visible than on the state and local levels. As recently as 1960 there were 39 states in the Union in which the majority of the population was urban, but there was not a single state in which the urban population controlled the state legislature. In consequence, urban populations whose needs were ignored by rural-dominated state legislatures were forced to appeal to the federal government. This is why the federal government is involved in such functions as public housing, urban renewal, civil rights, expressways and highways, mass transportation, and education. It is not so much that the federal government usurped "states' rights" as that the state legislatures ignored the needs of the urban population.

The very form of city government that prevails in the United States today is anachronistic, having been copied from that of England in the 17th century. At that time, no one anticipated the emergence of great cities, let alone of metropolitan areas that ignore municipal, township, and county lines and even state boundaries. As a result local government is fragmented, and individual metropolitan areas may contain as many as a thousand separate governmental units, each with powers to tax and to spend. In most cases there is no mechanism for dealing effectively with area-wide problems, such as water supply, drainage, sewerage, air and water pollution, traffic congestion, and crime prevention, especially the prevention of organized crime.

In urban United States today, place of residence, place of work, and place of political responsibility are often separated, as are also place of shopping, place of recreation, place of schooling, and place of worship. As a result, great disparities often exist between the need for essential public services, such as education and police protection, and the ability of the local government to provide such services. This problem has been exacerbated by the trend whereby more affluent persons move to governmentally independent suburbia and the poor remain in the central cities, where the tax base grows smaller and the problems grow larger.

The requirements of the mass society have led to an increase in the functions and powers of central governments throughout the world. Among the new functions that have evolved at various levels of government is that of "planning." City planning first evolved as a means of dealing rationally with the many physical problems of the city, but it soon became apparent that planning necessarily involved economic, social, and administrative considerations as well. Moreover, it also became evident that city planning could not proceed rationally if attention was directed only to the problems of the municipalities under the planning agencies' jurisdiction. The planning function, therefore, expanded, leading to comprehensive programs such as "public housing," "urban renewal," and "new-town" developments that included central governmental as well as local governmental participation. The proliferation of planning functions and agencies has, not surprisingly, led to the emergence of planning as a new profession—another product of the urban society.

The future: population

Much of the future of urban society is implicit in the above description of the past and present. What follows may now be better comprehended and seen in the context of what has gone before.

Short of the catastrophic, such as thermonuclear war, the population explosion and implosion will both continue, certainly to the end of the century. The rate of world urbanization will continue to accelerate. In 1800, 1.7% of the world's peoples lived in places of 100,000 or more; by 1850, 2.3%; by 1900, 5.5%; and by 1950, 13.1%. The continuation of this trend, as estimated by the economist Homer Hoyt, would place 28% of the world's peoples in cities of 100,000 or more by 1975 and 42% by 2000. By the century's end, over three-fourths of the population of northern America would be residents of cities of 100,000 or more, 55% in Oceania, and 48% in Europe. By 2000, 50% of the people in Latin America may be residents of cities of 100,000 or more, 39% in Asia, and 25% in Africa.

Growing world urbanization will take the form of increases in both the number and the size of urban places. In the more highly urbanized world of the future, profound changes will have occurred in the physical, economic, social, and political aspects of urbanism as a way of life. The transition from agrarian to mass society will be accelerated, and the social consequences of urbanization will become much more prominent and, perhaps, even dominant. Let us try to anticipate the situation by the mid-21st century, when the United States will have been an urban nation some 130 years, or about five generations.

The future: the physical city

By 2050 urban concentrations will have achieved much in the way of new form and structure, even while retaining some of their 20th-century physical heritage. The urban physical plant in both the economically advanced and the less developed nations will be more the product of central planning than of the play of market forces, and it will embody many dramatic technological developments.

In the economically advanced nations, the present-day metropolitan area will be a relatively old-fashioned form of urbanization, corresponding perhaps to what are now intermediate-sized cities. The advanced 21st-century urban agglomeration will be a megalopolis —a superagglomeration comprising large numbers of contemporary metropolitan areas merged into single concentrations that conceivably could encompass from 50 million to 100 million persons. Such an emergent megalopolis is visible in the almost unbroken clumping of people and economic activities reaching from Boston to Washington, D.C. In 1960 this area, defined by Jean Gottmann in his book *Megalopolis* (1961), already contained some 32 million persons.

Megalopolis as the form of future urban society will be both the consequence and the antecedent of vast technological developments in transportation and communications. The present major forms of intraurban transit, the automobile and the truck, will become little more than feeder vehicles to forms of mass transportation that are

now only speculative ideas. These could include fast trains and monorails; helicopter buses; automated expressways with continuous uninterrupted vehicular flow; and rocket vehicles, underground and on the surface.

Life in megalopolis will also be greatly facilitated by new developments in communications. A "home communication center"—available to every family—will provide mid-21st-century man with the potential for instantaneous communication, publication, sight and sound recording, and holography, including instantaneous transmission of anything in one's own hand, such as examination papers and signatures needed for banking transactions. Needless to say, the home communication center will give instantaneous sight and sound access to news, entertainment, special events, and the like—and without "commercials."

A home computer will permit the programming of many routine household tasks, including daytime and nighttime regulation of temperature and of fresh air intake and exhaust; turning ranges and ovens on and off and setting appropriate temperatures; signaling requirements for convenience goods; arranging for recreation and

travel; and shopping. A combination of three-dimensional TV and the computer will make it possible to do most shopping from the home communication center and will eliminate most present forms of retail trade—certainly for standardized goods.

By the mid-21st century, the urban plant will have been subjected to more than half a century of intense application of urban design and centralized planning. Many experiments in urban design will have been undertaken, and most of them will still be part of the mid-21st-century urban structure. These will include various forms of "new towns," occupying much of what is now exurbia and filling in the now-open spaces within and between metropolitan areas. With the development of megalopolis and increased central planning, land use and development will be largely controlled by government. Urban design will have become an accepted governmental function, with cooperation among all levels of government—central, regional, and local. Private property rights will have been further redefined so as to subordinate them to public needs. Slums will have disappeared because it will have become impossible to derive any profits from them. "Urban maintenance" will have eliminated the need for "urban renewal," for man will have learned to maintain urban plant on a continuous basis.

Urban design will have developed in various ways but with common principles, including the following:

1. Central control of land use in the interest of the entire urban society—the redefinition of the rights of private property at points where they conflict with the rights of society as a whole.
2. Adequate land for public use—for circulation of goods and persons, and for collective activities such as education, recreation, conventions, and meetings.
3. Public control of the environment so as to prevent all forms of environmental pollution.
4. A decent residence for every family.
5. Adequate provision for such urban amenities as water supply, sewerage, waste disposal, lighting.
6. The development of mass transit and the conversion of the role of the automobile to that of feeder for mass intraurban transport.
7. The development of a hierarchy of roadways balancing public and private transport and providing ready and safe access to collective activities; separation of pedestrian and vehicular traffic.
8. Creation of pedestrian malls, immune from invasion by vehicles that go to but not through such areas.
9. Bringing into all aspects of urban design consideration of the requirements of the human being—not only physical, but also psychological, aesthetic, and spiritual.

The implementation of such principles will undoubtedly transcend the present new town developments—which already represent great advances in urban plant, as is evident in the more ingenious new towns such as Tapiola in Finland, Cumbernauld in Scotland, and Welwyn in England. There will, of course, be important developments in materials and forms of construction. Intimations of these new forms can be seen in prefabricated housing, modular construction, and the "Habitat" complex shown at the Montreal exposition of 1967.

Finally, the future may bring control of the weather—or, at least, the control of temperature and humidity—over all or a major portion of the urban environment. Such control is already possible, of course, in individual structures, but in the future large parts of the urban agglomeration may be enclosed within a gigantic man-made envelope.

Needless to say, these developments may not occur in the urban agglomerations in the less developed regions. Between now and the mid-21st century many advances there are to be anticipated—or, at least, hoped for—but to a considerable extent progress will depend on the ability of the less developed areas to dampen their rates of population growth. If this can be done with at least moderate success, the less developed nations could make many notable advances, including improvement in infrastructure and, it is to be hoped, elimination of "squatter-town" developments. It is possible that new towns will be as important a part of the urban scene in the less developed areas as in the economically developed nations, but probably on a considerably lower level of affluence.

Less developed nations that achieve adequate population control may well have urban plants competitive with those in the present advanced nations—partly because they will be able to avoid many of the mistakes of the developed nations. It is possible that some less developed areas will be able to make the transition from their present urban plant to 21st-century urban plant without having to replicate the 19th- and 20th-century experiences of the advanced countries. But it would be wishful thinking in the extreme to suppose that this will happen throughout the less developed world.

The future: economic, social, and political organization

Economic, social, and political organization are considered together because by the mid-21st century they will not be as distinguishable as they are at present. The search for solutions to ever more difficult urban problems will necessitate increasing fusion of the economic, the social, and the political.

By the mid-21st century, the political ideologies consonant with 18th-century agrarian America will have been recognized as obsolete. In lieu of the tenet that "that government is best that governs least," it will be recognized that that government is best that provides the services essential to the maintenance of a viable urban society. In lieu of the tenet that "each man pursuing his own interest as if guided by an invisible hand acts in the interest of all," it will be recognized that, in an urban society, the impersonal and utilitarian nature of social interrelations requires government to use its powers to protect society against those whose self-interest leads to acts injurious to others. In lieu of the tenet that "taxes are funds taken away from the people by government and should be kept to a minimum," it will be

221

recognized that taxes are the price of services that only government can provide.

Many other examples of cultural lag will have been erased by mid-21st century. In the United States, for example, the right to possess guns will be severely restricted and controlled in accordance with the realities of urban society. Rigorous enforcement of provisions for reapportionment will have ensured the representative character of all legislative bodies. The use of force to resolve conflicts of interests—including labor-management disputes, intergroup differences, and intergenerational conflict—will have been completely outlawed. Mechanisms will have been evolved for the adjudication of all such conflicts by peaceful, nonviolent methods. The administration of criminal justice will have been revised to protect the interest of society in its battle with crime, especially organized crime. No longer will the rights of the individual and adherence to legal technicalities transcend the rights of the urban society. The organization and procedures of the Congress, state legislatures, and city councils will no longer permit tyranny by minorities, as is now possible through such devices as seniority appointments to committees and committee chairmanships, special-interest lobbies, undisclosed legislators' incomes, and the filibuster.

In brief, by the mid-21st century the United States will no longer be an anachronistic society, urban in demographic, physical, and technological structure but agrarian in economic, social, and political outlook. The laissez-faire orientation that has persisted to the present will have been replaced by recognition of the requirements of an urbanized and metropolitanized society. It will be understood that the personal, social, economic, and political freedoms of the populace can and must be assured and enhanced by positive governmental policies and programs. It will be recognized that the "welfare state" is not a pejorative term, but a necessity for the operation of an urban society.

By the mid-21st century the United States, as well as most urban societies throughout the world, will have adopted the following basic social goals and will have modified their constitutional and legal provisions accordingly:

1. To provide every person with the opportunity, freedom, and security that will enable him to achieve optimal development of the human potential.
2. To provide every child with a physical, social, and political setting for effective socialization, including formal education adequate to enable him to assume the obligations and responsibilities, as well as the rights, of citizenship and to enhance his life chances for opportunity, freedom, and security.
3. To provide every person with the opportunity for maximum length of life in good health.
4. To achieve positive control over the environment—both the physical environment and the social milieu—in the interest of society, including management of air, water, housing, adverse population densities, recreational facilities, natural resources, and urban design.

5. To provide every person with opportunity for employment commensurate with his education and skill and, if such employment cannot be provided, to assure him of an adequate income flow, preferably for services performed.

6. To provide every couple with the motivation and incentive as well as the knowledge and means to limit family size to a level consistent with family, community, national, and international welfare.

7. To assure equality to all in the administration of justice in a manner that will protect the interests of society while safeguarding the interests of the person.

8. To rationalize the system of national, regional, and local governance, including rational allocation of sources of revenue among different levels of government, and the preservation of basic democratic principles, including representative government and majority rule. It should be noted that, by the mid-21st century, existing totalitarian governments will have been forced to move in this direction by the pressures of modernizing urban societies.

9. To promote economic growth and the development of science, technology, the arts, and mass culture, and thus to provide a milieu in which opportunity, freedom, and security may be more meaningful in the attainment of the human potential.

10. To contribute to the development of a peaceful world order—a world of optimal economic, social, and political interrelationships; and to strive toward this end by maximum participation in international organizations, even at the expense of national sovereignty.

11. To maximize the areas of freedom of operation in the private sector consistent with the general goal of providing every person with opportunity, freedom, and security.

Thus, far from brutalizing and dehumanizing society, technological advances that permit agglomerative living and the emergence of urban society will also generate changes in social organization and goals in the interest of the person and the urban society. While the transition from the little community to the mass society will by no means have been completed by the mid-21st century, the character of the future urban society will have become clearly indicated in accordance with the goals outlined above. In the realm of the physical, environmental pollution, substandard housing, the commuters' crisis, and inadequate water, sewerage, and waste-disposal facilities will have been largely eliminated, especially in the economically advanced nations (which by then will include at least some of the present less developed nations).

In the realm of the economy, exploitative and monopolistic practices will have been subjected to control; more equitable income distribution will have been achieved; nonviolent means of resolving conflicts of interest will have emerged; and methods of distribution of goods and services will more nearly match the great advances in productivity.

In the realm of the social, methods of socializing the child will have been improved so as to produce adults possessing a healthy awareness of their obligations to society and concern for their fellow men without crippling their initiative and creativity. Racial prejudice as a vestige of the ethnocentrism of the little community will have largely disappeared, in recognition of the requirements of dense and heterogeneous urban living. Pluralistic societies will continue, but without animosity and intense intergroup conflict. Formal social controls will have evolved that can restrict undesirable deviate behavior to within tolerable limits. The family will have survived as the basic social institution, but it will have become a more egalitarian collectivity, in both spouse relationships and those of parent and child. Improved formal education will provide every child with the basic skills, the salable skills, and the citizenship skills that will enable him to stand on his own feet as an adult. Not unrelated to this development will be a great increase in the allocation of resources for educational purposes. Other social institutions will have developed to supplement the roles of the family and the school. Bureaucracies will still be with us, in all realms of life, but they will be controlled to maximize personal freedom within the framework of the social goals.

Finally, public and private policy and program development and administration will no longer be based on contemporary "conservative" or "liberal" attitudes or approaches. In the contemporary world, decision makers in both the public and the private sector come from diverse backgrounds, reflecting differential exposure to the social milieus of the little community and the mass society. In general, the conservative is the product of the little community—committed to the traditional order and its preservation. He is almost instinctively inclined to look to the past for answers to current problems. In contrast, the liberal is more often the product of the mass society—emancipated from the traditional order but not necessarily conversant with the genesis or implications of contemporary problems. He often confuses emotional zeal and energy—including their utilization in breaking with the past—with problem solving. The conservative is the representative of the past in the present; the liberal is more often the representative of the present, but he may also reflect the chaos and confusion of the present. Neither the conservative nor the liberal will provide the key to the resolution of the problems of the urban society of the future.

What then will be the basic approach to the resolution of those problems? The answer is "the social engineering approach," which is consonant with the needs of the future urban society because it is the product of urbanism as a way of life. The social engineering approach consists of the application of knowledge, rather than tradition or undirected zeal, to the solution of problems. In the urban society of the future it will be the social engineer, repository of the knowledge produced by the sciences—including the social sciences—who will be drawn upon for problem solution. It will be the analysis of the problem and the presentation of alternative solutions by the social engineer that will serve as a basis for decision making.

In the future urban society, the social sciences will have gained the prestige and acceptability that the physical and biological sciences enjoy today, and social science knowledge will be applied to social problems through the utilization of social engineers just as physical science knowledge is applied through the various engineering professions and as biomedical knowledge is applied through the medical profession. There are already some well-established social engineering professions—social worker, public administrator, city planner, criminologist, city manager. It is safe to predict that the social engineering professions will proliferate.

The role of the social engineer will, of course, be greatly enhanced by his access to and control of the accumulated and instantaneously available knowledge produced by the computer. But the social engineer will not be the philosopher-king in the urban society of the future. Rather, it will be his task to play the role of "expert" to the decision maker. It will be his role to find ways of achieving socially accepted goals, as conveyed by political leaders in a democratic society and by responsible executives in the private sector. It will be the role of the social engineer to displace both the conservative and the liberal approaches at those points in the decision-making process where the dead hand of the conservative or the undirected zeal of the liberal provide emotional rather than rational answers to problems.

All in all, the urban society of the future will be a society in which the social, economic, and political will have caught up with the transformed technological and physical world. At present, we live in a 20th-century technological and physical world but with 19th-century (or earlier) economic, social, and political ideologies and institutions. By mid-21st century the inevitable and irresistible forces of urbanization will produce a society much more coeval and synchronous than present society—an urban society with 21st-century social, economic, and political—as well as 21st-century technological and physical—elements.

FOR ADDITIONAL READING:
  Childe, V. Gordon, *Man Makes Himself* (Watts, 1941).
  "Cities and Urban Affairs," *1969 Britannica Book of the Year* (Encyclopædia Britannica, Inc., 1969).
  "City," "City Government," "City Planning," *Encyclopædia Britannica,* vol. 5, 1969, pp. 809–819. *See also* other articles relating to cities listed in the *Index* (Encyclopædia Britannica, Inc., 1969).
  "The City: Starting from Scratch," *Time* (March 7, 1969).
  Eldredge, H. Wentworth (ed.), *Taming Megalopolis,* 2 vol. (Anchor Books, Doubleday & Co., Inc., 1967).
  "The Sick, Sick Cities," *Newsweek* (March 17, 1969).

AUDIOVISUAL MATERIALS FROM ENCYCLOPÆDIA BRITANNICA EDUCATIONAL CORPORATION:
  Film: *Megalopolis—Cradle of the Future.*
  Filmstrips: *Man, Builder of Cities; The Rise of Civilization* (series)

Nature on the Rampage

by Robert C. Cowen

Modern man prides himself on his ability to control his environment. Yet, before the elemental forces of nature, he can do little more than stand in awe, as his primitive ancestors did before him. A leading science journalist views some of the more spectacular natural phenomena that can bring disaster to man and his works.

Sometimes nature helps to keep things in perspective. Early in 1969, for example, the wettest season in eight decades gave Los Angeles over twice its normal annual rainfall in two months and caused several hundred million dollars in damage throughout California. At the same time, drenched Angelenos read of anguish in Chile, where the driest period in a century had forced 120,000 persons to seek emergency supplies of food from the government.

These weather extremes along the Eastern Pacific emphasize that 20th-century man still clings to a planetary surface where vast natural forces play. In spite of his vaunted technology, he cannot stay them. He only imperfectly understands them and can only partially predict their courses. To speak as we often do of man's "conquest of nature" seems a little presumptuous. Man today faces these elemental forces with more hope than ever before. Earth science is

226

大 開來類燒

Great Kanto Earthquake, wood block print, kawara-ban, 1855. Photo, courtesy, University of Tokyo, Historiographical Institute

taking giant strides toward understanding and forecasting them, and even holds out a cautious promise of bringing them under some degree of control. Even so, man can do little more than stand in awe when nature goes on a rampage.

The unstable earth

The ill-fitting doors of my California house remind me of nature's dominance. Mild earth shocks over the years have warped their frames. Their stubborn refusal to latch testifies to the seismic liveliness of a region that experts consider "due" for a devastating quake. Earthquakes as powerful as the one that wrecked San Francisco in 1906 have rocked California on an average of twice a century, so another could come at any time. Seismologists know it will probably

227

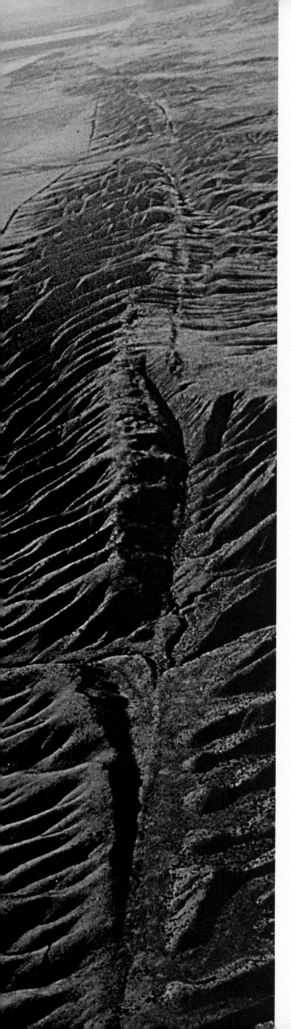

occur somewhere along the San Andreas Fault, but they cannot tell just when or where it will hit or how severe it will be.

Most quakes occur within the earth's crust, which is, on the average, 3 mi thick beneath the sea and 20 mi thick under land. About 80% take place along the coastal areas and deep ocean trenches that, with their associated volcanoes, mark the Pacific's so-called "ring of fire." Many other quakes occur along the great ridge system that bisects the North and South Atlantic, swings through the Indian Ocean, and stretches on into the Pacific. "Safe" areas cannot be complacent, however. The most widely felt series of quakes in North American history struck near New Madrid, Mo., in 1811–12, rocking an area from the Gulf of Mexico to Canada and from the Rocky Mountains to the Atlantic.

Earthquakes seem to be our planet's way of relieving strain in its outer rocks. In ways not yet understood, the underlying forces that shape the earth's surface create stresses that result in local tremors. However caused, earthquakes range from minishakes to city wreckers. Seismologists measure them according to several different scales. The one most frequently encountered is named for Charles F. Richter of the California Institute of Technology. It measures earthquake magnitude or the amplitude of the seismic waves produced. Because it is a logarithmic scale, a quake of magnitude 3, for example, would be ten times greater than one registering a magnitude of 2. The latter magnitude is about the smallest quake humans can perceive, while anything with a magnitude of 6 or higher ranks as a major shock.

Earthquake damage depends as much on local ground conditions and man's building practices as it does on the force of the quake itself. In the San Francisco earthquake of 1906 (magnitude 8.3), 700 people died and damage ran to $2.6 billion in 1966 dollars. To a considerable extent, the heavy damage was caused by fires that raced through flimsy buildings while broken water mains hampered the fire fighters. In the 1964 Alaskan earthquake (magnitude 8.5), in which 117 people died and damage amounted to more than $750 million, much of the damage occurred where buildings had been constructed on unstable land that slid away when the shock came.

Today, seismologists feel they are in a position to obtain the kind of knowledge that will help men to minimize earthquake disaster by defining safer building codes and by developing at least moderately reliable forecasting methods. Louis C. Pakiser, director of the U.S. Geological Survey's National Center for Earthquake Research, Menlo Park, Calif., believes that the ability to predict earthquakes in an active area is "a reasonable prospect for the next ten years." Much of the work in earthquake forecasting has been done in Japan, where seismic events are frequent and the need is urgent. Japanese scientists have discovered that surveys of long-term changes in leveling often herald the buildup of quake conditions and that, just before a shock, there may be a pronounced tilting of land, detectable by

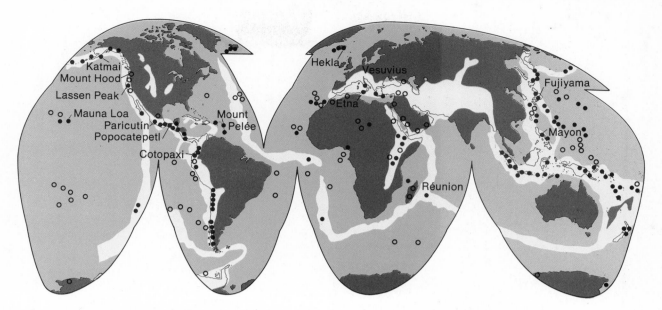

Labels on map: Katmai, Mount Hood, Lassen Peak, Mauna Loa, Paricutín, Popocatepetl, Cotopaxi, Mount Pelée, Hekla, Vesuvius, Etna, Réunion, Fujiyama, Mayon

sensitive meters. Some earthquakes are preceded by foreshocks, and these may also help to predict the force of the final event. Using these methods, scientists at the University of Tokyo's Earthquake Research Institute issued public warnings of danger periods for the Matsushiro area beginning in 1966, with about the same degree of success as that enjoyed by long-range weather forecasters.

Japan is planning a program of accurate and frequent leveling surveys throughout the country, using not only seismographs and tiltmeters, but also laser light beams, which measure land displacement with great precision. Meanwhile, scientists are searching for other quake indicators. Stresses and strains in rock strata, for example, can alter the ability of the rock to conduct an electrical current. Thus, monitoring electrical resistance under the surface of the ground might help to detect critical stress buildup. Rock strain can also change magnetic properties, so that stresses might show up in slight local changes of the earth's magnetic field. Because such magnetic changes are small (from 0.001 to 10 parts in 50,000), similar changes caused by magnetic storms and disturbances in the high atmosphere could mask them. However, Sheldon Breiner and Robert L. Kovach of Stanford University, Stanford, Calif., have found at least a time correlation between small magnetic changes and creep displacement along the San Andreas Fault near Hollister, Calif. Breiner and Kovach have seen distinctive magnetic change precede abrupt fault creep by some ten hours.

No one knows what triggers a quake once rock stress has accumulated. It might be as slight a stimulus as the gravitational pull of the sun and moon, which induces small tides in land as well as in the sea. Under certain circumstances, man may even initiate a quake himself, such as the secondary quakes set off by underground nuclear tests. J. P. Rothe, secretary-general of the International Association of Seismology and Physics of the Earth's Interior, suggests that

Earthquake regions are shown by the lightest areas on the map; solid dots represent active volcanoes and open dots denote dead ones. The coincidence of volcano and earthquake areas is particularly marked in the "ring of fire" circling the Pacific Ocean.

The San Andreas Fault (opposite page, as it appears about halfway between San Francisco and Los Angeles) extends nearly 600 mi, from the Salton Sea area in extreme southern California to the Pacific Ocean north of San Francisco.

the mass of water behind a dam, sometimes weighing as much as several billion tons, may upset local equilibria. Water seeping along deep cracks may lubricate rocks enough to cause them to slip; U.S. Geological Survey scientists think this kind of lubrication may have accounted for earth tremors that occurred near Denver, Colo., when chemical wastes were injected to a depth of over two miles at the nearby Rocky Mountain Arsenal. If so, injection or withdrawal of fluid in fault zones might provide a method of earthquake modification.

Such control, however, would be for the long-term future. Over the next decade the greatest progress can be expected in basic knowledge and forecasting of earthquakes, and in the application of that knowledge to building practices and zoning regulations so that damage from quakes, when they come, will be reduced.

Along these lines, the U.S. Federal Council for Science and Technology in January 1969 called for a ten-year National Earthquake Hazards Program, which would include mapping of hazard areas in the U.S., gathering of knowledge needed for earthquake prediction and construction planning, and investigation of the possibilities for earthquake control. The program would cost $220 million—figured on a yearly basis, about three times what was being spent on earthquake research in the U.S. in the late 1960s. On the other hand, a single great quake in an urban area could cause damage totaling billions of dollars, as well as incalculable suffering and loss of life.

The fiery mountains

Just as slowly building stresses within the earth power quakes, so pent-up pressures may quietly accumulate beneath "sleeping" volcanoes. The snowy panorama of the Cascade Range on the West Coast of North America, for example, may hide such a growing fury. Experts have been warning for several years that careful watch should be kept on these "extinct" fire mountains.

Nature stages a fireworks display as the fire pit of Halemaumau on Hawaii's Kilauea volcano erupts in November 1967. In this aerial view, molten lava is seen flowing from the fire pit at the left.

John Verde from Photo Researchers

*Residents of the Roman city
of Pompeii, attempting to escape
the great eruption of Mt. Vesuvius
in A.D. 79, were covered by volcanic
ash and their bodies preserved
in attitudes of flight. These
are plaster casts made
from the impressions of the bodies
in the ash when the city
was excavated many centuries later.*

When a volcano blows, it can release spectacular energy. Krakatan nearly obliterated an Indonesian island in 1883 when it exploded with the energy equivalent to 150 megatons of TNT. It disintegrated 5 cu mi of matter and killed 36,000 people, and for years the world's sunsets were reddened by the resulting dust cloud. And this was mild compared to an 1815 eruption in the same area that removed 36 cu mi of earth.

Some volcanoes sleep for centuries. Others, like Taal in the Philippines, have a turbulent history. Taal has erupted violently 26 times since 1572. Yet when it exploded again on Sept. 28, 1965, leaving a crater a mile long by a fifth of a mile wide and killing at least 208 persons, it took even the experts by surprise. Often such massive eruptions are heralded by minor earthquakes, ground swellings, and ground heating. In this case, a monitoring station on the mountain's flank had scarcely an inkling of danger. The only omen had been at a nearby hot lake, where the temperature rose from a normal 33° C to 45° C (91° F to 113° F) two months before the event.

Volcanic eruptions are not always sudden catastrophes, but a drawn-out period of activity can devastate a region with ash and noxious gases. Irazu in Costa Rica, quiet for 45 years, began erupting in March 1963; before it subsided 20 months later, 80 million tons of ash had been thrown over the heavily populated central plateau, depressing farming and choking the capital city of San José. As a kind of long-term reparation, the minerals in the ash enriched the soil.

The mechanism of volcanoes has yet to be fully understood. Their fiery lavas originate deep within the earth and rise along cracks in the crust. Experiments made by Hatten S. Yoder, Jr., at the Geophysical Laboratory of the Carnegie Institution, Washington, D.C., indicated that steam, resulting from the change in pressure as molten rock enters the chamber beneath a mountain, may provide the force that blows off the mountain's top. These experiments led Yoder to think about the sleeping giants of the Cascades, which are, after all, part of the "ring of fire." Even though Mt. Rainier's last major eruption was some 550 years ago, Yoder, in 1966, saw "a clear need to establish observatories near Mt. Rainier and Lassen Peak."

William T. Pecora, director of the U.S. Geological Survey, agrees. In July 1968, Costa Rica's Mt. Arenal, dormant for 500 years, exploded, killing over 100 persons and 300,000 cattle. Pecora returned from an inspection trip there to urge the establishment of a volcano watch in the Cascades. Admitting that eruptions have taken monitors unawares, as did that of Taal, Pecora explained, "From studies of volcanoes in Hawaii we know that we can catch the 'signature' of a volcanic hazard before it occurs, but it takes time and study." Warning that a number of volcanoes in the Cascade chain still could erupt explosively, he added that to go on ignoring the threat because there has been no recent activity is "out-of-sight, out-of-mind thinking."

Tsunamis: example of an early warning system

The success of the warning system against "tidal" waves in the Pacific demonstrates the value of being able to forecast natural phenomena. Actually, these waves have nothing to do with tides. They are generated by submarine landslides, volcanoes, or—most often—by earthquakes. The Japanese have a more apt name for them—*tsunami,* meaning "large waves in harbors."

These waves are scarcely noticeable on the open sea, even by a person floating on calm water in an open boat. They would rush past at speeds up to 500 mph with crests only a foot high. Once they reach offshore shallows or enter restricted coves or harbors, however, they rear into monsters that may be 100 ft high and can pack the energy of a 2.5-megaton hydrogen bomb. The April 1, 1946, tsunami, triggered by an earthquake in the Aleutian Trench, in the North Pacific, hit Hawaii with waves 50 ft high, caused $25 million in damage, and killed 173 persons.

To provide advance notice of such waves, the U.S. Coast and Geodetic Survey, working with some other Pacific countries, set up a tsunami warning system. An array of four seismic stations in Hawaii monitors earthquakes. A computer pinpoints their locations. If the quakes occur in regions likely to generate tsunamis, a network of tidal stations watches for the first sign of the waves. If waves are spotted, their courses and arrival times at populated areas can be computed and warnings issued. False alarms plague the system, however. Forecasters do not yet know how to predict accurately the local nature of tsunamis or their potential for damage in specific cases. Nevertheless, Survey scientists are confident that these difficulties will be overcome by continued research. Meanwhile, the system already provides useful warnings on an oceanwide basis.

Hurricanes: nature's blockbusters

Weathermen fooled by an unexpected snowstorm or an abnormal drought may wish they were dealing with such relatively simple phenomena as tsunamis. The weather threats they try to predict often depend on wide-ranging influences that interact in a complex way. Hurricanes illustrate this. They may decimate forests or flood coastal cities. Yet they seem to play a vital, though poorly understood, role in maintaining the earth's heat balance.

In very simple terms, the atmosphere can be thought of as a vast heat engine. The earth loses heat to space and receives energy from the sun. Overall, this balances out—otherwise the earth would slowly warm up—but regionally, there are imbalances. Tropical areas absorb more heat in their oceans than they lose to space, while the polar regions experience net cooling. Hurricanes are born along the line where temperate and tropical air mix.

These potent storms draw their energy directly from the warm ocean, chiefly in the form of water vapor which carries a hidden or "latent" heat energy. Heat is needed to evaporate water, and when the vapor condenses again as cloud drops or precipitation, this heat is released. A hurricane is an effective mechanism for this conversion. Winds, sometimes reaching speeds well above 100 mph, circle

Photograph of a hurricane, taken from the Apollo 7 spacecraft in 1968, clearly shows the circular path of the storm around the central eye. The island of Cuba is in the background.

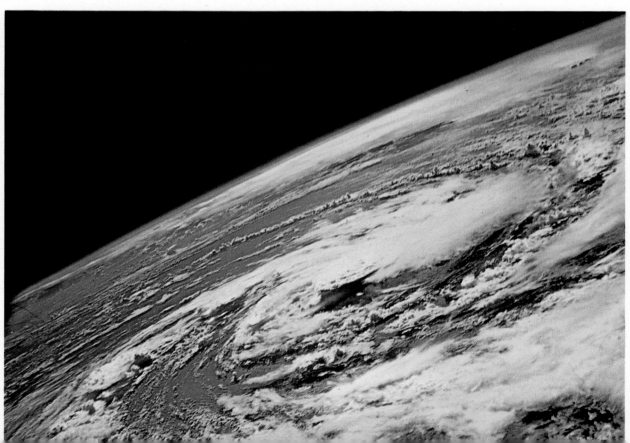

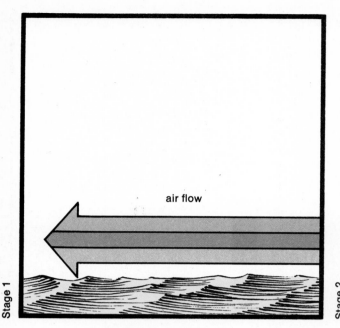

Stage 1

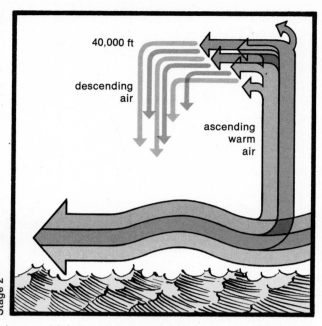

40,000 ft

descending air

ascending warm air

Stage 2

air flow

The life history of an Atlantic hurricane is shown in the series of schematic drawings above. (1) Hurricane conditions occur when there is a relatively steady air flow over the warm ocean, such as the trade winds or easterlies that blow across the ocean surface during the summer, absorbing both heat and moisture. (2) A hurricane is born when a low-pressure area disturbs the air flow. The winds "pile up," and the warm, moisture-laden air rises as high as 40,000 ft. At these altitudes cooling occurs and the contained moisture condenses, giving rise to precipitation.

around a central eye, which is calm and cloud-free. In the high walls of cloud surrounding the eye, air rises, drawing up water vapor. When the vapor reaches the upper atmosphere, where air pressure is low, it expands, cools, condenses, and releases its heat to power the hurricane. A hurricane traveling over land rapidly loses strength because its primary source of energy has been left behind.

Only superlatives can describe the energy of such storms. A single day's condensation in a medium-sized hurricane releases the energy of 400 20-megaton hydrogen bombs. In one hour, a hurricane puts out as much energy as all the generating plants of the United States could produce in a year. In September 1961, when Hurricane Carla passed over waters off the Gulf Coast of Texas, R. E. Simpson of Texas A and M University estimated that the storm took in energy from the sea at a rate of 2.2 billion billion calories (2.2×10^{18} cal) in 24 hours—enough to heat 62 million average homes in the Washington, D.C., climate for a whole winter season! Little wonder, then, that hurricanes—called typhoons in the Pacific—cause many hundreds of millions of dollars in property damage when they come ashore in populated regions. Since 1900 they have taken over 12,000 lives in the United States alone, although efficient tracking and warning systems now hold loss of life to a minimum.

Meteorologists are of two minds about these destructive storms, for they can also do much good. They have broken many a drought. They are prodigious desalting machines, producing perhaps two billion tons of fresh water a day. Typically, a hurricane passing through the Mississippi River basin may drop 50 billion tons of fresh water. When such storms pass offshore, they often bring badly needed rain as far north as New England and Canada. Certainly, too, the hurricane's enormous energy flow marks it as an important mechanism in the atmospheric heat engine. With this in mind, meteorolo-

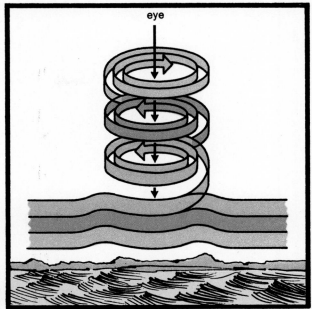

eye

gist Gordon Dunn, while director of the National Hurricane Center, Miami, Fla., remarked that, if man ever learned to suppress these storms, "nature would undoubtedly find some other method of maintaining the heat balance. And who can say that this method might not be even more disastrous . . . ?"

Twisters and thunderheads

As much can probably be said for severe local storms, especially tornadoes, which, within their limited compass, can outdo a hurricane in destructiveness. They too are working parts of the world weather machine. At any one time, an estimated 1,800 thunderstorms and tornadoes are raging throughout the world.

The concentrated violence of a tornado can rip apart even a strong building. Within the tornado funnel, winds of up to 500 mph circle a zone of very low pressure. When a funnel passes over a house, the building may literally explode as a result of the sudden drop in the pressure outside it. Tornadoes are famous for their bizarre effects. They may drive straws deeply into trees or hurl people and animals for hundreds of yards. One famous twister in Minnesota in 1931 picked up an 83-ton railroad car with 117 passengers and dropped it in a ditch 80 ft away.

Typically, a tornado has a small funnel, perhaps 1,200 ft across, and travels along the ground for 15 to 20 mi. There are wide variations between tornadoes, however. Some rise and touch down repeatedly, and there are recorded instances of funnels that have roared along the ground for hundreds of miles.

In a built-up area, a tornado can inflict death and injury and cause tens of millions of dollars in damage within a few minutes. Weather-
continued on page 238

(3) The ascending air currents are sustained by the continuous supply of warm, moist air near the ocean surface. The flow is somewhat similar to that in a chimney, except that, because of the rotation of the earth, a spiraling column is formed. This is the hurricane.
(4) A hurricane at sea can maintain itself indefinitely, as long as the supply of warm, moist air is not cut off. This supply is cut off, however, when the storm moves over land. Being relatively cool, the surface air over land will not rise enough to sustain the air flow in the column; the hurricane loses energy and, in a sense, dies of starvation.

The fate of the last man

(Extracted from the *Scientific American* of May 26, 1877.)

In all the discussion which has agitated the world over the Mosaic and geological accounts of the creation, no question has been more argued than that of the origination of the race. We have heard so much disputation as to whether Adam or an anthropoid ape was our primal ancestor, that we are now impelled to turn to the diametrically opposite end of creation, and consider not the beginning of the first but the end of the last man. Speculation as to future events—especially if several billion or so years distant—is not particularly profitable; but if a personal originator of the race is to be made an object of present theory, similar theorizing as to the personal terminator of the race is certainly just as useful.

M. Alphonse de Candolle points out that the terrestrial surface is constantly diminishing, and that elevated regions are being lowered through the incessant action of water, ice, and air. Besides, earthy matter, washed or ground away, is being carried into the sea, which is thus filling up; consequently in course of time the present configuration of the land will change. Continents will be divided into islands, and these will be gradually submerged. The human race will be driven by the encroaching waters from island to island. Finally the sun will rise on a vast waste of sea dotted perhaps with far-separated islets which once were mountain peaks. One by one these will be submerged until finally but one is left: Kunchainjunga, the loftiest summit of the Himalayas, perhaps; or more likely, some new coral reef. Therefore (1) *if the last man does not starve to death he will probably be drowned.*

Another theory is that of the periodicity of deluge, proposed by Adhemar, which depends on the fact of the unequal length of the seasons in the two hemispheres. Autumn and our winter last with us 179 days. In the Southern hemisphere, they last 186 days. These seven days or 168 hours of difference increase each year the coldness of the pole. During 10,500 years, the ice accumulates at one pole and melts at the other, thereby displacing the earth's center of gravity. Now a time, it is reasoned, will arrive when, after the maximum of elevation of temperature on one side, a catastrophe will happen, which will bring back the center of gravity to the center of figure, and cause an immense deluge. The hypothesis goes to show that (2) *the last man will certainly be drowned.*

Every few years or so we have a comet scare. It is, of course, not without the limits of possibility that a collision should occur. If it did, our globe would plunge into an atmosphere of gas, which, mingling with the air, would produce an explosion which would destroy every living thing. Such being the case, the person capable of breathing deleterious gas longest would survive the rest; and therefore (3) *if the last man is not suffocated by cometary gas he will be blown up.*

It is believed by many astronomers that there is a retarding medium in space, based on the fact that Encke's comet, in thirty-three years, loses a thousandth part of its velocity. If the ether resists our earth's motion in its orbit, then the centrifugal force will be constantly lessened, while the action of gravity will remain constant: so that the earth will describe a spiral path, always approaching the sun. The effect of this would be to convert the tropics into a desert, which would gradually expand toward the poles, from about which the ice and snow would be quickly melted. The probabilities in such event point to the supposition that (4) *the last man will be sunstruck.*

There are certain classes of rocks which are constantly becoming hydrated, and are thus occluding immense amounts of water. The theory has been broached that, in course of time, the seas will thus be dried up; and water being absent, our atmosphere will disappear, the earth becoming a waste similar to the moon. But before then, the atmosphere would probably become too rare for human existence. Consequently, in view of this theory (5), *the last man will be suffocated.*

Our sun itself may come to an end in two ways. First, as Mr. Proctor has recently very graphically explained, being but a variable star it may suddenly blaze up, and go out as other suns are known to have done. In this case, the intense heat of the colossal conflagration would destroy everything on the earth, and perhaps even vaporize the earth itself. Should this event occur (6), *the last man will be burned up.*

Or the sun may cool down. The glacial zones would thus enlarge, the race will be crowded nearer and nearer to the equator, by the encroaching glaciers coming from the poles. Finally, after the earth becomes covered with the vast ice sheet, man with his wonderful capacity of adaptation to surrounding circumstances will probably subsist for a certain period, but in the end (7) *the last man will be frozen to death.*

It has been suggested that the cooling of the earth will lead to the production of immense fissures in its crust similar to those already visible in the moon. The surface of the earth would thus be rendered extremely unstable, while the dwellers thereon for safety would be compelled to take refuge in caves. It is assumable that (8) *the last man will be crushed in some subterranean cavern.*

Or supposing that the people adapted themselves to their surroundings and managed to live on the surface, until the time when the earth becomes so cracked and broken that, as predicted, it falls apart, flying off in fragments into space. In such case (9) *the last man will be killed by the crash of orbs:* but if he is not, he will become an inhabitant of a new world. Evolution does not necessarily imply progress, and possibly the race may have retrograded until the human being possesses the nature of the plant louse: such being the case, this single inhabitant will spontaneously produce posterity of both sexes. A new race of men will begin, to continue *ad infinitum.* Hence (10) *there will be no last man.*

continued from page 235

men have become adept at spotting tornado conditions and they can issue general warnings, but they still cannot pinpoint where and when a tornado will strike. In the U.S., tornado weather occurs when cool, dry air from the west or northwest overrides significantly warmer, moist air coming from the south. The resulting unstable condition resembles a bucket of oil into which water has been poured. Just as the water would tend to sink beneath the oil, so the cold, dry air has a strong tendency to sink while the moist, warm air rises. In rising, the moist air cools, but not so much that it loses its buoyancy. Moisture condensing from it adds heat energy to the energy released by the upward movement.

Violent thunderstorms arise in this same way, and no one has yet satisfactorily explained what makes the funnel that turns a storm cloud into a tornado. Perhaps air currents, slowly rotating over a wide area, are somehow forced to converge. Then, like a skater who pulls in his arms, they whirl faster as their circle of rotation contracts. Perhaps a region of intense local convection gives rise to rotating winds. Perhaps both mechanisms operate at once. A few scientists think electrical forces may also be involved. Lightning discharges may sometimes concentrate in a narrow region where they heat the air to create powerful convection currents and then a tornado funnel.

Even if they never form tornadoes, convective storms can be destructive. Annual crop losses from hail in the United States run to $200 to $300 million, and insurance companies pay out millions of dollars to owners of mobile homes that have been dented by hailstones. Lightning, which may cause damage by starting fires, is also a killer. The Environmental Science Services Administration (ESSA) estimates that lightning kills 230 to 600 people a year and injures

Funnel cloud moving over the ocean draws water droplets into it to form a waterspout, such as the one near the Bahamas, shown below. Similar to a waterspout but potentially more destructive because it occurs over land, a tornado (opposite page, bottom, right) looms over Enid, Okla., in North America's "tornado alley." Opposite page, left, statue of the Virgin stands desolately in the mud-covered basilica of Santa Croce in Florence, Italy, after the disastrous flood of November 1966. Many priceless art treasures were lost when the rain-swollen Arno River surged into the city's oldest and most historic quarters. Top, right, swarms of locusts such as this, known and feared from biblical times, devastated crops throughout eastern Africa in the late 1960s.

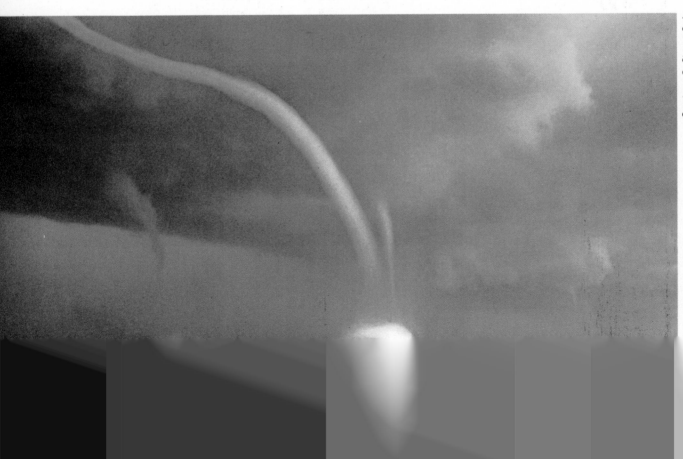

Courtesy, G. Steven Gwin

Photograph of a lightning stroke, taken with special equipment, reveals a color spectrum. Careful scientific analysis of such pictures can provide information about the stroke, including its size, electric current, and temperature.

1,500 others. Ferdinand H. Zegel of ESSA's Boulder, Colo., laboratory puts the average yearly death toll at 137, but adds that even at that lower figure "the lightning bolt causes more direct deaths than any other weather phenomena." Yet lightning too seems essential to the earth's healthy geophysical balance. The 100 lightning strokes that, somewhere in the world, flash between clouds and ground every second counter the small, steady upward flow of electric charge in the atmosphere.

Living with the elements

A little over 90 years ago, *Scientific American* published an essay on the fate of the last man (extracted on pp. 236–237), which shows a creature utterly at the mercy of the elements. Man still could not escape some of the fanciful fates the author imagined, and there are scientifically possible catastrophes—the melting of the polar icecaps, the expansion of the sun—before which he would be utterly defenseless. When it comes to the geophysical forces man has faced for millennia, however, he is making progress. He stands at the beginning of an era when he will be able to forecast these blows of nature with increasing precision and take action to dampen their effects. He may even find ways to soften the blows themselves.

On the whole, weather that threatens man is only part of the general mechanism that maintains a livable climate on earth. Gradually, man is increasing his ability to avoid its most destructive aspects by learning to forecast dangerous conditions. In 1958, for example, weathermen foresaw about 25% of severe storms 30 hours in advance. Ten years later, with the help of computers that simulate and project general weather, they caught approximately half. (See *1969 Britannica Yearbook of Science and the Future,* Feature Article: STUDYING THE EARTH.)

Perhaps the greatest challenge to meteorologists lies in the prospect of weather control. In attempting this, man faces awesome forces. A few statistics compiled by the U.S. National Academy of Sciences illustrate the problem. They are cast in terms of the time it would take the entire electrical generating capacity of the United States (estimated at 300 million kilowatts) to produce enough energy to change the natural motion of typical phenomena by 10%. For a tornado, the generators would have to run 30 seconds; for a small thunderstorm, 5 minutes; large thunderstorm, several hours; hurricane, several days; average nontropical storm, 5 to 6 weeks; and general circulation of the air over the Northern Hemisphere, 6 years. What modest success weather changers have had so far has been with cloud seeding, and even this has been problematical. The greatest hope lies in the development of computers that can simulate the mechanisms of the atmosphere.

As Roscoe R. Braham, Jr., of the University of Chicago puts it, man now has "one finger on the throttle of nature's weather machine. . . . By 'one finger,' I imply . . . that our knowledge of the inner workings of the weather machine is so fragmentary that we yet may not have identified the throttle handle." And, assuming that man does learn to grip the throttle, further problems arise. How do we know that stopping hurricanes would be a good thing? If we could stop flood-causing rains in California or ease drought in Chile, would this result in bigger weather problems elsewhere? While man may learn to avert some of nature's destructiveness, he will remain part of nature, in a world where natural forces may yet have the last word.

FOR ADDITIONAL READING:

Battan, Louis J., *Cloud Physics and Cloud Seeding* (Doubleday Anchor Books, 1962).

Battan, Louis J., *The Nature of Violent Storms* (Doubleday Anchor Books, 1961).

Leet, L. Don, and Leet, Florence, *Earthquake: Discoveries in Seismology* (Dell, 1964).

Furneaux, Rupert, *Krakatoa* (Prentice-Hall, 1964).

Roberts, Elliott, *Volcanoes and Earthquakes* (Pyramid Publications, 1967).

AUDIOVISUAL MATERIALS FROM ENCYCLOPÆDIA BRITANNICA EDUCATIONAL CORPORATION:

Films: *How Solid Is Rock?; Volcanoes in Action; What Makes the Wind Blow?; Atmosphere and Its Circulation.*

continued from page 177

The large increase in uranium requirements and enriching capacity has resulted from the relatively inefficient use that has previously been made of uranium. Uranium as it occurs in nature contains only approximately 0.7% of the ^{235}U isotope, while the balance consists of the ^{238}U isotope. ^{235}U is the fissionable isotope while ^{238}U is the "fertile" isotope; that is, it is not fissionable until it has been transmuted to plutonium-239 (^{239}Pu) after the absorption of a neutron. In most power reactors it is necessary to enrich the concentration of ^{235}U in the uranium to between 2% and 4%. Allowing for the losses in enriching and the losses in the reactor and fuel cycle, it is only practicable to utilize 1% to 2% of the potential energy contained in natural uranium, including the fissions which occur in the plutonium that has been formed from the ^{238}U in the reactor. It has, therefore, been recognized for some time that nuclear energy could only make a significant contribution to man's power needs if the "man-made'" fissionable isotopes (plutonium-239 and uranium-233) could be utilized more effectively and efficiently. This conclusion is based on the large abundance of uranium-238 (the source of ^{239}Pu) and of thorium-232 (the source of ^{233}U).

Advanced reactors are being developed which are more efficient in converting fertile isotopes to fissionable isotopes. They are called "advanced converters" because they "convert" fertile material to fissionable material. A special class of converters called "breeders" has commanded great interest because they convert fertile isotopes to fissionable isotopes at an even greater rate than the naturally fissionable isotopes can be fissioned. The most efficient breeder is a fast reactor using plutonium as fuel and ^{238}U as the fertile material. Such a reactor can produce not only enough new plutonium to satisfy its own requirements but also an excess to fuel new reactors. These reactors have the potential capability of utilizing all of the energy in natural uranium (as compared with 1% to 2% utilization in existing reactors). Although such a reactor in practice may be capable of only about 50% utilization, the impact of such increased efficiency and the equivalent reduction in uranium requirements offers virtually unlimited energy for the future.

Throughout the world considerable work was being undertaken on the development of fast breeders. The sodium-cooled fast breeder was the most popular of these. The idea for this type of reactor originated in the U.S., but it was under active development in other countries, as can be seen from the following.

The Soviet Union placed into operation in late 1968 a 60,000 thermal kilowatt (KWt) experimental fast breeder, which gave them an experimental capability comparable to the 60,000 KWt reactors in the U.K. and the U.S. The Soviets also had a 350,000 electrical kilowatt (KWe) prototype fast reactor plant under construction, and in 1968 they announced that a 600,000 KWe plant would soon be started. Underway in Britain was a 250,-000 KWe prototype fast reactor, and the French in 1968 started construction on a 300,000 KWe unit. In the U.S. three independent study teams were formed to develop three prototype sodium-cooled fast reactor designs, and one team began designing a gas-cooled fast reactor prototype. All of these programs had as their objectives the demonstration of prototype plant operation in the 1970s and commercial operation of very large plants in the 1980s. This use of such breeder plants is expected to reduce the rate of growth of uranium requirements, which would otherwise increase rapidly in the 1980s.

There has been far less emphasis to date on the thorium-232, uranium-233 system, but an important milestone was reached in regard to this program during the past year. In October 1968, the U.S. Molten Salt Reactor Experiment was fueled with uranium-233, the first time that any nuclear reactor had been so fueled. The molten salt reactor concept has the potential capability to utilize uranium-233 and thorium-232 effectively and, therefore, fits into a long-range program for nuclear power much like the fast breeder and its capability to utilize plutonium-239 and uranium-238.

Nuclear explosives. Legislation was introduced in the U.S. Congress which would have the effect of authorizing the AEC to engage in nuclear explosive projects with industry for other than research purposes. This had not been permitted previously. The proposed legislation would also permit the United States to meet the requirement of the nuclear nonproliferation treaty that nations possessing nuclear weapons make available on a nondiscriminatory basis the potential benefits of peaceful nuclear explosives to the nonnuclear weapon states that had signed the treaty.

Research and development in the peaceful uses of nuclear explosives continued at an accelerated pace, and test results of previous experiments continued to yield encouraging results. Flow tests on Project Gasbuggy began in June 1968. Gasbuggy had been detonated in December 1967 to release the flow of natural gas trapped far underground in New Mexico. (See *1969 Britannica Yearbook of Science and the Future,* Year in Review: ENGINEERING.) This experiment involved

*Fuel drawers of Argonne National Laboratory's
"zero power plutonium reactor" are inspected.
This reactor, in Idaho, is designed to simulate
fast breeder reactors over a wide range of sizes.
It will achieve a self-sustaining chain reaction,
while producing little power.*

private industry for the first time in the use of
nuclear explosives. The flow tests consisted of
allowing the well to produce at a rate of 5 million cu ft of natural gas per day for six days, shut-
ting the well for one day for pressure and temperature measurements, and resuming flow for
five more days. These were followed by additional
tests.

Many variables were being evaluated in the
Gasbuggy tests, including gas composition and
radioactivity levels as well as production rates.
Although no firm conclusions could be drawn,
some encouraging results were reported. Radioactivity levels were lower than anticipated and
had not constituted a hazard to test personnel or
to the public. The total gas production from January 1968 through April 1969 was about 167 million cu ft. By comparison, an existing conventionally completed well a little more than 400 ft away
had produced only 85 million cu ft from the same
rock formation during a nine-year period.

The nuclear excavation program expanded during recent months because of the need to establish the technical feasibility of nuclear explosives
for this purpose. Probably most important was the
desire to make appropriate information available
to the Atlantic-Pacific Interoceanic Canal Study
Commission, which was to report to the president
of the U.S. before Dec. 1, 1970.

A series of cratering experiments was started
early in 1968 in Nevada. Five explosives of about
one kiloton each (equivalent to 1,000 tons of TNT)
were detonated; they displaced more than 500,000
tons of the earth's crust and created a ditch about
250 ft wide, 850 ft long, and 70 ft deep. These
tests produced valuable data concerning the
effectiveness of using nuclear explosives for
excavating harbors, canals, and passes through
mountains.

Nuclear engineering for space. Although nuclear energy did not play a primary role in
man's first flight to the moon, major milestones
were reached in nuclear programs that were expected to play an important role in future space
exploration. Phoebus 2A, a prototype propulsion
reactor, operated for a total of about 32 minutes
with about 12 minutes at a power level above 4
million kw. This ground test exceeded the requirements of a manned lunar mission in respect to
both time and power level. The power level was
greater than that achieved by any previous rocket
reactor and it served to usher in the next phase
of the program, the development of a flight-rated
engine.

A major achievement also took place in the
SNAP (Systems for Nuclear Auxiliary Power) program. An advanced unit reached its full design
power of 600 KWt during ground tests in January
1969. This compact reactor was designed to provide the heat source for auxiliary power units
generating 20 to 75 KWe for two to five years
without refueling or maintenance. It could provide
power for manned orbiting laboratories and for
bases on the surface of the moon. This system
was destined to follow the SNAP-10A, a 0.5-KWe
unit that was placed in orbit around the earth in
1965.

Nuclear ship propulsion. Of the 108 nuclear
submarines and 7 nuclear-powered surface ships
authorized for the U.S. Navy, 80 submarines and
4 surface ships were in operation. Submarines
were being equipped with nuclear reactors designed to last for more than 10 years of normal
operation and to propel the ship for approximately
400,000 mi without refueling.

During the last year the world's first nuclear-
powered merchant ship put into port to refuel for
continued on page 245

Breakthrough in nuclear engineering

Help for some victims of heart disease may soon be on the way, as a result of a new development in nuclear technology. In May 1969 a compact nuclear-powered cardiac pacemaker was successfully implanted in a dog at the U.S. National Heart Institute, Bethesda, Md. If such a device is successful, it will operate within human beings without replacement for at least ten years, a considerable improvement over previous pacemakers. The U.S. Atomic Energy Commission developed the pacemaker and for three years tested it in the laboratory under conditions simulating those in the human body.

A pacemaker is designed to maintain normal heartbeat in people suffering from "heart block," a condition usually caused by injury to the system that conducts the contractive impulse through the heart. When functioning normally, this system originates and sends to all parts of the heart the electrical impulses that cause the heart to beat. Injuries, however, may disrupt the normal flow of impulses. This would cause the rate of heart beat to slow down, thereby decreasing the heart's output of blood to an extent that normal physical

A nuclear-powered pacemaker for a heart is implanted in a dog by a surgeon at the U.S. National Heart Institute. The plutonium-238 power source is expected to provide reliable and steady power for at least ten years. If successful on animals, the pacemaker will be tested on human beings.

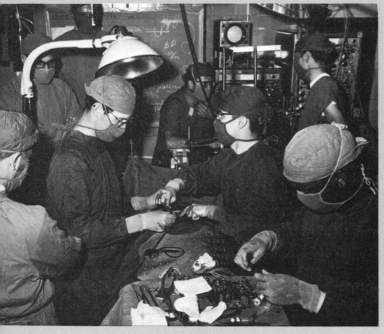

Thomas Joy, courtesy, National Institutes of Health

activity could not be sustained. Impeding the impulse flow can also cause disturbances in the rhythm of the heart beat which can lead to heart stoppage and death.

Battery v. *nuclear power.* Battery-operated pacemakers powered by mercury cells have been in use for some time. They have the drawback, however, of a limited lifetime because of battery depletion, usually within two or three years of the original implantation. In addition, the battery might fail with little warning to a patient, thus possibly jeopardizing his life.

Although surgical replacement of battery-operated pacemakers is not a difficult procedure, it does involve loss of time, expense, and some possible medical risk for patients. Therefore, a nuclear-powered pacemaker, which would have a reliable power source and would not have to be replaced for at least ten years, would be of considerable benefit.

Operation of a pacemaker. A nuclear pacemaker is about two-thirds the size of a pack of cigarettes and weighs 3½ oz. It is approximately 2½ in. long, 1¼ in. wide, and 1⅞ in. deep. The principle of thermoelectricity, the direct conversion of heat to electrical energy, is the basis of the pacemaker's nuclear power source. When certain metals are joined together, they form a thermocouple, which, when heated at one end, generates an electrical current. The thermocouple in the pacemaker consists of an alloy of copper and nickel and an alloy of nickel and chromium, each of which are drawn into wire strands and woven into a glass tape. Radioactive plutonium-238 is used as the energy source; the heat that it generates as it decays is used to heat the wire strands at one end. The heat causes the wires to generate electrical current, which is transmitted to a pulse generator that supplies the pacing pulses to the heart.

Plutonium-238 was chosen as the heat source because it emits particles that have high energy but low penetrating power. Because of this combination only about ½ g of plutonium-238 is required for each pacemaker, and no special radiation shielding is needed.

Future plans. Late in 1969 and early in 1970, nuclear-powered pacemakers were to be implanted in several additional healthy dogs. The dogs were then to undergo extensive tests; if the device is deemed successful, clinical studies on human patients would begin subsequently.

Besides pacemakers there are other potential biomedical applications for the plutonium-238 energy source. These include diaphragm stimulators for breathing, blood pressure control devices, and pain inhibitors.

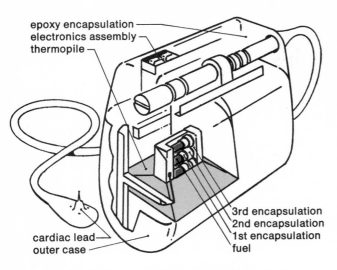

epoxy encapsulation
electronics assembly
thermopile

3rd encapsulation
2nd encapsulation
1st encapsulation
fuel

cardiac lead
outer case

Cutaway drawing of the nuclear-powered pacemaker, developed by the U.S. Atomic Energy Commission, shows the relationship between the plutonium-238 fuel and the thermopile, the unit that converts the heat from the fuel decay into an electrical current.

continued from page 243
the first time since it began operations. In 6 years the NS "Savannah" had sailed more than 300,000 mi and visited 77 ports in 26 countries. A conventional merchant ship would have consumed 150 million lb of oil, with frequent refueling, to cover the same route. The NS "Savannah" made the journey with 122 lb of nuclear fuel.

Future developments. Although significant progress will likely be made in many fields of nuclear engineering during the next year, the most exciting and perhaps the most important will probably be in the field of nuclear explosives. The emphasis in this area is expected to shift from research to applications and cost. This should generate appreciation of the tremendous potential capability of nuclear explosives to do jobs which previously were impossible or economically impractical.

A large increase in the number of tests to demonstrate these capabilities will almost certainly take place. They will include additional experiments on nuclear stimulation of gas fields and nuclear excavations. They will also include new projects involving mineral extraction and creation of underground gas storage facilities. International projects are expected to be developed, and significant progress is likely to be made on a joint Australian-U.S. venture to excavate harbors with nuclear explosives.

—Leonard J. Koch

See also Year in Review: PHYSICS, *Nuclear Physics.*

245

Environmental sciences

Conservation

Traditionally, the problems of conservation have been dealt with individually (if at all) as they have arisen. Action has followed crisis—food shortage, flood, or some other form of disaster. During the past year, however, there were increasingly hopeful signs that a new approach was developing. The ancient reminder that we are all travelers on the spaceship Earth was now being echoed by publicists, political leaders, and by the more thoughtful spokesmen for modern science. Significantly, too, it was being put forward by the representatives of religion, while the larger foundations were expanding their humanitarian concern by making substantial contributions for conservation purposes.

Marine resources. The demand for the biological resources of the sea, coupled with new and powerful methods for their exploitation, continued to threaten the supply, particularly of the larger sea mammals such as whales. While treaty agreements had enabled the fur seals to recover in number, the killing of baby seals at the mouth of the St. Lawrence River for their white fur aroused considerable protest. The very restrictions in time and take that were designed to pro-

Assisted by personnel from the U.S. Atomic Energy Commission, the Alaska Fish and Game Department moved about 360 sea otters from the wildlife refuge on Amchitka Island in the Aleutians. The colony had grown too large for the available food supply.

R. T. Wallen, courtesy, Atomic Energy Commission

tect the seals led to haste in slaughter and skinning. Even though the species might not be endangered as yet, strong humanitarian concern was voiced in many quarters.

For some years, the growing importance of marine resources had been underlined by the efforts of both large and small nations to extend their offshore jurisdiction, including rights to coastal fisheries and submarine mineral deposits. Peru, for example, claimed a 200-mi limit, and during the year several U.S. fishing boats were seized for transgressing on Peruvian waters. In the midst of these international complications, the need for some form of regulation was clear. For example, intensive mechanized fishing by foreign fleets off the New England coast had so depleted the supply of haddock and other food fish that a three-year moratorium might be necessary.

The tidal marshes or wetlands at the mouths of coastal streams, where nutrients from land and sea mingle, comprise an important habitat for fish, edible mollusks, and other forms of wildlife. Urbanization, with its attendant pressure for land and increasing waste accumulation, was making serious inroads on these wetlands, which were being filled in, rendered toxic, and reduced in area (in parts of New England by 80 to 90%). In many places coastal fisheries had declined proportionately. Citizen groups were becoming ac-

tive in an attempt to save this valuable resource, leading in some cases to strong legislative measures, notably in Massachusetts (see *Ecology*, below).

Industry and conservation. The number and diversity of natural resource problems increased rapidly in the 20th century, as did the growth of voluntary organizations concerned with such problems. That these organizations had become a major political force was evidenced by the fact that more than 40 pieces of legislation dealing with natural resources were introduced into the U.S. 91st Congress in less than two months.

The response of business and industry to this pressure was mixed but highly significant. The attempts of commercial interests to discredit and ridicule their critics appeared to have diminished. Instead, representatives of such interests were soberly explaining to legislative committees the enormous costs and threats to profit that would be involved in changes of practice. These considerations had a strong appeal, especially in the U.S., where stock ownership in corporations is widespread. On the other hand, such resource industries as commercial forestry and oil were taking considerable pains to express an interest in conservation and to demonstrate that interest through advertising. As commercial forestry passed from individual to corporate ownership, it had undergone substantial reforms. Manage-

Underwater cameraman photographs an oil slick as it begins to break up following application of Corexit 7664, a dispersant developed by a subsidiary of Standard Oil Co. (New Jersey). Said to be 90% effective and harmless to marine life, the chemical acts by coating oil droplets, which then disperse and are decomposed biologically. It can be applied by spraying.

246

*Swimmers returned to Lake Erie in July 1968, with the opening of this chlorinated "pool in the lake"
at White City Beach, Cleveland, O. The pool was the first of several planned for Cleveland,
where the lake had been off limits to bathers because of the high level of water pollution.*

ment became responsible not merely for providing a quick profit, but for ensuring a continuing supply of raw materials as well.

The astronomical demand for paper, however, had created special and complex problems for the industry involved in its production. Besides acquiring great tracts of land and placing them under scientific management, producers of pulpwood also cooperated with private owners, particularly in the southern U.S., in encouraging good management of farm woodlots. On the other hand, the manufacture of paper from wood pulp remained a major source of stream and air pollution. Stream pollution, because of its disastrous effects on game fish, was encountering opposition from politically powerful groups of sportsmen as well as from conservationists. Whether air pollution from pulp mills affects public health might be debatable, but its serious effect on the amenities of neighborhoods in the vicinity could not be questioned. Also without question was the technical difficulty of lessening this obvious nuisance.

The industry's traditional defense was exemplified by the response of a company executive to a complainant: "Strange of you to say that. All I can smell here is bread and butter." Less bluntly worded, perhaps, this payroll argument, with its

implicit threat to profits and taxes, continued to come into sharper focus, notably in the case of the electrical industry. Although this industry had done much to encourage the conservation of soil and water—for example, in Oklahoma, Ohio, and New England—its generating plants continued to be a major source of air pollution, as was clearly apparent to any air traveler. Yet many communities hesitated to press for abatement for fear of losing the wages and taxes so necessary to their well-being.

A problem that would grow with the increasing use of nuclear power was that of waste heat. Otherwise harmless waste water from a generating plant could raise the temperature of streams and coastal waters by several degrees, and the extent to which this heat could be added without seriously damaging water quality and aquatic life had come under consideration by regulatory agencies. Cooling devices, required by law in some parts of Europe, are costly. They also produce clouds of water vapor, which—the industry notes—may contribute to fog, already a major concern in regions of dense population. Clearly, there existed a need for intensive research, both public and private.

The damage to the atmosphere resulting from

247

industrial pollution was being compounded in many areas by steadily increasing amounts of dust resulting from the clearing away of native cover for agriculture and housing developments. In the Denver, Colo., area such dust made up at least half of the atmospheric contaminants, and in Tucson, Ariz., it was blamed for the occurrence of a respiratory disease known as valley fever. Its chief source in the latter area was land cleared of desert vegetation which, though seemingly sparse, had served to stabilize the soil. The dust problem in the deserts of both the Old and the New World had been greatly aggravated by the increase of traffic, military as well as civilian. West of Los Angeles much of this disturbance was due to motor vehicles ridden for sport, which caused not only dust but also dune drifting.

Early 1969 brought two major disasters to California—a vast oil slick from offshore drilling operations and mud slides resulting in destruction of lives and property. These slides, caused by heavy rains, were clearly predictable. The practice of building homes on steep slopes where the native clay had been leveled into terraces was an invitation to trouble, obvious for many years even to the casual observer. Yet this danger has been consistently ignored, exemplifying two great obstacles to sound land-use practices—the unchecked profit motive and disregard of plain warning.

Food and space. Among the somber possibilities facing mankind, only that of atomic war was more terrifying than the widespread famine predicted for the next decade. Here again, the ambivalence and conflict of interest so characteristic of resource problems were displayed. In this case, however, the conflict was to a large degree intellectual rather than economic: between those who

Thousands of dead fish were removed from the Rhine River, near Coblenz, W.Ger., after they were poisoned in June by a substance that could not be identified. Dutch authorities at first thought an insecticide caused the poisoning, but this proved to be false.

UPI Compix

emphasized the possibility of greatly increased world food production and those most concerned with the accelerating growth of world population. Meanwhile, evidence of hunger and malnutrition, particularly in Asia and Latin America, was incontrovertible, and their existence on a significant scale in the United States was becoming a matter of grave concern.

Curiously enough, this malnutrition was not due wholly to a lack of agricultural potential; it was most aggravated where production was concentrated on nonfood materials, such as tobacco and cotton. Another factor, which received too little attention, was the absorption of the family farm, with its tradition of near self-sufficiency in food, into large, heavily capitalized, and mechanized holdings. Subsistence farming had become a derogatory term associated with a low level of living, although in all fairness it should be compared with the ghetto existence of displaced farm workers. (*See* Year in Review: AGRICULTURE; FOODS AND NUTRITION.)

The problem posed by finite land area and human numbers growing at compound rates could not be questioned. Aside from the matter of population control, there had been increasing efforts, under the general rubric of "planning," to deal with this problem. Britain had developed green belts around its cities, with the mixed motive of restricting urban expansion and providing needed facilities for urban use. Unfortunately, this led to ambivalence in planning, further complicated by continued urban growth. At the same time, the American suburbs, once regarded as an escape from crowded city living, were threatened by urban problems that overflowed the city limits. In dealing with these problems, those who emphasize the benefits of the past face the charge of nostalgia, while those who try to envision a better future are accused of utopianism. Yet both points of view are needed to deal with the design of the environment and the prudent use of its resources. (*See* Feature Article: URBAN SOCIETY: A BLUEPRINT FOR THE CITY OF TOMORROW.)

—Paul B. Sears

Ecology

The extensive leakage of oil from a well off the beach at Santa Barbara, Calif.; the condemnation by the U.S. Food and Drug Administration of 34,000 lb of Lake Michigan coho salmon because they contained excessive amounts of DDT residues; the U.S. military's plan to dispose of obsolete chemical warfare materials in the ocean; the disclosure that earth tremors may occur as far as 30 mi away following large underground nuclear

Courtesy, Michigan Department of Natural Resources

Eaglet sits in a nest on Michigan's Muskegon River, beside a flaking egg that never hatched. Thin, easily broken eggshells, leading to population declines among several bird species, have been blamed by scientists on DDT, which is said to produce a hormonal breakdown that results in calcium deficiency.

explosions; and the admission by U.S. Army spokesmen before a congressional committee that the deaths of thousands of sheep in Skull Valley, Utah, in early 1968 had been caused by a nerve gas being tested at the neighboring Dugway Proving Ground—all were among the newsworthy events that focused attention on man's unintended effects on his environment.

Moreover, the discovery of a major new oil field at Prudhoe Bay on the Arctic slope of Alaska and the proposal for a new Miami jetport on the edge of Everglades National Park in Florida were examples of new developments that gave rise to conflicts among competing demands on the environment. In these two cases there were probably some steps that could be taken to ameliorate the undesired environmental effects; in other cases there might be no basis for compromise.

Public interest in man's environment. The amount of public discussion—among students, scientists, politicians, and diplomats—intended to call attention to environmental problems and to find solutions for them was clear evidence of continued concern with the quality of the world we live in. Of special interest was the recognition that environmental problems are of international concern. In September 1968, UNESCO sponsored a conference in Paris on the "Resources of the Biosphere," which was attended by delegates from 63 nations. The Council of Europe scheduled a conference on "Man and Environment" to be held at Strasbourg, France, in early 1970 to formulate ecological principles for preservation of the environment consistent with advanced economic and social development. The conference was to be a part of European Nature Preservation Year (1970). The Economic Commission for Europe, a regional organization of the UN, began preparations for a 1971 conference on "Problems Relating to the Environment," and the UN General Assembly acted favorably on a Swedish proposal for a 1972 ministerial-level conference on "The Problems of the Human Environment."

On the technical level, the Conservation Foundation in the U.S. sponsored a scientific symposium on "Ecological Aspects of International Development," the proceedings of which were to be published. The papers were case histories of inadvertent ecological events that resulted from well-meaning but inappropriate activities intended to help the less developed countries of the world. Several symposia at the 1968 meeting of the American Association for the Advancement of Science dealt with environment, and one of these, "Global Effects of Environmental Pollution," was carried on many National Educational Television network stations. At this symposium attention was devoted to the possible long-range effects on climate of carbon dioxide, dust, and water vapor, as well as the effects of toxic chemicals on the environment.

Within the United States, there was much discussion on how to cope with environmental problems. A Joint House-Senate Colloquium to Discuss a National Policy for the Environment was held in July 1968. This all-day session of congressmen, senators, Cabinet officers, scientists, and other distinguished citizens stimulated congressional interest in establishing a formal national policy for the environment. A number of bills providing for a Council of Ecological Advisers in the Executive Office of the President and for the setting forth of a national environmental policy were introduced in the early days of the 91st Congress. The executive branch also was actively involved in finding better ways of dealing with environmental problems. The most far-reaching action was the establishment of a Cabinet-level Environmental Quality Council, chaired by the president. This council would assign program responsibility and assure action on environmental problems that were beyond the scope of any one

Sensors designed to measure the dissolved oxygen content of lakes and streams, where insufficient oxygen resulting from pollution is detrimental to aquatic life, undergo temperature calibration tests at the Industrial Division of Honeywell Inc., Fort Washington, Pa. The two glass towers are filled with stones to break up the bubbles in aerated water.

department or that involved disagreements between agencies.

The International Biological Program. During the past year 54 nations were engaged in activities related to the International Biological Program (IBP). In the U.S. there was widespread support of the program and, for the first time, substantial federal funds were made available for it. The U.S. aspect of the program was concentrated on a series of integrated research projects directed at understanding in detail the functioning of the principal ecological systems of North America. Several hundred scientists were involved in these coordinated studies of grasslands, deciduous forest, coniferous forest, desert, tundra, and marine areas. In conjunction with the IBP, provision had been made for the U.S. National Science Foundation to maintain a clearinghouse for information on natural areas. It was hoped that this would

stimulate the preservation of areas on both public and private lands that would include examples of all of the natural environments of the U.S.

The IBP was scheduled to end in 1973. The interest in ecology that it had generated gave impetus to a move to establish a National Center for Ecology, to serve as a focus for IBP-like activities after the formal end of the IBP. The Ecological Society of America arranged for feasibility studies of such a center as a basis for further development of plans.

Hazardous substances. During the year much new information on persistent pesticides became available. Studies by Joseph Hickey and his colleagues at the University of Wisconsin demonstrated that shell thickness of eggs of certain predatory and fish-eating birds had decreased markedly since the mid-1940s, when DDT first came into use. (Alexander Sprunt IV, research director of the National Audubon Society, subsequently reported that on April 13, 1969, Audubon researchers found a bald eagle nest in northern Michigan containing an egg with no shell at all, only a membrane.) The decline in shell thickness had coincided with a decline in populations of these species. Further evidence was provided when experimental work by the U.S. Bureau of Sport Fisheries and Wildlife confirmed that DDE (a degradation product of DDT) causes decreased shell thickness in captive American kestrels. The mechanism by which shell thickness is reduced had not been completely established, but there was evidence from laboratory studies that DDT and related materials can affect calcium metabolism and thus, perhaps, shell deposition.

In 1965, D. E. Ferguson and his co-workers at Mississippi State University had demonstrated that some vertebrate species can become resistant to certain insecticides. ("Resistant" here means that, in a population to which a toxic material is being applied, the least susceptible individuals live and reproduce, thereby shifting the genetic structure of the population so that later generations are less susceptible to the toxicant.) In a report to the Entomological Society of America meeting in December 1968, Ferguson described work demonstrating that a resistant species can become a hazard to a species that preys on it. He exposed mosquito fish that were resistant to sublethal amounts of the pesticide endrin. These individuals in turn accumulated enough endrin in their bodies to be toxic to larger, nonresistant predatory fish to which they were fed. Thus, Ferguson proved experimentally that development of resistance to a pesticide, if it involves tolerance rather than detoxication, results in increased mortalities at other points in the food chain.

250

The seizure by federal officials of Lake Michigan coho for excessive levels of DDT residues (13 to 19 parts per million) demonstrated how a very small amount of a hazardous material can affect the use of a resource. At the same time, it called into question the premise on which today's pesticide regulation is based—that a pesticide will remain where it is placed. No one places DDT deliberately in Lake Michigan; rather, the DDT-related materials originate from applications at some distance from the lake and are brought to the lake by air or by tributary streams. Because of the phenomenal capacity of this material to become concentrated in the tissues of living organisms, the total amount of DDT-related materials in the lake's ecological system need not be large in order to have pronounced biological effects. If there are 10 million salmon in the lake, weighing 10 lb each and averaging 13 to 19 parts per million of DDT and metabolites, the total amount of DDT they contain would be between 1,300 and 1,900 lb. Viewed another way, 1,300 to 1,900 lb of DDT is enough to contaminate seriously 10 million fish. Along the same lines, Howard Johnson of Michigan State University showed that salmon from Lake Michigan have declined in their ability to reproduce.

Contamination of the marine environment was examined, among other places, in a public symposium on "Man's Chemical Invasion of the Ocean: An Inquiry," sponsored by Scripps Institution of Oceanography, La Jolla, Calif. Increasing levels of lead in the surface waters of the oceans, pesticides in marine fish and birds, petroleum products spilled onto the ocean, and disposal of sewage in the ocean or in streams that feed into it all came under intensive discussion.

There was evidence that some more or less contained areas of the sea were already undergoing changes. Thus, in the Baltic Sea, the level of dissolved oxygen had been decreasing to near zero at lower depths, while the level of dissolved phosphorus had more than doubled; both changes were believed to be the result of man's activities. So, too, were a number of incidents of pollution in these confined areas. The lesson was clear. Just as man has seriously damaged the Great Lakes, which once seemed beyond his capability to influence, so man *can* affect the oceans. It must be borne in mind that what would be vanishingly small amounts of some substances if they were equally distributed throughout the oceans as a whole can be so concentrated that, as with the DDT and the coho, they have a serious biological effect. (See *Conservation,* above.)

—John L. Buckley

See also Year in Review: ZOOLOGY.

From the work of Robert Sweeney,
State University of New York at Buffalo

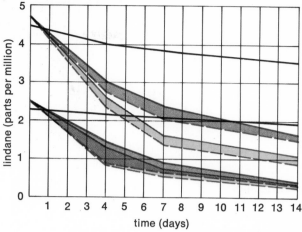

total concentration algae free solution ———

total concentration,
Chlamydomonas reinhardtii added _____

supernatant concentration,
Chlamydomonas reinhardtii added — — —

total concentration, *Chlorella vulgaris* added ———

supernatant concentration, *Chlorella vulgaris* added — — —

Ability of certain algae to metabolize the pesticide lindane suggests that these single-celled organisms might be used to clear lindane-contaminated water supplies. The graph contrasts the rate at which lindane normally disappears from water through evaporation with the disappearance rate when Chlorella vulgaris *or* Chlamydomonas reinhardtii *have been added. The results of two experiments, involving different levels of contamination, are shown.*

Foods and nutrition

During the past year, the twin specters of famine and obesity continued to pose a challenge in virtually all areas of the world. Somewhat paradoxically—as well as surprisingly—the two conditions often exist simultaneously.

Repeatedly, emphasis fell on a fundamental fact too often overlooked in the past: the nutritional well-being of a people depends equally on what they eat and on how much they eat. In the absence of the costlier fortified foods and of high-protein foods, economically disadvantaged people fall back on cheaper substances that are generally high in starch and fat. The average diet in Latin America, for instance, still consists of 78% carbohydrates, 10% fats, and only 12% protein.

New nutritional recommendations. In the U.S., the Food and Nutrition Board of the National Academy of Sciences–National Research Council issued the eagerly awaited revision of the "Recommended Dietary Allowances." The new

Food supplies on the table of a shack in Mississippi symbolize the paradox of hunger and malnutrition existing in the midst of an affluent society. Cheap foods such as cornmeal, beans, and lard, which often constitute the staple diet of the poor, tend to be high in starches and fats and low in the protein necessary to the maintenance of good health.

recommendations proved noteworthy in several respects. For the first time, they established recommended levels for seven nutrients now recognized as essential on a daily basis: folacin, vitamin E, vitamin B_6, vitamin B_{12}, and the minerals phosphorus, magnesium, and iodine. The board also made finer distinctions in terms of both sex and age categories. For example, requirements for infants under one year of age were divided into three groups, reflecting increased awareness of the special developmental needs of the newborn, the infant from two to six months, and the young child of six months to one year. In keeping

with the growing concern over obesity, the board also advised a reduction in caloric intake, commensurate with the general reduction in physical activity among Americans.

Recognizing the continued widespread prevalence of iron deficiency anemia, the board urged an intake of 18 mg of iron daily for females, from the age of ten through the reproductive years. The report emphasized, however, that this amount is not easily attained unless a woman eats far more than the desirable number of calories. Realistically, therefore, further fortification or enrichment of foods may be necessary.

Nutritional deficiencies. Worldwide, iron deficiency anemia is the most prevalent nutritional deficiency in both sexes and at almost all ages. It was becoming increasingly evident that this is due to factors other than mere lack of food. Even when there is an adequate supply of foods rich in iron, these are not necessarily the ones consumed; dietary customs or preferences often interfere. Furthermore, less than half the iron in foods is released into solution or is in a metabolically utilizable form. A study carried out at the American University of Beirut, for example, disclosed that the common plant sources of food in Lebanon—spinach, okra, lettuce, wheat, and chick-peas—are shockingly low in available iron, a fact that may account for the serious iron deficiency problem in that country.

A Canadian study brought a perplexing vitamin deficiency to light. A survey by the Food and Drug Directorate of that country, conducted in five cities, found that vitamin A levels were either very low or totally absent in the livers of the persons studied. The liver is believed to be the principal reservoir for vitamin A, and physicians have generally considered that vitamin A stores of this low an order would cause obvious clinical symptoms, often including blindness. No such symptoms were apparent in the Canadian subjects, however. Why this was so was a mystery that was undergoing further investigation.

Folic acid deficiency remained a target of study, not only in pregnant women, where it may pose a serious threat to both mother and fetus, but also among the aged. According to a report from the Royal Infirmary in Edinburgh, Scot., folate deficiency constitutes a considerable problem both in the U.S. and in the United Kingdom. It is particularly serious among alcoholics, those with cirrhosis of the liver, and the poor, especially those who are elderly and tend to neglect their meals.

Milk: less than the perfect food? Several reports clearly refuted the still widely held belief that milk is the perfect food for everyone. All the dietary minerals known to be necessary for good human nutrition are present in bovine milk, but not all are present in the requisite amounts. Milk is notoriously low in iron, and in the U.S. iron deficiency anemia is still prevalent among infants and children given excessively large amounts of milk to the exclusion of other foods. Similarly, copper deficiency develops among those fed a diet exclusively of milk. A team of scientists at Wayne State University in Michigan indicated that milk may also be lacking in adequate amounts of important trace minerals, such as iodine, fluorine, and zinc.

The phenomenon of intolerance to lactose, a major constituent of milk, caused much comment during the year. Mounting evidence pointed to the presence of a recessive hereditary trait in various ethnic groups that results in the absence or very low levels of an enzyme (lactase) needed to metabolize lactose. Among the groups in which this genetic trait has been reported are those of Asian derivation, Australian aborigines, natives of New Guinea, Greek Cypriots, Negroes, and possibly American Indians.

Persons with this deficiency may experience severe symptoms following the ingestion of milk. Because milk and milk products form a major part of food-aid programs in the less developed countries, the existence of such a biological drawback to milk consumption raises urgent questions. Sweeping changes may be called for in such programs, especially in countries faced with famine, where gastroenteritis and protein-calorie malnutrition are already prevalent. These conditions themselves often lead to secondary lactase deficiency. If a dietary lactase deficiency is superimposed on an inherent one, the ingestion of milk may result in extreme distress; for example, aggravation of an already present diarrhea.

Another study disclosed that the vitamin E content of both raw and homogenized cow's milk varies greatly, depending on the season and on the state of the individual animal. The role of vitamin E in human nutrition had been a subject of controversy for many years, but with recommended daily allowances for this vitamin having been established for the first time by the Food and Nutrition Board of the National Academy of Sciences–National Research Council, reliance on milk as a source for vitamin E came under question. This was especially so in the case of reconstituted nonfat dry milk, which supplies virtually no vitamin E at all. This is the form of milk most widely used in food programs, both in less developed countries and among the poor in the U.S. Nor had the debate over the possible link between saturated fats and cardiovascular dis-

ease lessened. On this score, too, milk had come under a cloud because of its saturated fat content.

One approach to overcoming the drawbacks of milk is through the development of synthetic milks and milk substitutes. Two "new milks" were receiving increased consideration by nutritionists and, to a lesser extent, by the public. The first is filled milk, in which the butterfat of cow's milk has been removed and replaced by vegetable fat, thus lowering the saturated fatty acid content. The second product is not a milk at all but a white substitute composed of vegetable fats and proteins with sugar and other nondairy ingredients added. Its advantages were said to include lower caloric content, greater ease of standardization, and lessened risk of spoilage.

By and large, nutritionists were far from neutral in this matter. Some looked to a future filled-milk product that would be both nutritionally sound and inexpensive. Others, however, were concerned about the possibility of general acceptance of synthetic or filled-milk products that do not meet this ideal. Thus, the Committee on Nutrition of the American Academy of Pediatrics recommended that properly designed and conducted clinical trials of all such products be made mandatory before they are marketed.

The struggle against malnutrition. Developments on both the scientific and the political level made it clear that there is an urgent need for definite studies to determine the exact extent of malnutrition and undernutrition in the U.S. The full implications of undernutrition were only beginning to be explored and evaluated. For example, recent data from Guatemala showed that undernutrition during pregnancy may have direct effects on the fetus, and studies at the Hospital Roberto Del Río of the University of Chile disclosed that severe early malnutrition can result in marked curtailment of cell division in all organs, including the brain. (See Feature Article: WHEN YOUNG CHILDREN GO HUNGRY: EFFECTS ON LEARNING AND BEHAVIOR.)

Another area of investigation related to the effect of the "population explosion" on future food supplies and the research being carried out to improve protein sources. Among the products that had been developed to meet special needs were Incaparina (an economical, grain-derived food developed for Central America), opaque-2 (a special variety of field corn, developed at Purdue University, West Lafayette, Ind., which contains certain essential amino acids), and IR-8 (a new rice variety developed in the Philippines). Current efforts at the University of Wisconsin were being directed toward the development of new strains of carrots that will be richer in vitamin A. Similarly, the combined efforts of three United Nations agencies—the World Health Organization (WHO), the Food and Agriculture Organization (FAO), and UNICEF—yielded Superamine, a balanced mixture of precooked flours from several sources, vitamin fortified and containing skimmed milk powder. (*See* Year in Review: AGRICULTURE.)

There was tremendous interest in the less developed countries in the possible enrichment of foods with four essential amino acids: lysine, methionine, tryptophan, and threonine. Cereal grains constitute the main food for millions of persons in such lands, and cereals are deficient in one or more of these vital substances. It was expected that, in the future, considerable emphasis would be placed on the restoration and addition of essential substances in cereals and other foods that are readily available for consumption.

At the same time, greater recognition was being given to other health problems that undermine nutritional status. A WHO report on infectious diseases in less developed countries pointed out that malnutrition destroys or interferes with the body's innate ability to resist infections. Conversely, many infectious diseases lead to a state of malabsorption that, in turn, aggravates existing malnutrition. Thus, the battles against infectious diseases and malnutrition are in reality part of the same war.

—Margaret Markham

Fuel and power

Explosive population gains and burgeoning economies in almost every country reemphasized the necessity of energy for the welfare and progress of mankind. More importantly, they underscored the need for continuous reappraisal of the changing patterns of energy supply and utilization in relation to both present demand and long-term expectancies.

Vast quantities of irreplaceable energy are being consumed daily throughout the world (an equivalent of more than 6½ million tons of coal, or 29 million barrels of oil per day in the United States alone in 1968). Thus, the adequacy of economically available supplies of energy assumes degrees of urgency among nations proportionate to their own resources or to their ability to obtain their requirements through international trade. In addition to the location, extent, quality, and forms of energy, their relative costs, availability, and technologies of production and utilization are prime factors in determining eco-

nomic growth and social development within as well as among nations.

Both globally and in the U.S. developments in fuel and power during the last half of 1968 and through mid-1969 covered a broad range. Typical of the constantly changing pattern of energy supply and demand, and of the factors that influenced that pattern, were: (1) substantial retrenchment from the recent optimism for rapid development of nuclear power generation in the U.S.; (2) discoveries of potentially large crude oil reserves on the North Slope of Alaska and of what could be the largest natural gas field in the world in western Siberia; (3) increased appreciation of the continental shelf as one of the largest potential sources of oil and natural gas in the U.S.; (4) acceleration of interest and of international trade in liquefied natural gas; (5) a reappraisal of the prospects for oil-shale development in Colorado, Utah, and Wyoming; (6) continuing progress toward the production of synthetic pipeline gas and of gasoline from coal; (7) a comprehensive survey of the potential supply of low-sulfur coal in the Appalachian area; (8) an increasing realization that the desire for a better environment, especially in terms of pollution, would have considerable impact on the development and utilization of energy resources; and (9) significant challenges for the development of new technologies tailored to changing energy patterns. These and other activities are summarized briefly below under related topic headings.

Nuclear energy and electric power

During the past year there was a surprising deceleration in the drive toward early attainment of large-scale nuclear power generation in the U.S. Following the upsurge in demand for nuclear systems in 1966 and 1967, optimism suddenly was replaced by caution. Principal among the reasons for this change in attitude were substantially increased costs of nuclear systems. Other problems included environmental restrictions against thermal pollution and the failure of some of the pioneer prototype nuclear power plants to achieve expected operating efficiencies.

The sobering influence of reappraisal, however, ultimately could mean more stable progress and earlier attainment than otherwise of the tremendous potentials for commercially competitive nuclear power, as well as an opportunity for better utilization of the fossil fuels within an overall plan. (*See* Year in Review: ENGINEERING, *Nuclear Engineering*.)

Bruce McAllister

Petroleum and natural gas

Additional exploration of the oil and gas reserves recently discovered on the North Slope of Alaska indicated that supplies from this area could influence considerably the future energy pattern of the U.S. The initial impact was expected to be felt in the western U.S. as pipelines or tankers, or a combination of both, move oil to that area. Other possibilities included a pipeline across Canada to the Middle West. Also, through new technologies of transportation, including supertankers and icebreakers for the development of a northwest passage, supplies could be made available to the East Coast of the U.S. A further possibility was the shipment of large quantities of liquefied natural gas to Japan.

The continental shelf appeared to have great potential as a major and rapidly expanding source of oil and natural gas in the U.S. Already accounting for 13% of the total U.S. oil production, principally from the Gulf of Mexico, offshore sources could reach at least 25 to 33% of the nation's total output by 1980. Expectations for offshore natural gas from these areas are even greater, estimated as high as 40% of total output by 1980. The possibility of significant deposits off the North Atlantic coast was not being discounted, with Canada beginning exploration off Nova Scotia.

Reports about Soviet gas finds indicated that the new Urengoiskoye field in western Siberia may be the largest natural gas reserve in the world, ranging from approximately 91.8 trillion cu ft of proved and probable reserves to overall reserves of about 141 trillion cu ft. Moreover, the Soviet Union claimed that Samotlorskoye, also in western Siberia, was one of the world's giant oil fields, although it had not been developed to its fullest capacity. The largest gas field in the West was generally considered to be the Groningen field in the Netherlands, with reserves of 58.2 trillion cu ft.

The potential of liquefied natural gas (LNG) to become an important factor in international trade captured the imagination of many who envisioned large-scale, worldwide shipments of this product as an energy source for nations with limited energy supplies. LNG also seemed likely to be useful for special purposes in industrialized nations where its unique qualities, including low

Drilling for oil is under way on the North Slope of Alaska, that part of the state bordering on the Arctic Ocean. A potentially large reservoir of petroleum and natural gas was recently discovered in this area.

Courtesy, Atlantic Richfield Co.

sulfur content, were in increasing demand. Shipments from Algeria to Great Britain and France already were a reality, shipments from Libya to Spain and Italy were soon to begin, and extensive plans were being made for expanded international trade, with the United States as a major target. Research and development, and the application of LNG to commercial and other purposes in the U.S., were proceeding at an accelerating rate.

Throughout the U.S. regulations were established or were under consideration which severely restrict the allowable sulfur content of fuels consumed for electric power generation and for other purposes. As a result, the demand for low-sulfur oils was increasing substantially, particularly along the East Coast. To meet these requirements, oil desulfurization plants and processes already were initiated or were under study in Venezuela and the Caribbean area. Also, it appeared likely that there would be considerably increased imports of natural low-sulfur oil from North Africa.

Coal

Long-term expectancies for coal were optimistic, with predictions for new highs in output between 1969 and 1980 resulting from coal's high efficiency

Two major projects in the Western Hemisphere involved the discovery and transportation of oil.
On the North Slope of Alaska at Prudhoe Bay potentially large crude oil and natural gas fields were being explored. A pipeline over the Andes Mountains in Colombia connected the oil field at Orito with the seaport of Tumaco.

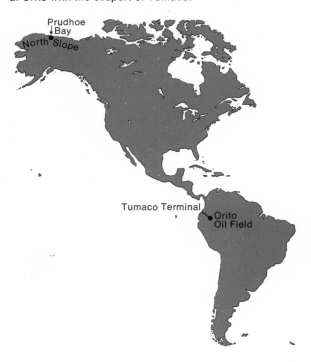

in electric power generation (which had become its primary market) and high productivity rates in the coal industry. The degree of its ascendance will be affected over the short term principally by the extent to which it can conform to requirements for a pollution-free environment, and over the longer term by economic capabilities for the generation of power by nuclear sources and by the commercial availabilities of synthetic gas and oil production from coal.

Low-sulfur coal. Principal among the environmental factors, as related to coal's competition with other energy sources, were restrictions which required the use of low-sulfur coal for power generation and other purposes. The U.S. Bureau of Mines, in cooperation with the U.S. Public Health Service, was conducting a comprehensive survey of the availability of coal, by sulfur content, in the Appalachian region. When completed, this information was expected to be valuable not only to the government but also to the coal industry, to coal consumers, and to the public, in determining the qualities and quantities of coal available from the region and whatever utilization standards, or modifications thereof, might be appropriate. Also, the Bureau of Mines and others were studying the development of economical processes for the removal of sulfur from coal and of sulfur oxides from stack gases.

High-quality gas from coal. Spurred by an apparent need for additional natural gas supplies within the next decade, researchers were nearing the capability of producing pipeline-quality gas from coal. Several processes were so encouraging that pilot plants were either under way or planned, with some construction scheduled for 1969, according to the Office of Coal Research, U.S. Department of the Interior. Among the most promising processes was the hydrogasification of coal, a type of hydrogen treatment that was being jointly supported by the Department of the Interior and the American Gas Association. Experimental work on this process indicated a projected gas cost as low as 40 cents per 1,000 cu ft (from an earlier cost of $1 per 1,000 cu ft). Later studies of the effect of incorporating improved hydrogen sources, along with additional experimentation, indicated the possibility of further cost reductions.

An added attraction was the removal, and availability, of sulfur in the gasification process. This was important in regard to uncertainties regarding future sulfur reserves and expectations for a heavy increase in the demand for sulfur. The U.S. Department of the Interior estimated that by 2000, when other supplies may be limited, one-half or more of the needed sulfur supplies in the U.S. could come from coal gasification.

Liquid fuels from coal. Because coal inherently contains many of the chemical constituents common to petroleum, the possibility of producing gasoline from coal has been a challenge to technologists for many years. Critical examination of future availabilities of and demand for petroleum, in the light of heavily increasing requirements for gasoline and related products, has generated positive action to develop processes that will make the production of gasoline from coal economically viable.

Several conversion processes being tested showed promise of commercial feasibility. However, the timing of the availability of gasoline from coal was expected to depend on many factors, particularly the cost of conversion. If there should be a technological breakthrough which would make liquid fuels from coal economically competitive with natural petroleum, the demand for such fuels would be immediate. Otherwise, their availability would probably be determined by such factors as the demand for oil, which was increasing steadily; the extent of domestic reserves of petroleum; the status of oil imports; and comparative costs with the process of obtaining oil from oil shale.

Energy resources and the natural environment

Of paramount interest throughout much of the industrialized world were demands for clean air, clean water, and a more attractive landscape. That the production and utilization of energy resources contributed to air and water pollution and to disturbance of the landscape could not be denied. It was also true, however, that many leaders in energy-producing and energy-consuming industries were among the most active in the drive to attain higher environmental standards, and in the expenditure of large sums of money to gain these objectives.

Whether by self-imposed standards or in conformance with governmental regulations, the preservation and improvement of the environment was time-consuming and costly to the producers and consumers of energy and to the public. Among major objectives were the restoration and improvement of land features damaged in the extraction of mineral fuels; the removal of pollutants from raw materials before combustion or from gas emissions afterward; diminution or prevention of acid drainage into streams and other water bodies; the use of cooling towers or other devices to eliminate thermal pollution from nuclear and other power-generating facilities;

"Operation Hannibal," the building of a pipeline 193 mi across the Andes in Colombia, was completed in 1969. It transports up to 50,000 bbl of crude oil per day from the interior to offshore oil tankers at the port of Tumaco.

and the prevention of land subsidence and of mine fires, and of the noxious fumes that emanate from the latter through fissures in the earth. (*See* Year in Review: ENVIRONMENTAL SCIENCES, *Conservation.*)

Future technological needs

Problems generated by the changing patterns of energy availabilities and utilization throughout the world suggest significant challenges for the development of new technologies that can perform new and bigger tasks with increased efficiency. Included are overriding needs for protecting environmental qualities, and massive problems pertaining to the logistics of supply, all of which will be influenced by changing proportions in the types of energy being used.

Some of the problems and needs are indicated by the following: (1) new and changing techniques in underwater production of oil and natural gas as exploration extends into deeper waters of the continental shelf; (2) super-pipelines and other

257

means of transportation for long-distance transmission of oil and gas from large reserves remote from eventual markets, some of which will require special types of equipment and materials to withstand wide ranges in temperature and in geologic conditions that are hostile to current systems; (3) new storage facilities—underground, underwater, or otherwise—to supplement pipeline distribution of energy resources, or to eliminate the need for additional pipelines if adequate supplies of energy are to be available when needed; (4) larger oil tankers, and either larger ports or offshore tanker and pumping stations; (5) specially designed vessels and storage facilities for large-scale international trade in liquefied natural gas; (6) commercially acceptable technology for the desulfurization of fuels, or of gases resulting from their combustion; and (7) research toward new, more efficient methods of extraction, processing, distribution, and utilization of the respective energy resources.

—Thomas W. Hunter

Honors

The following were recipients of certain major scientific honors during the period from July 1, 1968, through June 30, 1969.

Alexander, Tom: *Science Journalism;* AAAS-Westinghouse Science Writing Award

Alvarez, Luis Walter: *Physics;* Nobel Prize for Physics

Barker, Horace A.: *Miscellaneous;* National Medal of Science

Bartlett, Paul D.: *Miscellaneous;* National Medal of Science

Béhar, Moisés: *Medical Sciences;* Bronfman Prize

Bohr, Aage: *Miscellaneous;* Atoms for Peace Award

Brodie, Bernard B.: *Miscellaneous;* National Medal of Science

Bronk, Detlev W.: *Miscellaneous;* National Medal of Science

Bumpus, F. Merlin: *Medical Sciences;* Stouffer Prize

Cairns, Robert W.: *Chemistry;* Perkin Medal

Culler, Floyd L., Jr.: *Miscellaneous;* Atoms for Peace Award

Cunningham, R. Walter: *Aeronautics and Astronautics;* Haley Astronautics Award

Dirac, P. A. M.: *Physics;* J. Robert Oppenheimer Memorial Prize

Eckert, John P.: *Miscellaneous;* National Medal of Science

Eisele, Donn F.: *Aeronautics and Astronautics;* Haley Astronautics Award

Eisenhower, Dwight D.: *Miscellaneous;* Atoms for Peace Award

Eklund, Sigvard: *Miscellaneous;* Atoms for Peace Award

Friedman, Herbert: *Miscellaneous;* National Medal of Science

Fuglister, Frederick C.: *Earth Sciences;* Alexander Agassiz Medal

Gibbon, John H., Jr.: *Medical Sciences;* Albert Lasker Clinical Medical Research Award

Gilmore, C. P.: *Science Journalism;* Albert Lasker Medical Journalism Award

Giovannitti, Len: *Science Journalism;* Albert Lasker Medical Journalism Award

Goddard, James L.: *Medical Sciences;* Bronfman Prize

Hanchette, John: *Science Journalism;* AAAS-Westinghouse Science Writing Award

Hill, Lister: *Medical Sciences;* Albert Lasker Public Service Award

Holley, Robert W.: *Medical Sciences;* Nobel Prize for Physiology or Medicine

Hooker, Stanley G.: *Aeronautics and Astronautics;* Goddard Award

Hoyle, Fred: *Science Journalism;* Kalinga Prize

Ioffe, M. S.: *Miscellaneous;* Atoms for Peace Award

Kaplan, Henry S.: *Miscellaneous;* Atoms for Peace Award

Katz, Morris: *Chemistry;* R. S. Jane Memorial Lecture Award

Khorana, Har Gobind: *Biology;* Louisa Gross Horwitz Prize; *Medical Sciences;* Albert Lasker Basic Medical Research Award, Nobel Prize for Physiology or Medicine

Lilienfeld, Abraham: *Medical Sciences;* Bronfman Prize

Lorenz, Edward N.: *Earth Sciences;* Carl-Gustaf Rossby Research Medal

Lush, Jay L.: *Miscellaneous;* National Medal of Science

Moser, Jürgen K.: *Astronomy;* James Craig Watson Medal

Mottelson, Ben R.: *Miscellaneous;* Atoms for Peace Award

Newmark, Nathan M.: *Miscellaneous;* National Medal of Science

Neyman, Jerzy: *Miscellaneous;* National Medal of Science

Nirenberg, Marshall Warren: *Biology;* Louisa Gross Horwitz Prize; *Medical Sciences;* Albert Lasker Basic Medical Research Award, Nobel Prize for Physiology or Medicine

Onsager, Lars: *Chemistry;* Nobel Prize for Chemistry; *Miscellaneous;* National Medal of Science

Parker, Eugene N.: *Astronomy;* Henryk Arctowski Medal

Peart, William S.: *Medical Sciences;* Stouffer Prize

Pratt, Perry W.: *Aeronautics and Astronautics;* Goddard Award

Rennie, Compton A.: *Miscellaneous;* Atoms for Peace Award

Salam, Abdus: *Miscellaneous;* Atoms for Peace Award

Schirra, Walter M., Jr.: *Aeronautics and Astronautics;* Haley Astronautics Award

Schwyzer, Robert: *Medical Sciences;* Stouffer Prize

Seaborg, Glenn T.: *Miscellaneous;* Arches of Science Award

Siegel, Seymour N.: *Science Journalism;* Albert Lasker Medical Journalism Award

Simmonds, Sofia: *Chemistry;* Garvan Medal

Skeggs, Leonard T.: *Medical Sciences;* Stouffer Prize

Skinner, Burrhus F.: *Miscellaneous;* National Medal of Science

Smyth, Henry DeWolf: *Miscellaneous;* Atoms for Peace Award

Sullivan, Walter: *Science Journalism;* AAAS-Westinghouse Science Writing Award.

Turkevich, Anthony: *Miscellaneous;* Atoms for Peace Award

Wheeler, John Archibald: *Physics;* Enrico Fermi Award

Wigner, Eugene P.: *Miscellaneous;* National Medal of Science

Wild, J. P.: *Astronomy;* Henryk Arctowski Medal

Windle, William F.: *Medical Sciences;* Albert Lasker Basic Medical Research Award

Wood, William B., III: *Biology;* U.S. Steel Foundation Award in Molecular Biology

Yuncker, Barbara: *Science Journalism;* Albert Lasker Medical Journalism Award

Aeronautics and astronautics

Goddard Award. The American Institute of Aeronautics and Astronautics annually awards the Goddard Medal and a $10,000 honorarium for a brilliant discovery or a series of outstanding contributions over a period of time in the engineering science of propulsion or energy conversion. The 1969 award was shared by two men: Stanley G. Hooker, technical director of Bristol Engine Division, Rolls-Royce Ltd., Bristol, Eng., and Perry W. Pratt, vice-president and chief scientist, United Aircraft Corp., East Hartford, Conn. They were cited for developing the gas turbine engines that power modern aircraft.

Haley Astronautics Award. The Apollo 7 crew, Capt. Walter M. Schirra, Jr., Lieut. Col. Donn F. Eisele, and R. Walter Cunningham, were the

Marshall Nirenberg

Ralph Bredland, courtesy, National Institutes of Health

Robert W. Holley

Wide World

Har Gobind Khorana

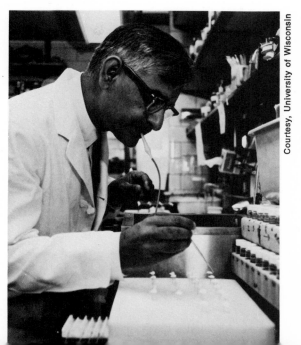

Courtesy, University of Wisconsin

Apollo 7 astronauts (left to right), Walter Cunningham, Donn F. Eisele, and Walter M. Schirra, Jr.

recipients of the 1969 Haley Astronautics Award, which is given annually by the American Institute of Aeronautics and Astronautics for "an outstanding contribution by test personnel who undergo personal risk in the advancement of space flight." The three astronauts made the first manned flight test of the Apollo spacecraft.

Astronomy

Henryk Arctowski Medal. In 1969 the U.S. National Academy of Sciences awarded the first Henryk Arctowski Medal for studies of solar activity changes and their effects on the ionosphere and the terrestrial atmosphere. The recipients of this new award were Eugene N. Parker of the University of Chicago and J. P. Wild of the Commonwealth Scientific and Industrial Research Organization (CSIRO) in Sydney, Austr. Parker was honored for his contributions to the theoretical understanding of the interaction between the magnetic fields of the sun and earth and the ion plasmas that surround those bodies. Wild was chosen for his many contribu-

tions to solar radio astronomy, including a technique for studying solar disturbances.

James Craig Watson Medal. Approximately every three years the U.S. National Academy of Sciences awards the James Craig Watson Medal for contributions to the science of astronomy. The 1969 winner was Jürgen K. Moser, director of the Courant Institute of Mathematical Sciences at New York University, who was cited for his contributions to dynamical astronomy. In 1962 Moser constructed a geometrical theorem that led to the stability proof of periodic orbits of Hamiltonian systems.

Biology

Louisa Gross Horwitz Prize. The Louisa Gross Horwitz Prize is presented annually by Columbia University for outstanding research in biochemistry. In 1968 the $25,000 award was given to the biochemists Har Gobind Khorana of the University of Wisconsin and Marshall Warren Nirenberg of the U.S. National Heart Institute, Bethesda, Md., both 1968 Nobel laureates (see *Medical*

Sciences, below), for their work in genetics. Khorana was cited for synthesizing the subunits (trinucleotides) of the genetic code and for explaining the way in which they are read in the cells. Nirenberg received credit for two major discoveries that made it possible for his group of workers to establish the exact sequence of letters in the biochemical code by which genes determine hereditary characteristics.

U.S. Steel Foundation Award in Molecular Biology. Administered by the U.S. National Academy of Sciences, the U.S. Steel Foundation Award in Molecular Biology is given annually for a recent, notable discovery in molecular biology by a young scientist. The recipient of the 1969 award was William B. Wood III, a biochemist at the California Institute of Technology, who used the virulent virus T4 as a model in his genetic and biochemical studies of the mechanisms by which the DNA of a virus enters a bacterial cell and reprograms it to produce and assemble new viruses. (*See* Year in Review: MOLECULAR BIOLOGY, *Biochemistry.*)

Chemistry

Garvan Medal. Each year the American Chemical Society presents the gold Garvan Medal and $2,000 to a U.S. woman chemist chosen for her distinguished service to chemistry. In 1969 the award was given to Sofia Simmonds, associate professor of biochemistry at Yale University, whose research in the amino acid metabolism of bacteria showed that some leucine peptides seem to inhibit utilization of free leucine. This led to the hypothesis that certain peptide antibiotics (e.g., gramicidin) also may inhibit utilization of amino acid because they are not hydrolyzed as easily as simple peptides.

Nobel Prize for Chemistry. The person chosen by the Royal Swedish Academy of Sciences to receive the 1968 Nobel Prize for Chemistry and its cash prize of $70,000 was Lars Onsager, J. Willard Gibbs professor of theoretical chemistry at Yale University. Onsager, who was also a recipient of the U.S. National Medal of Science (see *Miscellaneous,* below), was cited for work published in 1931 concerning the discovery of the reciprocal relations bearing his name (the reciprocal relations of Onsager), which are fundamental for the thermodynamics of irreversible processes. His ideas, formulated while at Brown University, Providence, R.I., (1928–33), make up a system of equations demonstrating the reciprocal relations of various kinds of activity.

Perkin Medal. The Perkin Medal, which is given annually by the Society of Chemical Indus-

try, is the highest honor bestowed for outstanding work in applied chemistry in the U.S. In 1969 the medal was awarded to Robert W. Cairns, vice-president of Hercules, Inc., Wilmington, Del., who was chosen because of his ability for leadership of group effort in the field of polymer chemistry, especially in the development of a polymerization method for making polypropylene.

R. S. Jane Memorial Lecture Award. The highest honor in Canadian chemical engineering, the R. S. Jane Memorial Lecture Award is given annually by the Chemical Institute of Canada. In 1969 the recipient was Morris Katz, professor of atmospheric sanitation in the department of civil engineering at Syracuse University, Syracuse, N.Y., who was cited for his internationally known work in air pollution. Katz pioneered in methods for analyzing sulfur dioxide in the atmosphere and for observing its effects on forest and crop plants.

Earth sciences

Alexander Agassiz Medal. The U.S. National Academy of Sciences presents the Alexander Agassiz Medal, usually at three-year intervals, for original contributions in oceanography. In 1969 the medal was awarded to Frederick C. Fuglister, a senior scientist at the Woods Hole (Mass.) Oceanographic Institution, in recognition of his observations of the Gulf Stream and its vortices. Fuglister developed the theory that the Gulf Stream may sometimes shorten its course by cutting across the shortest distance between sides of the loops in its channel, thus causing large, independently moving vortices (rotating rings) of warm water that could be 100 km or more in diameter.

Carl-Gustaf Rossby Research Medal. The American Meteorological Society's highest honor, the Carl-Gustaf Rossby Research Medal, is presented to an atmospheric scientist for outstanding contributions to man's understanding of the structure or behavior of the atmosphere. In 1969 the medal was awarded to Edward N. Lorenz, professor of meteorology at the Massachusetts Institute of Technology, for "his fundamental innovations in dynamic meteorology."

Medical sciences

Albert Lasker Medical Research Awards. Each year the Albert and Mary Lasker Foundation awards a number of $10,000 cash prizes in recognition of advances made in the medical field. *Basic Medical Research Award.* This prize is given for fundamental investigations that provide techniques, information, or concepts prerequisite to the elimination of the major causes of death and disability. It was shared in 1968 by three men: the biologists Marshall Warren Nirenberg of the U.S. National Heart Institute and Har Gobind Khorana of the University of Wisconsin for their work in elucidating the genetic code (see *Nobel Prize for Physiology or Medicine,* below, and *Biology: Louisa Gross Horwitz Prize,* above); and the physiologist William F. Windle, research professor at the Institute of Rehabilitation Medicine, New York University Medical Center, who was cited for his basic discoveries in developmental biology and for his contributions to the treatment of brain-damaged children. *Clinical Medical Research Award.* The 1968 prize in clinical research was given to John H. Gibbon, Jr., emeritus professor of surgery at Jefferson Medical College, Philadelphia, for his work in developing the heart-lung machine that maintains life during open-heart surgery and heart transplantation, and for his contributions to techniques in heart and blood vessel surgery. *Albert Lasker Public Service Award.* Presented for devotion to the cause of medical research, the 1968 Albert Lasker Public Service Award was received by former Senator Lister Hill of Alabama for his leadership in guiding more than 80 enactments of health legislation through the U.S. Congress during his 46 years as a member of that body. *Albert Lasker Medical Journalism Awards* (see *Science journalism,* below).

Bronfman Prize. The American Public Health Association awards the Bronfman Prize annually for efforts in improving the health and life expectancy of large numbers of people. The three 1969 recipients were: Moisés Béhar, director of the Institute of Nutrition of Central America and Panama at Guatemala City, Guatemala, who was cited for his contribution to the conquest of malnutrition among children throughout the world; James L. Goddard, vice-president of EDP Technology, Atlanta, Ga., who received his prize for the "judicious use of regulatory power for the protection of the consumer" while he was U.S. Commissioner of Food and Drugs (1966–68); and Abraham Lilienfeld, professor of chronic diseases at the Johns Hopkins University School of Hygiene and Public Health, who was recognized for his leadership in the development of chronic disease epidemiology, and as a brilliant teacher.

Nobel Prize for Physiology or Medicine. The Swedish Royal Caroline Medico-Chirurgical Institute awarded the 1968 Nobel Prize for Physiology or Medicine to three U.S. scientists for their pioneering research in genetics that led the way in the struggle against hereditary illness, and that could one day give man the power to control

his biological destiny. (1) Marshall Warren Nirenberg (see *Biology,* above), head of the biochemical genetics section of the U.S. National Heart Institute, who prepared a cell-free system that synthesized protein in the presence of amino acids and energy sources (adenosine triphosphate) from the bacterium *Escherichia coli.* He then demonstrated for the first time that messenger ribonucleic acid (RNA) is needed for cell-free protein synthesis. (2) Har Gobind Khorana (see *Biology,* above) of the University of Wisconsin's Institute for Enzyme Research was chosen for his major contribution in solving the genetic code by synthesizing short, biologically active chains of deoxyribonucleic acid (DNA) with known sequences of bases. Khorana and his co-workers developed two general synthetic approaches which aided in obtaining direct proof that the genetic code is nonoverlapping and is read three bases at a time, in triplets. (3) Robert W. Holley, resident fellow at the Salk Institute for Biological Studies in San Diego, Calif., who was associated with Cornell University when he and his co-workers were the first to elucidate the nucleotide sequence of an amino acid-specific transfer RNA, alanine transfer RNA (ala-tRNA). The ala-tRNA was subjected to enzymatic digestion, separating the 16 smaller fragments (oligonucleotides) that were obtained by using solution chromatography. Each fragment was hydrolyzed with alkali and the component mononucleotides were identified by chromatographic, electrophoretic, and spectral properties.

Stouffer Prize. Awarded by the American Heart Association, the Stouffer Prize is in recognition of a scientist or scientists who made outstanding contributions to the understanding of hypertension (high blood pressure) and atherosclerosis (hardening of the arteries). In 1968 the $50,000 prize was shared by four scientists: (1) Leonard T. Skeggs, professor of biochemistry in the department of pathology at Case Western Reserve University, Cleveland, O.; (2) F. Merlin Bumpus, chairman and scientific director of the division of research at the Cleveland Clinic Foundation; (3) William S. Peart of St. Mary's Hospital, London; and (4) Robert Schwyzer of the Swiss Federal Institute of Technology, Zürich.

Physics

Enrico Fermi Award. The U.S. Atomic Energy Commission presented the 1968 Enrico Fermi Award of $25,000 to John Archibald Wheeler, Joseph Henry professor of physics at Princeton University, for his pioneering contributions to the understanding of nuclear fission, for develop-

Lars Onsager

ing the technology of plutonium production reactors, and for his continuing broad contributions to nuclear science.

Nobel Prize for Physics. The Royal Swedish Academy of Sciences awarded the 1968 Nobel Prize for Physics, and the amount of $70,000, to Luis Walter Alvarez, professor of physics at the University of California, Berkeley, for his decisive contributions made during the early 1960s to the physics of subatomic particles and for his development of a technique for their detection. This technique, which is known as stereophotography, is used for photographing and analyzing the strings of bubbles left by ephemeral particles as they descend through liquid hydrogen.

J. Robert Oppenheimer Memorial Prize. Established in 1968 by the Center for Theoretical Studies of the University of Miami, Coral Gables, Fla., the J. Robert Oppenheimer Memorial Prize is given in recognition of important contributions to the theoretical natural sciences and to the philosophy of science. The first recipient of the gold medal and $1,000, presented in 1969, was P. A. M. Dirac, Lucasian Professor of Theoretical Physics at Cambridge University, who was cited for work on quantum electrodynamics, for his prediction of antiparticles (later verified), for his spin theory of elementary particles, and for his discovery of the states of polarization of gravitons.

Science journalism

AAAS-Westinghouse Science Writing Awards. The American Association for the Advancement of Science presented the 1968 AAAS-Westinghouse

Science Writing Awards to three people for outstanding writing on the natural sciences and their engineering and technological applications (excluding medicine). For general circulation magazines, the recipient was Tom Alexander, associate editor of *Fortune* magazine, for his articles "The Costly Hunt for the Heart of Matter" (March 1968) and "The Shimmery New Image of Matter" (June 1968). For newspapers of more than 100,000 daily circulation, Walter Sullivan, science editor of the *New York Times,* received the award for 10 articles on pulsars (March–July 1968). For newspapers of less than 100,000 daily circulation, the award was presented to John Hanchette, a reporter for the Niagara Falls (N.Y.) *Gazette,* for his series of 11 articles on air pollution (April 6–16, 1968).

Albert Lasker Medical Journalism Awards. Presented by the Albert and Mary Lasker Foundation, the Lasker Medical Journalism Awards for 1968 were given to Barbara Yuncker of the *New York Post;* C. P. Gilmore, free-lance writer; Len Giovannitti of the NBC network; and Seymour N. Siegel of WNYC, New York City Municipal Broadcasting System. Each received $2,500 for articles or broadcasts concerning public health and the prolongation of life through medical research.

Kalinga Prize. Each year UNESCO awards the Kalinga Prize for the popularization of science in writing. The 1968 recipient was Fred Hoyle, British astronomer and author, who has been Plumian professor of astronomy and experimental philosophy at Cambridge University since 1958. Hoyle is credited as being one of the creators of the steady-state theory of cosmology. Among his

Glenn Seaborg (center)

publications are *Some Recent Researches in Solar Physics* and *Frontiers of Astronomy.*

Miscellaneous

Arches of Science Award. Sponsored by the Pacific Science Center, Seattle, Wash., the Arches of Science Award is presented to an American who has made an outstanding contribution to the public understanding of the meaning of science to contemporary man. The 1968 award of $25,000 was made to Glenn T. Seaborg, chairman of the U.S. Atomic Energy Commission, who was cited for his writings, speeches, and new approaches in science teaching.

Atoms for Peace Award. Established in 1955 by the Ford Motor Company Fund as a memorial to Henry Ford and his son Edsel, the Atoms for Peace Award is to encourage the promotion of international efforts in the development of nuclear energy for peacetime purposes. The eighth presentation of the award, in the fall of 1968, honored three men, each of whom received $30,000: Sigvard Eklund, director-general of the International Atomic Energy Agency (IAEA); Henry DeWolf Smyth, U.S. representative on the IAEA board of governors; and Abdus Salam of Pakistan, director of the IAEA International Center for Theoretical Physics at Trieste.

In the spring of 1969 the ninth and last Atoms for Peace Award of $15,000 each was given to seven scientists: (1) Aage Bohr (son of Niels Bohr, recipient of the first Atoms for Peace Award in 1957) and (2) Ben R. Mottelson, both associated with the Nordic Institute for Theoretical Atomic Physics in Copenhagen; (3) M. S. Ioffe of the I. V. Kurchatov Institute of Atomic Energy in Moscow; (4) Compton A. Rennie of Great Britain, chief executive of the Organization for Economic Cooperation and Development high-temperature reactor project; (5) Henry S. Kaplan, professor of radiology at Stanford University School of Medicine; (6) Floyd L. Culler, Jr., assistant director of the Oak Ridge (Tenn.) National Laboratory; and (7) Anthony Turkevich, professor of chemistry at the University of Chicago.

In 1969 a special honorarium of $50,000 was awarded posthumously to Dwight D. Eisenhower in recognition of his great contribution to international efforts for the peaceful uses of atomic energy. Accepted by his grandson David, the honorarium was given to Eisenhower College in Seneca Falls, N.Y.

National Medal of Science. The U.S. government's highest award in science, mathematics, and engineering, the National Medal of Science, is presented annually by the president of the

Walter Sullivan

Luis Alvarez

United States to those persons who "in his judgment are deserving of special recognition by reason of their outstanding contributions to knowledge in the physical, biological, mathematical, or engineering sciences."

Of the 12 recipients in 1968, five were in the biological sciences: (1) Horace A. Barker, professor of biochemistry at the University of California, Berkeley, who was cited for his study of the chemical activities of microorganisms, especially the unraveling of fatty acid metabolism, and for the discovery of the active coenzyme form of vitamin B_{12}; (2) Bernard B. Brodie, head of the chemical pharmacological laboratory at the U.S. National Institutes of Health, Bethesda, Md., for his pioneering of qualitative concepts that revolutionized the development, study, and effective use of therapeutic agents in the treatment of human disease; (3) Detlev W. Bronk, emeritus president of Rockefeller University, New York City, for research in physiology and for his contributions to the advancement of science and its institutions in the service of science; (4) Jay L. Lush, professor of animal science at Iowa State University, who applied the science of genetics in animal breeding and so helped remold the herds and flocks of America and Western Europe; and (5) Burrhus F. Skinner, professor of psychology at Harvard University, for his contributions to the study of behavior that have influenced those working in psychology and in many other related areas.

Three men were honored in engineering science: (1) John P. Eckert, vice-president of Remington-Rand Univac division, Sperry Rand Corp., for pioneering and continuing contribution in the creation, development, and improvement of the high-speed electronic digital computer; (2) Nathan M. Newmark, professor of civil engineering at the University of Illinois, for contributions to the development of powerful and widely used methods for analyzing complex structural components and assemblies under a variety of loading conditions; and (3) Jerzy Neyman, professor of mathematics at the University of California, Berkeley, who laid the foundations for modern statistics, and who devised tests and procedures essential to all statisticians.

In the physical sciences four men received medals: (1) Paul D. Bartlett, professor of chemistry at Harvard, whose leadership advanced the understanding of the mechanisms by which chemical reactions take place, and for his success in training young teachers and researchers; (2) Herbert Friedman, superintendent of the U.S. Naval Research Laboratory's atmosphere and astrophysics division, who was cited for his pioneering work in rocket and satellite astronomy, particularly for his contributions in gamma-ray astronomy; (3) Lars Onsager, professor of chemistry at Yale University (see *Nobel Prize for Chemistry,* above), for a number of contributions leading to the understanding of electrolytes and other chemical systems, especially the thermodynamics of systems in change; and (4) Eugene P. Wigner, professor of mathematical physics at Princeton University, for his innovations in the physical, mathematical, and engineering sciences that have included quantum chemistry and nuclear theory.

Medicine

Increasing concern with the development of systems to provide better health care, the discovery that virus infections can cause chronic degenerative diseases of the central nervous system, the increased application of cell-culture systems to the detection of defects before birth, and the further refinement of organ transplant procedures were among the significant issues and developments in medicine during the past year. The relative priorities for these and other significant issues were being discussed both within and without the medical profession.

The critical social issues surrounding medical practice were well known. First, while large segments of the population in both urban and rural areas did not receive adequate health care, when preventive health care rather than emergency treatment was considered, much more of the population also received inadequate attention. Second, at the same time that there was an extreme shortage of health-care professionals, physicians were performing tasks that they did not need to do. Physicians needed to reexamine their responsibilities and roles and to determine what they could do best, what others could do better, and whom they might train in order to extend their services more effectively.

There were also other, less publicized, problems. For example, there was a need to learn much more about the effects on health of urban pressures, both environmental and social. In addition, old medical yardsticks, such as mortality rates, hospital days, or sick days, were no longer satisfactory measures of health-care delivery. Perhaps most important of all, however, was the need to recognize that there was a limit to what could be accomplished at any one time; priorities had to be established from among all of these demands.

—Donald N. Medearis, Jr.

Immunology

Structure of the antibody molecule. One of the most dramatic developments in medical research during the year was the announcement of the deciphering of the complete structure of a gamma globulin molecule by Gerald M. Edelman and his colleagues at Rockefeller University in New York City. The immunoglobulins, including gamma globulin, are antibodies, specialized chemical substances produced by the body to counteract foreign substances (antigens) by neutralizing them. It had been established earlier that an immunoglobulin molecule contains two kinds of polypeptide chains, termed heavy and light chains. Each molecule is composed of two identical heavy chains containing about 446 amino acids each and two homologous (of the same chemical type) light chains containing about 214 amino acids each. The chains are linked by four disulfide bonds—two between the heavy chains, and one between each light chain and its corresponding heavy chain.

Intensive investigations from a number of laboratories in the U.S. and U.K. demonstrated that both the light and heavy polypeptide chains consist of two portions, one part having a constant amino acid sequence and the other a variable combination of amino acids. The variable sections of the light and heavy chains are in close proximity and together, through an almost infinite number of combinations, develop the specificity of recognition for the site of the antibody molecule that combines with the invading substance. The constant sections carry out other immunological functions after the antigen is bound by the antibody.

The group at Rockefeller solved the formidable problem of identifying the entire amino acid sequence of the heavy as well as the light chains, and of identifying the 16 locations of the disulfide bonds that hold the chains in their characteristic three-dimensional shape. Analysis of the amino acid sequence of the stable portion of the chains revealed that they are composed of 8 homologous groups (homologues) of about 110 amino acids each. The variable ends of the light and heavy chains, despite differences in composition at certain points within them, contain four homologues. These homologues resemble one another but do not resemble the homologues of the stable parts of the molecule. The amino acid sequence analysis, which took three and a half years to complete, was conducted on a gamma globulin (the Bence-Jones protein) from a patient suffering with myeloma tumor. This protein is the same as a light chain. (See Year in Review: MOLECULAR BIOLOGY, Biochemistry.)

Because it is universally accepted that one gene codes for the formation of only one protein molecule, the puzzle remaining unsolved was how the antibody-forming plasma cell synthesizes a molecule containing both a variable and a constant amino acid sequence. One hypothesis for this remarkable phenomenon proposed the existence of a special genetic process involving two cellular genes that undergo recombination during cell division, exchanging only those parts of the genetic message that code the variable sections of the polypeptide chains. To prove this, however, would require a considerable effort.

Chemical Structure of Gamma Globulin Molecule

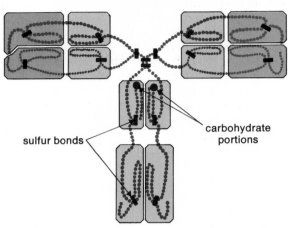

sulfur bonds

carbohydrate portions

The gamma globulin molecule deciphered at Rockefeller University consisted of 1,320 amino acids in two chains, one heavy and one light, represented here by the blue beads. The 16 sulfur bonds (small black bars) determine the globulin's configuration. Eight stable sections of the molecule are shaded in gray; the four areas shaded in blue are the variable sections.

Identification of the antibodies responsible for allergic disease. Immunoglobulins can be separated into different classes by virtue of variations in the structure of the heavy polypeptide chains. It is the differences in the composition of the heavy chains that determine the individual immunologic properties of the molecule. Until recently only four classes of immunoglobulin had been identified in human serum, termed gamma G, gamma A, gamma M, and gamma D immunoglobulin.

Although it had long been known that a particular type of antibody, called a reaginic antibody, was responsible for the allergic reactions in such diseases as hay fever and asthma, it was only recently that these immunoglobulins had been isolated in pure form and their structure characterized. These investigations, primarily from the laboratory of Kimishige and Teruko Ishizaka, a husband and wife team at the Children's Asthma Research Institute & Hospital in Denver, Colo., demonstrated that this antibody belongs to a distinct immunoglobulin class, named gamma E.

The Ishizakas separated and purified all five immunoglobulin components from serums of ragweed-sensitive individuals and demonstrated that only the newly discovered gamma E immunoglobulin component contained reaginic activity to ragweed pollen extract. Reaginic activity was established by inoculating a small amount of the gamma E from an allergic individual into the skin of a normal person. In a non-allergic individual the reaginic antibodies have the unique property of combining with cells of the skin, thereby sensitizing the skin so that a subsequent injection with the allergen results in the rapid development of a typical erythematous wheal reaction (abnormal redness) at the site of the injection.

Utilizing a technique of immunofluorescence, these investigators demonstrated gamma E antibody-forming cells in lymphoid organs of the tracheal mucosa, pharynx, and intestinal tract, although they were essentially absent in the spleen and lymph nodes, which synthesized the bulk of the serum antibodies. This finding may explain why gamma E is found only in low concentrations in normal serum, and suggests that the local production of the antibody at the site of the target tissues may be necessary for the development of the state of reaginic hypersensitivity in the allergic patient.

The secretory antibody systems. Investigations at a number of laboratories, principally those by Thomas B. Tomasi and his co-workers at the State University of New York at Buffalo, demonstrated that, in addition to the humoral immunoglobulin system (that which involves the body fluids), there exists in man a separate antibody-forming system that produces those antibodies found in such "external" secretions as saliva and nasal and intestinal fluids. These antibodies consist predominantly of a particular type of gamma A immunoglobulin, termed secretory gamma A. This secretory immunoglobulin is composed of two gamma A antibody molecules, which are coupled into a single molecule by a globulin component called the secretory piece. This component has been related to the ability of the antibodies to be actively secreted into the digestive and other external body fluids. Additionally, it appears to protect the molecule from the enzymes that degrade proteins, which are often found in these secretions.

The construction of this molecule is unusual, as its components are synthesized in two separate cell types. Whereas the gamma A immunoglobulin is produced by plasma cells of the mucous tissue, the secretory globulin piece is produced by epithelial (surface) cells lining these tissues. Investigators were attempting to discover the mechanism responsible for the coupling of these two components of the molecule. Recovery from certain infections, such as viral respiratory disease, seems to correspond more to the levels of virus-neutralizing antibodies within the respiratory secretions than to those of serum antibody. This suggests that the secretory antibody is produced by a local immunoglobulin-forming system in response to regional stimulation by the antigen.

In addition, it was reported recently that immunization of humans with aerosol sprays of inactivated influenza virus stimulated antibodies in respiratory secretions. In contrast, inoculations in the skin with an equivalent amount of the vaccine did not stimulate the production of the secretory antibodies. Similarly, oral immunization with polio virus has been shown to stimulate intestinal antibody production, whereas skin inoculation did not.

These findings proved that the gamma A immunoglobulin found in human external secretions arises as a result of local antibody synthesis. They also suggested that in the development of resistance to certain viral infections the specific stimulation of this local antibody system may be more important than the humoral antibody system. The discovery of the secretory antibody system also pointed out the importance of stimulating the full immune potential of an individual.

Cell-mediated immunity. It was generally accepted that the lymphoid system of a properly stimulated animal mediates two distinct types of immunity. In one type, the immunoglobulin-producing system develops humoral immunity through the production of antibodies by plasma cells in the lymph nodes and spleen. These antibodies enter the bloodstream and react with and inactivate infecting microorganisms or their toxic by-products. The mechanism of the other immune response, termed cell-mediated immunity, was less well known. In this immune response, immunologically activated lymphocytes are mobilized and apparently attracted by cells foreign to an animal. Recent investigation indicated that immunologically committed lymphocytes become attached to foreign target cells because of the specific recognition of the foreign cells by an antibody, or antibodylike configurations, on the lymphocyte's surface.

Through a mechanism as yet not well defined, the attached lymphocytes are triggered to release a substance that causes lysis (disintegration) of the target cells. Although this response is immunologically specific, it was shown recently that even lymphocytes from animals without specific immunologic recognition can be manipulated to adhere to foreign cells and destroy them. It was hypothesized that the primary reaction of target cells and immune lymphocytes may also result in a biologic signal leading to the local mobilization of normal blood lymphocytes, which aid in the elimination of the foreign cells.

Robert A. Good and his colleagues at the University of Minnesota examined the development of these two immune responses and demonstrated that they are mediated by two distinct lymphoid systems. A lymphoid cell population arising from the thymus gland is responsible for cell-mediated immunity, while lymphoid cells most probably developing from the lymphoid tissues in the lower intestine are the progenitors for cells forming the humoral antibody system. The cell-mediated immune system was currently of great interest because of its role in the immune rejection of organ transplants. Furthermore, observations of patients with developmental failures of the thymus system strongly suggested that the cell-mediated immune system participates in the eradication of certain viral and fungal microorganisms that remain primarily intracellular and, therefore, protected from circulating antibodies.

Immunosuppression. The greatest hazard to successful organ transplantation remained the recipient's immunologic rejection of the foreign tissue. In addition, a variety of clinical disease states appeared to result from development of an immune response that is directed against one or more of the patient's own tissues. Thus, many of the current investigations in immunology were concerned with methods of eliminating such undesirable responses.

No unanimity of opinion had been reached on how the mechanism of the immune response functions. The current medical management of immune rejection of organ transplants, however, used drugs known to destroy the rapidly dividing immune cells. Because of this, patients on immunosuppressive drugs were extremely susceptible to infection. A promising addition to this therapy came from reports that it was also possible to interfere with the immune response through the administration of antihuman-lymphocyte serum. Recent studies, however, suggested that this effect did not necessarily depend on the destruction of lymphocytes, but might occur because the antibody attached to a specific site on the lymphocyte membrane, thereby blocking one of the necessary stages of antigen sensitization. Much effort was going into ways to purify this lymphocyte membrane and to prepare antiserums that block an expected undesirable immune response without abolishing the total immune response of the individual. (See *Surgery,* below.)
—Robert Keller

Infectious diseases

Infectious disease problems were diverse in recent months, varying from smallpox in India—where vaccination was not practiced widely enough—to the infective complications following immuno-suppressive therapy used in organ transplantation. Fundamentally, infectious diseases were dealt with through public health measures, such as adequate environmental sanitation, which interrupted the spread of pathogens, the specific causes of disease. To a lesser extent, physicians could preserve health or prevent the spread of disease with vaccines or the use of drugs.

Bacterial diseases. Bacteria continued to prove their ability to adapt to the newer antibiotics and to changes in the usage patterns of old antibiotics. Adaptation occurs when the infecting organism either acquires or loses antibiotic resistance. A current example of this was the appearance of staphylococci (bacteria that cause serious skin and mucous-membrane infections) that were resistant to the action of methicillin, one of the semisynthetic penicillins that had been made especially to act against the staphylococcus. This penicillin had been chemically altered to resist the action of the penicillin-destroying enzyme penicillinase, which the staphylococcus produced and which frequently had provided the bacteria with a resistance to regular penicillin.

In another study of antibiotic resistance, the ability of staphylococcal strains isolated from patients at the University of Washington in 1966–67 to react to treatment with various antibiotics was compared with similar sensitivity tests made in 1960–61. Careful study showed that the bacteria had regained a significant sensitivity to a variety of commonly used antibiotics. This increase in sensitive strains of staphylococcus was believed to be attributable to the fact that the antibiotics tested had not been used to treat this type of infection since the semisynthetic penicillins became available. Another factor affecting test results was that patients were more carefully isolated from one another in the later period, thus minimizing the spread of organisms.

Another bacterial disease against which antibiotic effectiveness seemed to be on the decrease was tuberculosis. Two efficacious drugs were developed for use in those instances where resistance to streptomycin, the most generally used antituberculosis agent, had occurred. (See *Pharmacology,* below.)

Several centers in the world reported that the antibiotic sensitivity of the gonococcus (the cause of gonorrhea) had also shifted somewhat in the last few years. As yet, the degree of penicillin resistance that was occurring was not strong enough for it to be clinically important. Almost surely, however, it would be a problem for the future, in light of the great increase in venereal disease that had taken place in the last few years.

Another bacterial infection that was receiving much interest was melioidosis. This disease has a high incidence in Vietnam, but the attention paid to it in the U.S. was occasioned by its occurrence among soldiers who had returned home before symptoms developed. The infection is signaled by abscesses in the internal organs and therapy is complicated by the fact that the causative organism is highly resistant to many antibiotics commonly used in clinical medicine. Successful therapy, therefore, required exact diagnosis and the use of combinations of antibiotics and other drugs.

Another problem that appeared in Vietnam in recent months was an increased incidence of bubonic plague among military personnel. Programs for vaccination and increased research were underway.

The melioidosis problem and the interest it received was typical of the observation that a frequent by-product of war is the necessity for increased study of infectious disease. The reason for this is obvious: transients in an area lack resistance to indigenous diseases; whereas the native population not only has resistance but also serves, in many cases, as carriers of the disease-causing organisms.

Protozoal diseases. Military activity in Southeast Asia led to an increased international awareness that one of the protozoan malarial parasites had developed a resistance to both synthetic and natural antimalarial treatments. Cases of this agent-resistant malaria were reported in Vietnam, Thailand, Cambodia, Malaysia, and as far away as Brazil.

The parasite involved is the *Plasmodium falci-parum,* which causes a severe, malignant form of malaria. By 1969 a program led by the Walter Reed Army Institute of Research had produced a new antidote that was actually two drugs, each of which was somewhat effective (and toxic in man) when administered singly in large doses. But, when combined in small amounts, one dose cured the malaria and prevented its return without harmful side effects. There was as yet, however, no prophylactic drug, that is, no agent that would provide immunity to the resistant strain. Regular use of the curative drugs, while depressing the disease, would also depress human blood formation.

These experiences also taught that attempts to eradicate the malarial parasite by killing the mosquito carrier through the use of DDT was only a partial approach to control of the disease. In South America it was found that when surveillance ceased following an intensive eradication program, the incidence of the parasite in mosquitos and people increased and, in fact, surpassed previous levels of infection. In Africa political difficulties that prevented the initiation of proper public health measures resulted in a breakdown in malaria control programs and an increased incidence of the disease. Most experts emphasized the need for continued surveillance and the intensification of control programs as the incidence of malaria fever rose.

Viral diseases. Perhaps over the years the most important public health finding has been the great efficacy of vaccination against certain virus diseases. Occasionally, however, there are complications following vaccination, including involvement of the central nervous system and general vac-

The growth of tissue culture cells on three successive days shows what the SV40 virus does to the cells it infects. Little distinguishes normal cells (top series) from infected ones (bottom series) on the first two days (left and center); a difference in density and arrangement is obvious by the third day (right).

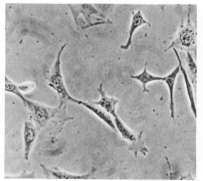
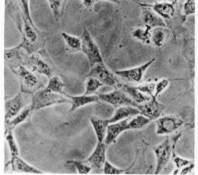
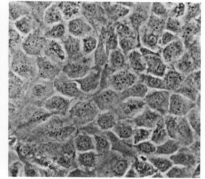

Courtesy, Renato Dulbecco, The Salk Institute for Biological Studies

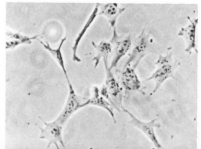
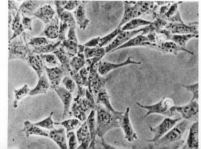
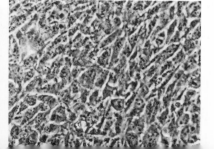

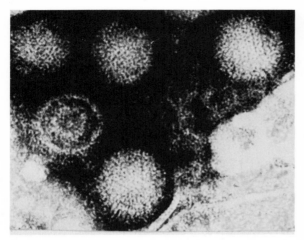

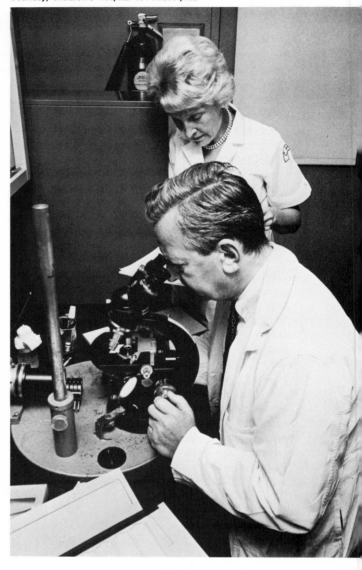

At the Children's Hospital of Philadelphia, virologists Gertrude and Werner Henle (right) successfully identified the virus that is most likely the cause of infectious mononucleosis. They found that blood samples from patients with the disease contained antibodies to a specific herpes virus, the EB virus (above, magnified 240,000 times). These antibodies were not present before the patients became ill.

cinal infection. This was especially true of smallpox vaccination, and recently several approaches that might reduce the occurrence of such complications were being considered. One suggestion was that vaccination could be made less mandatory in countries that are free of the disease, but most experts did not agree with this.

The complications and danger of smallpox vaccination did appear to lessen when more highly attenuated, or weakened, strains of the vaccine were used. Unfortunately, as yet there was no experience with individuals so vaccinated under epidemic conditions. Perhaps future study would increase confidence in the protective value of these attenuated vaccines, and their use could decrease the complications of vaccination.

In the meantime, it was likely that various national governments, acting both independently and within the World Health Organization (WHO), would continue programs to eradicate smallpox in the areas of Asia and Africa where it still persisted. Findings indicated that vaccination could produce a dramatic decrease in the number of cases of the disease.

Along the same lines, in the U.S. the last few years had shown that a widespread program of vaccination against measles (rubeola) could eradicate the disease in the vaccinated population. The U.K. was also undertaking such a program within the next year, and it was likely that other countries would adopt this vaccine. In addition, a live mumps vaccine, presently in the early stage of wide clinical use, appeared to be successful in

decreasing the attack rate and was likely to give solid protection against disease in the vaccinated population. Attempts to grow the rubella (German measles) virus in culture produced several strains that were under trial as vaccines. At least one of these was expected to be available commercially soon in the U.S. (see *Pediatrics,* below). There were also efforts underway to combine several of these vaccines in a single jet-type inoculation for use in populations where medical care is not obtained easily.

In the last year, all were made aware again of the ability of the influenza virus to mutate enough to overcome the immunity a host had acquired from prior attacks of influenza. The pandemic infection of the new strain of influenza A2, or Hong Kong-68, spread rapidly and had a very high attack rate (see *Public Health,* below).

Although the U.S. Public Health Service and the WHO rapidly distributed strains of the virus to vaccine manufacturers, there was some difficulty obtaining enough fertile eggs to produce the large quantities of the virus needed for a widespread vaccination program. Therefore, in most areas of the U.S. the vaccine arrived at the time that cases of flu were already appearing and its use had to be reserved for those who would suffer most from infection with the virus. It was highly significant, however, that a vaccine for the specific strain that was to become pandemic could be prepared within a few months.

Investigators at the Children's Hospital of Philadelphia made an important observation in their association of a specific herpes virus with infectious mononucleosis, the so-called "kissing disease" of the young adult. It was likely that either this virus, or something very closely related to it, was the hitherto undetected agent causing the disease.

Also of potential importance was the finding that an antigen, a substance that stimulates the production of an antibody, appears in the circulation of individuals just prior to the yellow or jaundiced phase of infectious hepatitis. This antigen could represent the virus causing the disease.

The finding that the virus that causes cold sores on the lips, *Herpes simplex*, is really two separate strains of virus with two major sites of predilection, one oral and the other genital, led to recent speculation that this virus is also the cause of cancer of the cervix. This suggestion grew out of the increased incidence of antibodies against the genital strain of *Herpes simplex* observed in patients with cancer of the cervix. Unfortunately, this lead was only an indirect one; there was still no definite proof that any human tumor is caused by a virus.

An area of emerging importance for medicine was the research being done on the role of virus infection in degenerative neurological disease. There was growing evidence that in some diseases the major degenerative effects occur years after the initial virus infection. A neurological disease called kuru, which has been observed only among the native population of New Guinea, was found to be caused by a virus that persists in the tissues for long periods of time before symptoms appear. A similar finding was also made for a type of encephalitis that seems to be associated with infection by the measles virus some years before the development of severe neurological symptoms. (See *Pediatrics,* below.)

Another important developing area involved the possible medical use of interferon, or of inducers that stimulate cells in the body to produce interferon, against human or animal virus infections. Interferon is a protein involved in the natural recovery process from viral infection; it acts to

Photomicrographs of the thin membrane lining the left ventricles of year-old chickens contrast a normal membrane (left) with the degeneration of connective tissue, or endocardial fibroelastosis (right), in the membrane of a chick whose egg had been injected with mumps virus 12 hours after fertilization.

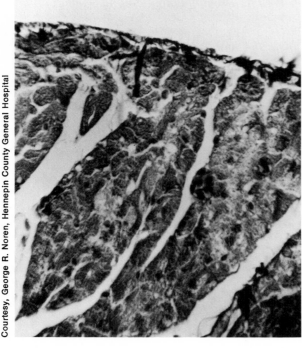 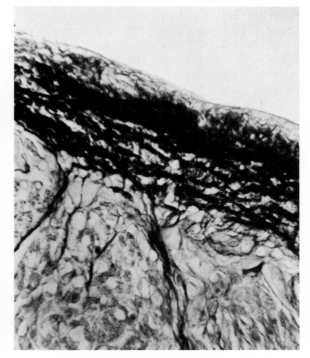

271

Medicine

(Left) Courtesy, National Communicable Disease Center; (others) Courtesy, Eli Lilly and Company

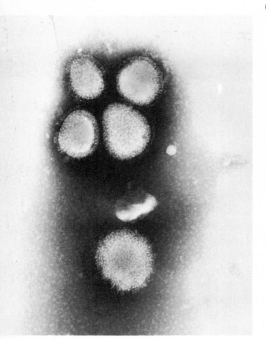  

New techniques aided the production of a vaccine for the A2 Hong Kong-68 influenza virus (left).
Cell debris, egg protein, and other residue found in conventionally produced influenza A2 vaccine (center)
were removed by a special centrifuge leaving only the ultrapure vaccine (right).

block virus multiplication in infected cells and is relatively nontoxic. Therefore, it is a potentially ideal therapy in virus infections where the exact cause is unknown and prompt treatment is needed. There were many practical problems associated with administering to humans interferon prepared in tissue culture, but in the last year several synthetic molecules were discovered that stimulate interferon production when given directly to animals. Some of these appeared relatively nontoxic and would very likely be used in experimental trials against certain virus infections in man in the near future.

—Thomas C. Merigan

Lunar Receiving Laboratory. All of the refinements in the techniques of detecting, defining, and controlling infectious diseases were brought to bear in mid-1969 on an infection no man had ever had. Although man's knowledge of the moon had indicated that it could not support life, all manner of precautions were taken against the extremely remote possibility that a bacterium, fungus, spore, virus, or other form of life could be picked up on the surface of the moon and brought back to earth.

The greatest medical danger to be anticipated was that an infection-causing organism (pathogen) brought back to earth would be a new one— one against which man had no resistance. Just as the Hong Kong flu, a new strain of the A2 influenza virus, had spread in a matter of months in

1968–69 around a planet that had never before been exposed to it, an extraplanetary infection could also spread without interference.

The Lunar Receiving Laboratory (LRL) set up in Houston, Tex., by the U.S. National Aeronautics and Space Administration was designed to prevent such an occurrence, to test the effects of space flight on man, and to establish procedures in anticipation of the day when man would return from a celestial body more capable of supporting life (*see* Feature Article: LIFE BEYOND THE EARTH). While the LRL was also the site of the preliminary examination of lunar materials—a complex of physics, chemistry, geology, and biology laboratories—its first use was as a medical clinic and isolation ward. As such it incorporated elaborate safeguards against the spread of pathogens. (The same safeguards also protected the lunar samples from earthly contaminants.)

To prevent organisms from escaping, the LRL was completely sealed and equipped with its own air conditioning, purification, and pressure systems. Lunar materials placed in a moonlike environment were subjected to numerous tests that yielded information about the moon's surface and its history.

Most important to man's health, however, were tests introducing lunar samples to a variety of terrestrial life forms that had been bred and raised in germ-free conditions. Because they had never been exposed to infections of any kind,

272

these test animals and plants were extremely susceptible to any pathogen. In order to prevent misreading any symptoms the test subjects might develop, the results were compared with other tests performed on microbial samples taken from the spacecraft and astronauts before the start of their lunar mission.

In a separate part of the LRL, the astronauts, their doctors, and other personnel who came in contact with lunar materials also served as guinea pigs for certain tests. In addition, the astronauts were examined to determine what physical effects space travel might have had on their bodies. If the LRL was not one of the most complex biomedical centers in the U.S., it was certainly the one searching out the most curious disease on earth.

See also Year in Review: MICROBIOLOGY.

Medical genetics

During the past year genetics, the scientific study of heredity, had a major impact upon other related and dependent sciences, such as cytology, biochemistry, taxonomy, bacteriology, and anthropology. In addition, the many contributions made over the years by genetics to the scientific basis of medicine were now forming an essential part of daily medical practice. The public awareness of the relationship between genetics and medicine was, in fact, one of the most significant developments in the area of human genetics. The genetic counselor, a new specialist trained in both the principles of genetics and the practice of medicine, gained widespread acceptance, and the numbers of such people were increasing rapidly. Current developments in biology also were providing genetic counselors with new concepts and techniques that had a tremendous impact upon the practice of medicine and on society in general.

Genetic counseling techniques. New techniques permitted physicians to identify those couples that had a high risk of transmitting genetic defects to their offspring. Most persons who were being referred for genetic counseling either had previously borne a child with a birth defect or had a history in which a closely related family member had been affected with a particular genetic disorder. Genetic counseling for such patients was usually quite easy, especially if the disorder had a classical mode of inheritance. Counseling was more difficult, however, when the carrier state of the disorder could not be specifically identified.

The utilization of tissue-culture techniques for the study of familial disorders had resulted in de-

tecting approximately 25 genetic defects in which the carrier state could be defined. The detection of most of these had depended until recently upon a biochemical analysis that specifically measured the deficient or abnormal enzyme. Recently, however, investigators demonstrated that granules that can take certain dyes (metachromatic granules) are present in cultivated cells from patients with a number of familial disorders. Despite its lack of specificity, this method proved extremely useful; cystic fibrosis, a respiratory disease that is the most common and significant genetic disorder affecting Caucasians, could now be studied on a cellular level and its carriers, one of every 25 Caucasians, could be identified.

This approach and many others, including the studies of red and white blood cells, serum, urine, and biopsies of organs, also permitted the detection of carriers without family histories of genetic defects. In order to be more successful in identifying the high-risk patient, however, screening procedures that could be available for large groups of people would have to be developed.

Investigators working at Children's Memorial Hospital in Chicago and at the National Institutes of Health in Washington, D.C., developed additional techniques that permitted precise determination of sex and the detection of genetic disorders in unborn children. By means of a technique called transabdominal amniocentesis, small samples of amniotic fluid that surrounds and protects the fetus can be obtained by placing a needle through the abdomen into the uterine cavity at approximately 12–16 weeks of pregnancy. Amniotic fluid contains cells that have been shed by the baby at an earlier stage of development. Recent methods permit the growth of these cells in tissue culture so that about 20 familial biochemical disorders can be detected. In addition, chromosome analysis using these cultured cells provides a means of prenatal identification of the 1% of all live births in which a child has a chromosomal aberration.

Transabdominal amniocentesis was found to be simple, reliable, and safe to both the baby and mother. It was used successfully in the detection of a number of chromosomal and familial biochemical disorders including cystic fibrosis; Down's syndrome (mongolism), in which the presence of an extra chromosome 21 causes mental and physical retardation; Turner's syndrome, in which the absence of an X chromosome results in the lack of gonadal development; and galactosemia, the lack of the enzyme needed to metabolize milk sugar. When these or other defects were detected, a therapeutic abortion could be considered by the parents.

The disorders of an infant that could be detected before it is born were primarily those producing congenital deformities, mental retardation, or severe illness, and leading to death within the first decade of life. For these disorders, the genetic counselor no longer needed to rely upon known risk factors such as one in four births, one in three, or one in two, but could determine accurately whether or not the unborn child would be affected. While the management of the high-risk genetic pregnancy currently consisted of defining the status of the fetus and, if abnormal, recommending termination of pregnancy, it was quite possible that within the next few years there could be a new medical speciality that would concern itself with the care of the fetus while in the womb. Additional new techniques were expected to permit the treatment of genetic disorders early in pregnancy and the significant modification of the particular defect. (*See* Feature Article: HUMANICS AND GENETIC ENGINEERING.)

Research on embryos. Other studies dealt with some of the genetic components of reproduction. A number of investigators in different countries were studying the possibility of maturing human eggs in a chemically defined medium, fertilizing them with sperm, and observing the first signs of growth outside the uterus. This was accomplished first for a number of laboratory animals and, most recently, for man.

Using egg cells taken from women for medical reasons, scientists at the University of Cambridge bathed the eggs in a mixture of body fluids and allowed donor sperm to be mixed with them. Of the 56 eggs used, 34 matured and divided at least once, 18 were definitely penetrated by sperm, and 7 were known positively to have been fertilized. Some of the embryos had developed to the blastocyst stage when they were removed from their culture for detailed study. At that point, however, they lacked the nourishment that would have allowed them to continue to grow.

Scientists working in this area eventually hoped to be able to implant a fertilized egg in certain women who could not otherwise have babies, to select eggs in which the genetic disorder would not be present and, finally, to unravel the events that occur as the single fertilized egg develops into a well-differentiated child. Biologists, however, had a long way to go before any of these possibilities could become reality. Many problems had to be overcome, the most significant of which was the ability to have the fertilized egg continue to develop outside the uterus after the first few cell divisions.

Genetic variations. More precise knowledge of genetic variation in man was also being sought. Genetic polymorphism (normal variations of a single protein or enzyme) was being investigated in many centers throughout the world. The potential of damage that would cause a mutation was being studied. In addition, many commonly used drugs, both legal and illegal, were being evaluated for their potential to produce genetic damage. Reports described chromosomal damage to the unborn children of women who had taken LSD and other similar drugs during pregnancy. Other investigations in progress were attempting to define relationships between many environmental factors and potential genetic damage.

In recent months a number of new familial disorders leading to mental retardation and/or death in early infancy were described, and the

By extracting amniotic fluid from the area surrounding a developing fetus and separating cells shed by the baby from the other material, it is possible to cultivate the cells and analyze them for biochemical disorders and chromosomal aberrations.

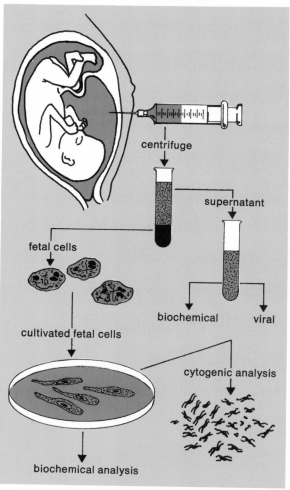

basic defect for a number of other genetic defects was elucidated. In addition, studies in which human cells were hybridized with mouse cells attempted to identify the specific locus of certain genes on human chromosomes.

Behavioral traits. Attention also focused on chromosomal abnormalities and the behavioral traits associated with them. Special concern dealt with the so-called XYY syndrome in males, which appeared to cause aggressive and even criminal behavior.

While a normal female has two X chromosomes and a normal male has one X and one Y, occasionally one or the other of the parental chromosomes can be doubled, causing an XXX, XXY, or XYY pattern in offspring. Such defects often result in physical and/or mental retardation. Recent observations of males with an XYY chromosomal pattern have also suggested that these men show a tendency toward tallness, severe cases of the adolescent skin disease acne, mental dullness, and aggressive behavior.

Because the XYY chromosomal aberration had originally been observed among inmates of prisons and hospitals for the criminally insane, the trait had come to be known as a "criminal" syndrome. In a number of court cases, the fact that a defendant had the XYY pattern was used in a plea for acquittal of a murder charge.

It was not yet possible, however, to conclude that all males with the XYY chromosomal pattern were predestined to be criminals, or even to be aggressive. Control studies of the general population would have to be carried out before such a conclusion would be valid. While examinations of about 3,700 infants in the U.S., Canada, and Scotland indicated that the actual incidence of the XYY pattern could be as high as 1 of every 300 males, there was also evidence that a number of males with the abnormal chromosomal pattern did not appear to exhibit any of the behavioral abnormalities assumed to be connected with it.

It was not yet known how these and other chromosomal abnormalities occurred in the course of meiosis, the process of sperm and egg formation. It was known, however, that fathers with the XYY pattern seemed unable to transmit the defect to their sons. Presumably a sperm carrying the extra Y would be heavier than one with a single Y and would not be able to move as quickly toward the egg.

It was not unlikely that as geneticists refined the methods for analyzing chromosomes they would discover other traits that indicated the probability of criminal behavior.

—Henry L. Nadler

Pediatrics

The research developments that occurred throughout the various branches of medicine in recent months took on a special importance in the field of pediatrics, where the identification or elimination of a disease was often seen in terms of the increased numbers of children who could be promised a healthier life. In addition, the efforts being made to improve the delivery of pediatric health care were among the best examples of a developing pattern in medical practice that would, hopefully, bring better health to more people more efficiently and economically.

Pediatric health care. For some time, C. Henry Kempe and Henry K. Silver, pediatricians at the University of Colorado Medical Center in Denver, had been in the forefront in developing new systems for improving the delivery of pediatric health care. They began programs in which specially trained nurses operate child care clinics in rural areas where there are no physicians. These pediatric nurse practitioners may, for example, make one of four diagnoses: the child is well, the child's illness is mild and self-limited, the child should be seen again soon, or the child needs the immediate attention of a doctor.

The program made optimal use of personnel, and in Colorado it brought health care to populations that were previously not receiving it. It was also a forerunner of another innovation by Silver and Kempe: a three-year Pediatric Associates Program for students who had completed two years of college. This program provided courses in human biology, clinical training, and the prescription and use of certain drugs, as well as an internship in an appropriate health service facility. According to a bill before the Colorado state legislature, these pediatric associates would be licensed health professionals and could prescribe certain drugs.

Slow virus infections. A discovery of great importance to pediatrics was made by Carleton Gajdusek and his co-workers at the U.S. National Institutes of Health, Bethesda, Md. Gajdusek had previously described kuru, a disease that afflicts certain tribes of the New Guinea highlands, as characterized by progressive ataxia (the inability to coordinate voluntary muscle movement) and trembling, wasting, and finally death. He knew that veterinarians had discovered that virus-like agents caused scrapie, a progressive degenerative disease of the central nervous system of sheep, and that there was a similarity between the pathologic changes of scrapie and kuru. Therefore, he inoculated specimens of nervous tissue of kuru victims into the brains of chimpanzees

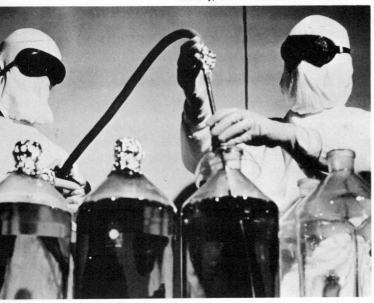

Researchers at a Belgian pharmaceutical firm pool harvests of a strain of rubella (German measles) virus as a step in the production of a new vaccine against the disease. One version of the rubella vaccine was licensed for manufacture in the U.S. in June 1969 and was to be administered to children.

and, after a period of one to two years, they became ill with a similar disease.

The very long incubation period, which gave rise to the term "slow virus infection," and the fact that a progressive degenerative disease of man's central nervous system could be caused by a virus were the two aspects of this discovery that were of transcendent importance. Accordingly, diseases that heretofore had not been suspected of being viral must now be so considered. For example, some believed that multiple sclerosis is a similar though more variable and milder infectious disease.

This discovery was a stimulus for defining the cause of another more acute disease of the human central nervous system. Subacute sclerosing panencephalitis (SSPE) is an extremely rare affliction of children characterized at the onset by poor performance in school and an inability to concentrate, leading eventually to seizures, coma, and death. Scientists in France noticed in 1965 that particles that looked like viruses of the family to which the measles (rubeola) virus belongs could be found in cells from children with SSPE. Confirmatory discoveries demonstrated conclusively that the same virus may cause SSPE several years after ordinary childhood measles has occurred. Measles virus was recovered from the brains of individuals who died from SSPE, and antibodies against measles virus were de-

tected in very much higher concentrations in those individuals than in those with usual measles.

A very important question remained: how does measles, with an incubation period of about two weeks, cause this disease, which has an incubation period of many years? Occasionally, measles is complicated by encephalitis, but SSPE is quite a different disease than measles encephalitis. Sir MacFarlane Burnet, a Nobel Prize winner from Australia, proposed that certain individuals fail to develop the hypersensitivity to measles that is necessary for a complete recovery. Instead, they form only those antibodies that can be found in the blood and other body fluids. After many years the progressive multiplication of the measles virus in the brain becomes associated with this acute disease of the nervous system.

A new vaccine. German measles (rubella), a mild viral infection, is most feared for its effect on an unborn baby. Congenital heart disease, cataracts, deafness, and mental retardation are among its devastating effects when infection occurs during the first part of pregnancy. A number of years ago two investigative teams recovered the rubella virus, and after that time a great deal of work was done to develop a vaccine to prevent these consequences. Following a review of these efforts at an international conference held in Bethesda, Md., in February 1969, it was generally agreed that there was sufficient evidence to justify the immediate licensing and production of a vaccine for German measles.

One feature of the mild infection caused by the vaccine virus was of some concern; the virus is "shed" by the recipient, that is, it can be recovered from throat washings after vaccination. Therefore, one important phase of the studies was to determine whether excreted (shed) virus could cause infection in individuals who were exposed to those who had been vaccinated. Apparently, this occurs with extreme rarity, if at all. If a woman in early pregnancy should be exposed to vaccinated individuals and, as a result, became infected, it is conceivable that the baby she was carrying might be affected. Extremely large, indeed almost impossible, studies would be required to determine whether or not such an infection could cause damage to the developing human embryo-fetus.

Accordingly, it was of cardinal importance to show that the virus does not spread from vaccinees to pregnant women, and this was demonstrated to the satisfaction of virologists and U.S. federal officials. It was expected that the wise use of this vaccine in children would so reduce the incidence of German measles that mothers or women in the childbearing age would not be exposed in the future even though these women themselves would not and should not be vaccinated.

Light treatment of jaundice. Soon after birth many babies have a period when their skin is stained yellow by bilirubin, a breakdown product of red blood cell hemoglobin. This jaundice is due to the inadequate development of the enzyme system and its related chemical factors, which convert indirect, or slowly reacting, bilirubin into direct, or rapidly reacting, bilirubin. Generally this condition is temporary and harmless, but other conditions, such as Rh blood group incompatibility (erythroblastosis), can contribute to the harmful accumulation of bilirubin. Conversion of bilirubin is essential because the indirect reacting component, if freed from its transport protein in the blood albumin and allowed to pass into the nerve cells of the brain, will disrupt the oxidation process within these cells and destroy them, causing brain damage manifested by a disease called kernicterus.

In recent months, the use of filtered sunlight and artificial blue light therapy for jaundice received much attention in the U.S. So far it had not been complicated by toxic or deleterious

A four-year-old deaf child receiving special training in a New York school is one of the estimated 20,000–30,000 children born with a handicap as a result of the 1964 rubella epidemic in the U.S. The new rubella vaccine was expected to prevent another severe epidemic anticipated for the early 1970s.

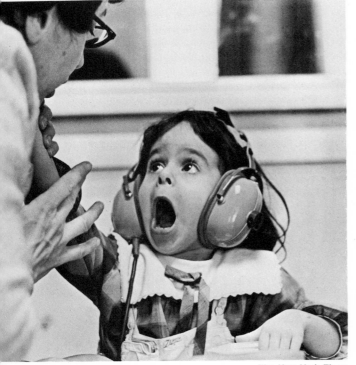

The New York Times

effects. If further studies establish definitely that this phototherapy reduces the quantity of indirect reacting bilirubin in the blood and thus lowers the incidence of kernicterus without causing any toxic effects, its widespread use might significantly reduce the incidence of a cause of mental retardation.

Detection of congenital defects. Hurler's disease is caused by an accumulation of complex carbohydrates (mucopolysaccharides) in various body tissues and is associated with dwarfism, grotesque skeletal deformities, joint restriction, deafness, cardiac deformities, and mental retardation. In the mid-1960s scientists at Rockefeller University, New York City, demonstrated that the accumulation of these chemical substances could be detected in the cytoplasm of skin cells (fibroblasts) of patients with this disease when these cells were cultivated in the laboratory. The cells had many granules that take on different colors (metachromasia) when stained with the dye tolidine blue and studied under a microscope. This technique was now being applied to the detection of cystic fibrosis, a respiratory disease. Abnormal cells were detected in both carriers and victims of these diseases.

Studies of the biochemical activity of cultured cells, their chromosomes, and their sex chromatin content were also being used to detect congenital defects and other characteristics of babies prior to birth. Amniotic fluid and cells could be extracted from the uterus by a needle and syringe (see *Medical Genetics,* above). The increasing applicability of these techniques made it quite clear that we are on the threshold of being able to know very much about those who are yet unborn. This knowledge was giving rise to the critical issue of what man should do with this knowledge. (*See* Feature Article: HUMANICS AND GENETIC ENGINEERING.)

Interaction of physiological, psychiatric, and social factors. An important recent series of observations demonstrated the interrelationship between physiological, social, and psychiatric factors in the control of growth. Infants suffering from a psychiatric disorder termed "parental deprivation" often show a retardation of growth. By interview and observational techniques, it can be determined whether these children are receiving affection and beneficial attention from their parents. The children of ineffective and sometimes abusive parents have been found to suffer no organic disease but to be severely retarded in their growth and to have a deficient level of growth hormone. When they are placed in a more protected, less hostile environment, however, they begin to grow and their growth

Medicine

hormone levels return to normal. A most important focus for pediatrics in the future would be that dealing with a definition of the interaction between social, psychiatric, and physiological factors in the health of infants and children.

Such efforts, however, would be severely handicapped by the current decrease in federal support for biomedical research in the U.S. If federal assistance was not forthcoming to replace the funds for research that medical schools had been receiving, medical education as well as federal health care programs would suffer greatly.

—Donald N. Medearis, Jr.

Pharmacology

Developments in pharmacology, with regard to both the use of existing drugs and the introduction of new ones, revolved around a growing interest in the different ways in which patients responded to treatment. This theme was apparent in the announcements of recent months as well as in the research being conducted on the drugs of the future.

Genetic differences in man. A body of knowledge, called pharmacogenetics, was accumulating that showed that the fate of a drug in the body, or even the nature and extent of its therapeutic effect, depends in certain cases upon a discrete genetic trait. Pseudocholinesterase, for example, is an enzyme present in the liver and blood plasma of man. Its physiological role is not completely known, but when certain drugs are given, such as the muscle relaxant succinylcholine, the enzyme can usually destroy them in a short period of time. To achieve relaxation of skeletal muscle for surgery, anesthetists commonly infuse succinylcholine by vein. Muscles involved in respiration become paralyzed momentarily, but the anesthetist can overcome this handicap by the use of positive pressure respiration (a form of artificial respiration). When the infusion of the drug is stopped, the residual drug is quickly inactivated by the action of the enzyme pseudocholinesterase. Occasionally, however, patients do not resume spontaneous respiration, and require artificial respiration for several hours. Careful examination of their pseudocholinesterase showed that the enzyme, although present, lacked the usual degree of activity with respect to this drug. The trait appeared in about one out of 2,000 persons tested, and was found to be genetically transmitted.

Many examples of such extraordinary responses to drugs could be cited. Most of them involve a small percentage of people, but some genetic traits are widely distributed. For example, about half the population in the U.S. may be classed as "slow" metabolizers of isoniazid, a drug used in the treatment of tuberculosis. The balance of the population consists of "fast" metabolizers of the drug. Of course, the physician would have to find out to which class his patient belongs by the use of a trial dosage.

These differences in drug handling by the body that are caused by discrete changes at a specific gene locus are called idiosyncrasies. If they present a hazard to health or to life, the physician learns to test each patient or to be prepared for the application of corrective measures. There are other differences between patients, however, that do not present themselves in such a dramatic fashion. These are graded differences that reflect the fact that most drug responses fall on a normal distribution curve. As an extreme example, among 11 adult patients treated continuously with the same daily dosage schedule of desmethylimipramine (DMI), a treatment for psychiatric illness, there was a 30-fold difference in the final blood level of DMI. In a strict sense these differences are also inherited, but their genetic basis is not so sharply defined as is the case for the idiosyncrasies.

Changes in drug metabolism. Many of the processes by which drugs are chemically altered in the body are mediated by enzymes in the liver, notably by a group of enzymes localized in tiny, intracellular structures called microsomes. These enzymes normally metabolize such substances as hormones, carbohydrates, proteins, and some of the intermediate metabolites. Their effectiveness in the alteration of drugs is a fortunate by-product. These enzymes convert drugs into less active, more water-soluble compounds that are more efficiently removed from the body by the kidney. This enhanced excretion plus the chemical alterations effectively terminate the actions of most drugs.

One remarkable feature of these enzyme systems, shown first in animals and recently in man, is the fact that their activity can vary widely in an individual depending upon the kinds of drugs, hormones, or diets that have been ingested. For example, a patient given the usual daily dose of DMI, the drug mentioned above, will achieve a certain "steady-state" level of drug in his blood after a reasonable time. If he is then given an ordinary daily dose of phenobarbital, a sedative, the blood level of DMI may drop by 50% after a few days, even though the DMI is being continued.

This effect was established in the mid-1950s, when it was observed that feeding carcinogenic (cancer-producing) chemicals such as benzpy-

278

rene to animals caused increased activity of their liver enzymes, due to an actual increase in the amount of enzyme present in the liver. Several stimuli can bring about such a response, which is called enzyme induction. One powerful agent that causes it is phenobarbital, which causes the rate of its own metabolism, as well as that of several other drugs, to be markedly increased after a few daily doses. Animals pretreated with phenobarbital exhibit enhanced metabolism of such diverse drugs as chlorpromazine (a tranquilizer), chloramphenicol (an antibiotic), procaine (a local anesthetic), and others. The tranquilizer meprobamate, like phenobarbital, hastens its own metabolism—by up to four times—after one month's daily administration.

Drug interactions. Many of these drug interactions were confirmed for man. Thus, serious problems could arise in patients receiving several drugs at the same time.

Patients with certain types of epilepsy are routinely treated with diphenylhydantoin. When such patients are also given phenobarbital, the metabolism of diphenylhydantoin is speeded up. The physician then has to raise the dose of diphenylhydantoin to maintain the body level of this drug that he had achieved before phenobarbital was added. A variety of such interactions came to light in recent years and led to a much more cautious use of therapies that include more than one drug.

For animals, and presumably for man, diet can also influence the activity of enzymes involved in drug metabolism, and insecticides such as DDT can stimulate these enzymes. In man, the metabolism of cortisone is influenced by the presence of large doses of DDD, a close relative of DDT. In animals, accidental exposure to DDT or related insecticides affects liver enzyme systems. This probably occurs in man too, but it would be difficult for study purposes to find human subjects who have not been exposed to insecticide residues.

The chlorinated hydrocarbons, such as DDT and DDD, are extremely resistant to ordinary processes of degradation. Through their widespread use as insecticides they have found their way into the body fat of man from food crops, water, and livestock that have eaten contaminated forage. Because there was a possibility that these agents had toxic hazards to man, and obvious devastating effects on certain animal species, there was a trend among biologists and agronomists to seek less crude methods of insect control.

An interesting observation showed a relationship between cigarette smoking and enzyme activity. Benzyprene is a chemical in cigarette smoke and is thought to be carcinogenic. Benzyprene hydroxylase is the enzyme that degrades benzyprene and is normally found in the liver. Placentas were obtained from women who had experienced normal labor and delivery in childbirth, and their benzyprene hydroxylase activity was measured. There was appreciable activity of the enzyme in the placental tissue of the 11 women who were cigarette smokers, but no detectable activity in those of the 13 nonsmokers.

Drug resistance. Drug resistance refers to cases where a drug does not exert its usual therapeutic effect at ordinary dosages. One example is the resistance to antibiotics shown by some rather ordinary bacterial infections. Mutations occur in any population of growing bacteria at a small but finite rate. If a mutant happens to appear that is resistant to penicillin, the mutant and its progeny flourish simply because competing, "normal" bacteria are being wiped out. Such experiences were carefully studied when antibiotics were being discovered at a rapid pace, and new insights into microbiology attended these discoveries. If the body's own defenses could not cope with bacteria resistant to an antibiotic, it was a simple matter to prescribe another.

Resistant strains of common organisms were most prevalent among hospital personnel. They did not necessarily cause signs and symptoms of disease among nurses, house staff, and other full-time employees, but they were readily transmitted to patients unless extraordinary precautions were taken. It was reported recently that 83.6% of the 482 strains of *Staphylococcus aureus,* a common pathogen (disease-producing organism), isolated in a one-year period from patients at Boston City Hospital were resistant to penicillin.

But another dimension was discovered recently. In certain bacterial species resistance to several drugs may be acquired simultaneously. Gram-negative bacilli such as *Escherichia coli* can become resistant to as many as nine antibiotics by virtue of a single genetic event. The genetic alteration in these cases appears to involve the transfer of DNA (deoxyribonucleic acid, the compound in which genetic information is encoded) from one bacterium to another by conjugation (bacterial mating). Thus far, this "R-factor" type of resistance, as it is called, had not led to many serious clinical cases. There were enough antibiotics at hand so that there was generally one which the organism did not resist. But the discovery of this kind of broad-spectrum resistance makes it imperative that the search for new antibiotics continues.

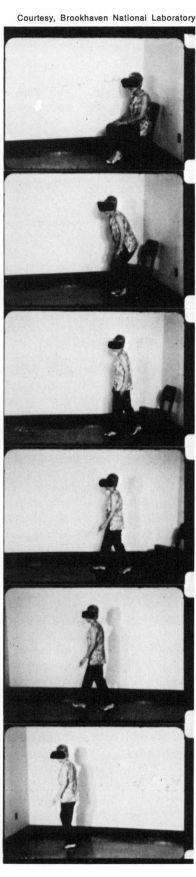

Antibiotics were also being used in agriculture to treat infections of swine, poultry, and cattle and as a supplement in animal feeds. In fact, use as a feed supplement accounted for the great bulk of antibiotics used in agriculture. It was not certain that this practice enhanced meat and poultry production but it did appear to cause the emergence of resistant pathogens in the animals. Because these pathogens might pose a serious health hazard to man, the problem was being carefully studied internationally by public health officials.

New drugs. Parkinson's disease (paralysis agitans, or "shaking palsy") usually afflicts people in the fifth and sixth decades of life. Each year about 50,000 new cases are discovered in the U.S. alone. The disease involves the basal ganglia of the brain, located deep within the cerebral hemispheres. Normal functions of the basal ganglia are not completely known, but they have an influence on muscular reflexes and complex body movements. Parkinson's disease is progressive; it leads to increasing degrees of debility due to tremor, muscular rigidity, and the loss of normal postural reflexes. Until recently therapy was confined to drugs that afford symptomatic relief and to an occasional attempt at surgical amelioration by interrupting certain central nervous pathways.

Recently, treatment of Parkinson's disease with the drug L-dopa was demonstrated to be effective by several groups of workers. The *New England Journal of Medicine* called it "the most important contribution to medical therapy of a neurological disease in the past 50 years." A group of investigators at the Medical Research Center of the Brookhaven National Laboratory, Upton, N.Y., showed that chronic administration with gradually increasing dosages of L-dopa can reverse the distressing signs and symptoms of the disease. Typical symptoms that are ameliorated include tremor, muscular rigidity, and akinesia (poorly coordinated muscular movements).

The remarkable aspect of this work was the fact that administration of dopa (dihydroxyphenylalanine) was based upon the observation that dopa and/or related substances are depleted in

The remedial effects of a new drug being used to treat Parkinson's disease are evident in two sequences of photographs of a patient before and during therapy with the drug, called L-dopa. At left, the patient shows the major symptoms of the progressive neurological disease: tremor, muscle rigidity, and loss of normal postural reflexes. At right, during treatment with individually tailored doses of L-dopa, the patient walks normally and unassisted. The drug apparently replaces a natural chemical deficiency in the midbrain.

the brain of the patient with Parkinson's disease. In other words, the symptoms of this disease can be ameliorated by the replacement of a normal metabolite of the brain. Quite remarkably, Linus Pauling suggested that reduced concentrations of vital substances in the brain may be a cause of mental illnesses. He postulated that the brain is more sensitive than other organs to concentrations of such things as amino acids and vitamins. Certainly the promising results obtained in this case will give impetus to the exploration of Pauling's views.

There were important implications, too, for future investigations of drug efficacy. L-dopa was tested in treatment of Parkinson's disease several years earlier at a low dosage level and deemed to be ineffective. It is entirely possible that other known drugs could affect a variety of diseases if larger dosages are used.

A new semisynthetic derivative of an antibiotic from the mold *Streptomyces mediterranei* was being studied. Test tube, animal, and clinical studies indicated that this drug has activity against many different strains of *Mycobacterium tuberculosis.* And early clinical trials just reported gave hope that this drug, called rifampin, would be useful in the therapy of tuberculosis in man.

Modern treatment of tuberculosis involved the use of a chemical compound, isoniazid, along with the antibiotic streptomycin, which together reduced the tendency for streptomycin-resistant strains to grow. Resistance, however, continued and prevented eradication of the disease. Rifampin promised to add to the weapons against tuberculosis. It appeared to be relatively nontoxic. But already it seemed that resistant strains of the tubercle bacillus appear during treatment of man with the new drug. This means that this new agent will probably find a role to play in combination drug therapy, where resistant strains have less chance to gain a foothold.

Schistosomiasis is a tropical disease caused by blood flukes that live in the intestinal or urinary bladder veins of man. The disease was estimated to afflict approximately 200 million people. Until recently the primary form of therapy was treatment with compounds of antimony. Although effective, these drugs had potent side effects and toxicities. New and potentially important drugs for the control of this serious disease have, however, recently appeared. Typical of them was niridazole, which had the formidable, complete chemical name 1(5-nitro-2-thiazolyl)-2-imidazolidinone. It was reported to be quite effective in the treatment of two of the three important species of schistosomes that afflict people in Africa, South America, and parts of Asia. It was less effective in the treatment of *Schistosoma japonicum,* the species that is indigenous to the Far East. New chemotherapeutic agents are difficult to evaluate because it takes time to see whether resistant strains or organisms will appear and whether there are serious toxicities among people receiving the drug. Nevertheless, any new hope in the treatment of such a destructive and widespread disease as schistosomiasis deserves mention even though optimism about its actual value must be qualified.

New directions. Certain trends in drug therapy are a direct consequence of the developments of recent months. Because of a new awareness about the development of resistance, antibiotics were being used more cautiously and much more wisely. In addition, there was less tendency to use many drugs at the same time for "shotgun therapy." Reasons for this included the discoveries about drug interactions and the remarkable degree of individual variability in drug metabolism and drug excretion. This could make the prescribing of even one drug a complicated affair.

These are accomplishments of restraint. There were also exciting positive developments. More research was being done on methods for estimating blood levels of drugs in an individual patient. This will enable the physician to prescribe a dosage regimen tailored to the "metabolic personality" of each patient. Even more exciting was the search for new methods of introducing drugs into the body. We look forward in two directions: (1) more careful control of dosage, for example, by the use of small automatic injection systems that will deliver a drug at a previously set rate; and (2) techniques for releasing a drug on demand, such as by the development of a feedback control whereby insulin is delivered to the body when the blood sugar level of the diabetic reaches a preset value. Preliminary studies of such systems were being conducted.

—Sumner M. Kalman

Psychiatry

Neither as an applied medical science nor as a larger field of research does psychiatry change rapidly by means of sudden "breakthroughs." Psychiatrists have had sufficient experience in the last several decades to affirm this statement. Cutting off parts of the frontal lobes of the brain was once heralded widely as a cure for agitated and aggressive patients, but it has now been completely abandoned. Insulin shock therapy did not, when adequate follow-up studies were made, cure those suffering from schizophrenia. Depressions were not obliterated by electric shock therapy. The so-called "miracle drugs" alone are unreliable, and although they permit early discharge from state hospitals they have generally been followed by equally early readmissions. Psychosomatic specificity, a concept that contended that for each psychosomatic disease (peptic ulcer, hypertension, ulcerative colitis, migraine, allergy, eczema, etc.) there was a specific emotional cause, endured as a "breakthrough" discovery for only a brief period. Thus, apparently forward steps have often ended in retreat. Psychiatry is still in the midst of uncertainty which must be endured, and the positive dogmatic statements published in popular magazines often do more harm than good.

Diagnosis. The need for research on specific disease entities has increased general interest in developing a logical system of classification for diagnostic categories. Recently published was an international manual, to which all countries must adhere by treaty; it did not, however, include the latest advances in the redefinition of categories of depression, schizophrenia, or borderline conditions. U.S. psychiatrists attempted to resolve this confusion by publishing a separate manual of definitions.

The debate as to whether there are separate disease entities or only one large graded system of disturbances, and as to whether psychiatric conditions should be termed disease, behavioral deviance, or faulty education continued. The first logical classification carried with it concepts of specific causes, the course of the disease, and its final outcome. Classification gradually became less rigid and more dynamic, however, until many psychiatrists, especially psychoanalysts, began to consider each patient as a special and individual case.

Phases of the life cycle. Psychiatrists and psychologists have become more interested in naturally demarcated aspects of the life cycle in their studies of normal, healthy, or coping behavior. Childhood, adolescence, youth, middle age, and old age are crude demarcations of man's passage through life. Each phase has its critical period of sensitivity to stress, disease, and conflict. Each has its rites of passage associated with internal or external turbulence.

Chief among the issues discussed at the Pan-American Congress for Psychoanalysis, held in New York City in February 1969, was the divergence between most U.S. and Latin-American psychiatrists caused by their respective orientations toward Sigmund Freud and Melanie Klein. The Latin-American followers of Mrs. Klein have stressed her belief that the first few months of a person's life are the crucial ones in determining

The "idiot" was one of several engravings used to illustrate J. E. D. Esquirol's Des maladies mentales, *published in Paris in 1838. The work was the first scientific treatise on the types of mental illness.*

later development. This concept conflicts with Freudian views, which put less emphasis on that particular stage of life.

Therapy. The traditional methods of long-term individual therapy for the purpose of uncovering deep-seated conflicts has been less favored lately than short-term services oriented toward the relief of symptoms or crises. These have been termed brief psychotherapy, crisis intervention therapy, suicide prevention, etc. Such services increase the amount of manpower time available to more patients and may prevent many chronic careers as patients in custodial hospitals.

Despite the fact that psychiatry is moving toward briefer forms of psychotherapy oriented toward the relief of symptoms, and even though psychoanalysis has not fulfilled its therapeutic ambitions, psychoanalysis has had a profound effect on psychiatry. Psychoanalysis has focused on the development of personality as a result of experiences acting on instinctual or drive functions. It deals with conflicts and defenses, and "explains" behavior on the basis of hypothetical structures such as the id, ego, and superego. Although these inferences have never been scientifically substantiated, as working hypotheses they have had a tremendous impact on a previously sterile descriptive approach.

The public has shown itself increasingly reluctant to spend the time, money, and painful effort to be psychoanalyzed with the hope that personality and character will be "reconstructed." Most people seem to be content with the relief of their symptoms, which generally take the form of anxious or depressed feelings, or some variety of deviant behavior. People appear willing to settle for being able to play better, love better, work better, and expect better.

The behaviorists, utilizing reinforcement and conditioning methods, have extended their efforts from laboratory experiments on animals to the treatment of human distress. Various forms of group and family therapy and hospital milieu treatment are being used with confident claims for positive results. As of this time, all forms of therapy—psychotherapy, psychoanalysis, behavioral, complementary, family and group—have not proved subject to the type of analysis that results in conclusive evaluations. Claims for success have been many, but to date all have been poorly validated. (*See* Year in Review: BEHAVIORAL SCIENCES, *Psychology*.)

Social and community psychiatry. This aspect of psychiatry has burgeoned greatly in the last few years, based on a report in 1961 implemented by funds from the U.S. National Institute of Mental Health. Social psychiatry involves consideration of the family, groups, communities, society, and culture as entities within which mental illness develops, thrives, and destroys people. Its theoretical approaches may suggest methods of "social engineering" by means of which mental illness may be prevented or aborted. Already, family and group therapy are being explored as substitutes for individual treatment. Social studies of adolescent development and adolescent failures that result in delinquency are increasing.

Since 1964 there has been an increasing interest in improving the availability of psychiatric services to all people, regardless of economic or social status, on the principle that all our citizens have a right to adequate care. Community mental health centers during the past year have sprung up throughout the U.S. and many other countries. These centers are based on consent, cooperation, and participation by members of the community; they aim to provide backup facilities for traditional outpatient and inpatient services. By at least one criterion—decreased admission rate to state hospitals—the community effort has been successful. A major problem in obtaining the cooperation of black communities, where providing psychiatric services most needs improvement, is the fact that there are few black professionals. The use of trained black nonprofessional workers is being attempted.

Psychopharmacology. Much work is being done on the chemical constitution of parts of the brain in an effort to improve our understanding of their functions. A considerable amount of this research has been stimulated by the discovery of new drugs applicable to various emotional states.

A large group of drugs, called tranquillizers, have been used to quiet patients with intense anxiety or aggressive behavior, permitting psychotherapy to be used on them and sometimes even permitting their direct discharge from the hospital with no further treatment. Another group of energizing drugs counteracts depressive states. One of the most striking discoveries of recent months was that the element lithium has proven valuable in lowering a patient's level of excitement during manic conditions. Another of the promising new drugs is propanolol, which has been tested in recent months in London and South Africa and has demonstrated some effectiveness in reducing or eliminating anxiety states. All of these new pharmacological agents have led to increased interest in long-term state hospital patients, who had previously been considered untreatable, and have facilitated the return home and to work of many of them.

The future. Because of the slow pace of good research, predictions for even the near future are not easy. One can expect that new drugs will be discovered, but the evaluation of their benefits and dangers will almost surely be slow. Perhaps we will learn how to determine what forms of treatment are specifically applicable to special problems. The disorders of mental activity involve all men because man is an animal who lives with and by the symbols produced by his thought processes. Especially important to achieve is the understanding and prevention of violence. This is just beginning and is essential for the survival of all.

The major problem that hinders the development of all aspects of psychiatry is the manpower shortage. The more therapists that are trained, the greater is the demand for them. Also, as new forms (group, family, milieu, and community) of psychiatric services are developed, more people are becoming acquainted with them. The pool of intelligent youngsters available for higher specialized education is sliced ever thinner so that each particular occupation has become underpopulated. As a result of their long and expensive education, young psychiatric graduates tend to move into private practice, which is relatively highly paid. Many clinical psychologists with Ph.D. degrees prefer to treat patients rather than teach or do research. As a result, the manpower available to fill positions as teachers and research specialists is scarce despite the recent decided improvement in academic salary scales. Universities, consequently, compete fiercely for talented staff. On the other hand, the basic scientists still shy away from psychiatric treatment facilities, where their knowledge and research abilities are often badly needed.

—Roy R. Grinker, Sr.

See also Feature Articles: FREUD'S PLACE IN MODERN PSYCHIATRY; SLEEP AND DREAMS; THE BRAIN.

Public health

In recent months more public health professionals than ever before were becoming involved with the problems of medical care and the delivery of health services. There was a growing awareness and consensus that the traditional preventive and screening services of public health needed to be viewed as part of a total system of comprehensive health care.

Health legislation. While no new national laws covering the health fields were enacted in the U.S., legislation passed in previous years was being implemented. Among those programs were Medicaid (Title 19 of the Social Security Act of 1965), the Comprehensive Health Planning Act, and the Neighborhood Health Centers section of the act that had established the Office of Economic Opportunity (OEO).

By February 1969, Medicaid had been implemented in 43 jurisdictions, which included 39 states. It was designed to provide financial assistance for medical costs to low-income families and to individuals who were not on welfare but did not have sufficient income to pay for medical expenses. There were 16 states that did not include persons in this group within the scope of their medical aid programs. For the jurisdictions that did include them the financial eligibility varied. Income ceilings ranged from $2,448 to $6,000 for a family of four persons, and these families had to meet certain other requirements before becoming eligible. Families of four with incomes above these levels were generally not eligible for the Medicaid programs.

Despite these restrictions the costs of the program rose beyond those anticipated, and some states were forced to cut back on their original eligibility criteria. In 1968 the program had fallen far short of its stated goals of making medical care of high quality readily available to those unable to pay for it. Clearly one of the major problems was in defining the medically needy. The American Public Health Association passed a resolution urging the federal government "to undertake or finance a major study that would determine the appropriate relationship between maintenance standards for the needy and the income level at which a nonneedy family becomes eligible for medical assistance." Reevaluation of the Medicaid program was expected to be accomplished by the end of 1970.

The Comprehensive Health Planning Act stimulated the development of joint professional and community committees to plan for more and better health services. Emphasis upon community participation in health planning, especially when it related to the "grass roots" residents of poverty areas, was relatively new in the U.S., but as a result of discussion, heightened interest, and the increased involvement of the community, the demand for health care was added to the other demands of civil rights and community organizations. Under the Comprehensive Health Planning Act, the U.S. Public Health Service was encouraging communities to develop comprehensive care programs similar to those developed through the Neighborhood Health Centers program of the OEO.

During the past year the neighborhood health centers had emerged as the most innovative and promising method for increasing health services to the poor, and their techniques were being incorporated into the Model Cities programs. Basically, the neighborhood health center was designed to bring together health personnel with a wide range of professional and semiprofessional skills to work as a team in the delivery of comprehensive medical care to defined population groups. Because community involvement and, eventually, community control were inherent in the program, some problems were presented. However, various experiments that would allow community control without interfering with medical decisions were being tried, including the establishment of nonprofit corporations in which those using the health services had one-third representation.

Currently, 51 neighborhood health centers were being funded under the OEO; 11 neighborhood service programs funded under the Comprehensive Health Planning Act were in varying stages of planning and development. It was estimated that 800 such centers and programs eventually would be required.

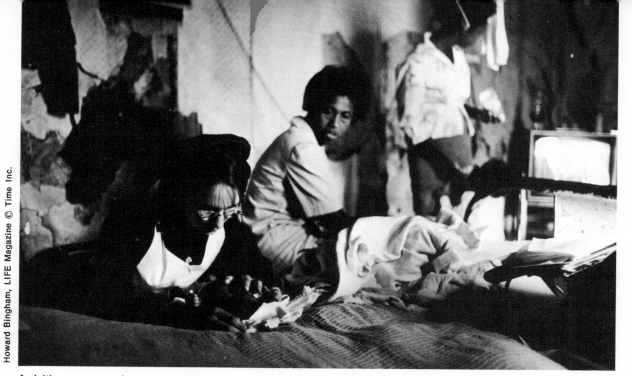

A visiting nurse conducts a postnatal examination on an infant in a home in Mississippi. Projects such as this one, which provide medical care in areas where none had existed previously, were funded by the U.S. Office of Economic Opportunity.

At its annual meeting in November 1968, the American Public Health Association (APHA) commended the Office of Economic Opportunity for its innovative approach. By resolution the APHA urged continuation of the Neighborhood Health Centers program and urged that certain concepts associated with the centers be respected. These were: "the need for innovation in the organization of comprehensive health care; participation by the community in policy making; training for new health careers; the development of alternatives to the fee-for-service model of delivering health services; the need to relate Comprehensive Neighborhood Health Services with those in contiguous neighborhoods and with more specialized area wide health service."

Organization and financing. The problems of providing health services were not limited only to needy populations; there was increasing concern among all income groups relative to the availability and cost of medical care services. There was an expanded interest in the establishment of group practices, especially in combination with prepaid insurance programs, as one possible solution to such problems. The U.S. Public Health Service sponsored a three-day conference on group practice medical care at the University of Chicago in the fall of 1968, and recommendations were made for the development of incentives and special grants to encourage group practice programs. The federal Housing and Urban Development Act of August 1968 authorized the U.S. Secretary of Housing and Urban Development to insure mortgage loans that would finance the construction or rehabilitation of, and the purchase of equipment for, facilities for the group practice of medicine, dentistry, or optometry.

There was also growing concern about the rising cost of hospital care and the lack of insurance coverage for outpatient care. In an address to the APHA, Walter Reuther, president of the United Automobile Workers union, announced the formation of a Committee of 100 to work for national health insurance legislation. This marked the revitalization of a demand that had lain dormant since the late 1940s. Participants at the U.S. National Health Forum, held in March 1969, went on record in support of this approach. The forum brought together both providers of health services and representatives from urban poverty areas. Although there was little likelihood that this type of legislation would be passed in the next few years, one could expect a growth in the demand for it.

Municipal hospitals. Another major crisis centered around the continued viability of the municipal hospitals in major urban areas. In New York City, a commission on the delivery of personal health services, reporting on its study of all aspects of the system by which public funds are used for health services, concluded: "In providing inadequate and substandard care and in serving only the indigent population in its own hospitals and clinics, the city is perpetuating a dual system of medical care with a built-in invidious double standard of private and welfare medicine." Simi-

285

lar attacks were made against the continuation of a dual system of hospital care in other urban centers. The New York commission recommended the creation of a nonprofit health services corporation to operate the city hospitals and clinics.

Although it was generally agreed that the cities faced a crisis in relation to the future of municipal hospitals, there was little agreement on the solution to this problem. As yet the proposals in the New York City report had not been implemented. Other proposals included converting the city hospitals to community-controlled, nonprofit, voluntary institutions. This problem was expected to remain one of the major public health issues of the next few years.

Medical manpower. The shortage of medical personnel continued to receive major attention. Programs to deal with the shortage by using non-physicians, such as the one introduced at the University of Colorado medical center to provide public health nurse practitioners (see *Pediatrics,* above) and the physicians' assistants program at Duke University, Durham, N.C., were being expanded and were receiving increasing attention from a number of institutions. There was also increasing interest in the training and licensing of midwives. Institutes to provide training in allied health sciences were being established by major medical schools as well as by junior colleges through affiliation with teaching hospitals.

—Joyce C. Lashof

Epidemics and disease control. A major development in the control of disease in 1969 was the successful testing and licensing for prescription use in the U.S. of a vaccine against rubella, or German measles (see *Pediatrics,* above). Rubella can cause serious birth defects in the child of a mother who is infected by the virus early in pregnancy. The vaccine was developed following a serious epidemic of rubella in the U.S. in 1964 in which an estimated 50,000 pregnancies were affected. Another major outbreak was expected in the early 1970s. The vaccine, which was being made by three drug manufacturers, was based on a live, attenuated virus, HPV-77, and was expected to be used in inoculation programs for school-age children.

In a recent survey on venereal disease in the U.S. the American Social Health Association reported that the incidence of gonorrhea was up 35.3% while the rate for syphilis was down by 29.3%, compared with similar reports for 1962. The major problem involved in efforts to control the diseases was that only 14 states permitted the administration of therapy to infected minors without parental consent. Because teen-agers were

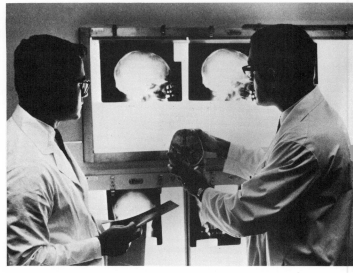

A physician assistant at Duke University Medical Center compares X-ray photographs with a model of a skull being held by a physician. The program at Duke is one of several efforts to relieve the shortage of medical personnel by developing new, nonphysician career opportunities.

reluctant to inform their parents, the spread of the diseases went unchecked and constituted a health hazard to the community.

In January 1969 the United Nations Narcotics Commission began examining the draft of a treaty designed to bring international control to the use of psychotropic (acting on the mind) substances. Sir Harry Greenfield, chairman of the International Narcotics Control Board, reported that abuse of the various pep pills, tranquilizers, and hallucination-inducing drugs had "assumed the proportions of an epidemic" in all of the more developed nations, particularly the U.S., Sweden, the Netherlands, and the United Kingdom. The international effort to prevent illicit distribution of drugs was aided by new efforts on the part of the governments of Turkey, Lebanon, and Burma to cut back on the amount of acreage assigned to the cultivation of opium- and marijuana-producing plants.

The most widely publicized epidemic of 1968–69 was that of the strain of influenza virus officially named A2-Hong Kong-68 because it was first isolated in Hong Kong in July 1968. A major mutation of the A2 influenza virus of 1957–58, the strain was resistant to all available vaccines and spread rapidly throughout Southeast Asia and the Western Hemisphere before a new vaccine could be developed and distributed. By the first week of January 1969, when outbreaks of varying degrees of severity were reported in 47 U.S. states and before the virus had posed a serious threat in Europe, a vaccine was available in limited quantities. A direct result of the epidemic in the U.S. was a severe national shortage of blood supplies. Because of a general inability to find blood donors without flu symptoms, all but emergency surgery had to be postponed in many cities. (See *Infectious Diseases,* above.)

Food processing. Reports from several sources suggested that the unrestricted consumption of cyclamates, the most widely used of the non-nutritive, or artificial, sweeteners, could be hazardous. While studies had revealed only one known side effect in humans, a moderate intestinal complaint, from the use of substantial amounts of the sweetener, there was evidence that in some persons cyclamates were converted into another compound, cyclohexylamine. Rats injected with this compound had shown an abnormal number of broken chromosomes.

In December 1968 the U.S. Food and Drug Administration (FDA) recommended that cyclamates be consumed in limited amounts until current research could be evaluated. Earlier, the UN Food and Agriculture and World Health organizations had recommended that daily use of cyclamates be limited to 50 mg per kg of body weight, or about five bottles of artificially sweetened soft drinks per day for adults. The cyclamate content in soft drinks varied from a quarter of a gram to over one gram per 12-oz bottle. In April 1969 the FDA announced its intention to require manufacturers to indicate on labels the amounts of cyclamates their foods contain. The proposed labeling regulations would also require a statement indicating safe daily consumption levels for both adults and children.

In another action involving food processing, the FDA revoked the approval it had given the U.S. Army two years earlier to serve irradiated bacon at its installations. While a U.S. Department of Commerce survey had reported that about 50 countries were conducting programs on the use of radiation to preserve various grains, fruits, vegetables, meats, and fish, the Army experiment was the only one that had been approved for human consumption in the U.S. In effect, the FDA action raised the standards to which irradiated foods would have to conform before they could be released for general use. The irradiated bacon was reported to have been "unwholesome."

Antismoking campaign. Five years after the publication of the report to the surgeon general of the U.S. Health Service on smoking and health, the American Cancer Society reported in January 1969 that there were 21 million former cigarette smokers in the U.S., including 100,000 physicians. In addition, the year 1968 had marked

the first decline in cigarette consumption—slightly less than a quarter of 1%—since the 1964 report. The decrease was believed to be the result of warnings by various government agencies and public health organizations linking cigarette smoking not only to death rates from lung cancer but to a variety of other illnesses and even to the number of days a person lost from work or spent in bed with an illness.

In addition, various research, educational, and propaganda campaigns, including a Federal Communications Commission ruling that radio and television stations had to balance the advertising from cigarette manufacturers with antismoking messages, were credited with having caused a decrease in the number of persons who started smoking. A Public Health Service survey indicated that the number of 17-year-old smokers was 10% less than it had been ten years before.

See also Feature Article: WHEN YOUNG CHILDREN GO HUNGRY: EFFECTS ON LEARNING AND BEHAVIOR; Year in Review: AGRICULTURE; FOODS AND NUTRITION.

Surgery

Transplants of human organs. Organ transplantation in 1969 was among the most publicized developments in the field of surgery. One of the most urgent problems which physicians faced was to determine whether a patient's system would accept the new organ. A typing procedure similar to matching a blood donor with a recipient of that blood was devised by a group of scientists. This procedure, which is based on a classification of the small lymphocytes, seemed to be important in determining how well the patient will receive the donor's organ. Through the collaborative efforts of medical research in the U.S., 12 antigens (substances that stimulate the production of antibodies) were identified which related to the lymphocyte. Most surgeons who attempted transplantations were satisfied if at least 10 of the 12 lymphocytic antigens matched.

The rejection phenomenon is characterized by an accumulation of the patient's lymphocytes at the site of the transplanted organ, the clotting of blood in the capillary vessels of the organ, and disturbance of the lining of the blood capillaries. In an effort to prevent rejection, various methods were employed to reduce the patient's capacity to produce antibodies in the small lymphocytes. Azathioprine was one of the agents used for this purpose. Another agent was an antilymphocyte serum prepared from another human. Its effect was to suppress the lymphocytes of the patient. A third mechanism was the use of ionizing irradiation to suppress the formation of lymphocytes within the patient's own body. Newer, potentially more effective drugs were still in the experimental stage in 1969.

The problem with all the agents tested, however, was that they tended to suppress the patient's antibodies, which protect the body against all infections, thereby making him susceptible to such conditions as pneumonia. But it also appeared that once the patient had sustained his transplanted organ for six months or longer, he would likely have little need for immunosuppressive agents, at least for several years. In fact, some form of tolerance appeared to develop after six months or longer. This made the requirement for immunosuppressive agents minimal.

The first transplants, begun during the 1930s, were of the cornea of the eye. This worked reasonably well because the cornea, which is the clear part of the eye, carries no blood vessels and is generally readily accepted by a recipient without any form of typing.

The next important step in transplantation was that of the kidney, which was first accomplished by a team of surgeons in Boston in the early 1950s. The first such transplants were done by using a patient's twin sibling to avoid the problem of typing, a technique for which, at that time, had not been developed. Although this procedure was remarkably successful, it was also quite

limited because the patient had to have a twin. With the advent of azathioprine and similar immunosuppressive agents, attempts were then made to transfer kidneys from unrelated human donors. Gradually, the immunosuppressive agents used in this procedure were adjusted until the rejection problem appeared to have been solved. By 1969 a patient with a kidney transplant who survived the first three months had approximately an 80% chance of living three years or longer. Many patients showed signs of rejection, but when the immunosuppressive agents were increased in frequency and in quantity, they almost always accepted the transplanted kidney.

On Jan. 2, 1968, Christiaan Barnard, of Cape Town, S.Af., used a technique developed in 1959 by Norman Shumway and Richard Lower of Stanford University, Stanford, Calif., to perform the first successful human heart transplant upon Philip Blaiberg. Blaiberg continued a relatively active life into 1969, but died August 17 as a result of the rejection process.

After Barnard's initial success, other surgeons attempted heart transplants employing almost the same immunosuppressive methods as used by those performing kidney transplants. But one serious problem plagued these heart transplant attempts. Because lung and kidney damage usually accompany severe chronic heart disease, the transplanted heart functioned unusually strongly in an unusually sick body. It also appeared that patients who received heart transplants were a little more susceptible to the immunosuppressive effects of azathioprine and other drugs than was true for many of the kidney transplants. Technically, however, the operative procedure itself was relatively simple.

Unlike kidney transplants, for which cadaveric kidneys can be used, a heart to be transplanted must be removed from a donor who has just died. This necessity brought into sharp focus the question of the certainty of the moment of the donor's death. Determination of death seldom presents a problem to the experienced physician. It was, however, a question of concern to many other persons who were not knowledgeable in this field. Rules, therefore, had to be established as guidelines.

During the past year, transplants of other organs also were attempted, particularly of the liver, the pancreas, and the lung. In order to develop procedures for transplanting the larynx (voice box) into patients who had had theirs removed for reasons of cancer, studies were conducted with animals. Satisfactory results were not obtained, however.

Artificial organs. It was expected that artificial

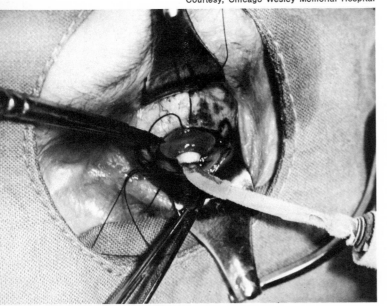

Courtesy, Chicago Wesley Memorial Hospital

A new instrument in eye surgery was the cryoptor, the white, frost-covered tube used here to remove an opaque lens, or cataract. The tube is connected to a console that lowers its temperature to −32° C, causing it to stick to the wet lens surface.

organs would, in time, supplant or augment the use of natural transplants. Transplanted kidneys illustrate one disadvantage in the use of natural organs. Once a kidney transplant has been rejected, it is implied that the patient's lymphocytes have developed strong antibodies for any kidney: a second kidney transplant in the same patient is, therefore, seldom successful. However, several excellent mechanical devices were developed to use in case the kidney should be rejected. But these all had a common drawback: for approximately 12 hours two or three times a week, the patient had to be dialyzed (hooked up to a filtering machine that removes blood impurities). Some of these procedures could be done at home by a trained member of the family, but not without expense and inconvenience.

More efficient and smaller artificial kidneys reached the experimental stage of development in 1969. One device under investigation was produced by the Dow Chemical Co. It consisted of two small portable units in which great lengths of capillary tubing were encased. The dialyzable surfaces of the tubing were bathed in fluids favorable to the "excretion" of salt and urea into a container, which is then disposed of. It was expected that the portable kidneys would be clinically tested by 1970.

Artificial hearts also received much attention during 1968 and 1969. Two purposes were envisioned for them. First, such devices should be able to maintain a person's circulation until an appropriate human heart becomes available for transplantation. And second, a mechanical heart should ultimately be developed which can maintain the circulation of the patient indefinitely and be placed within his own body. In trying to perfect such a device, scientists encountered a number of problems: (1) the need for an inexhaustible energy source to drive the heart indefinitely; (2) a means of increasing cardiac output by the machine in response to the patient's various body demands, such as exercise; (3) a means for preventing coagulation within the structure of the device; and (4) a means to prevent the destruction of red blood cells on the inner surface of the mechanical heart.

On April 4, 1969, an artificial heart was clinically tested for the first time in history by Denton Cooley of St. Luke's Episcopal Hospital in Houston, Tex. The synthetic heart, designed by Domingo Liotta, kept the patient, 47-year-old Haskell Karp, alive for two and one-half days until the device could be replaced by a human heart. Karp died of complications a day after he received the human heart. General use of artificial organs was not anticipated until the mid-1970s.

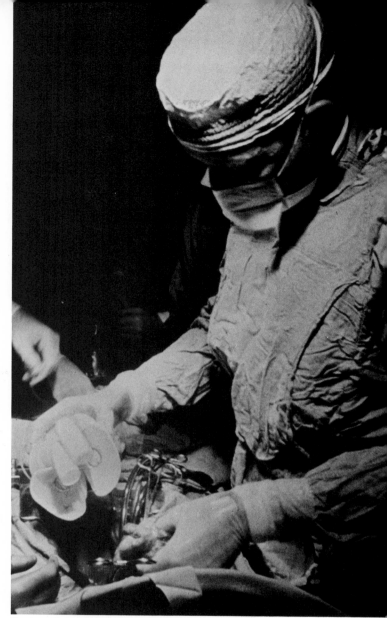

Courtesy, Texas Heart Institute, Houston

Denton Cooley holds an artificial heart in his right hand and the patient's original heart in his left hand at the moment when the device was substituted for the damaged heart. The artificial organ kept the patient alive for more than two days until a suitable human heart donor could be found.

Treatment for respiratory disorders. In recent years many hospitals have developed units for the specific management of acute respiratory disorders. These facilities have improved the rates of recovery and the avoidance of both surgical and medical treatment of complications for many patients.

The goals achieved by the new respiratory units were significant. Methods for keeping the trachea, or windpipe, clean and for supplying an adequate flow of air, as well as means for washing out the bronchial tree were greatly improved.

Need for new plasma standards. In April 1968, after four cases of hepatitis with jaundice and eight more cases of chemical hepatitis had been known to develop following blood transfusions, the Division of Biologic Standards of the U.S. National Institutes of Health threatened to exclude the use of pooled plasma. These cases occurred in the Los Angeles area, where the blood donors for the most part were of the skid-row variety. This type of donor was found to carry the hepatitis virus with a frequency of almost 75 times that of other donors, and usually in a much higher concentration. Unfortunately, this skid-row population had been used most frequently as blood donors by most commercial blood banks and the Red Cross. Since the early 1950s no standards had been set by the Division of Biologic Standards that would guard against the use of this kind of donor, either for plasma or for whole blood. Because no substitute had been discovered for plasma, it was important that appropriate guidelines be devised which would be simple but effective and also assure a safe product.

—J. Garrott Allen

See also A Gateway to the Future: A HOUSE FOR LIVING MOLECULES; Year in Review: BOTANY; MICROBIOLOGY; MOLECULAR BIOLOGY; ZOOLOGY.

Microbiology

Research in microbiology continued to cross paths with many other disciplines. For example, the interrelationship of microbiology and medicine was evident in the ongoing efforts to control the viruses that infect man. In recent months, live, attenuated rubella (German measles) viruses for use as vaccinating agents were developed independently in three laboratories, two in the U.S. and one in Belguim, and an experimental influenza vaccine using killed influenza viruses that are sprayed directly into the lungs was under evaluation. Another promising approach to the prevention of viral diseases was interference with infection by utilizing interferon, an antiviral protein produced by animal cells in response to infection by a virus. There was also continued interest in slow-acting viruses that were said to cause at least 30 human diseases of the nervous and muscular systems, some rare, some common. In addition, there was a growing body of evidence linking viruses with certain forms of human cancer. (*See* Year in Review: MEDICINE.)

Primarily, however, the study of microorganisms, living bodies visible under a microscope, and of how they function and interact continued

to be the best way to seek out an understanding of the actions and reactions of all living things. In this regard, developments in microbiology in recent months dealt with how substances outside the cell are converted into cellular material, how the cell membrane functions, and how cells develop different roles within the same organism and are altered during the various stages of development. Microorganisms also continued to be the principal tool in the efforts of molecular biologists to synthesize genetic materials. (*See* Year in Review: MOLECULAR BIOLOGY.)

Bioenergetics and applied microbiology. The efficiency with which growing microorganisms convert the substances on which the live (substrates) in culture media into cellular material has long been of interest. From knowing the amount of adenosine triphosphate (ATP) that bacterial cells can generate by fermenting anaerobically (in the absence of oxygen) a specific quantity of sugar, it was learned early in the 1960s that 10.5 g of bacterial cells are produced per mole (gram-molecular weight) of ATP utilized. ATP is the energy currency generated by respiration and expended during growth by all types of cells. The values obtained from anaerobic systems cannot be transferred to considerations of aerobic growth yields, for there is no certainty of the quantity of ATP generated for the latter.

Quite recently, workers from the University of Georgia presented evidence that 3.14 g of aerobically grown microbial cells are produced per available electron in an organic growth substrate. Furthermore, they formulated an equation whereby the yield of bacteria may be predicted from any type of microbial growth as related to the kilocalories (kcal) of energy involved. (One kcal is 1,000 g-cal, or the amount of heat required to raise the temperature of a kilogram of water 1° C.) The predicted value, which was experimentally shown, was 0.118 g of bacterial cells per kcal. The practical importance of these observations lies in the usefulness in predicting the yield of bacterial cells that one may expect from aerobic microbial utilization of industrial or domestic waste organic materials, or the contributions of microorganisms to the total energy flow in a specific habitat (ecosystem).

Several countries were building manufacturing facilities that employed microorganisms to convert waste organic chemicals or hydrocarbons into edible proteins as a food supplement. The usefulness of such "single cell protein" to supplement certain protein-deficient diets had been amply demonstrated. Another approach was to utilize microorganisms that can economically produce feasible quantities of certain essential

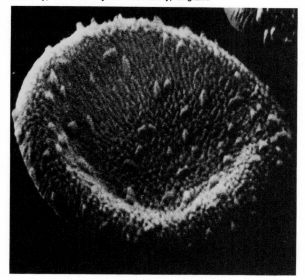

To study the internal structures of normal and abnormal cells, British scientists adopted a physical science technique called ion etching. Materials are eroded atom by atom by bombardment with high-energy ions. Here, hemoglobin aggregates known as Heinz bodies are visible in red blood cells after ion etching.

amino acids, such as lysine or tryptophan. These amino acids could then be used as supplements to cereal products.

The enzyme L-asparaginase was known to be a potent antineoplastic (tumor-preventing) agent in animals, and it was said to have given complete remission in some human leukemias. Extensive clinical trials were not possible in the past because of inadequate production of this substance. Recently, however, it was found that L-asparaginase could be produced by a bacterial fermentation process in sufficient quantity for more extensive clinical evaluation.

Another recent practical application was the incorporation of water-soluble enzymes of microbial origin into detergents. One could predict that there would be expanded uses for enzymes produced by microorganisms, as well as for microorganisms themselves, in the disposition of organic wastes of all types.

The bacterial cell membrane. The cell membrane of bacteria constitutes a barrier to nutrients brought into the cell and to the waste products excreted. Specific systems are associated with the cell membrane to provide for selective transport of these substances. Several proteins that appear to be parts of cell membrane transport systems have been isolated and characterized. The evidence linking these proteins with transport is indirect, but one known correlation was that mutant cells that cannot carry out the transport lack the corresponding protein.

One recent advance in transport studies was to use specific enzymes to remove the cell wall, after which the resulting exposed material of the cell was allowed to distintegrate. The cell membranes were collected and washed free of cytoplasmic materials. These membranes were shown to form hollow vesicles that retained the ability to transport and accumulate substrates while further metabolism of these substrates by intracellular enzymes was thereby avoided. This was an especially useful technique for studying the dynamics of transport mechanisms.

The bacterial cell membrane is also the site of aerobic energy-generation processes that are analogous in function to the role of mitochondria, the sites of the main energy transfer system in higher forms of life. Recent evidence, although somewhat preliminary, indicated that the bacterial cell membrane may also have a structure analogous to the membranes of mitochondria.

Microbes and cellular differentiation and morphogenesis. Some bacteria have the capacity to transform themselves, via an intricate sequence of organized steps, into small ovals or spheres that are highly resistant, dormant cells known as spores or endospores. When such spores are transferred into a medium or environment favorable for growth, or when they are experimentally exposed to certain chemical or physical agents, they germinate and grow into new vegetative cells. Bacterial spore formation and spore germination are examples of cellular differentiation (specialization) and morphogenesis (growth and development), which, in turn may be defined as any nonmutational, large-scale, and reasonably permanent variation from the norm of cellular composition, structure, or behavior.

Myxobacteria represent a class of bacteria that undergo another type of cellular differentiation and morphogenesis. In the course of a complex life cycle their vegetative cells, which are unicellular, flexible rods, swarm together and are transformed into resting cells or microcysts that are spherical and have rigid cell walls. The massed microcysts form fruiting bodies, some of which have elaborate structure.

Most features of the differentiation and morphogenesis of these bacterial forms remained poorly understood. They were, however, receiving increasing attention from biologists. It was expected that, due to the relative simplicity of bacterial systems, detailed analyses of the genetic and biochemical controls, and of the events that occur in the orderly and sequential processes involved in the life cycles of the spore-forming bacteria and of myxobacteria, would lead to a better

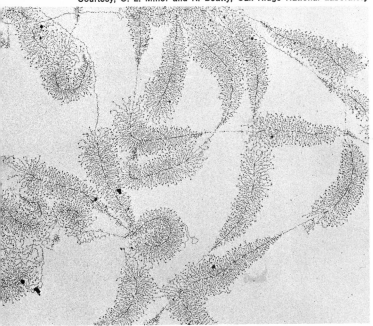

An electron micrograph of genes in the process of coding for precursor ribosomal RNA molecules was made possible by the use of several techniques that stretched out and exposed to view the core areas of the genes. The genes are those of the nucleoli of amphibian egg cells. RNA molecules that are initiated sequentially for each of about 100 enzymes before completion of the first molecule can be seen as graduated fibrous material within the nucleolar core.

understanding of cellular differentiation and morphogensis in higher organisms.

Microbes and molecular biology. Microorganisms continued to be useful experimental models for the study of molecular biology. One of the more exciting areas of study involved the experimental attempts to synthesize genes. Recently, Har Gobind Khorana (*see* Year in Review: HONORS, *Medical Sciences*) and his co-workers at the University of Wisconsin reported that they had synthesized approximately two-thirds of a small gene found in yeast cells. Their approach involved chemically producing small segments of the 80-unit deoxyribonucleic acid (DNA) chain of the gene and then using an enzyme called DNA-ligase to join the segments in the precise order of the naturally occurring gene. The small individual segments of the gene were produced by chemically adding the individual units of the DNA chain one at a time.

Many strains of the bacterium *Escherichia coli* (*E. coli*) can recognize and destroy DNA from "foreign" strains of the same bacterium. There is considerable evidence that this ability depends on the detailed pattern of methylated bases, the four atomic side groups (adenine, guanine, thymine, and cytosine) in the DNA molecule. The destructive bacterial strains contain both methylating enzymes that are highly specific and selective, and nuclease enzymes that destroy any DNA lacking their particular pattern of methylated bases. These data suggest that if this mechanism is also used by higher organisms it could be an important factor in regulating infection by the DNA-containing viruses.

Genetic information is transcribed from the DNA of the genes to messenger ribonucleic acid (m-RNA). The latter carries the genetic information to the ribosomes (particles in the cytoplasm composed of protein and RNA), where it is translated into a specific protein. A group of workers from the University of Wisconsin achieved the synthesis of biologically active ribosomes by mixing free RNA with proteins obtained by dissociating ribosomal subunits of *E. coli.* Their experiment provided proof that the molecular components of a ribosome contain all the information needed for ribosomes to assemble themselves.

Another interesting approach to the study of molecular biology is via the use of bacteriophages, viruses that infect bacteria. It was known that when the larger viruses develop in their host cells, they express the information of different genes at different times. Developing bacteriophages, therefore, were splendid models in which to study the biological mechanisms involved in the steps of transcription of the genetic information, and to study the repressor substances that turn genes off, inhibiting transcription.

—Robert G. Eagon

See also Feature Articles: HUMANICS AND GENETIC ENGINEERING; LIFE BEYOND THE EARTH; A Gateway to the Future: A HOUSE FOR LIVING MOLECULES; Year in Review: BOTANY; ZOOLOGY.

Molecular biology

Molecular biology maintained its position through mid-1969 as an active frontier of science, filled with excitement and discovery. Few areas of current research could match the keen competition, the talent, and, to a lesser extent, the financial support that was devoted to molecular biological research. The possibility of being able to synthesize and perhaps sensibly alter the biological building blocks fired the imaginations of scientists and laymen alike. Noteworthy in this regard was the fact that *The Double Helix,* by Nobel laureate James D. Watson, made the best seller list in the U.S. for 17 consecutive weeks.

Biochemistry

The chemistry of life, which involves such common elements as hydrogen, carbon, nitrogen, oxygen, sulfur, and phosphorus, presents the problem of how these elements first combined some billions of years ago to form the principal biochemical substances. These substances, which are found in most living forms, include proteins, enzymes (proteins that speed up, or catalyze, chemical reactions), and the nucleic acids, deoxyribonucleic acid (DNA) and ribonucleic acid (RNA), that regulate protein production and determine the function each cell will perform (differentiation). Biochemists have not only learned many of the secrets of protein and nucleic acid structure in recent years, they are also beginning to learn the techniques required to synthesize them.

Molecular synthesis. The recent development of the "solid phase" method by Robert B. Merrifield of Rockefeller University was a giant step forward toward the artificial synthesis of proteins (see *Biophysics,* below). Using amino acids as the individual building blocks of a polypeptide chain, scientists at Rockefeller employed the solid phase method in 1968 to synthesize successfully an enzyme, ribonuclease (RNA-ase), for the first time (see *Breakthrough in Molecular Biology*). In 1963 the synthesis of insulin, a protein, had been accomplished by a different method. Following his achievement, Merrifield predicted that other small proteins whose structures are already known, such as myoglobin, cytochrome *c,* ferredoxin, and growth hormone (somatotrophin), might be synthesized next. Early in 1969, the first commercially made peptide-synthesizing machine, based on the Merrifield method, was put on the market under license from the Danish Institute of Protein Chemistry.

Another major step forward toward the synthesis of living systems involved viruses, which multiply only within other susceptible living cells. In 1969 Paul Kaesberg and Ilan Sela of the University of Wisconsin synthesized the protein coat of the tobacco mosaic virus (TMV) and then combined it with viral RNA to make TMV itself. In the meantime, William B. Wood III of the California Institute of Technology successfully reconstructed another virus, the T4, and revealed its assembly mechanism. When the T4 virus invades the cells of the bacterium *Escherichia coli,* its DNA reprograms the host cell to produce and assemble new viruses.

In a 1968 report, E. J. Corey and his associates at Harvard University announced that they had developed methods for the total synthesis of five biologically potent prostaglandins, which are hormones found in a variety of body fluids and organs. The prostaglandins influence heart rate, blood pressure, the firing rate of nerves, and the contraction of the uterus and smooth muscle. They may even hamper the production or action of other hormones, and specifically of serotonin, a brain hormone.

The synthesis of amino acids. Scientists believe that before proteins and amino acids existed on earth other simpler chemical compounds and elements existed: hydrogen, water vapor, methane gas, and ammonia. It was theorized in 1924 by the Soviet scientist Aleksandr I. Oparin that amino acids might be made from these substances. Since 1953 several research groups had synthesized many amino acids by using various techniques, such as by passing electric sparks through Oparin's suggested mixture; by exposing a chemical mixture to ultraviolet light, ionizing radiation, visible light, or heat; or by using the chemical silica for a catalyst. In 1968 Gary Steinman of Pennsylvania State University and Adolph E. Smith and Joseph J. Silver of Sir George Williams University, Montreal, reported synthesizing the sulfur-containing amino acid methionine, one of the protein-forming amino acids that had not yet been created under simulated pre-life conditions.

In other experiments amino acids were heated together to produce "proteinoids," which are protein-like peptide chains. It was also possible to heat proteinoids in water and produce tiny "microspheres" that resembled simple earth bacteria, and that would produce new "microspheres" when placed in a concentrated proteinoid solution. It was argued that these experiments had demonstrated that a protein-like substance could be made to multiply without the presence of DNA or RNA.

The sugars ribose and deoxyribose form the backbone of the RNA and DNA structures, respectively, and therefore are essential to their formation. In 1967 scientists at the Atomic Energy Laboratory at Ames, Iowa, produced ribose, deoxyribose, and other sugars by passing ultraviolet light into a dilute solution of formaldehyde. That a similar action may have occurred in nature was suggested in March 1969 when astronomers at the U.S. National Radio Observatory in Green Bank, W.Va., identified formaldehyde in the dust and gas of 15 interstellar clouds. The presence of formaldehyde is strong indirect evidence also of the presence in space of methane, one of the four building blocks of amino acids. Regarding the three other ingredients, it had been known since

continued on page 295

Breakthrough in molecular biology: the synthesis of an enzyme

During the past year two teams of U.S. scientists succeeded in totally synthesizing an enzyme, ribonuclease, by making it out of a certain sequence of amino acids. Ten years ago, almost no one would believe that such a thing could be done. This fact alone would have made the effort to synthesize an enzyme worthwhile, but because much that had practical value could be learned from the study of enzymes, the achievement took on added significance.

No living cell could function without enzymes, the proteins that break down amino acids and recombine them into new proteins. In the absence of enzymes vital body functions would take place too slowly or not at all, while the presence of enzymes, in other cases, can save lives. The enzyme L-asparaginase, for example, breaks up asparagine, an amino acid needed by a certain type of leukemia cell. In other words, the enzyme is a specific cure for one type of leukemia. Another enzyme, urokinase, dissolves blood clots. A timely injection of it may prevent heart attacks or strokes.

Chemists recently learned how to produce L-asparaginase and urokinase commercially. But the two lifesaving enzymes are expensive and very difficult to extract from the substances in which they already exist. If men understood their structure better and could make them synthetically, perhaps new, cheaper cures would be found.

Being able to produce synthetic enzymes is also important because scientists still do not know exactly how they work. The theory is that the enzyme has an active site—one specific portion of the enzyme that performs the catalysis because it fits exactly a crucial portion of the substance upon which it acts. If chemists could choose to include or exclude particular amino acids from synthetic enzymes, they could learn more about the active sites. Perhaps they could then design simpler enzymes by including the active site and leaving off the unnecessary parts.

In addition, if more were known about how the active sites of enzymes work, better nonenzyme catalysts—which also have active sites—might be created for industrial use. Many industrial catalysts require high temperature or high pressure to function. Enzymes, however, perform their catalytic function extremely rapidly, at normal pressure, at moderate temperatures, in water solutions, and usually only on one chemical substance.

Ribonuclease (RNA-ase), the first enzyme to be totally synthesized, breaks down ribonucleic acid (RNA). Possibly it stops RNA from stimulating new cell growth after RNA has done its job; possibly without it, cells would go on proliferating— and the result would be cancer. (The RNA-ase synthesized in 1968 is found naturally in cattle, not human beings, but knowing about it may point the way to a better understanding of human cell growth and cancer.)

Although RNA-ase was isolated and named in 1938, it was not until 1959 that its exact amino acid sequence was identified. RNA-ase is a

Synthesis of Ribonuclease

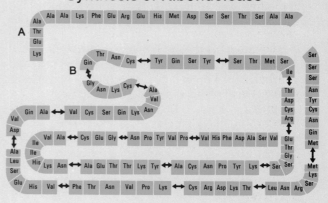

Ala—Alanine
Arg—Arginine
Asn—Asparagine
Asp—Aspartic Acid
Cys—Cystein
Gin—Glutamine

Glu—Glutamic acid
Gly—Glycine
His—Histidine
Ile—Isoleucine
Leu—Leucine
Lys—Lysine

Met—Methionine
Phe—Phenylalanine
Pro—Proline
Ser—Serine
Thr—Threonine
Tyr—Tyrosine
Val—Valine

To accomplish the synthesis of ribonuclease, the Merck team assembled the 124 amino acids in two sections (A and B, above) and joined them chemically. The Rockefeller group built the complete enzyme (C) by adding the amino acids one at a time starting at the carbon-terminal end of the first amino acid (arrow on C), which was bound to a polystyrene bead. The enzyme assumed its twisted shape and catalytic activity when placed in an aqueous solution.

relatively simple enzyme 124 amino acids long and containing 1,876 atoms with a molecular weight of only 13,683. (Some enzymes have molecular weights in the millions.) In 1967 scientists at Roswell Park Memorial Institute, Buffalo, N.Y., described its three-dimensional geometric structure.

In the meantime, Robert B. Merrifield of Rockefeller University, New York City, had developed a peptide synthesis machine, a device that would automatically bring together chemically a chain of amino acids (see *Biophysics,* below). Using this device, in 1968 Merrifield and Bernd Gutte created synthetic RNA-ase. The procedure began with a tiny polystyrene bead about 0.002 in. in diameter to which the first amino acid was anchored. The other 123 amino acids were then added in the proper sequence. The chain was freed of the plastic bead and placed in an aqueous solution, where it assumed the proper geometric shape needed to perform its typical catalytic activity. (The proper configuration is vital; under unfavorable conditions, such as heat, an enzyme's geometric shape may change and it may lose its enzymatic ability.)

At the same time, another group of researchers in Rahway, N.J., were creating their own synthetic RNA-ase by another method. Robert G. Denkewalter, Ralph F. Hirschmann, and associates of the Merck Sharp & Dohme Research Laboratories of Merck & Co. assembled the 124 amino acids in subgroups containing 6 to 17 amino acids each. They used a process developed by Denkewalter that involved amino acid compounds with protecting groups that could be removed easily when the molecule was completed.

While the Rockefeller University and Merck teams succeeded in completely synthesizing a known enzyme, a Northwestern University scientist, Myron Bender, pursued the problem from a different angle. Working with a visiting Hungarian scientist, Laszlo Polgar, in 1966, Bender succeeded in altering the active site of the bacterial enzyme subtilisin and creating a new active site by adding a sulfur group. Bender and his associates also discovered that a cyclodextrine made up of glucose units instead of amino acids acted much like chymotripsin, an important digestive enzyme. Possibly, completely new enzymes could also be synthesized by adding an active site to a non-amino acid compound. As more is learned about the essential characteristics of the "business end" of an enzyme—the active site—it may be faster and simpler to create new catalysts than to re-create an entire already existing one.

continued from page 293

1951 that vast amounts of hydrogen are present in huge interstellar clouds, the presence of ammonia in space was detected in December 1968 by radio astronomers at the University of California, and the existence of interstellar water was reported in *Nature* in February 1969. (*See* Year in Review: ASTRONOMY, *The Galaxy.*)

Molecular structures. The first step in the body's production of insulin, Donald F. Steiner of the University of Chicago demonstrated, is proinsulin, a long single chain of amino acids. Steiner found that the chain, produced in the pancreas of humans and animals, spontaneously folds into a stable arrangement that permits disulfide bonds to form, linking the smaller insulin chains. The "end loop" portion of this larger, proinsulin molecule then is removed by an enzyme (Steiner used trypsin in his tests), leaving a two-chain, disulfide-bridged insulin molecule.

Steiner suggested that an enzyme deficiency may lead to the release of proinsulin, rather than insulin, in the circulation of a diabetic. Steiner also indicated that medically useful insulin might one day be produced commercially from proinsulin.

Early in 1969 Gerald M. Edelman of the Rockefeller University reported that he had discovered the amino acid sequence in a gamma globulin, a protein molecule of antibodies found in blood serum. Gamma globulin is used in medicine to give passive immunity to measles, poliomyelitis, infectious hepatitis, and other diseases. Edelman showed that gamma globulins consist of two light chains of about 220 amino acids each and two heavy chains of about 440 amino acids each. The chains are linked by four disulfide bonds, one between each light chain and its corresponding heavy chain and two between the heavy chains. There are also two disulfide bonds within each light chain.

Edelman found that each amino acid chain had a variable and a constant region. In the variable regions, the amino acid sequences can vary in billions of ways; in the constant regions they are the same in all gamma globulins. Each of the variable regions is coded to spot one specific type of invading protein, known as an antigen. When the variable region locks onto the invading substance (bacteria, viruses, or even transplanted tissue), the gamma globulin starts multiplying. Soon there is a proliferation of gamma globulin antibodies that lock onto other invading antigens. Scavenger cells then remove both antigen and antibody. (*See* Year in Review: MEDICINE, *Immunology.*)

—James Stouder Sweet

Biophysics

Determination of the structure of complex biological molecules may be done by the synthesis approach, building the whole molecule out of its basic components, or by breaking the intact molecule down into its component parts. Either of these approaches is the work of the biophysicist in that both require competence in the principles and techniques of contemporary physics and physical chemistry. Both also require the use of sophisticated and expensive equipment. The cost of such apparatus, coupled with the need for highly trained people to use and maintain it, essentially limited the number of laboratories capable of advanced molecular biological studies to major research institutions. A similar restriction applied to the investigation of the function of a particular molecule or its subunits.

Double helix observed. There is always a very human desire to actually "see" a structure rather than conceive of it mathematically or in some other nonvisual way. Improvements in instrument design and techniques, coupled with perserverance, continued to yield new insights in recent months. Using a high-powered electron microscope, Jack Griffith of the California Institute of Technology was successful in obtaining photographs of what appeared to be intact deoxyribonucleic acid (DNA) molecules. DNA molecules from pea-plant chromosomes were sprayed with a thin coating of tungsten to increase the contrast in the electron beam. The image, magnified more than seven million times, showed two strands woven into a double helix, as predicted by Francis H. C. Crick and James D. Watson in the early 1950s. (See *1969 Britannica Yearbook of Science and the Future,* Feature Article: THE LANGUAGE OF LIFE.)

Griffith, however, was careful to point out that he was not sure he had photographed the double helix:

We cannot be certain that the helical structure observed in the present micrograph is real, and not an artifact or a fortuitous structure that *looks* like the Watson-Crick structure. It is seen in only a few regions of a few DNA molecules. . . . These rare glimpses into molecular structure may be hints of statistically sound micrograph data to come, or they may be erroneous artifacts created by the machines that visualized them.

Radioactive labeling. The continuing discovery of new ribonucleic acids (RNAs) has led to the suggestion that two classes of RNA exist: one that moves between the nucleus and the cytoplasm, the other confined to the nucleus itself. Studying RNA from liver cancer (hepatoma) cells, Harris

Courtesy, Jack Griffith, California Institute of Technology

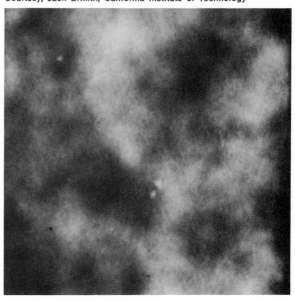

A thin coating of tungsten sprayed onto DNA molecules from pea-plant chromosomes increased the contrast in electron micrographs enough to allow what appears to be DNA to be captured on film for the first time. The object photographed had the twisted, double spiral configuration that has been proved by other techniques to be characteristic of DNA.

Busch at Baylor University College of Medicine found ten different nucleolar types, including a new one of low molecular weight. By adding radioactive phosphorus-32 to sites on the RNA molecules, Busch found that the hepatoma RNAs all showed patterns of radioactive distribution that were distinctly different from the same RNA types obtained from normal liver tissue. This suggested a difference in phosphorus positioning in the molecule in the diseased state. In addition, the finding of a new kind of RNA might help to explain how genes and proteins are related.

Artificial ribosomes. A major accomplishment reported in recent months was the synthesis of biologically active ribosomes by allowing a reaction between the RNA and proteins of the bacterium *Escherichia coli.* Ribosomes are cellular particles upon which amino acids are polymerized into proteins. They consist of two subunits, designated 30S and 50S because of their sedimentation properties. The actual function of ribosomal RNA and ribosomal proteins was not clearly understood, and the ability to reconstitute ribosomes would now permit further study.

Masayasu Nomura and Peter Traub of the University of Wisconsin were able to prepare a series of ribosome derivatives, each lacking a specific ribosomal protein. By comparing the characteristics of these deficient particles with those of normal ribosomes, it should be possible to define the role of a specific ribosomal protein as well as to discover why more than a single ribosomal particle is necessary to carry out the ribosome's role in protein synthesis.

Automated protein synthesis. The synthesis of protein molecules continued to be a long and painstaking process, as witnessed by the few molecules synthesized in quantity to date. An automated protein synthesizer developed by Arnold Marglin and Robert Merrifield of Rockefeller University greatly reduced the time requirements. Based on the Merrifield scheme, in which the growing protein chains are linked to a resin, the synthetic method allowed all the chemical reactions and intermediate purification steps to be conducted in a single reaction chamber.

Amino acid molecules have a common chemical structure in which a carbon atom (C) has four other atomic groups linked to it—an amino group (NH_2), a hydrogen atom (H), a carboxylic group (COOH), and a fourth group or side chain that is different for each amino acid. As several amino acids come together to form a protein, condensation between the COOH group of one molecule and the amino group of another creates what is called a peptide bond between the two amino acids. When several of these bonds have occurred, a polypeptide chain is formed.

In automated protein synthesis, first the supporting resin containing the C-terminal amino acid is put in the chamber; building a polypeptide chain then consists of injecting the proper solvents and reagents and withdrawing them in the proper sequence. The critical components in the automated system are two motor-driven circular selection valves, one for amino acids and the other for solvents. The cycle timing is controlled by rotating drums with appropriate positioning pins. The drum advances on a signal from a timer. The cycle timing can be easily modified to permit changes in reaction chemistry. With this procedure, using two reaction chambers, the two polypeptide chains that comprise insulin can be made at once by a single operator in ten days, compared with about six months by more conventional means. Using this procedure, in 1968 Merrifield and Bernd Gutte were the first to synthesize an enzyme (see *Breakthrough in Molecular Biology,* above).

Zonal centrifuge. Another boon to the collection and separation of sizable quantities of specific cells and cellular components is the zonal centrifuge developed at Oak Ridge (Tenn.) National Laboratory by Norman G. Anderson and co-workers. A centrifuge is a machine in which substances of different densities are whirled about

rapidly until they separate from one another. Centrifuge rotor systems were being developed to separate cell nuclei, cell membranes, mitochondria, polysomes, ribosomes, ribosomal subunits, and macroglobulins. A commercial model was used for purifying large quantities of viral and bacterial vaccines. In a test run Eli Lilly Research Laboratory used the machine to produce enough influenza vaccine to make large-scale clinical tests. The ultrapure vaccine obtained from the zonal centrifuge exhibited almost none of the troublesome side effects shown by the regular vaccine.

In practice the effectiveness of a zonal centrifuge for a particle of any given size is limited by rotor speed and the degree to which turbulence can be suppressed (by rotor design). Present speeds of up to 35,000 rpm had yielded good results for viruses and DNA. The Oak Ridge group hoped to attain 400,000 rpm to separate proteins with molecular weights in the 50,000 range.

Relaxation spectra. Use of the relaxation technique whereby enzyme reactions may be examined by disturbing a specific enzyme substrate from its steady state by means of pulsed thermal pressure or electric shock was extended by a group at the University of Pennsylvania Medical School. Relatively large pulses were used to remove the reaction far enough from equilibrium so that the entire sequence of transformation to a new steady state could be followed. Reactions that do not achieve measurable steady states could also be studied in this way. The binding of oxygen to hemoglobin was the first reaction to be examined. A promising application was that of enzymatic reactions in membrane-bound systems, such as those associated with mitochondria and chloroplasts. These systems contain multienzyme sequences in which the time sequence of reactions involving electron transfer can be read out by electrical or optical methods.

Mitochondrial DNA. Self-replication of mitochondrial DNA (M-DNA) and the fact that there is protein synthesis in mitochondria were demonstrated in work done at Kansas State University and at Stony Brook (State University of New York). Mitochondria are cytoplasmic bodies that oxidize foods and release or store energy. Electron micrographs of DNA taken from rat liver mitochondria gave evidence of DNA synthesis; circular molecules apparently in the process of self-replication were observed.

Some of the circular DNA molecules had an extra segment that looped from one forked region on the circumference of the molecule to another forked region. The length of the looped segment was the same as that found between the forks of the original segment, strongly suggesting that the loop is a piece of newly replicated DNA. Support for this suggestion was given by the fact that if the length of either of the two equal segments is added to the length of the remaining DNA, the total is within the range of lengths found by unforked, circular DNA molecules.

—Philip F. Gustafson

Molecular genetics

Since the description of the replicon model was first proposed in 1963, molecular geneticists had attempted to find experimental evidence to test its validity. This model considers that deoxyribonucleic acid (DNA) replicates, or produces a copy of itself during cell division, as a unit and that this unit possesses peculiar properties. For example, each replicating unit, or replicon, has a distinct and unique origin from which replication begins. Other characteristics attributed to these units of replication are that each unit exists as a closed structure or, formally, a circle, and that each replicon contains the genetic information that controls its own replication. Recent months saw activity on a number of fronts that brought to bear new information on how DNA replicates.

Identifying the site of replication. In the bacterium *Escherichia coli* (*E. coli*), which is among the organisms best suited for study, almost all of the genetic information is known to reside in one structural element, which is circular. This structure is referred to as the bacterial chromosome. Using different methods, a number of laboratories attempted to identify the origin of chromosome replication in this organism. There was reasonable agreement that, during routine cell growth, chromosome replication begins near a position identified as eight o'clock on the standard circular genetic map and that it proceeds in a clockwise direction.

Various strains of *E. coli* exist, some of which have mating properties caused by the presence of a sex factor, which itself is a replicon. According to these studies, replication may originate in some strains from a position that is almost directly opposite the most common position—at two o'clock on the genetic map. Furthermore, the direction of replication from this position is counterclockwise.

To account for the regular distribution of copies of the bacterial chromosome among newly divided cells, it was proposed that the chromosomes are attached to the membrane of the cell and that they segregate to new cells via this attachment. In fact, evidence existed to indicate

that the actual synthesis of new DNA, which makes up the replication process, occurs at a membrane site. New information available in 1969 showed that, in addition to the actively replicating site of DNA being attached to the membrane, sites associated with the origin and terminus of the bacterial chromosome of *Bacillus subtilis* are also permanently attached to the cell membrane.

Other evidence from work with *E. coli* implied that there may be as many as 30 sites at which the chromosome is attached to the membrane, and that the attachment at the replicating point is only one of them. The evidence did not indicate, however, whether these multiple sites are specific or whether they change with time. It was also shown that replicating DNA in animal cells is attached to the nuclear membrane, a situation analogous to the attachment of replicating bacterial DNA to the cellular membrane.

In contrast to bacterial chromosomes, which appear to consist of only one replicon, the true chromosomes of mammalian cells contain many replicons. A recent report of DNA synthesis in mouse leukemic cells illustrated their difference in complexity in organization of the genetic material as compared with the simple bacterial cell. While the average growing bacterial cell contains from two to four chromosomes, each being a replicon, this mammalian cell contains 41 chromosomes and the average number of replicons per mouse leukemic cell was estimated to be between 200,000 and 400,000. (The average number of replicons in the chromosomes of a normal mouse cell was found to be between 1,000 and 4,000.) During the time when active DNA synthesis occurs (the S period), 37–100% of the replicons are replicating at any given moment. This agreed with visual, autoradiographic observations that replication in animal cells appears to be initiated simultaneously at many sites in a complex chromosome. Moreover, recent evidence obtained from Chinese hamster cells showed that mammalian chromosome replication initiated at one point proceeds in two directions from that point. The average size of the mammalian replicon was determined as 10–30 million daltons, a measure of atomic mass unit, compared to about 3 billion daltons for the bacterial replicon.

The rolling circle model. All that was certain about DNA replication was that it is semiconservative, which means that the integrity of each original DNA strand of a double-stranded molecule is maintained even though they separate and are found paired with new complementary strands after replication. A new model of DNA replication, however, was stirring interest. Referred to as the rolling circle model, it was proposed to explain

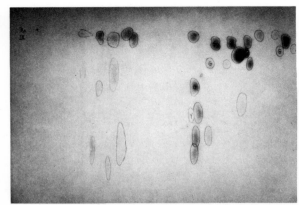
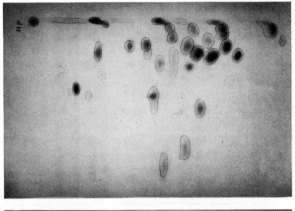
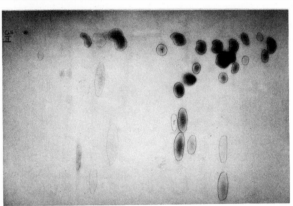
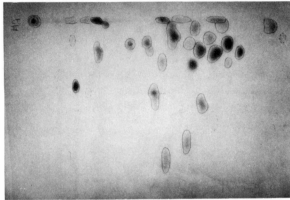

The common ancestry of plants and animals was confirmed in studies of the amino acid sequences in histones, simple proteins attached to DNA in cell nuclei. Peptide maps of histone-3 (top, left) and histone-4 (top, right), as isolated from buds of garden peas, differ only slightly from maps of histone-3 (bottom, left) and histone-4 (bottom, right) from the thymus of a calf.

certain aspects of bacterial and phage (a bacterial virus) DNA replication.

The rolling circle model could be visualized in the following way. The original DNA molecule that is to be copied (the template) consists of two strands that are complementary to each other and that are attached end to end to form a closed loop, or circle. (All bacterial and phage chromosomes studied in detail were known to have this configuration at some time in their existence.) When one of the strands opens and is peeled away from its complement, a new complement, or replica, is produced to take its place. The replica is attached to the free end of the original complement that was the last to come off the circular strand. This process is repeated, resulting in replicas attached end to end. Then, new complementary strands are made, using these replicas as templates. This results in completed, double-stranded DNA replicas as the finished product.

Two important features of this model need to be emphasized. First, the replication points for each strand may be at different sites, a condition that is termed asynchronous replication. Second, and

genetically significant, only one of the two parental DNA strands is used to transmit hereditary information to daughter molecules. This phenomenon is aptly described as master-strand replication. It explains some observations made on replicating phage chromosomes, such as the existence of a series of phage chromosomes structurally linked together end to end.

A number of laboratories reported that newly synthesized DNA appears as short segments. Some data were also interpreted to show that all newly made DNA is synthesized in a discontinuous manner. These discontinuous segments are then joined by an enzyme, called ligase, to produce a continuous strand.

Recombination studies. Recent reports demonstrated that two systems for forming new combinations of genes exist in one of the phages, the lambda. (Recombination allows for the exchange of genetic information between two organisms.) One of the systems is generalized and accounts for the genetic recombination that occurs during vegetative reproduction of the lambda. The other is a site-specific recombination system that directs recombination in the region where the phage is attached to its host and in a state in which it is harmless to the host (prophage form). This type of recombination brings about the insertion of the phage genome (reproductive cell) into the genome of its bacterial host, a relationship called lysogeny. Increasing evidence indicated that the bacterial-phage interactions are strikingly similar to those between animal viruses and the complex animal cells they infect.

Another report showed that repeated sequences of the base pairing units occur in the DNA of evolutionarily higher organisms. Some segments are repeated hundreds of thousands of times. These repeated sequences were detected by their rapid reassociation in experiments designed to measure the rate at which the separated single-stranded DNA molecules reestablish themselves in their double-stranded or native form. The rate for a fraction of the DNA was more rapid than would have been expected if all the sequences of a certain size had been unique.

It was proposed that during evolution the repeated sequences change slowly and diverge from each other, and that, occasionally, certain segments of DNA were extensively reduplicated. This replenished the dwindling redundancy. The function of these repeated sequences may be to provide for high rates of synthesis of certain much-needed proteins, such as ribosomal RNA. An intriguing question remained whether or not the same sequences are repeated in different tissues from the same animal.

In contrast, the genome of another phage, the T4, does not contain recurring nucleotide sequences longer than 12 in length. It was thought that any freely recombining genome that has two identical sequences larger than this size has a high probability of losing a part of its information content in the course of internal recombination. Evidently, a mechanism to prevent such loss in higher organisms must exist.

Trends in genetic research. The most recent achievement in the study of test-tube replication systems, this time derived from the RNA of the phage Qβ, was the asexual production of progeny (cloning) of several different RNA molecules. This means that a collection of molecules having the same single molecule as their parental template can be isolated and studied for their particular properties. Eventually the sequence of each of the different molecules will be determined. The various molecules that were isolated and cloned must be treated in a way analogous to that used in working with different strains of bacteria or viruses. This system provides a novel approach to studying the properties of self-replicating macro-

molecules. An artificial "universe" can be created in the test tube, and the effects of different "natural" selections can be determined as the evolution of these molecules proceeds in a controlled manner. (*See* Feature Article: HUMANICS AND GENETIC ENGINEERING, *Vegetative Propagation.*)

Recognition of the achievements that provided the groundwork for current efforts to understand the translation of the genetic message into amino acids was bestowed on three U.S. scientists in 1968. The Nobel Prize for Physiology or Medicine was awarded to Marshall W. Nirenberg, Robert W. Holley, and Har Gorbind Khorana. (*See* Year in Review: HONORS, *Medical Sciences.*) Working independently, the three had established the process by which DNA directs the synthesis of amino acids.

In 1969 Khorana was engaged in an attempt to synthesize totally the gene for yeast alanine transfer-RNA (t-RNA), which converts the genetic message into the appropriate amino acid. The DNA molecule was being built segment by segment in known sequence. Eventually, once the gene is made, it will be attached to the DNA of a lambda phage, which will then be used to infect a spheroplast (a cell that has no cell wall) of *E. coli.* In this way the man-made gene will be amplified, and the gene product (t-RNA) can be isolated and its function determined.

The upcoming months would also see the continued effort to determine the exact location for the origin of replication on the bacterial chromosome. Present evidence favored the interpretation that replicons have one origin, the location of which may differ among closely related organisms, and that replication proceeds sequentially in one direction from that origin. Continuing investigations, however, will have to determine the generality of this interpretation. The rolling circle model for DNA replication accounts for a number of observations made on replicating phage and bacterial chromosomes, and we can expect that the next few years will show a vigorous effort to find evidence to support or refute the general applicability of this model.

Whether or not DNA is synthesized discontinuously and whether this discontinuous synthesis involves both strands of the double helix will also occupy the attention of molecular geneticists in the future. The intriguing observation on Chinese hamster cells that shows replication starting from a common point and proceeding in opposite directions will stimulate attempts to determine if this mode of replication is also operative in other animal cells.

—James C. Copeland

Future trends in molecular biology

Determination of the structure and function of a specific biological molecule is a complex problem in itself, but the relationships and reactions between species are admittedly even more difficult to unravel. Molecular biologists were coming to realize, therefore, that a successful detailed understanding of the human cell would require a major effort nationally and internationally.

A step in this direction in the U.S. was the establishment of the MAN (for molecular anatomy) program at Oak Ridge National Laboratory supported by the Atomic Energy Commission and the National Institutes of Health. The purpose of the program was to develop additional biophysical and biochemical tools and to extend the use of devices such as the zonal centrifuge for the study of human cells on the molecular level. The future may see specialized centers established at other national laboratories and, perhaps, the drawing of talent from the universities into a strictly research atmosphere. In Britain quite the opposite tack was being followed, namely the removal of existing research in molecular biology from the laboratory at Harwell to the universities.

The hardware for the automated synthesis of large molecules and for the ultrapure separation of biological molecules will undoubtedly lead to an accelerating rate of discovery in molecular biology, the destruction of old theories, and the construction of new ones. At the same time, renewed interest in cellular and intercellular research will tend to blend the findings of molecular biology into a more complete understanding of life processes on a larger scale.

—Philip F. Gustafson

See also A Gateway to the Future: A HOUSE FOR LIVING MOLECULES; Year in Review: BOTANY; MEDICINE; MICROBIOLOGY; ZOOLOGY.

Obituaries

The following persons, all of whom died between July 1, 1968, and June 30, 1969, were noted for distinguished accomplishments in one or more scientific endeavors. Biographies of those whose names are preceded by an asterisk (*) appear in *Encyclopædia Britannica.*

Alter, Dinsmore (March 28, 1888—Sept. 20, 1968). Alter, a U.S. astronomer and director of Griffith Observatory in Los Angeles from 1935 until 1958, further advanced the theory of the planetoid origin of the moon when, in 1956, he observed gaseous mists in the crater Alphonsus. His observations were little noted by astronomers

Charles William Mayo

until 1958–59, when Nikolai A. Kozyrev of the U.S.S.R. also saw what seemed to be outbursts of gas from the moon's surface. These independent observations led astronomers to reevaluate certain concepts of the moon.

Anslow, Gladys Amelia (May 22, 1892—March 31, 1969). A U.S. physicist and an authority on mass spectroscopy, Dr. Anslow became emeritus professor of physics at Smith College, Northampton, Mass., in 1960, having been associated with that institution from 1914. Her work included a spectrochemical study of the structure of proteins and antibiotics, which is of great importance in the production of synthetic foods and drugs. Because of her knowledge of mass spectroscopy, Dr. Anslow was the first woman to work on the cyclotron at the University of California.

Browne, Benjamin Chapman (April 29, 1911—Aug. 14, 1968). A British scientist, Browne was head of the department of Geodesy and Geophysics at Cambridge University from 1948 until 1960. He made an important contribution to the measurement of gravity when, during his study concerning the effect of the movements of a ship in relation to gravity, he came to realize that the usual methods needed correcting. In making the necessary recalculations, he came up with what is known as the "Browne Correction."

Cannon, Berry Louis (March 22, 1935—Feb. 17, 1969). One of the first U.S. aquanauts, Cannon died while working 600 ft beneath the Pacific in connection with the U.S. Navy's Sealab III project. Cannon, an electronics engineer and a veteran of the 1965 Sealab II experiment, was at the site of the Sealab III habitat for a last check of the tank-car-type structure, which was to be the home of the project's nine first-team divers for a period of 60 days. The aquanauts, using the $10,000,000 Sealab III as a base of operations, were slated to study the effects of prolonged underwater life upon man.

Carlson, Chester F. (Feb. 8, 1906—Sept. 19, 1968). Carlson, a U.S. physicist, invented the reproducing process known as xerography ("dry writing"). The process was developed by the Battelle Memorial Institute of Columbus, O., and commercially introduced in 1959 by Haloid-Xerox (later the Xerox Corporation) of Rochester, N.Y.

*Dale, Sir Henry Hallett (June 9, 1875—July 23, 1968). British physiologist and Nobel Prize winner, Sir Henry received his education at Cambridge University and at St. Bartholomew's Hospital in London. He began his research career at the Wellcome Physiological Research Laboratories in 1904 and served as director from 1906 until 1914. He was concerned with investigating the chemical composition and effects of ergot of rye, and during this period performed his important research into the pharmacologically active substances histamine and acetylcholine. In 1914 Sir Henry became a member of the staff of what was to become the Medical Research Council, and from 1928 until 1942 he was director of the National Institute for Medical Research. He was president of the Royal Society (1940–45) and of the British Association for the Advancement of Science (1947). In 1936 he was awarded the Nobel Prize for Physiology or Medicine (with Otto Loewi) for his work on the chemical transmission of nerve impulses.

Davies, William (April 20, 1899—July 28, 1968). A British agronomist, Davies was director of the Grassland Research Institute at Hurley from 1949 until his retirement in 1964. He trained at the Welsh Plant Breeding Station at Aberystwyth in the 1920s, then was plant geneticist at Palmerston, N.Z., from 1929 until 1931. He returned to Aberystwyth in 1933 as head of the department and from that time until 1940 he worked on completing the first grassland survey of England and Wales. At Hurley, Davies gave strong leadership in developing his view that grassland research should be based on the interrelationship between the plant and the soil, and the animal consuming the forage.

Gamow, George (March 4, 1904—Aug. 19, 1968). A U.S. theoretical physicist and astronomer,

Gamow was a professor of physics at the University of Colorado from 1956 until 1968. He first attained recognition in 1928 when he published his quantum theory of the atomic nucleus, which led to the later theory of nuclear fission and fusion. With other scientists Gamow attempted to apply his formula for calculating the rate of induced nuclear transformations to the so-called thermal nuclear reaction in the interior of the sun and other stars. In recent years Gamow was a proponent of the "big bang" theory concerning the origin of the universe. In 1956 he received the UNESCO Kalinga award for his popular, nontechnical books on atomic energy and other scientific subjects. Gamow also contributed to *Encyclopædia Britannica.*

Garrod, Dorothy Annie Elizabeth (May 5, 1892—Dec. 18, 1968). A British archaeologist and an authority on the Paleolithic Age, Dr. Garrod was Disney Professor of Archaeology at Cambridge University from 1939 until 1952. Her most widely recognized work was the excavations (1932–34) of Paleolithic cave dwellings at Mt. Carmel in Palestine, which she described in *The Stone Age of Mount Carmel* (1937).

Greene, Harry S. N. (Sept. 22, 1904—Feb. 14, 1969). A U.S. pathologist and cancer researcher, Green was chairman of the department of pathology at Yale University School of Medicine from 1950. He conducted extensive research in tissue transplantation, and in 1946 discovered that healthy human tissue transplants would not grow in animals but that cancerous human tissue would, as would embryonic tissue. This study suggested a relationship between cancerous and embryonic tissues, and was a contribution to understanding of diseased tissue and tissue growth.

*Hahn, Otto (March 8, 1879—July 28, 1968). German nuclear chemist, Hahn won the 1944 Nobel Prize for Chemistry for his discovery in 1938 that nuclear fission was possible. At the Kaiser Wilhelm Institute for Chemistry in Berlin, Hahn and his associate, Fritz Strassmann, had long worked on the problem of the identity of radioactive elements that were produced by neutron bombardment of uranium. The results of their experiments showed the products to be barium, lanthanum, and cerium. In 1966 Hahn shared the $50,000 Enrico Fermi Award with Strassmann and his lifelong associate, the nuclear physicist Lise Meitner (*see* below). Hahn's autobiography appeared in 1962 (Eng. trans. *Otto Hahn: a Scientific Autobiography,* 1966).

*Heymans, Corneille Jean François (March 28, 1892—July 18, 1968). Heymans, a Belgian physiologist, succeeded his father as professor of pharmacology and as director of the Institute

Otto Hahn and Lise Meitner

of Pharmacodynamics and Therapeutics at the University of Ghent in 1930. At the institute, which examines the effects of medicines on the human body, Heymans studied the physiology of the respiratory and circulatory systems. His most celebrated discovery concerned the functions of the carotid sinus, the carotid body, and the aortic bodies in the neck. He found that their role in the regulation of blood pressure and respiration lay in their response to pressure stimuli and to changes in the oxygen tension of the blood. For this achievement, Heymans received the 1938 Nobel Prize for Physiology or Medicine.

Lambert, Walter Davis (Jan. 12, 1879—Oct. 27, 1968). Lambert, a U.S. geodesist and mathematician, was chief of the gravity and astronomy section of the U.S. Coast and Geodetic Survey from 1942 until 1947. He was a contributor to *Encyclopædia Britannica.*

*Mayo, Charles William (July 28, 1898—July 28, 1968). A U.S. surgeon, son of Charles H. Mayo and nephew of William Mayo, co-founders of the Mayo Clinic in Rochester, Minn., Charles W. Mayo was the last family member to practice at the clinic, where he served as senior surgeon and board member until retiring in 1963. At the clinic Mayo specialized in abdominal surgery and had perfected a one-stage operation for cancer of the lower colon and rectum. He was alternate dele-

gate to the United Nations General Assembly in 1953 and in the following year served as president of the American Association for the UN.

*Meitner, Lise (Nov. 7, 1878—Oct. 27, 1968). An Austrian physicist, Lise Meitner was a pioneer in the study of radioactivity and a joint discoverer of nuclear fission. After receiving a doctorate (1906) at the University of Vienna, she studied under Max Planck in Berlin, then joined Otto Hahn (*see* above) in research on radioactivity. Their partnership, which lasted over 30 years, included the discovery of the element protactinium (1917). In 1938 she left Nazi-occupied Austria for Sweden, where she worked until retiring in England in 1960. In 1966 she shared the Enrico Fermi Award with Hahn and Fritz Strassmann for their joint research that led to the discovery of uranium fission in the late 1930s.

Pickering, James S. (1898—Feb. 14, 1969). Pickering, a U.S. amateur astronomer, did not become a professional until he was 60 years of age, and only then as a part-time lecturer at Hayden Planetarium, New York City. When he reached retirement age he was given the honorary title of emeritus astronomer of the planetarium. He was the author of *The Stars Are Yours, Windows to Space,* and *Famous Astronomers.*

Rees, John (June 25, 1890—April 11, 1969). Rees, a British psychiatrist, was director of the World Federation for Mental Health (1949–62) and honorary president after 1962. He served as director of psychiatry for the British Army during World War II and reviewed many of his cases in *The Shaping of Psychiatry by War* (1945).

Sanger, Paul Weldon (Sept. 17, 1906—Sept. 8, 1968). Sanger, a U.S. surgeon and a pioneer in open-heart surgery, was head of thoracic and cardiovascular surgery (from 1938) and director (from 1946) of Heineman Research Laboratory at Charlotte (N.C.) Memorial Hospital. Sanger's orlon artery graft was called a stepping-stone toward the development of modern-day processes in heart surgery. His recent work concerned the storage of heart valves and full hearts.

Scheffey, Lewis Cass (1893—March 13, 1969). A U.S. gynecologist, Scheffey was professor of gynecology and obstetrics at Jefferson Medical College, Philadelphia, from 1946 until 1955. He was a pioneer in applying cystology (the study of intrinsic characters and functions of cells) to early diagnosis and treatment of cancer in women. In 1962 he received the American Cancer Society's gold medal for outstanding contributions to the control of cancer.

Schneirla, Theodore C. (July 23, 1902—Aug. 20, 1968). A U.S. animal psychologist, Schneirla was curator of the department of animal behavior at the American Museum of Natural History in New York City from 1947. Capturing a 20,000-member colony of army ants in the jungles of the Panama Canal Zone, he brought the ants to the museum and duplicated their living arrangements in order to study their habits. He also observed the behavior patterns of bees and various animals in an effort to better understand human psychology. Schneirla wrote a number of books and was a contributor to *Encyclopædia Britannica.*

Siple, Paul Allman (Dec. 18, 1908—Nov. 25, 1968). Siple, a U.S. polar explorer, had been chosen at age 19 from among 600,000 Boy Scouts to accompany Adm. Richard E. Byrd on his first voyage to Antarctica in 1928. Subsequently, Siple made six trips to the South Pole, which were written about in four books, including *90° South* (1960). He was awarded the Hubbard Medal of the National Geographic Society in 1958.

Vestine, Ernest Harry (May 9, 1906—July 18, 1968). Vestine, a U.S. geophysicist, was associated with the Carnegie Institution from 1938 until 1957, when he joined the RAND Corporation at Santa Monica, Calif. An authority on geomagnetism and auroral sciences, Vestine led a Canadian expedition into northern Alberta Province during the Second International Polar Year (1932–33). There he made a near-first series of observations of night-luminous clouds, which he described in a paper that became a classic authoritative work on the subject. While there he also set up an observatory that was still providing important data in the late 1960s. Vestine received the 1967 John Fleming Award from the American Geophysical Union for original research on fundamental aspects of geomagnetism, atmospheric electricity, aeronomy, and related sciences. He was a contributor to *Encyclopædia Britannica.*

Vogt, William (May 15, 1902—July 11, 1968). A U.S. naturalist and conservationist, Vogt was a lecturer for the National Association of Audubon Societies from 1935 until 1939. As chief of conservation of the Pan American Union (1943–49) he wrote *Road to Survival* (1948), stressing the danger of wasting natural resources. In 1951 Vogt became national director of the Planned Parenthood Federation of America and again warned against exploding populations and waste in *People! Challenge to Survival* (1960).

Walker, Edmund Murton (Oct. 5, 1877—Feb. 14, 1969.) Walker, a Canadian entomologist, discovered scores of new insect species, including the Canadian ice-bug (part cricket, part cockroach). He was emeritus professor of Zoology at the University of Toronto, having been head of its zoology department from 1934 until 1948.

Oceanography

Much was done during 1968 and 1969 to establish guidelines for the development of the ocean sciences on an international level. These plans involved proposals for a more rational restructuring of the international scientific community so that scientists who study the oceans might be brought into more effective contact with each other, a thorough study of the many areas of activity undertaken by various governments so as to coordinate efforts to study the oceans by means of conventional methods and space technology, and the formation and strengthening of regional consortiums within certain nations, including the United States, so as to pool research resources and develop joint programs.

In January 1969, the Commission on Marine Science, Engineering and Resources, appointed by the president of the United States, concluded a two-year investigation into the possibilities of U.S. involvement in the understanding, exploiting, and preserving of the world's oceans. Julius A. Stratton, chairman of the commission, stated that "a vigorous, systematic investment in the oceans will yield a tremendous return over the years ahead—a tangible return to the economy and an intangible return of priceless value, the quality of the environment in which we live."

International developments. A division of the International Union of Geodesy and Geophysics (IUGG), the International Association of Physical Oceanography (IAPO), changed its name to the International Association for the Physical Sciences of the Ocean (IAPSO). This broadening in emphasis of the organization from physical oceanography to the physical sciences involved an increase in the number of scientists who became members of the association. The new group included scientists working in marine geochemistry, marine meteorology, and marine geology, as well as oceanography. This change was expected to provide a more effective international forum for the discussion of all aspects of the scientific study of the oceans.

In July 1968, technical specialists from 35 nations, including the U.S. and the Soviet Union, reported to the United Nations that commercial exploitation of the extreme depths of the oceans for minerals could be easily realized within a few years. An international agreement was proposed to give the UN control, or title, to the deep-ocean floor. The agreement would also involve an accord among all nations not to use the ocean bottom for nuclear testing.

The report stated that beneficial uses of the largely unexplored ocean bottom are much closer to realization than most people imagine. But the scientists also found that the financial investment necessary may be too high to make rapid development worthwhile. Some oceanographers, however, doubt some of the conclusions of this report, especially with reference to projected time scales.

Australia, because of its 12,000-mi coastline and, therefore, ideal conditions for oceanographic research, inaugurated in 1968 an Institute of Marine Sciences at the University of New South Wales in Sydney. The institute focused its attention on the future and established itself as a coordinating body for any faculty or school within the university interested in oceanographic study.

Japan, one of the four leading nations in the world in oceanographic research, showed a continuously expanding interest in the sea. To meet the prohibitive cost of equipment, many of Japan's ocean-oriented industries (for example, the Mitsubishi, Mitsui, and Sumitomo groups) coordinated efforts and pooled resources.

Concern about future food resources led the Japanese government to make tentative plans to establish various agencies to study the problem.

The Science and Technology Agency would consider exploitation of the continental shelves, the Ministry of Agriculture and Forestry would study the sea's food sources, and the Ministry of International Trade and Industry would be interested in the technology of offshore oil drilling.

On March 8, 1968, U.S. Pres. Lyndon B. Johnson proposed the launching of "an historic and unprecedented adventure," an International Decade of Ocean Exploration for the 1970s. The National Council on Marine Resources and Engineering Development asked the National Academy of Sciences and the National Academy of Engineering to develop more fully the scientific and engineering aspects of the Decade. The report that they prepared, "An Oceanic Quest," described broad-scale cooperative programs leading toward more effective utilization of the ocean's resources. This report was expected to serve as a basis for further U.S. planning for the Decade, as well as provide a focus for similar discussions by the other ocean-oriented nations.

President Johnson's proposal for the International Decade of Ocean Exploration emphasized
continued on page 372

"Lanka," a two-man miniature submersible designed by Soviet scientists, was tested recently near the town of Gelendzhik on the Black Sea. Despite its size, the boat is equipped with all the instruments necessary for underwater work. The "Lanka" is made of aluminum and plastic and is open at the top to allow the divers to enter and exit easily.

Tass from Sovfoto

Sleep and Dreams

by Julius Segal and Gay Gaer Luce

Sleep that knits up the ravell'd sleave of care,
The death of each day's life, sore labour's bath,
Balm of hurt minds, great nature's second course,
Chief nourisher in life's feast —

WILLIAM SHAKESPEARE
MACBETH, ACT 2, SCENE 2

All men sleep. A third of life is spent in that profoundly mysterious state to which we submit nightly, removed from the waking world. Throughout his history man has attempted to unravel the mysteries of this remarkable experience. Many centuries ago, for example, sleep was regarded as a type of anemia of the brain. Alcmaeon, a Greek physiologist who lived during the 5th century B.C., believed that blood retreats into the veins, after which the partially starved brain goes to sleep. Plato, on the other hand, supported the idea that the soul leaves the body during sleep, wanders the world, and then wakes up the body when it returns. More recently, chemical and neurological explanations of sleep have been proposed. According to one theory, the brain is put to sleep by a chemical agent that accumulates in the body when it is awake. Another theory postulates that weary dendrites (branches) of certain nerve cells break connections with neighboring nerve cells, thereby disrupting the flow of impulses required for staying awake. But in order to establish their validity, these more recent theories first had to be subjected to the scrutiny of laboratory research.

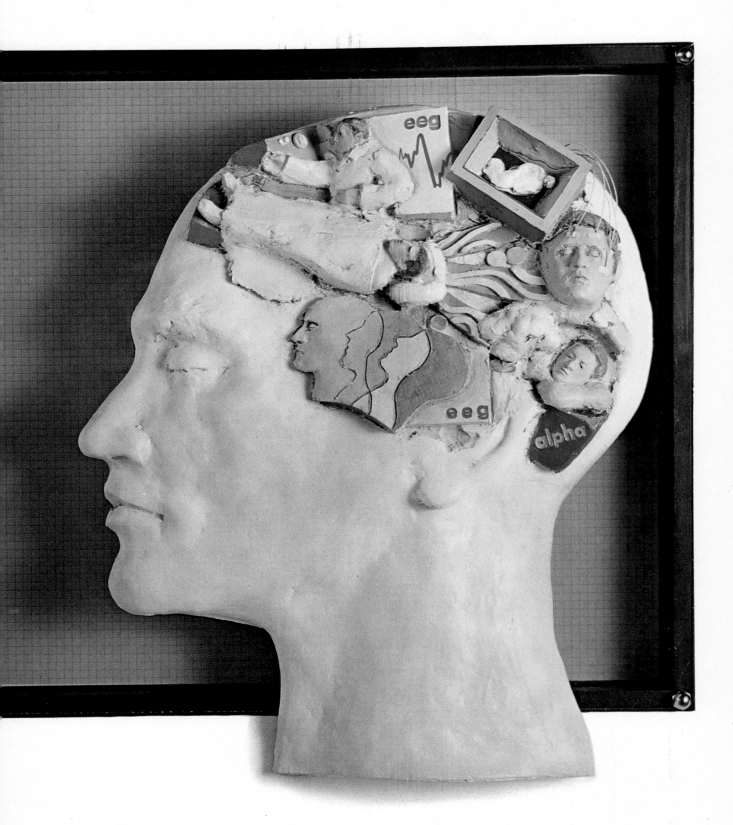

The beginning of modern sleep research

Why do we sleep? Why do we dream? What is the meaning of our nightly journey through unremembered levels of consciousness, through hidden aspects of ourselves? Although neurologists, physiologists, and psychologists have sought answers to these questions for many decades, modern sleep research is said to have begun in the 1950s, when Eugene Aserinsky, a graduate student at the University of Chicago, and his professor, Nathaniel Kleitman, observed recurrent periods of rapid eye movements (REM's) in sleeping subjects. When awakened during these REM periods, subjects almost always remembered dreaming. On the other hand, when awakened during non-REM phases of sleep, the subjects rarely could recall their dreams. Thus, guided by REM's, it became possible for investigators to "spot" dreaming from outside and then awaken the sleepers to collect dream stories. They could also alter the dreamers' experiences with noises, drugs, or other stimuli before or during sleep.

Since the mid-1950s nightfall has become a time that draws hundreds of researchers around the world into sleep laboratories, where a bedroom adjoins another room that contains an amplifier-recorder known as the electroencephalograph (EEG) machine. The EEG amplifies signals from sensors on the face, head, and other parts of the body, which together yield tracings of respiration, pulse, muscle tension, and changes of electrical potential in the brain that are sometimes called brain waves. These recordings constitute the decipherable clues to the changes in the activities that are going on within a sleeping person.

It has also been found that the sleep of cats and other mammals reveals EEG configurations corresponding to the REM—or dreaming sleep—in man. Because this recurrent sleep rhythm occurs throughout the animal kingdom, investigators have been able to use animals as subjects for sleep research and to employ procedures that extend well beyond those possible with human volunteers. Concurrent with animal studies to enhance our knowledge of the biologic foundations of the dreaming rhythm, advances have also been made with human subjects in the psychiatric exploration of the dreaming process.

One fact was clearly demonstrated by the early sleep researchers: one part of the night is not just like another. As scientists began to compare the records of volunteers during the 1950s, they observed that human sleep follows a rhythmic schedule. They noted, too, that not only was this schedule much the same in healthy persons of the same age with similar habits but, from night to night, each individual had an EEG record almost as consistent as a signature.

The many shades of sleep

Sleep and wakefulness, once considered to be the light and dark of consciousness, no longer seem to differ so sharply. To sleep does

not mean to drown in an ocean of darkness. Actually, sleep is not a unitary state; it involves many shades or degrees of detachment from the surrounding world. Bedroom observations can hardly detect the many subtle changes constantly occurring in the body and mind during a normal night of sleep. While sleep may feel like a blanket of darkness punctuated by dreams, a time when the mind is asleep, nothing could be less true. All night long a person drifts down and up through different levels of consciousness, as if on waves. With laboratory methods, researchers have been able to chart the typical stages of the human journey into sleep.

The journey starts while the subject is still awake but beginning to relax. His brain waves, which have been low, rapid, and irregular, begin to show a new pattern. This new pattern, which is known as alpha rhythm, is an even, electrical pulsation of about 9 to 12 cycles per second. Most people do not know what the alpha state feels like, but during the last few years researchers have been able to teach subjects how to recognize and control their alpha rhythm.

When their EEG shows an alpha rhythm, the subjects are notified, either by a sound or by the appearance of·a color on a screen. Because the alpha state tends to be pleasant and relaxed, the ability to sustain it can help tense people ease their passage into sleep. A

The first step on the journey from wakefulness to sleep is the alpha state, a pleasant, relaxed condition characterized by even brain-wave rhythms of 9–12 cycles per second. Researchers can teach recognition and control of the alpha state. When the subject's EEG shows an alpha rhythm, he is notified by a sound or the appearance of a color on a screen.

moment of tension, a loud noise, or an attempt to solve a problem, however, and the alpha rhythm may vanish. Curiously, the alpha rhythm is sustained by the Zen practitioner when he is in a state of meditation. It also occurs sporadically in other individuals throughout the day and night.

As the subject passes through the gates of the unconscious, his alpha waves grow smaller, and his eyes roll very slowly. For a moment, he may wake up during this early part of the descent, alerted by a sudden spasm that causes his body to jerk. Like the brain waves, this spasm is a sign of neural changes within. Known as the myoclonic jerk, it is caused by a brief burst of activity in the brain. Although it is related to epileptic seizures, the myoclonic jerk is normal in all human sleep. It is gone in a fraction of a second, after which descent continues. The subject has not felt the peculiar transformation, but now he is said to be truly asleep.

Here, in Stage I, the pattern of the sleeper's brain waves is small and pinched, low, irregular, and rapidly changing. Occasionally, however, the regular waves of the alpha rhythm break through. During this period the sleeper may be enjoying a floating sensation or drifting with idle thoughts and dreams. His muscles are relaxing, his heart rate slowing down. He can be awakened easily, and might insist that he had not been asleep at all. If not disturbed after a few minutes at this stage the sleeper will descend to another level, another step removed from the world.

As the sleeper passes into Stage II, his brain waves change again. Now they trace out quick bursts—a rapid crescendo and decrescendo, resembling a wire spindle, and unmistakable on the EEG chart. The eyes roll slowly from side to side, but if the experimenter gently opens a lid the sleeper will not see. If awakened, which can be accomplished easily with a modest sound, the sleeper may still think he has been awake all along. At this point, however, he has been sleeping soundly for perhaps ten minutes. Whatever happens now in the imagination of the sleeper will be mainly beyond his conscious grasp.

Still the sleeper descends—to Stage III, which is characterized by large, slow brain waves (about one a second) that are sometimes about five times the amplitude of the waking alpha rhythm. Now it will take a louder noise to awaken the subject, perhaps a repetition of his name. His muscles are very relaxed and he breathes evenly. His heart rate slows, his temperature declines, his blood pressure drops.

Some 20 or 30 minutes after he first falls asleep, the sleeper reaches Stage IV, the deepest level. Marked by large, slow brain waves (delta waves) that resemble jagged buttes, Stage IV is a relatively dreamless oblivion. The breathing is even; heart rate, blood pressure, and body temperature are slowly falling.

High-amplitude delta waves in sleep are almost typical of youth. With increasing age, however, the EEG of the delta waves becomes

smaller and flatter. Most delta sleep occurs during the first part of the night, those first few hours when children are characteristically difficult to awaken. During middle age delta sleep begins to vanish from the nightlong pattern; older people actually do not sleep as deeply as the young.

Stage IV sleep was initially thought to be a time when the mind idled; when awakened from this state, most sleepers rarely recalled thinking or dreaming. Actually it is not quite a time of oblivion. In a "nightmare" laboratory at a New York hospital, it was found that most volunteers with recurrent dreadful dreams experienced them during delta sleep. Such dreams tend to differ in quality from other dreams, often being unelaborated repetitions of a fragment of a real trauma, such as a fire. It appears that the nightmares of delta sleep can also be induced by outside stimuli delivered to a susceptible person during this deep phase of sleep.

It is during deep delta sleep, too, that somnambulism (sleepwalking) occurs. Sleepwalking, which is actually a kind of waking trance, apparently is quite common among very young children, although often undetected by their parents. Somnambulism can be instigated externally by calling the sleepwalker by name when he is in delta sleep or by standing the sleeping child on his feet.

The sleeper does not remain long in Stage IV. After 20 minutes or so of delta sleep, he begins to drift back up through the lighter levels. About 90 minutes after he fell asleep, he will show the low-voltage, fast brain waves that are characteristic of the lightest sleep. Because the brain waves at this level are practically indistinguishable from those recorded in the alert state, this period is called paradoxical sleep. Yet the sleeper is not easy to awaken. Lying limply, his eyes move jerkily under closed lids as if watching something.

Stage IV sleep, the deepest level, is marked by large, slow brain waves and is a relatively dreamless oblivion. It is also, however, the state during which nightmares and sleepwalking occur.

311

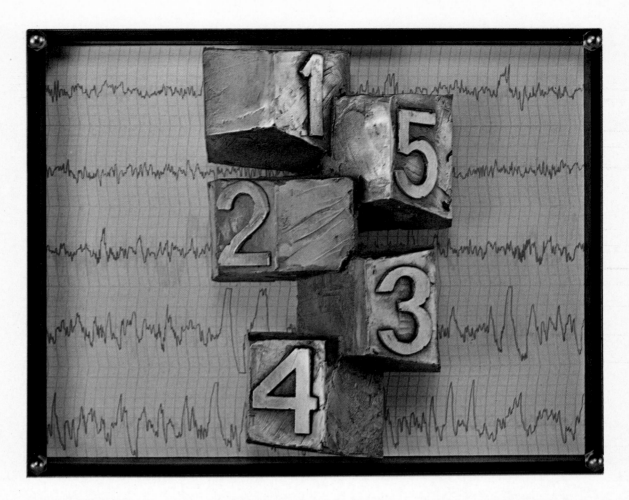

Each of the five patterns of brain waves is characteristic of a different stage of sleep. Because human sleep follows a rhythmic schedule, one part of the night is not just like another. During the night the cycle of five distinct states of sleep is repeated four or five times.

He is in a special variety of Stage I that is known as REM sleep. If awakened now the sleeper would almost certainly remember dreaming, probably in very vivid detail.

During REM sleep, the visual system of the brain exhibits great excitement. Nerve cells in the system fire sudden bursts of impulses that originate in a region of the brainstem called the pons. When the pons is damaged, the paradoxical state of sleep drops out of the sleeper's repertoire.

After perhaps ten minutes in the REM state, the sleeper will probably turn over in bed and again begin descending through the levels of sleep to the depths, only to return in another hour or so for a longer REM dream. Sometime between 3 A.M. and 5 A.M. the average sleeper's body temperature reaches its lowest point, after which it starts to rise. As morning approaches, the REM periods grow longer and delta slumber decreases. A dream that is remembered in the morning was probably the last REM dream of the night, an episode lasting perhaps as long as 40 minutes.

Each night the entire cycle of sleep stages is repeated four or five times. This schedule of night rhythms, which is moderately consistent for each individual, changes with increasing age. It can also be altered by fatigue, illness, emotional upset, and alcohol or drugs.

The deprivation of sleep

What does sleep do for us? What are its mysterious restorative functions? Why do some persons react more poorly than others to sleep deprivation? Although we do not know what lies behind our basic requirement for sleep, it seems to be an essential need of higher mammals. A man can survive starvation for over three weeks with few ill effects, but after three weeks without sleep he may act like a psychotic. We do not yet understand, however, why such mental illness sometimes attends severe sleep loss.

We can demonstrate that sleep is essential by depriving people of it for just a few days. The first effect seen in men taking part in such experiments was one of overwhelming sleepiness. They needed constant attention, activity, and stimulation to keep them awake. As the days went by, the subjects became irritable, sometimes volatile, unwilling to exert any muscular or mental effort without strong incentive. Memory faltered and they were unable to perform simple tasks reliably. They lapsed into momentary blackouts called microsleeps and were beset by hallucinations, imagined sensations, nonsensical thoughts, and a sense of disorientation. Those who held out long enough finally began to act like madmen.

Experiments demonstrating dramatic deterioration of performance and behavior, as well as the experiences of men at war, do not, however, give the entire picture of effects of sleep deprivation. Some healthy young men have gone without sleep for over 200 hours without suffering any hallucination or major decrements in behavior. While they did suffer lapses in performance, they did not become psychotic. What subtle damages may accrue from such sleep deprivation are not known. Obviously, just as people vary in their susceptibility to drugs, fatigue, and illness, they also appear to vary in their tolerance of sleep loss.

Chronic sleep loss, which is far more common and less dramatic than total deprivation, has also been studied in several laboratories. These investigations indicated that a person who abbreviates his sleep to four hours or less will not exhibit his usual sleep pattern. He will maximize some stages at the expense of others, sometimes shifting his pattern on successive nights, often showing more delta and REM sleep and less of the transitional light levels.

Studies have also demonstrated that a reduction in sleep for just a few nights causes pronounced decrements in vigilance performance. In tests at Cambridge University, scientists discovered what usual laboratory tests of short duration had failed to reveal. The English volunteers were subjected to testing for a full day, not just for an hour, following varying periods of sleep. Anyone can muster his resources for an hour's test, but after about 10 hours of testing a person begins to demonstrate the difference between rested performance and performance after 2, 3, 5, or 7 hours of sleep.

The results of the Cambridge study indicated clearly that sleep does something for our ability to sustain attention. Thus, by implication, it acts as a process of recovery that we are ill-advised to ignore. It does not, however, spell certain disaster to go without sleep for several days.

New studies of dreaming

Universal interest in dreams was the reason why the REM stage became the most studied aspect of sleep. In the laboratory an observer can note the clues that the sleeper is dreaming and awaken him rapidly before the memory of the dream has faded. At home, however, most dreams cannot be recalled. Those we do remember are often from the final REM period, just before we awaken in the morning. Indeed, laboratory studies show that one important factor in recall and dream quality seems to be the time of night when a person is aroused. During the second half of the night dreams are easier to recall; awakening at almost any time during this period seems to produce at least a memory of dreaming or of a vague dreamlike experience.

When a person enters the REM period after quiet sleep, his brain

In one recent experiment designed to test the idea that dreaming might be a way of fitting a day's experience into the special organization of memory, the subjects wore goggles during the day that allowed only red, orange, and yellow light to enter their eyes. When awakened during REM periods, the subjects reported that reds and oranges were the predominant colors in their dreams.

and body exhibit dramatic changes. His already relaxed postural muscles become altogether flaccid. If awakened from this state before muscle tone returns, a person may feel paralyzed temporarily. Yet in REM sleep the closed eyes dart—sometimes furiously—and the face twitches; even breathing and pulse become irregular, blood pressure fluctuates, and oxygen consumption rises, as do brain circulation and brain temperature. Adrenal hormones in the blood increase and males of all ages have penile erections during 80–90% of their REM periods.

Although the REM period resembles a slowly increasing physiological storm, comparable to a state of fright or excitement in waking, no one has yet established any clear connection between this intense body activity and the intensity of the dream experience. People have reported most innocuous dreams, such as "sitting at the dinner table at Grandpa's house," after showing physiological changes during the dream period that once might have been interpreted as extreme stress.

Physicians have long suspected but have not proved that violent or disturbing dreams during REM intervals might be the cause of nocturnal heart attacks. It is also during these intervals that the abnormal stomach acidity of ulcer patients is at its peak. As we learn more about the relationship between these events and specific sleep stages, it may be possible to anticipate and prevent such nighttime medical crises.

Anyone who has observed the half-open, darting eyes of a drowsing pet or the movements of a sleeping child's eyes under closed lids would be convinced that the sleepers were watching an internal movie. REM's, however, also occur in congenitally blind people, although such people usually dream in terms of touch and sound rather than in visual images. Thus, it may be possible that REM's have nothing to do with the events and action perceived in dreams but may be associated instead with bursts of bioelectric activity that occur during REM sleep in the visual system of the brain.

Although we still do not know what REM sleep does for us, we do seem to require a certain amount of it for our well-being. Abnormally little REM sleep has been noted in the records of some psychiatric and senile patients, among psychologically disturbed restless sleepers, and among people who have taken heavy doses of alcohol, barbiturates, amphetamines, or other drugs. William C. Dement of Stanford University observed that, when people or animals were deprived of REM sleep, they invariably exhibited signs of mounting excitation in the brain, even when behavior seemed unaffected. On each successive night of deprivation, a person would try more and more often to dream. When finally left to sleep uninterrupted, he would go into an orgy of REM sleep, as if making up the loss.

A similar REM orgy has been observed in alcoholics and drug addicts undergoing withdrawal. It has even been speculated that such symptoms as DT's (delirium tremens) may result from long suppression of REM sleep, the dreams finally erupting as hallucinations when the person is awake. What makes drugs as different as alcohol (a depressant) and dexedrine (a stimulant) suppress REM dreaming is not yet known.

In addition to noting the brain's unusual excitability in REM-deprived animals, Dement and his co-workers demonstrated that such animals were easily convulsed by a mild electric shock. Following shock treatment, it was found that the REM-deprived animals no longer indulged in an orgy of REM sleep, yet their brain waves returned to normal. It was as if the shock had performed the same function as REM sleep. This discovery may lead to a better understanding of the mysterious effectiveness of electroshock therapy, which somehow provides relief to depressed mental patients. Such patients show less REM sleep after shock therapy than before.

Although it is possible to plunge a person rapidly into REM sleep or to increase it by giving him an amino acid found in foods or microscopic doses of LSD, most drugs that induce sleep suppress dreaming. Scientists, however, are now searching for specific chemicals in the brain that trigger REM sleep. Michel Jouvet and his co-workers in France have already demonstrated that REM sleep is initiated in cats, and probably in man, by what appears to be a combination of several chemicals in the brainstem. As a result of such work, sleeping pills of the future may be formulated to initiate a specific stage of sleep. Thus, it may then be possible to supply more REM dreaming to the person who is in need of it.

The meaning of dreams

As a person is awakened from REM periods in the course of a night, his dreams tend to progress from vague and almost thoughtlike incidents—revolving about such everyday realities as work, studies, home, or friends—to more vivid scenarios that grow increasingly bizarre as the night wears on. To explain this trend, some theorists have suggested that dreaming may be a time during which a person assimilates his present life into the whole of his past. During REM sleep in cats, for example, investigators have found unusual activity in the brain centers associated with memory and emotion. Perhaps during the bizarre sequences new memories are being filed or associated with the old, releasing a horde of details from the brain's almost infinite storage of experience—of which the conscious person remains almost totally unaware.

In one experiment to test this idea, subjects wore special goggles during the day that colored their visual experiences in orange-reds, eliminating all blues and greens. When asked the color of their dreams, the hues described by the volunteers were more frequently the reds and oranges, not blues or greens. Such results could mean that dreaming may be a way of fitting the day's experience into what is already organized in memory.

Films, posthypnotic suggestion, isolation, and a variety of other stimuli have been used to influence subsequent dream content. A man who goes to bed thirsty after eating a highly spiced meal tends to dream of thirst and drinking—but not always. A hissing sound played in the ear of a REM dreamer occasionally may evoke a dream of a waterfall. Thus, it appears that body states and outside stimulation may indeed influence our dreams, though not invariably.

Other experiments have revealed that time seems to pass at the same rate in dreams as when awake, although a few dreams may occur in split seconds. In other words, five minutes of dream time are equivalent to five minutes of clock time. Furthermore, many dreams are in color, although sleep-study volunteers often fail to say so unless specifically asked.

Although the biochemistry and neurophysiology of REM sleep are indeed complicated, we are likely to understand these aspects of our nightly dream cycle before we fathom the meanings of the dreams themselves. Whether phrased in evocative Freudian language or the language of neurophysiology, however, it is obvious that the meaning of a dream must be as complex as the dreamer. As yet there is no generally acceptable formula for understanding dream symbols or for giving a quick, unequivocal interpretation of a stranger's dream. Do penile erections mean that every dream is sexual? Is dreaming, as Freud postulated, the bursting forth of repressed drives and wishes in some symbolic form? (*See* Feature Article: FREUD'S PLACE IN MODERN PSYCHIATRY.) Is there a hidden and coded relationship between the dreamer's experiences of fantasy, the contents of his dreams, and the physiological changes in his body? Each new discovery about sleep and dreams seems to make such questions more difficult to answer.

FOR ADDITIONAL READING:

Foulkes, William David, *The Psychology of Sleep* (Charles Scribner's Sons, 1966).

Hartmann, Ernest, *The Biology of Dreaming* (Charles C. Thomas, 1967).

Kleitman, Nathaniel, *Sleep and Wakefulness* (University of Chicago Press, 1963).

Lessing, L., "Sleep," *Fortune* (June 1964).

Luce, Gay Gaer, and Segal, Julius, *Sleep* (Coward-McCann, 1966; Lancer, 1967).

MacKenzie, Norman, *Dreams and Dreaming* (Vanguard Press, 1965).

Freud's Place in Modern Psychiatry
by Paul R. Miller

Mental illness caused by personal relations or defective psychological development? Impossible! So most doctors believed until Sigmund Freud demonstrated otherwise.

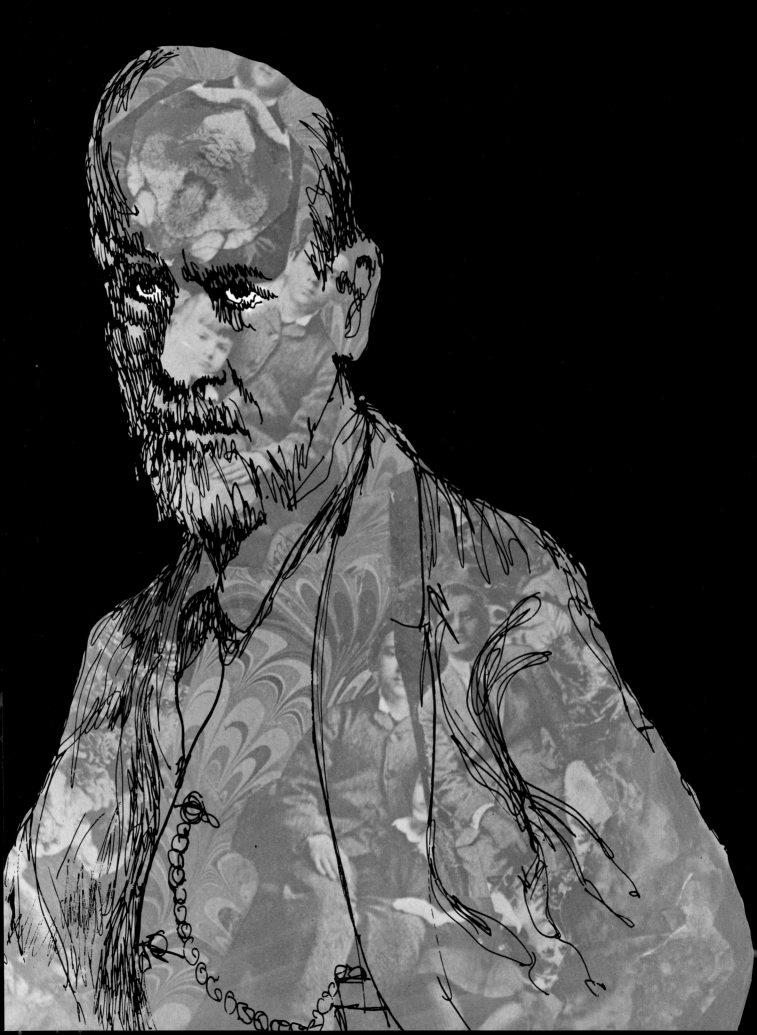

Sigmund Freud, to whom psychiatrists of the last 50 years have been deeply indebted, has been probably one of the most outstanding yet controversial individuals of the 20th century. Praised by those who agreed with him, maligned by those who did not, Freud's work, nevertheless, stands as a monumental milestone in the study and treatment of mental illness. Prior to his time all such disorders were considered simply the product of brain disease. It was Freud, however, who first demonstrated that many neuroses and psychoses may be caused or aggravated by early family or environmental influences or by environmental stress.

Freud's major contributions were in three areas: (1) a theory about unconscious processes in the human mind, (2) a technique for investigating such functions (free association), and (3) a therapy for mental and emotional problems (psychoanalysis). Of the three, his

theory about unconscious processes has been the most relevant to psychiatry for the last 50 years. Moreover, it has had great influence on the art and literature of the 20th century, especially on such writers as James Joyce, D. H. Lawrence, and Eugene O'Neill. It was these men of letters, among others, who made household words of Freud's terms "compensation" and "repression."

Freud's discoveries

Born in 1856, Freud made his basic contributions to psychiatry in the last 15 years of the 19th century. Many of them were published in 1899 in his book *The Interpretation of Dreams.* It is interesting to note, however, that the copyright date of this book was shifted to 1900, indicating its symbolic relation to the new century rather than the old.

One of Freud's most important contributions was his theory of the unconscious, which dominated his life's work. Freud defined the unconscious as "any mental process the existence of which we are obliged to assume—because, for instance, we infer it in some way from its effects—but of which we are not directly aware."

The idea of an unconscious mind was at least as old as the ancient Greeks, and was part of the thinking of many others long before Freud. But it was Freud who added much that was unique. He studied the evidence for unconscious processes in new ways, and his understanding of these processes enabled him to treat psychiatric patients with a new technique (psychoanalysis) that promised results for mental illnesses previously considered untreatable.

Perhaps the simplest example of unconscious influences occurs in what Freud called the "psychopathology of everyday life," in which people misplace objects or forget names and dates. If we think we like a person when we unconsciously dislike him, we may "unintentionally" snub him, or "forget" an appointment with him, or "forget" his name. "I'll never forget good old what's-his-name" is a standard joke implying that "good old what's-his-name" is best forgotten as soon as possible. Not all errors are "Freudian slips," nor are they all worth a lengthy analysis, but some are.

Other important knowledge about unconscious processes came from the study of neurosis by Freud and his collaborator, Josef Breuer, which they documented in the landmark book *Studies on Hysteria,* published in Germany in 1895. By allowing a patient with a hysterical symptom (such as blindness or paralysis not caused by physical injury or disease) to "remember" emotionally painful events while under hypnosis, Freud and Breuer learned that patients might eventually discuss personal experiences that seemed to be connected to the hysterical symptom. These were associations the patient apparently had never consciously made before. Often the patient did not understand their possible meaning until they were interpreted for him. After these experiences had been discussed

321

with the doctor, the symptoms sometimes disappeared, either temporarily or permanently. However, Freud later broke with Breuer and replaced hypnosis with his own technique of "free association" (spontaneous verbalization by the patient of any thought that came to mind, without conscious censorship).

Freud considered his study of unconscious processes in dreams to be his major achievement. (In a self-analysis of his motivations for writing *The Interpretation of Dreams,* Freud concluded that the death of his father released him from an unconscious inhibition against creative writing and thinking.) According to his theory, the dream portrayed a compromise solution of the conflict between instinctual drives and acquired needs to conform to the rules of society, learned first from parental control and later from experience with other people. These two conflicting forces clashed on an unconscious level and produced the dream. In other words, the dream began as a wish (instinct, drive) and continued by being modified by the reality of experience ("the ego"). As a result of his studies, Freud believed that his theory of dreams was the "royal road to the unconscious."

Today this theory is being greatly modified. Modern research on sleep and dreaming has shown that dreams and nightmares are mainly the result of physiological and biochemical variations. It has also been found that dreams occur every one or two hours throughout the night, but only the dream just before waking is remembered. The content of a dream is, of course, a psychological phenomenon, but it seems to be largely random or irrelevant material, although, as might be expected, any intense subject of preoccupation or anxiety may recur again and again. (*See* Feature Article: SLEEP AND DREAMS.)

Freud also sought evidence for influences of earlier experience on a person's current life. He observed that what happened in childhood could be important to the adult many years later. This seemed to hold for relatively normal adults as well as for severely neurotic ones. Freud thought it likely that the child who was reprimanded or punished for sexual curiosity would be sexually inhibited as an adult. He also expected that the child who had no demonstrations of affection from his parents would feel unloved, and as an adult would be less capable of loving others.

Recent experiments with primates at the University of Wisconsin have dramatically confirmed these ideas. Monkeys reared from birth in a wire cage and fed from a bottle, without having any contact with a monkey mother or with playmates, become very "neurotic" adults. They are fearful and incapable of normal relations with other monkeys, including sexual intercourse. If the females reared in this way do have babies, they ignore the babies and do not "mother" them. No way to cure this behavior has been found after the adult stage has been reached. As a result of these and other studies, most researchers now believe that when the nervous system has not formed the right connections at the critical time in infancy and childhood, it is unable to do so later with any treatment. In the case of human beings, an adult whose childhood has been distorted in this way frequently cannot account for his feeling of being unloved, less capable of loving, or sexually inhibited.

Freud's basic theory

Freud himself stated that his basic contribution was *the interpretation of unconscious processes, especially through dream images and dream formation.* There are, however, other aspects of Freud's theory that have played an important role in later thinking. These include his ideas on sexuality (the "libido," which is the source of all energy, including sexual); instincts; childhood origins of neurosis; the structure of "the human mind" ("the ego," "the superego," "the id"); "the Oedipus Complex"; and so on. But none of these other ideas is as basic as his theory of unconscious processes.

Freud concluded that unconscious processes, despite their apparent chaos and contradictions, are orderly and follow definite rules, especially as inferred from dreams. He said that the orderliness is true for content (dream images) and for style or process (dream formation). In dreams the images tend to be visual (less frequently are they images of touch or sound), and are packed with meaning. When enough dreams are collected, common images can be found that usually seem to have the same meaning for one person, and often have the same meaning for different persons. Freud, however, overestimated the universality of dream images. But dream images tend to be consistent in what they symbolize for a person, and many images do suggest a common meaning, at least within a given group or culture.

Freud also said that unconscious processes follow their own rules of "logic." These rules may be quite different from those of conscious thinking, although the latter also includes "daydreaming" and "fantasy." First, the logic of unconscious processes permits "symmetry": a relationship may be equally and exactly reversed. In Aristotelian logic, if John is the father of Peter, then Peter must be

323

the son of John. In Freudian logic of unconscious processes, if John is the father of Peter, then Peter also may be the father of John. Second, unconscious logic permits "classlessness": a relationship between groups may shift back and forth between exclusiveness and inclusiveness. In Aristotelian logic class relations are fixed and irreversible: vertebrates include mammals, which include primates, which include *Homo sapiens* (man). But the reverse is not correct: *Homo sapiens* cannot include all primates, mammals, or vertebrates. In unconscious logic, all of these reverse groupings are possible. But this is not chaos or randomness; it follows definite rules. Perhaps this is similar to the alteration of rules in some types of mathematics, as in the case of non-Euclidean geometry and Boolean algebra, which reverse many traditional rules to make their own kind of sense and lead to new and useful discoveries.

It was Freud's contention that unconscious logic shows its effects in dreams, which were supposed to alter time by reversal, compression, or expansion, and which seemed to change the image of a person to "represent" several other persons or only a part of one person. (Recent studies of the time-duration of dream content have been done by waking people during their dreaming stages, when their eyeballs are moving rapidly under the eyelids. It appears that the dream sequence usually appears to have taken about the same length of time that the person has been dreaming, in spite of these earlier myths to the contrary, which seem to be based on careless observation.) To the extent that such distortions of waking experience appear in dreams, they are understandable according to Freud's theories. Artists seem to have sensed this long before Freud; witness the dreamlike surrealism of Hieronymus Bosch (*c.* 1500). And later James Joyce wrote his novel *Finnegans Wake* (1939) in a kind of dream language that follows the supposed rules of unconscious logic.

The limitations of Freudian theory

Freud was so convinced of the validity of his theory of unconscious processes that he never tested it scientifically. Moreover, his closest followers and disciples have tended to accept all of his other theories as valid also. Except for the theory of unconscious processes, however, most of Freud's other theories have been found to be incorrect, equivocal, or metaphysical (beyond scientific study).

Freud was a neurologist (a physician specializing in diseases of the nervous system) and did some fundamental neurological research. Nevertheless, his biological thinking reflected essentially 19th-century ideas, including such unsophisticated concepts as "energy in the brain." His views of sexual activity, for example, were not basically biological. He saw sexual needs as an accumulation of energy, which he termed libido, that built up like water behind a dam and had to be drained off periodically to relieve the tension that would produce neurotic symptoms. We now know that this is not so. Freud did acknowledge, however, that new biological data would alter his theories, and this is happening today.

Freud's theories about man's sociocultural nature have been criticized as speculative because they have little basis in verifiable, direct experience. As a result, his theories about civilization, anthropology, and religion are generally ignored by empirical scientists.

Behavioral science: a new basis for modern psychiatry

Freudian theory dealt with the mind; it did not extend to all human behavior. Because modern psychiatry attempts to understand the totality of human behavior and to treat all behavioral dysfunctions, a broader basis than Freudian theory provides is necessary.

That broader basis is supplied by what is coming to be called *behavioral science* (sometimes the *behavioral sciences*), a large area of study comparable in size to the whole range of the physical or biological sciences. In studying the totality of human behavior, not just "the mind," behavioral scientists go beyond traditional Freudian limits by trying to integrate biological, psychological, and social behaviors; they view man as a biopsychosocial phenomenon. Behavioral science has the potential to provide the kind of scientific foundation for modern psychiatry that anatomy does for surgery, or physiology and bacteriology do for medicine, or physics does for engineering.

Behavioral science is exactly what the words imply—the study of behavior, using the scientific method. It has been mainly behavioral scientists—not psychoanalysts—who have tested Freud's theories empirically. And it is the behavioral scientists who are providing the basic knowledge from which psychiatry can develop the practical techniques for treating today's human problems.

Some of the research in behavioral science has supported Freud's theory of unconscious processes. In one experiment, for example, subjects were told to push a key with their thumbs when they heard a

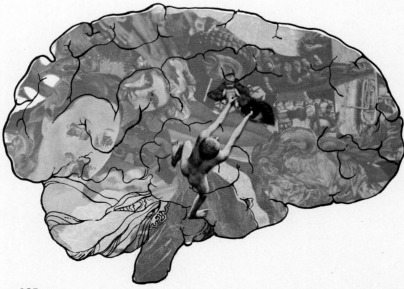

325

bell. A recording pickup was attached to a thumb muscle of each subject; each time this muscle twitched, the bell rang. The twitch of the muscle was so slight that the subjects were not conscious of it, but the twitch was recorded by a machine called an electromyograph. In other words, the subjects were unconscious of the thumb-muscle twitch. While the subjects continued to push the key each time they heard the bell (which was activated by the muscle twitch), the sound of the bell was gradually reduced to zero. Still, the subjects continued to push the key whenever the thumb muscle twitched, because they had *unconsciously* learned to respond to the other real stimulus—the muscle twitch—even though they were not aware of the twitch or of learning to respond to it. When asked why they continued to push the key, none could answer correctly. Many subjects made up answers; others said they still heard the bell.

The study of sleep and dreams is another area in which behavioral science is demonstrating its technical ability to explain human behavior as biopsychosocial events. Current research suggests that the rapid-eye-movement (REM) period of sleep is biological, the dream that occurs during this period is psychological, and the discussion of the dream and its interpretation are social. Thus, behavioral science enables the clinician to cross the boundaries between man's systems and to integrate them.

Freud, psychiatry, and social problems

Our brave new world in the last third of the 20th century has gone far to ensure our survival through the maintenance of physical health and the prevention of many devastating diseases; the production of abundant food; the construction of cities linked by mass transportation and communication; and the development of multiple sources of energy, including atomic fission. In spite of these technological advances, however, society is faced with greater problems than at any time in history: the threat of nuclear war, the population explosion, poverty, conflicts between groups (especially blacks and whites), crime, mental illness, and the decay of our cities. These problems are all related to the triumphs of technology: medical science has reduced infant mortality and death from infection, thereby contributing to the population explosion; engineering permits us to build vertical cities, which breed poverty and crime; splitting the atom poses the threat of nuclear war.

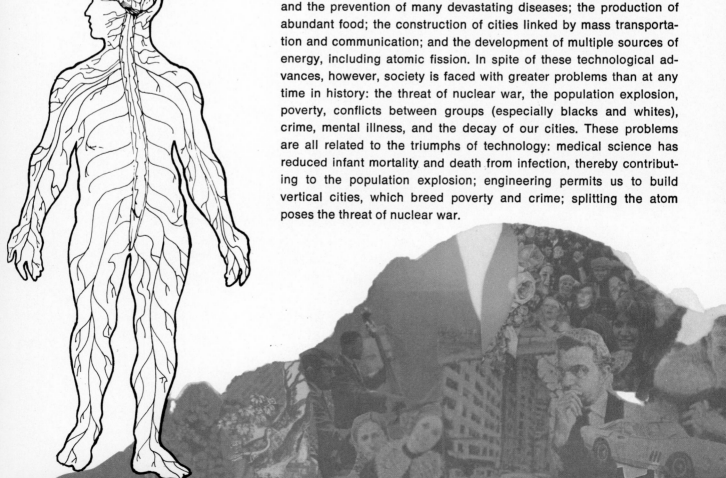

All of these problems are uniquely social, not physical or biological. In the past we have ignored social problems while giving priority to the solution of physical and biological problems. But we are now at a critical point: we must decide how much we are going to shift our resources to solving these broader human problems.

During the era of technology in Western culture (roughly the last 200 years), the little empirical attention given to human problems came mainly from the fields of medicine and psychiatry. Psychiatry, however, is now reconsidering its role. Instead of confining itself to its traditional field of mental illness only, psychiatry is broadening its focus from mental and emotional disturbances to the whole spectrum of human behavior and its problems. In order to study current social problems and to devise new methods of coping with them, psychiatry is shifting its emphasis from the Freudian theory of the mind to the behavioral science of man.

Man needs the discipline of science in developing his understanding of human behavior. Behavioral science promises help with the human problems of living, just as the physical sciences have helped us manage our physical environment and the biological sciences have helped us control disease. Freud's place in this process is now mainly historical. He gave us one great discovery, the function of unconscious processes, which was a major contribution to the understanding of human behavior. Now, however, our concern must extend beyond the study of man's mind to the totality of human behavior. The challenge of the present is to seek the biopsychosocial knowledge necessary to understand and treat the social problems of today and tomorrow.

FOR ADDITIONAL READING:

Freud, Sigmund, *The Interpretation of Dreams* (Basic Books, 1955).

Gorer, Geoffrey, *et al., Psychoanalysis Observed* (Coward-McCann, 1967).

Miller, Paul R., *Sense and Symbol* (Hoeber Medical Division, Harper & Row, 1967).

Seeley, John R., *The Americanization of the Unconscious* (International Science Press, 1967).

Whyte, Lancelot, *The Unconscious Before Freud* (Basic Books, 1960).

AUDIOVISUAL MATERIALS FROM ENCYCLOPÆDIA
BRITANNICA EDUCATIONAL CORPORATION:

Film: *Karl Menninger.*

Exploring the Ocean Frontiers
by Edward Wenk, Jr.

The rapidly expanding world population is forcing oceanographers and statesmen to intensify their studies of potential marine resources. The Executive Secretary of the U.S. Council on Marine Resources and Engineering Development analyzes the discoveries of marine scientists and their plans for future exploration and exploitation of the oceans.

In all of the satellite photographs taken of the earth, the predominant feature has been the blue of the world's oceans. This has confirmed what geographers have long known—that the earth is a water planet, and that its 330 million cu mi of water cover 70.8% of its surface. Despite the fact that almost three-quarters of the earth's surface is water, scientists have only begun to comprehend the seas and nations have only begun to develop their potential to serve man. (*See* Year in Review: ASTRONAUTICS AND SPACE EXPLORATION, *Earth-Oriented Satellites.*)

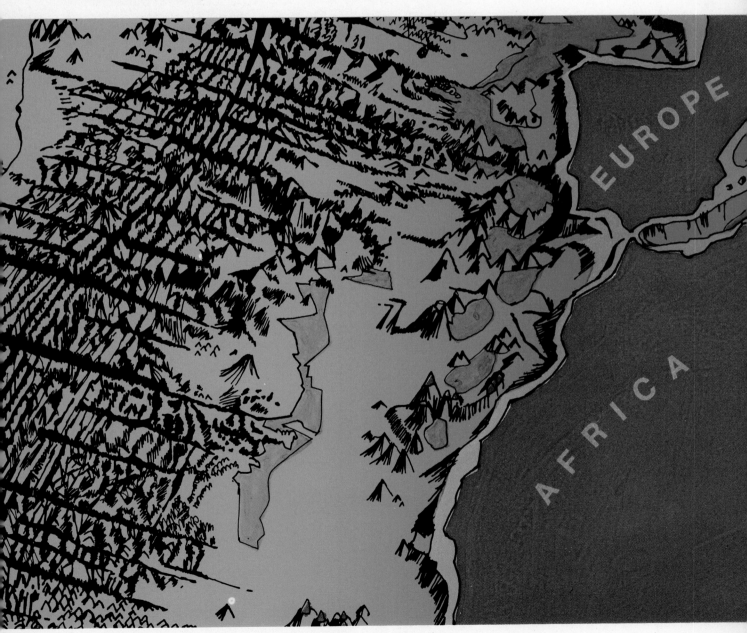

Since the middle of the 19th century, scientists have rigorously analyzed the motions and the contents of the sea. They have probed the energy generated by its tides, waves, and surges and they have mapped the great horizontal surface, the submarine currents, and the powerful upthrusting vertical currents near the continents. Oceanographers have charted the bottom topography of the seabed with its shallow continental shelves, slopes, and submarine canyons that plunge abruptly to almost seven miles below sea level—much farther below the sea than Mt. Everest is above. These charts describe broad sweeping abyssal plains, freckled with volcanic mountains called "seamounts" and flat-topped mountains called "guyots." They have been used to pinpoint pockets of oil and gas locked in the seabed and mineral-rich, potato-shaped manganese nodules resting on the ocean floor.

Biologists, working with oceanographers, have counted tens of thousands of different species of animal and plant life inhabiting the oceans, from microscopic bacteria and miniscule plankton to 100-ton whales—life that swims, drifts, or rides piggyback as a parasite. Swirling interactions have been found at the boundaries of the sea, between sea and coast, between sea and seabed, and between sea and atmosphere. And meteorologists have studied the interaction between ocean and atmosphere where energy and matter are exchanged to generate our global weather and ocean water evaporates to become the source of rain, snow, and the polar ice caps.

During the 1960s, man's relationship with the sea has undergone spectacular changes. The importance of the ocean as an aid in meeting the pressing needs of society has been realized by governments as well as scientists. Along with the rapid progress in technology, the concerned interest of individual nations in shaping policies and developing institutions has facilitated cooperative approaches to international problem-solving. The concept of oceanography as a pure science has become archaic. The application of oceanographic discoveries affects more than the scientist and university professor. It affects the engineer, industrialist, fisherman, vacationer, government official, and diplomat as well.

At depths of 2,000 to 3,000 ft aquanauts will live in a mysterious world of exotic sea creatures. The shrimp-like Sergestic prawns (below), about an inch long, were netted at 3,000 ft. Galathan crabs (right), shown clinging to a black coral tree with which they are believed to have a symbiotic relationship, were photographed at 1,200 ft on the Coronado Escarpment off the California coast. The sea anemones on the opposite page are attached to a rock deposited off the Connecticut coast by glacial action.

The coastal zone

Man's exploitation of the sea has been most extensive where land
and sea meet—in the coastal zone. Most of the world's population
has settled within a short distance of the sea, or along the navigable
rivers leading to the sea. In the United States, for example, 75% of
the population inhabits states bordering on a 17,000-mi coastline
and 45% of its urban population lives directly on the coast. Because
the bulk cargoes of ore, fuel, and chemicals, which underpin a technological society, are transported easily by sea, the majority of the
nation's heavy industry has always been attracted to the coastal
zone. Moreover, the industrial concentration generates further com-

331

Even as man explores the oceans, he threatens them with pollution. Oil from a leak caused by offshore drilling operations was washed ashore near Santa Barbara, Calif., in 1969, fouling beaches and killing thousands of seabirds. Waste heat, which endangers temperature-sensitive fish, is illustrated by the thermogram (below, right), showing heat pollution in the Connecticut River near an electric power plant. The black and blue areas represent the coolest water; the red and magenta areas, the hottest.

mercial markets and labor pools, so that by the year 2000, most of our megalopolises, the super cities, should be packed along the coastal zone.

Long before they were utilized by man, the coastal zone's estuaries and lagoons, wetlands and beaches, were sanctuaries for waterfowl, nurseries for coastal fisheries, and habitats of a rich variety of plants and animals. But the coastal ecology is fragile and perishable, and some of the most fearsome ravages of nature visit there each year, eroding beaches and filling channels. (*See* Feature Article: NATURE ON THE RAMPAGE.) But much more damaging have been the vast quantities of municipal and industrial wastes, the chemicals —pesticides and fertilizers—and the hot waters poured into the convenient sink of the sea, polluting the brackish waters and the freshwater streams and the swamplands. These wastes kill many forms of animal life, thus upsetting nature's balance; in some instances, marine organisms concentrate these pollutants and pass them on through the food chain. A stark example of extensive destruction is Lake Erie, which has actually been suffocating to death in man-made pollutants. In the Soviet Union as well, scientists and conservationists have been fighting to preserve the polluted Lake Baikal.

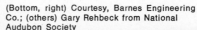

(Bottom, right) Courtesy, Barnes Engineering Co.; (others) Gary Rehbeck from National Audubon Society

In the mid-1960s, a new peril emerged: the threat of massive oil pollution from wrecked tankers such as the "Torrey Canyon," which ran aground off England in 1967, and the "Ocean Eagle," which broke up off Puerto Rico in 1968, and from runaway underwater oil wells such as those that fouled the Santa Barbara Channel, Calif., in 1969. Even greater hazards could result from the 300,000-ton supertankers (roughly 15 times larger than their counterparts of World War II) and the increased amount of offshore deep-sea drilling.

Simply stated, there is an increasing pressure for more intense and more variegated use of a scarce, perishable resource. Solutions must be found that will provide for the many diverse and often conflicting coastal demands, public and private, while still preserving the ocean environment so that it will continue to yield long-term social and economic benefits. Science and engineering are tools in this undertaking. The wise and prudent use of our water resources involves planned management of bays, estuaries, and coastal lands. It means setting water-quality standards and shaping an administrative and legal framework to promote an optimal balance among uses and conservation.

The technologies, employed to facilitate commerce, that have brought about this ecological imbalance have also been employed to combat it—for example, chemical compounds have been manufactured that will disperse oil slicks without doing more harm to the sea and shore life. Also, a new branch of biological engineering has emerged that studies the feasibility of stabilizing beaches with grass, moving river-spawning fish over dams, exploiting offshore platforms as fish havens, and employing estuaries for intensive mariculture (aquiculture). So man has utilized science and engineering to assist him in defining the ecological balance; in describing the natural forces at work and predicting the consequences of man's activities; in managing the ocean resources; in controlling water quality, inhibiting beach erosion, fostering construction of offshore airports, nuclear power plants, or supertanker terminals; and in sculpturing the coastline so as to enhance the earth's natural endowment. (*See* Year in Review: ENVIRONMENTAL SCIENCES.)

Food for a growing population

Since World War II, the world seafood catch has grown at a faster rate than agricultural production. In 1968 it amounted to over 60 million tons (live weight), and was valued at $7 billion. Even conservative estimates have indicated that the world fish catch could be increased at least 4 and perhaps 40 times without depleting stocks. With advances in marine research, it has been possible to predict the distribution and abundance of fishery stocks and thus provide a sound basis for fish harvests of optimum yield consistent with resource-conservation policy.

Marine technology has advanced the art of fish finding and

harvesting so that greater numbers of rare as well as common species can be caught more efficiently. It is expected that men will eventually look to aquiculture to cultivate, augment, herd, and select fish. Raised in suitable estuaries, artificially cultured fish could yield more protein per acre than beef cattle or grain.

Almost every study of human nutrition has concluded with the view that the scale, severity, and duration of the world's food problems are massive, so great in fact that only a long-range, innovative effort unprecedented in human history can master them. Food from the sea offers a partial answer; fish are 15% protein and contain a favorable amino acid balance necessary for the human diet. Modern engineering has made possible the production of fish protein concentrate (FPC)—a pure, tasteless, odorless, and relatively imperishable powder, made from whole fish, that can be added to other foods as a dietary supplement. FPC could be manufactured to meet a child's minimum daily protein requirement of ten grams for about one cent. (*See* Year in Review: ENGINEERING, *Chemical Engineering;* FOOD AND NUTRITION.)

Energy and minerals for an industrialized society

After World War II, industrialists began to turn to the sea for energy, principally from petroleum and gas. During the 1960s, fuel was produced from some 6,000 offshore wells on the continental shelf of the United States and eight other countries. In 1968, offshore petroleum production accounted for 16% of the world output, and was expected to comprise 30 to 40% by the year 2000. Gas, too, was extracted from seabed reserves, but this supplied only a small amount of the world's total gas production.

Virtually all existing offshore wells have been drilled into the continental shelf (the submerged coastal terrace between 400 and 600 ft in depth, extending an average of 50 mi seaward). The world's continental shelves comprise an area equal to one-quarter of the continents; in such countries as Canada and Indonesia, the contiguous shelf almost doubles the land area. Few of these expansive undersea extensions of the continent have been surveyed, but the increasing demand for shelf resources has precluded any further delay. (*See* Year in Review: FUEL AND POWER.)

The world's demand for minerals has also increased rapidly and was expected to double by 1980. The ocean holds and hides an abundance of minerals—placer deposits of gold; ilmenite and diamonds; shallow-water commercial concentrations of sand, gravel, oyster shells, and lime mud; deep-ocean nodules containing cobalt, nickel, copper, manganese, and other metals; phosphorite; metalliferous muds rich in copper and zinc; and others. The demand for these natural resources will necessarily mount as world markets grow and improved technology makes marine sources competitive with terrestrial ones.

The deep-sea drilling project ship "Glomar Challenger," depicted in the schematic drawing on the opposite page, must remain in a stable position while 400,000 lb of flexible pipe are lowered 20,000 ft into the water. Pulses from acoustic beacons on the ocean floor, shown beaming toward the ship, are fed into an especially designed computer, which automatically makes the delicate adjustments needed to keep the ship on station.

Technological development

In the past, man's innate curiosity about the world around him has been the strongest motivation for his study of the ocean. But in order to satisfy the increasing demands for more productive use of the ocean, he needs a great deal more knowledge about the marine environment. Obtaining that knowledge is the task of the oceanographer and marine scientist. Oceanography (or, as some prefer, oceanology) is not a single science but a composite of many basic sciences applied to the marine environment: biology, geology, chemistry, physics, mathematics. Synthesizing these specialized branches of knowledge is the domain of descriptive oceanography, and complementing them are all the fields of engineering—civil, mechanical, electrical, and metallurgical.

The science of oceanography was not quite 100 years old in 1969. (Most oceanographers give 1872 as the year of its birth, when the HMS "Challenger" weighed anchor and set off on its three-year round-the-world cruise.) In less than 100 years of investigation since the "Challenger" expedition, the ocean sciences have yielded some remarkable discoveries. Since World War II, especially, oceanographers have learned much about the topography of the ocean floor. They have discovered the 40,000-mi mid-ocean ridge, which reaches upward, in places, 15,000 ft from the ocean bottom and curves in a great arc from the Arabian Peninsula to the Crozet Islands. They have found that land and seabed rocks are distinctly different and that the continents' granitic base is lighter and thicker than the seabed's basaltic crust. They have discovered evidence of a ridge-rift system throughout all ocean basins which has led to a new concept of sea-floor spreading that may hold the key to the origin and development of ocean basins and continents and may help unravel the riddle of the earth's structural history. They have unveiled vast, unsuspected subsurface countercurrents, as big and as powerful as the Gulf Stream, flowing underneath the known surface currents. And they have brought up the curious and rich mineral nodules that rest in vast quantities on the deep-ocean floor.

The ocean is the primary source of much of the world's weather and the source of most of the moisture upon which life depends. With a better understanding of the relationships of the total land-air-sea environment, oceanographers, working with meteorologists, will be better able to predict, influence, and perhaps control weather phenomena—a matter of major importance to everyone.

Since the early days of the space age, scientists have had the advantage of observations from spacecraft that have enabled them to ascertain and study sea temperatures, currents, wave conditions, and underwater conditions in clear, shallow coastal areas. Unmanned buoys, which were to be established in a worldwide network, would provide periodic data transmissions about sea conditions below the surface and above, via satellite to central data banks.

335

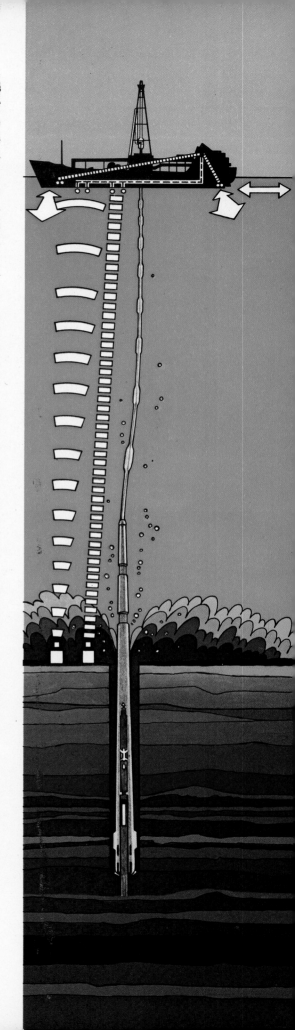

Sonar has been used to locate and sample fish populations. Underwater television has made possible reconnaissance at almost any depth; wreckage of the USS "Scorpion" was sighted in more than 10,000 ft of water. Geological cores have been taken of sediments at depths of many thousands of feet.

On Aug. 19, 1968, the deep-sea drilling vessel "Glomar Challenger" held station in 11,720 ft of water and drilled 422 ft into the bottom of the Gulf of Mexico, locating oil indications. The vessel participated in the National Science Foundation's National Ocean Sediment Coring Program, which was planned and guided by members of the Joint Oceanographic Institutions for Deep Earth Sampling (JOIDES), and which included a number of leading U.S. universities and oceanographic institutions. Later in 1968 the vessel set a drilling record for a ship in 17,567 ft of water, before starting out on other exploratory drilling assignments on the Mid-Atlantic Ridge and in the Pacific Ocean. The "Glomar Challenger" was a specially designed drilling vessel with a dynamic positioning system that enabled the ship to remain on station while drilling. The ship was one of the first nonmilitary vessels to use a new navigation satellite for precise positioning to within 200 yd.

As is true in all sciences, discoveries raise more questions than they answer. Unlocking the secret of the oceans with conventional ships and instruments would be an overwhelming task, involving hundreds of ships for decades. With advancing ocean technology, however, tasks once considered unaccomplishable in the ocean's demanding and corrosive environment have begun to yield to human initiative and skill. With the aid of modern technology, man has learned more about the oceans since 1940 than he had in the preceding 2,000 years.

Man in the sea

Nowhere is the new ocean technology more dramatic in its extension of the scientist's abilities to observe than in the development of an effective way to put man himself in the sea—either in deep-diving research submersibles or with a self-contained underwater breathing apparatus (SCUBA) strapped to his back. More than any other single tool, the deep submersible has added a new dimension to man's quest to use the sea.

The first such vehicle, a bathyscaphe, was built in 1948 under the direction of Swiss scientist-engineer Auguste Piccard. This device was an underwater blimp that gained its vertical mobility by means of a large gasoline-filled buoyancy tank. The second bathyscaphe, "Trieste," skippered by Piccard's son Jacques and an American, Don Walsh, although cumbersome and without much horizontal mobility, made a record-breaking descent of 35,800 ft into the Mariana Trench in 1960.

The second generation of such vehicles were designed as true submarines which gained depth capabilities by using high-strength materials in the pressure hull. "Aluminaut," the first such design, was distinctive because of its 15,000-ft depth capability—fully 20 times that of the true submarines then operating. Construction of the "Aluminaut" was undertaken in the early 1960s with private rather than governmental funds and initiative. Following that technological pioneering, more than 30 submersibles have been developed in the United States alone. Scientists and industrial workers have been able to use these vessels to study and work on the ocean bottom and to examine resources and marine life.

In 1969, the U.S. Navy's five-man nuclear research vessel NR-1 joined this underwater fleet. The NR-1 was distinctive because of its nuclear power plant, which was a marked advance over the range-limited battery power of its deep-diving precursors. Another submersible, the "Benjamin Franklin," was launched late in 1968 and gained immediate recognition because its first mission, expected to begin in 1969, was to drift submerged in the Gulf Stream.

One group of these vehicles under construction by the U.S. Navy was intended for undersea search, rescue, and recovery. These submarines, small enough to be air-transportable to any location in an emergency, were expected to be deployed primarily to assist disabled submarines. These minisubs would ride piggyback on a mother sub to the site of the disaster, where they would join to the hatch of the stricken sub to allow the safe transfer of personnel.

All of these vehicles were to be equipped with portholes for viewing, underwater communications systems and cameras, as well as special manipulators for doing work while submerged. But no substitute has been invented for the human diver, who is able to observe and to perform all of the necessary tasks with the aid of special tools.

Jules Verne's hero Captain Nemo and his crew explore the ocean depths in a scene from a 1954 movie adaptation of 20,000 Leagues Under the Sea. *Written in 1870, Verne's book described a submarine and sophisticated diving gear prefiguring that in use today.*

The U.S. Navy's Man-in-the-Sea project, France's Pre-Continent operations, and the Ketzeh operation by the Soviet Union have sought to develop new equipment to enable man to live and work under water—eventually at a depth of 1,000 ft. Should these techniques be successful it would be possible to engage in any type of industrial activity—oil production, mining, or aquiculture—on the bed of the continental shelf as easily as on land. In fact, in a series of U.S. Navy Sealab experiments, aquanauts have lived in habitats on the ocean floor at depths of 200 ft for several weeks. In Sealab III, which began in February 1969 and which was temporarily suspended because of the death of one of the divers, aquanauts used saturated diving techniques in 600 ft of water off San Clemente Island, Calif. (The word "saturation" refers to the physiological conditions of their bodies under gas pressure.) The men were to live in an artificial helium and oxygen atmosphere with the pressure equalized to that of the surrounding seawater, enabling them to swim in and out without need for decompression. Along with the Sealab project, a joint industry-government program, called Tektite, was conducted early in 1969 in the Virgin Islands. This operation placed four scientists on the ocean floor at shallow depths for a record-breaking 60 days using saturated-diving techniques.

International cooperation

Approximately 100 nations front on the sea, and as they expand their activities in the oceans with new technology for exploitation, the likelihood of conflict increases. Some countries have already asserted jurisdiction hundreds of miles seaward, thus diminishing the traditional freedom of the seas. Long-range fishing fleets of certain countries have threatened coastal fisheries historically essential to others, and the possibility for stationing weapons of mass destruction on the sea floor has raised the specter of an arms race in the oceans.

The U.S. Navy's Sealab deep-ocean habitat (opposite page, top) is lowered to a site 610 ft below the surface. Bottom, the General Oceanics research submersible "Nekton," capable of descending 1,000 ft, prepares to dive. Below, left, a diver examines the Tektite underwater laboratory, which housed four scientists for 60 days in 1969. Center, an ancient amphora is found on the ocean floor. Right, a deep-sea current-measuring device has been carefully positioned for accuracy by a specially built submersible, rather than lowered from a ship.

(Left) Courtesy, General Electric, (center) Flip Schulke from Black Star, (right) Ron Church

Because the seas are so vast and generally beyond national sovereignty, international cooperation has been widespread in oceanography for many years. The International Geophysical Year (1957–59) was a healthy stimulus to cooperative efforts begun earlier, particularly because an international exchange of data from scientific investigations was encouraged. Since then, much successful international collaborative planning has been undertaken, including the International Indian Ocean Expedition (1962–65), the International Cooperative Investigation of the Tropical Atlantic (1963), and the Cooperative Study of the Kuroshio Current (1965–69). International fisheries commissions have been empowered to study, to conserve, and to regulate regional fisheries.

Since 1960, intergovernmental and scientific interest in the oceans has grown markedly. In that year, the secretary-general of the United Nations undertook a study of the importance of marine resources. In 1967, Malta proposed internationalizing the seabed, and the UN General Assembly appointed a 35-nation ad hoc committee to study the issue. In general, the discussion of the oceans by the United Nations has revolved around questions of cooperation in research and exploration, the reservation of the seabed for peaceful purposes, and the establishment of guidelines for nations in the use of the sea and seabed. In 1968, the General Assembly created a 42-nation standing committee, replacing the ad hoc committee, which has held productive preliminary discussions on creating meaningful, workable principles to guide the international community in the marine environment. Ahead lie complex problems such as determining the seaweed limit of national jurisdiction and establishing an international regime to govern seabed activities beyond this limit.

The two-man submersible SP 350 retrieves a sample from the ocean floor. Developed by the French, who have pioneered in underwater exploration, the SP 350 is capable of descending to 350 m (1,148 ft).

Photos, Les Requins Associés

During the 1968–69 period, moreover, the science of the sea entered a new phase marked by increasing world interest, expanding activities, and greater emphasis on international collaboration. One major step in this development was the U.S. proposal on March 8, 1968, for an International Decade of Ocean Exploration. Building on existing scientific exchanges, the Decade would involve close coordination among nations and international organizations. Its goal would be the determination of the distribution of fish and mineral resources and the development of the oceanographic capabilities of individual nations.

Looking to exploration of its continental shelf through the combined efforts of government and industry, France has outlined a six-year program which began in 1969 and was expected to cost $200 million. The program called for the construction of a National Oceanographic Center at Brest employing 400 persons. Late in 1968, Germany announced a four-year oceanographic program which would cost the government $50 million by 1971. Japan's 1969 marine science budget of $8.8 million for developing ocean technology, exploiting the continental shelf, and investigating the ocean doubled the budget of the previous year. Oceanographic expenditures in Canada doubled between 1965 and 1967. Chile established a Committee of Investigation of the Resources of the Sea and Continental Waters at the university level. Israel opened a new Marine Biological Station, and Italy established a similar institute on the northeast Adriatic near Trieste.

Many of these nations and their industrial sectors have developed and put into use sophisticated oceanographic technology. The French have had a highly advanced submersible and man-in-the-sea program since 1948. The Soviet Union has experimented with diver

An aquanaut leaves the "Etoile de Mer," an underwater base and garage for the SP 350 located at a depth of 11 m (35 ft). The base can house six aquanauts for one week.

Courtesy, John H. Dearborn, University of Maine

Oceanographic research ship "Hero," the first vessel to be stationed permanently in Antarctica, lies at anchor off Anvers Island near the Antarctic Peninsula. Built with a wooden hull and outfitted with sails, the "Hero" carries a modern research laboratory equipped for the study of volcanoes, marine life, and ocean currents.

teams living in shallow water habitats and, in March 1969, completed tests of its first deep-diving submarine. In 1968, Britain unveiled a mobile sea-bottom vehicle and habitat projected to operate for salvage and other bottom work for several days at 600 ft. The Germans have made plans to undertake a man-in-the-sea experiment at a 200-ft depth off Heligoland in the North Sea. Japan and Australia have announced intentions to study jointly the sea floor off northern Australia during 1969 in a 45-ft Japanese submersible.

In 1966, with the passage of the Marine Resources and Development Act, the United States took a major step toward a systematic exploration and development of the marine environment. This act declared it to be the policy of the United States "to develop, encourage, and maintain a coordinated, comprehensive and long-range national program in marine science for the benefit of mankind."

Looking to the future, the Marine Sciences Act established a

342

public advisory commission to recommend the major steps in a plan for developing the oceans that would reflect the long-term interests of the U.S. government. The commission submitted its report in January 1969. Among its broad-ranging recommendations, it called for U.S. government reorganization in the marine sciences, which would pull together many of the agencies, now organizationally separated, into a new National Oceanic and Atmospheric Agency. In the words of the commission, the organization would serve as a "strong Federal focus for marine activity . . . essential to a national effort [to] direct a civil program to the Nation's economic and social needs, conducting the scientific, technological, and management programs required to ensure that those needs are met." The commission recommended that the agency study the possibility of support for coastal-zone authorities, designation of national and coastal-zone laboratories, development of a legal regime for the deep seabed, and establishment of national marine engineering projects, such as a continental-shelf laboratory. Some have referred to the proposed agency as a "wet NASA."

As man looks to his future relationship to the sea, it is evident that the 1960s have been a turning point. The time now seems propitious for us to move seaward. We need the ocean's resources; we have developed the technology to exploit them. As we move across the continental shelf and reach toward the ocean floor, we face complex new questions of how we can best mobilize our resources to meet our needs. While the task is formidable, its accomplishment promises to inspire and reward those who accept the challenge to probe the secrets of the sea. (*See* Year in Review: OCEANOGRAPHY.)

See also *1969 Britannica Yearbook of Science and the Future,* Feature Article: STUDYING THE EARTH.

FOR ADDITIONAL READING:

Carson, Rachel, *The Sea Around Us* (Oxford University Press, 1961).

Gaskell, T. F., *World Beneath the Oceans* (Natural History Press, 1965).

Hardy, Sir Alister Clavering, *The Open Sea: Its Natural History* (Houghton Mifflin Company, 1965).

Joyce, E. A., Jr., "Project Hourglass Explores the Continental Shelf," *Sea Frontiers,* pp. 352–359 (November 1968).

Pell, Claiborne, and Goodwin, Harold L., *Challenge of the Seven Seas* (Morrow, 1966).

Shepard, F. P., *The Earth Beneath the Sea* (Johns Hopkins, 1967).

Stewart, H. B., *Deep Challenge* (Van Nostrand, 1966).

AUDIOVISUAL MATERIALS FROM ENCYCLOPÆDIA BRITANNICA EDUCATIONAL CORPORATION:

Films: *Ocean Tides; The Beach—A River of Sand; Waves on Water.*

Filmstrips: *Oceanography: Understanding Our Deep Frontier.*

When Young Children Go Hungry: Effects on Learning and Behavior
by Nevin S. Scrimshaw

Terrible in itself, malnutrition in young children may have long-range effects on learning and behavior. An expert on nutrition examines the evidence and the implications, especially for the less developed nations.

The hunger of children is always heartrending, whether it occurs in the Biafran countryside, in an Indian village, or in the pockets of poverty that mock the affluence of today's industrialized societies. Yet there is strong and growing evidence that the immediate suffering may be only one, and perhaps not the most significant, of its effects. Malnutrition in the young child during the crucial period of most rapid growth may result in physical underdevelopment and mental impairment in the adult.

The report of an International Conference on the Effect of Malnutrition on Mental Development, Learning, and Behavior, held at the Massachusetts Institute of Technology, Cambridge, in March 1967,

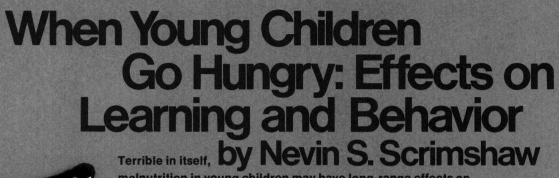

emphasizes that in both experimental animals and man either malnutrition or social deprivation at an early age can have a pronounced adverse effect on subsequent physical and mental development. The report concludes that in less developed countries malnutrition is likely to be a major factor in both the smaller size and the poorer test performance of children, and that its effects on mental development are generally reinforced by an inferior social and educational environment. In industrialized countries, on the other hand, social factors are probably mainly responsible for the impaired intellectual and school performance of underprivileged children, although in some individuals malnutrition may be involved.

The magnitude of the problem becomes apparent immediately. Experts estimate that millions of young children in less developed countries may be experiencing some degree of permanent retardation as a result of inadequate nutrition. These malnourished children of today will be the young adults on whose performance the economic and social progress of their countries will depend in the decades ahead.

Physical effects of early malnutrition in animals

The urgency and seriousness of the problem of early malnutrition in children can best be appreciated by first reviewing some of the evidence from experiments with animals, since such experiments are relatively uncomplicated by social and psychological factors. This evidence will serve as background for a review of the growing number of long-term field studies of the physical and mental development of groups of malnourished children in various parts of the world.

When rats, which are weaned at about 21 days, are subjected to a relatively short period of severe undernutrition immediately after weaning, their brains are smaller than normal at maturity. This is true even if the rats receive a balanced diet before and after the period of deprivation. If malnutrition is produced during the nursing period by having 12 to 14 rats suckle a single mother, rather than a normal litter of 6 to 10, subsequent brain growth is affected still more, even when the diet after 21 days is adequate. Similar results have been obtained with pigs, in which the nursing period normally lasts eight to ten weeks. In both rats and pigs 80% of adult brain size is achieved by the normal weaning time, compared with only 20% of the anticipated body weight at maturity. Clearly, the brain is vulnerable to damage as a result of malnutrition during the period when it is growing rapidly.

A number of recent experimental studies have shown that changes in brain size are accompanied by alterations in the distribution and appearance of nerve cells in the brain. Formation of the sheath around certain nerve fibers is defective in animals malnourished at an early age, even after a long period of refeeding. In studies by

Biafran children, victims of famine brought on by the Nigerian civil war, show the classic physical signs of starvation. For those who survive, the future may hold a lifetime shadowed by mental impairment.

S. Heydinger © The Daily Telegraph Magazine from Pictorial Parade

346

R. J. C. Stewart and B. S. Platt at the National Institute for Medical Research in London, young pigs fed low-protein diets also showed abnormalities in the nuclei of certain large motor nerve cells in the spinal cord, swelling of the nerve sheaths, and some loss of nerve cells from key areas of the brain. These changes persisted in spite of an extended refeeding period.

Myron Winick and his collaborators at Cornell University Medical School have made important contributions toward understanding the timing of nutritional effects on the brain and central nervous system. Since the amount of deoxyribonucleic acid (DNA) in the nucleus of each cell is constant for a given species, the total amount of DNA in an organ is a measure of the number of cells it contains. By determining the quantity of DNA in the brains of rats subjected to various periods of malnutrition and refeeding, Winick found that those fed during the first 21 days following birth as part of a litter of 18 had fewer brain cells than normal, even if they were well nourished after weaning. If they received only half of their caloric requirements during the second 21 days, the number of cells at maturity was below normal in some organs but not in the brain and lungs. Caloric restriction during the third 21-day period had no permanent effect on the number of cells in any tissue.

Rats nursed in litters of only three had an above average weight for every organ, both at the time of weaning and at maturity; they also showed a clear increase in the number of cells in the brain. When the mothers were chronically undernourished before and during pregnancy, their young were small at birth and the number of brain cells was below normal. However, if these smaller progeny were well nourished from birth onward by being foster-nursed in small litters, the damage that occurred during pregnancy was corrected; at least, organ weight and number of brain cells were normal at 21 days.

Behavioral effects of early malnutrition in animals

The evidence from experimental work with animals leaves no doubt that the function of the nervous system, as well as its morphology, can be seriously and permanently impaired by malnutrition during the nursing and early postweaning periods. The severely undernourished pigs produced by Stewart and Platt walked on tiptoe, with a stiff-legged "hobble-skirt gait," and stumbled readily. Electroencephalography revealed an increase and irregularity of the slow brain wave components and a striking decrease in the fast ones. The changes were still more pronounced in animals that had been forced to consume greater amounts of carbohydrate relative to protein.

Stewart and Platt also found that in puppies born of and suckled by mothers fed a protein-calorie-deficient diet, abnormalities present at weaning gradually disappeared when the animals were given

Courtesy, Richard H. Barnes, Cornell University

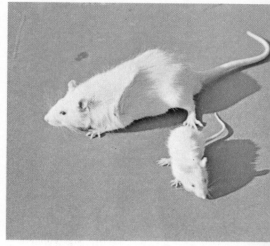

Both of these rats are eight weeks old. The large rat was well nourished during the three-week nursing period and was weaned to a diet containing 25% protein. The small rat, restricted in its milk intake during nursing and weaned to a diet containing 3% protein, shows symptoms resembling those of human infants suffering from marasmus, a form of severe, generalized malnutrition.

a high-protein diet. Puppies born of and nursed by normal mothers stopped gaining weight when they were given a generally deficient diet following weaning. At about 11 weeks of age they developed fine head tremors and stiffness of the hind legs. They ran less and lost interest in their environment. When the puppies were weaned onto diets specifically restricted in protein, the head tremors were more marked and the gait was stiff-legged and unsteady. The animals were restless and excited, and a few had convulsions. After the dogs had been on an improved diet for some time, these signs receded but rarely disappeared. When the puppies were born of and nursed by malnourished mothers and were weaned onto either generally deficient or protein-deficient diets, the changes were still more dramatic; convulsions were frequent and behavior remained decidedly abnormal even after long periods of refeeding.

Richard Barnes and collaborators at Cornell University imposed varying degrees of malnutrition on pigs from the 3rd through the 11th week of life. The pigs were then fed a nutritionally adequate diet for a period of five to nine months, after which behavioral studies were carried out. Animals initially fed a diet low in protein relative to calories were able to learn a conditioned stimulus normally but were unable to adapt to changed conditions as quickly as animals with no history of malnutrition.

To induce nutritional deprivation, the group at Cornell University also used the technique of foster-nursing rats in large litters from the 2nd to the 21st day of life, placing newly weaned rats on a very low protein diet for eight weeks, or applying both procedures to the same animals. Five to nine months after rehabilitation from these forms of malnutrition, the rats were studied in a discrimination test involving a Y-shaped water maze. A significantly higher rate of learning was consistently observed in the control rats than in the doubly deprived ones; singly deprived rats showed intermediate or inconsistent differences in learning ability.

The findings of John Cowley, now at Belfast (N.Ire.) University, are also highly relevant. When weanling rats were fed a diet that was only mildly deficient in protein, no significant change was observed in their problem-solving ability as adults, as assessed by a maze test of animal intelligence. If these rats and their offspring remained on the diet, however, problem-solving ability was progressively reduced in the first, second, and third generations.

The adverse effects of sensory deprivation on the young animal parallel those resulting from severe malnutrition. Scientists at the Institute of Human Nutrition in Prague, Czech., combined both factors. Rats were placed on different dietary regimens during the first months after birth. In each experiment some animals were stroked and handled every day while others were not intentionally stimulated. The animals were then tested between the 90th and 110th day. The stimulated rats fed in litters of 17 showed less spontaneous activity and fewer standing-up reactions than those fed in smaller litters and

Symptoms similar to those of kwashiorkor were induced in the smaller of these two 20-week-old pigs by feeding it a diet high in sugar and low (2%) in protein. Especially notable is the swelling about the jowls, resembling the "moon face" seen in children with this acute deficiency disease. Both pigs received sufficient vitamins and minerals, but the larger pig's diet contained 18% protein.

Courtesy, Richard H. Barnes, Cornell University

better nourished after weaning. Animals that were both underfed and unstimulated showed still less activity. Unhandled animals fed in litters of four showed less spontaneous activity than stimulated animals that were similarly fed. Thus, the studies demonstrate that both environmental stimulation and an adequate diet are essential for normal development, even in rats.

Physical effects of early malnutrition in children

As in animals, there is evidence of a link between early malnutrition and brain size in children. When Winick, in collaboration with pediatricians at the University of Chile in Santiago, applied the technique of measuring brain DNA to Chilean children who had died of various causes and who had a history of severe malnutrition in infancy, he found that in all cases the number of brain cells was markedly below normal. The findings were the same even when the early deprivation had been followed by a period of more adequate nutrition.

Fernando Mönckeberg of Santiago provided an even more dramatic demonstration of the effects of severe malnutrition in infancy on the brains of Chilean children. If the head of a normal, well-nourished child is photographed while a powerful light is held against it, a zone of transillumination about two centimeters in width is revealed, surrounding the dark brain shadow. In children with cases of severe generalized undernutrition, known as marasmus, this zone is much larger—in some subjects almost the entire skull appears lighted. Apparently spinal fluid fills the space designed to hold a much larger brain.

All mammalian brains pass through a similar developmental sequence, but the period of most rapid brain growth varies in different species, depending mainly on the maturation period and life span of the animal. The brain of the human infant attains 80% of its adult weight by age three, when the body is about 20% of adult weight. For the child, therefore, the first two to three years after birth are equivalent to the first three weeks for the rat and eight to ten weeks for the pig. It is important to keep these differences in mind when comparing the evidence from animal experiments with that obtained from observations involving young children.

Children in the less developed countries are generally breast-fed, and, as a result, they grow well for the first four to six months. After six months, however, breast milk does not provide adequate protein to meet their needs. Supplementary food, if given, is usually grossly lacking in protein and often in calories as well. As a result, growth and development are slowed and susceptibility to infection is increased just at the age when the children are being exposed to an unsanitary environment.

When breast feeding is interrupted during the first year, the traditional substitutes are generally so inadequate that the child develops marasmus. This disease is increasing in frequency as women in

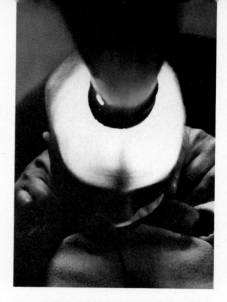

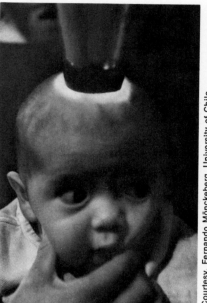

Courtesy, Fernando Mönckeberg, University of Chile

When held against a powerful light, the head of a normal child (bottom) reveals a narrow zone of transillumination around the brain shadow. The much larger zone in the head of a child with marasmus (top) indicates the reduction in brain size that may result from early malnutrition.

Scientists are taking many roads in their attempts to combat malnutrition. One involves better utilization of existing but underused resources, as in the manufacture of high-protein flour from trash fish. Another is the effort to increase the quantity of food by developing high-yield varieties of food crops and more efficient strains that can be grown under marginal conditions. To combat protein deficiency, plant geneticists are endeavoring to produce plants with a higher and better-quality protein content. Most exotic of all is the search for a method of synthesizing edible protein from otherwise inedible substances such as petroleum.

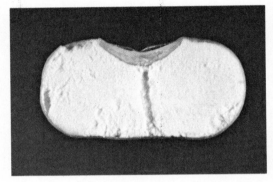

(Above and right) courtesy, Edwin Mertz and Oliver Nelson, Purdue University

(Above and left) Ivan Masser from Black Star

U.S. Department of Agriculture researcher (left) measures the photosynthesis rate of a plant, using the air-seal device shown above. The cornstalk at right is of a type high in lysine and other vital amino acids, developed by scientists at Purdue. Cross section of a kernel of ordinary corn (top) contrasts with the kernel of high-lysine corn below it.

One possible source of protein consists of single-celled organisms such as algae and yeasts. The fermentors above are used in a British Petroleum Co. Ltd. laboratory for continuous fermentation of yeast cells, shown below growing on a hydrocarbon substrate.

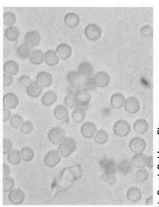

Proteinoid with many of the properties of protein has been synthesized at the University of Miami. Eighteen amino acids common to protein, heated in a flask (above, left), ground to a powder (below), and combined with water, react to form the microspheres shown above, right. The taste is said to resemble that of cooked fish.

lower socioeconomic groups, particularly in the burgeoning cities of the less developed countries, imitate the weaning practices of middle- and upper-class women without having either the knowledge or the economic resources to provide a proper substitute for breast milk. After the first year of life, the children still being breast-fed are likely to receive additional foods that supply calories rather than protein. Such a dietary imbalance, often exacerbated by infection, may result in kwashiorkor, an acute and often fatal deficiency disease.

Although they may never show overt clinical signs of either marasmus or kwashiorkor, nearly all young children in less developed countries experience sufficient malnutrition during the preschool years to impair growth and development. The crucial question is whether this malnutrition, severe enough to stunt their growth, occurs early enough and is serious enough to influence brain growth and subsequent learning and behavior.

It is clear that head circumference, at least, is affected, and head circumference is a reasonably good indicator of brain size. While differences in head circumference among normal, well-nourished children are primarily determined by genetic factors and show no correlation with intelligence, the situation is different among children who have been poorly nourished at an early age. For example, in 1950 Mavis B. Stoch and P. M. Smythe began to follow a group of 20 children in Cape Town, S.Af., who had been severely malnourished during the first year of life. Their head circumferences ten years later averaged a full inch smaller than those of adequately nourished children matched for age and racial background. This implies an average 14% decrease in intracranial volume. Workers in many other less developed countries have made similar findings.

Learning and behavioral effects of early malnutrition in children

Pioneer studies of the effects of malnutrition on the learning and behavior of children were conducted by Joaquín Cravioto, Rafael Ramos-Galván, and their collaborators in Tlaltizapán, Mex. When these workers began their studies in 1958, social and economic differences among families in the town seemed sufficiently small to enable them to detect differences attributable primarily to malnutrition. They found a high inverse correlation between deficits in height and weight at various ages and the results of tests measuring motor performance, adaptive behavior, language skills, and personal social development. In other words, the smaller the children were for their age, the lower their test scores tended to be. Retarded growth among children in the community depended on individual dietary history and infectious disease experience. Significantly, growth retardation proved unrelated to differences in housing, personal hygiene, proportion of income spent on food, and other indicators of social and economic status.

Six-year-old Guatemalan boys in the lower and upper height quartiles for their village, as delineated by Joaquín Cravioto and his co-workers in their study of the effects of malnutrition on growth and behavior. Height differences appeared to be related to the children's nutritional and epidemiological history rather than to their genetic background.

Photos, courtesy, Joaquín Cravioto, Hospital Infantil de México

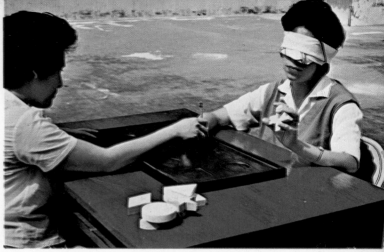

To pursue this work with a somewhat different ethnic group, Cravioto and several co-workers carried on a study in Guatemala, in cooperation with the Institute of Nutrition of Central America and Panama (INCAP). They selected the town of Magdalena Milpas Altas, a predominantly Mayan Indian village of 1,600 people. In this village, as in others throughout the region, more than 10% of the newborns died during the first year and deaths in the one-to-four-year age group were over 45 times more frequent than in the United States and Europe. Nearly all the preschool children showed retarded growth, which was judged to be due primarily to malnutrition since variations in height and weight for age within the community were unrelated to the height of the parents or to the minor differences in economic and social status among families.

Tests were given to the children, designed to measure their ability to integrate stimuli received from the various senses. While all children improved in test performance as they grew older, those in the lowest height and weight quartile for their age had consistently lower scores than those in the upper quartile. Similar tests given to children in a second Guatemalan village, Santa Catarina Barahona, and in Tlaltizapán produced the same general results.

When these tests were repeated among well-nourished children of middle- and upper-income families in Guatemala City and Mexico City, no differences in test performance by quartiles for height and weight were encountered. In these more favored populations, differences in growth were due mainly to heredity rather than to nutritional deficiencies. Clearly, genetically determined differences in growth have no relationship to mental development as judged by these tests, but differences in growth reflecting early malnutrition appear to be correlated with learning ability. The significance of these test results for performance in later life remains to be determined, but the fact that they persist to the age when children begin school is sufficiently serious to warrant urgent attention.

Mönckeberg reported a study with similar implications. Fourteen Chilean children with severe marasmus, diagnosed at ages one to five months, who had been hospitalized for long periods, were followed during visits to the outpatient department of the hospital. Each

Examiner administers two of the tests used by Cravioto to determine ability to integrate stimuli received by different senses. Left, the subject looks at a geometric shape and is asked whether it corresponds to the path through which her hand, hidden behind an opaque screen, is being moved by the examiner. Right, the subject, now blindfolded, must decide whether the path through which her hand is moved is the same as the shape she is touching.

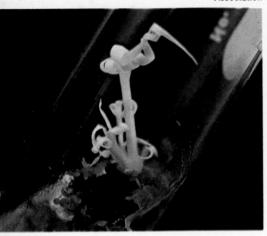

Gamma radiation induces an albino mutation in a sugarcane plant at the experiment station of the Hawaiian Sugar Planters' Association in Honolulu. The resulting strain, lacking normal plant color, is more easily used by plant geneticists in developing improved varieties to meet the world's food needs.

mother received 20 liters of free milk per month for each preschool child, along with systematic advice on proper feeding of her children. At the end of three to six years, the children were all clinically normal and some even appeared obese. Height, head circumference, and IQ were nevertheless far below the average for Chilean children of corresponding ages with no history of early malnutrition. Similar results were reported by S. Champakam, S. G. Srikantia, and C. Gopalan, who observed 13 children 8 to 11 years of age in Hyderabad, India, and by V. Cabak and R. Najdanvic from their follow-up of 36 Yugoslavian children hospitalized with marasmus between the ages of 4 and 24 months.

The most comprehensive field investigation yet attempted to determine the interrelationship of malnutrition, learning, and behavior has been organized in Guatemala by INCAP with the support of the U.S. National Institute of Child Health and Human Development. In three villages the preschool children, as well as pregnant and nursing mothers, are being given a daily food supplement; children and mothers in three other villages are serving as controls. Medical care and preventive immunization are being provided for the people of all six villages. Relevant social, economic, and cultural information is being obtained on each child. A battery of tests, involving perception, learning, memory, language, and behavior, is being administered periodically.

The definitive phase of this study, in which each child will be followed from birth to age eight, has only begun, but some results are available from the three-year developmental and pilot phase that preceded it. The findings suggest that if children who have experienced severe malnutrition at an early age are examined several years later, when malnutrition is no longer present, they still show impaired performance on four of the ten psychological tests employed, when compared with children in the same village whose heights are within 10% of normal. Two of the tests measure the subject's ability to retain and immediately reproduce serially ordered material—digits and short sentences of two-syllable words. The other two also involve short-term recall, but reflect the child's ability to learn things incidental or peripheral to the central problem. The most important contribution of the definitive study should be a demonstration of the extent to which supplementary feeding during and after weaning can improve both physical development and intellectual performance.

Conclusions and implications

To sum up, in man, as in experimental animals, malnutrition during the period when breast feeding should be supplying adequate nourishment can have a permanent effect on brain size relative to final body size. This will also occur, but to a lesser degree, if the malnutrition occurs only in the immediate postweaning period. Later than this, malnutrition has many other adverse effects but little permanent influence on the physical development of the brain and central nervous system. If the mother is malnourished during pregnancy, there is probably little permanent effect on the child's central nervous system *if* it is well fed from birth onward. Malnutrition of the mother during pregnancy, however, predisposes the newborn to more consequences from malnutrition soon after birth.

The effects on brain size are paralleled by demonstrable abnormalities in brain cells, brain chemistry, and brain function. Their permanence and severity depend on the timing, degree, and duration of the malnutrition. It is clear, however, that once significant damage is produced at an early age, residual effects remain, regardless of the child's—or animal's—subsequent life history.

Malnutrition interacting with infection is recognized as a major factor in the high morbidity and mortality of infants and preschool children in less developed countries. It not only results in nutritional diseases such as marasmus and kwashiorkor, but also lowers resistance to the infectious diseases responsible for so much illness and death among young children in these areas.

Malnutrition also interacts with infection, heredity, and social factors to impair both physical and mental growth and development. Many of the social factors are difficult to correct within a single generation, but malnutrition and much of the heavy burden of infection can be eliminated by programs of preventive medicine, applied nutrition, and public health.

The prevention of malnutrition in young children, whenever and wherever it occurs, is an obvious and urgent necessity if they are to have an opportunity to attain their full physical, mental, and social potential. This is the birthright of every child and an indispensable prerequisite to the full social and economic development of any country.

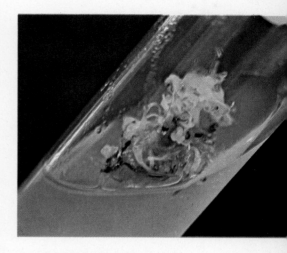

Growing plants from single cells is an important process in scientists' efforts to improve plant characteristics at the cellular level. Here a new sugarcane plant begins to differentiate itself from the tissue formed by a cell in a culture tube.

FOR ADDITIONAL READING:

Eichenwald, Heinz F., and Fry, Peggy Crooke, "Nutrition and Learning," *Science,* pp. 644–648 (Feb. 14, 1969).

Scrimshaw, Nevin S., "Infant Malnutrition and Adult Learning," *Saturday Review,* pp. 64–66, 84 (March 16, 1968).

Scrimshaw, Nevin S., and Gordon, John E. (eds.), *Malnutrition, Learning, and Behavior* (Massachusetts Institute of Technology Press, 1968).

AUDIOVISUAL MATERIALS FROM ENCYCLOPÆDIA BRITANNICA EDUCATIONAL CORPORATION:

Films: *Food and People; Foods and Nutrition.*

Horsehead Nebula in Orion.

A Gateway to the Future
The Mount Wilson and Palomar Observatories:
Two Rooms with a View
by Jesse L. Greenstein

In the forefront of those making new discoveries in astronomy are the people who work at the Mount Wilson and Palomar Observatories, the hub of a sophisticated complex of astronomical facilities.

Gazing into a clear night sky, a man, using his eyes alone, can see thousands of stars. Vast as this array is, however, it represents only a small fraction of the celestial bodies that can be viewed with the aid of telescopes. These instruments, and their auxiliary devices, have helped to probe far into the universe. As they have become more powerful and refined, they have thrown ever-greater light on our eternal quest to understand the mysteries of the cosmos. They have also revealed new mysteries that still defy explanation.

A large share of the most significant astronomical discoveries has been made at two sites in southern California, the Mount Wilson and the Palomar observatories. Eventually, the Space Age may provide satellite telescopes that can take advantage of the permanently clear, darker, and more transparent skies above the atmosphere. But until then the southern California climate and its mile-high mountains, well above the sea-fog level, will continue to give us one of the most favorable locations on earth for astronomical facilities.

The observatories and auxiliary facilities

The Mount Wilson Observatory, 20 mi from Pasadena, was established in 1904–05 by the Carnegie Institution of Washington. Astronomers selected the site because of its extraordinary

356

viewing conditions: between 250 and 300 nights a year with a clear and relatively steady atmosphere. Three solar telescopes and a 150-ft-high solar tower were erected for studies of the sun, and in 1908 a 60-in. reflecting telescope was built for planetary and stellar observations. Next, a daring instrument was constructed that was for many years the world's largest telescope, the 100-in. Hooker reflector, completed in 1918. All of these instruments are still in use.

In 1948, with funds provided by the General Education Boards of the Rockefeller Foundation, the California Institute of Technology (Caltech) completed what is still the largest telescope in the world, the 200-in. Hale reflector. This installation, which is located on Palomar Mountain, 130 mi from Pasadena, now includes 18- and 48-in. Schmidt mapping telescopes, a 20-in. photoelectric telescope, and a sophisticated, special-purpose, 60-in. photoelectric telescope which is nearing completion.

The scientists who work at these observatories have offices in Pasadena, traveling to the telescopes to observe the skies for short periods and then returning to Pasadena to analyze their results. Among the facilities for astronomers in Pasadena are the Hale Solar Laboratory, where the solar magnetograph, a device for studying the sun's magnetic field, was developed and the Henry M. Robinson Laboratory of Astrophysics, center of Caltech astronomy, inside of which George Ellery Hale built a 150-ft solar tower. Recently put into operation, this tower is being used to test instruments for still another solar station at Big Bear Lake, which is 60 mi from Pasadena.

Not directly connected to but operated in close harmony with the Mount Wilson and Palomar facilities is Caltech's Owens Valley Radio Observatory, 250 mi north of Pasadena, in the shadow of the Sierra Nevada mountains. This radio observatory, which is largely federally supported, includes one 130-ft and two 90-ft paraboloidal radio telescopes that may be used together as an interferometer, an instrument used in radio astronomy to measure extremely small angular separations. The rapid growth of radio astronomy, as indicated by the discovery of radio galaxies, explosions in galaxies, quasi-stellar radio sources (quasars), and pulsating radio sources (pulsars), has made this cooperation particularly fruitful.

Organization of staff and facilities

The organizational structure of the Mount Wilson and Palomar complex provides for independent

When George Ellery Hale, the founder of Mount Wilson Observatory, and Andrew Carnegie, its benefactor, visited the site in 1910, part of the trip had to be made by horse-drawn carriage.

choice of scientific programs by the staff members of the observatories and by faculty members in physics and the geological sciences at Caltech. Generally, the permanent staff at the two observatories consists of about 20 scientists, 6 associates, and 25 postdoctoral fellows. A large support group is also necessary because of the many problems involved in maintaining two mountain observatories. Mechanical and electric maintenance is handled on both mountains by a permanent resident group, to whom astronomy remains deeply indebted. If pumps fail or circuit breakers trip in the middle of the night, within a few minutes a maintenance man will appear to trace the circuits and improvise a repair. Night assistants help the astronomers at all the major telescopes. They make settings on the object being studied and, when the complex electronic auxiliaries are in use, they monitor the performance of the various components and report on any malfunctions.

Special responsibilities for the Mount Wilson and Palomar complex of instruments and auxiliary facilities are allocated to individual staff members. In Pasadena new optical and electrical instruments are developed by a staff of 25 engineers, technicians, and machinists. One of the leaders in this group is Bruce Rule, a Caltech engineer who was responsible for the completion of the 200-in. telescope after World War II and for the mechanical design of most of its auxiliaries. The optical devices that were so necessary for the success of the 200-in. reflector were the work of

A Gateway to the Future

Ira Bowen, the director at that time. Though now retired, he has continued to provide ingenious new designs for many of the most modern astronomical instruments.

An optical shop, located in the laboratory of the Carnegie Institution in Washington, is capable of producing optical components as large as the 60-in. primary mirror for the new photoelectric telescope at Palomar. The mirror for the 200-in. Hale reflector was ground and polished in a special shop at Caltech. Sophisticated electronic devices for amplification, control, and data-recording systems, now used with the telescopes on both mountains, are designed and built in the Astro Electronics Laboratory at Caltech.

Educational and research programs

The entire complex of instruments at the observatories and in Pasadena is used in free interchange by scientists associated with either Caltech or the Carnegie Institution, as well as by graduate students at the former school and by guest investigators from other universities in the U.S. and abroad. Supported largely by its own funds, this complex has been for many decades the world's largest privately operated facility of its kind.

Graduate education is an important function of the observatories. Begun in 1948 under the leadership of the author, the graduate program now includes several postdoctoral fellowship programs. The facilities for research are so varied and flexible, and the introduction of novel techniques is so rapid, that a Ph.D. degree marks only the beginning of a young scientist's career. The postdoctoral programs, though strictly limited by the availability of funds and telescope time, have led to the advanced education of a large number of active astronomers throughout the world.

Almost every year, the staff, associates, and students publish 150 technical papers in journals, encyclopedias, monographs, and annual reviews. In addition, guest observers from other institutions publish their own results independently. About 15% of the total observing time of the largest telescopes (the 48-in. Schmidt and the 60-, 100-, and 200-in. reflectors) is assigned to guest investigators, without charge, in keeping with the public responsibility that attends private ownership of these large instruments.

Although economically operated, the costs incurred by the observatories for education, research, and new instruments exceed $2 million a year. A large share of the costs for education and operation comes from private gifts and from endowments to the Carnegie Institution and Caltech. Recently, the funding of new auxiliary instruments has been assumed mainly by the U.S. National Aeronautics and Space Administration, the National Science Foundation, and the Advanced Research Projects Agency. The postdoctoral fellowship programs are also largely supported by U.S. government agencies.

The work of the observatories: pioneering in spectroscopy

George Ellery Hale's move to California to establish the observatory at Mount Wilson occurred at a time when solar astronomy and the attempt to understand solar physics were dominant. While at the observatory, Hale invented the spectroheliograph, a device to observe the sun's surface in the light of a single spectral line of a chemical element. Eventually, the lines present in the spectrum of the sun were completely mapped in the so-called *Revised Rowland Tables*. In 1966 a second revision of the tables was published with worldwide collaboration. It included wavelengths and strengths for about 20,000 lines in the solar spectrum, with the atoms or molecules responsible for each.

The Hale telescope at Palomar is inspected at close range. At the bottom of the girderlike structure is the 200-in. reflecting mirror. The crosswise yoke rotates parallel to the earth's rotation about its axis.

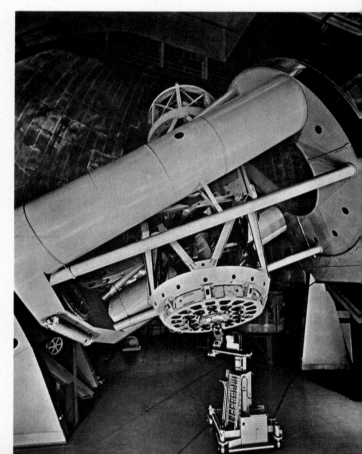

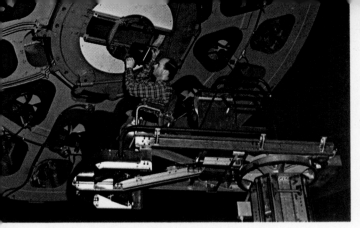

An astronomer on an elevated chair views the underside of the mirror cell of the Hale telescope at Palomar. For many years this was the world's largest optical telescope.

Because stars are so faint, it was not until the large reflecting telescopes and more efficient spectrographs were developed at the observatories that similar information about stellar spectra could be provided. The evolution of the fixed-position coudé spectrograph (an instrument used with large telescopes to photograph stellar spectra) for the 100-in. Hooker telescope, from a prism-and-lens design to a mirror-and-grating type, permitted advanced stellar spectroscopy on relatively faint stars. The quantitative analysis of stars began with the identification of thousands of spectral lines in stars that could be seen by the naked eye and developed into studies of the abundances of the chemical elements and isotopes. Qualitative studies of stellar spectra resulted in an enormous increase in our knowledge of what types of stars existed. High-resolution solar spectra were first published in the form of

The coudé spectrograph of the Hale telescope has permitted astronomers to analyze chemically the different types of stars at varying stages of their evolution.

an atlas prepared at Utrecht, Neth., using plates taken on Mount Wilson. The first equivalent atlas of a stellar spectrum, that of Arcturus, has been completed and is expected to provide a similar storehouse of information about a star.

Beginning in 1948 Ira Bowen, then director of the observatories, started to design a coudé spectrograph for the new 200-in. Hale telescope. When the spectrograph became operational in 1952, the author and many collaborators began a series of chemical analyses of different types of stars at various stages of their evolution. This large body of information has been critically important to the theory of the origin of chemical elements inside stars. Thus, in a period of only 30 years methods of solar spectroscopy developed at the observatories have been applied to stars and have helped create new insights into the origin and evolution of matter.

Lower-resolution stellar spectra were obtained soon after the 60-in. telescope on Mount Wilson was built. A group headed by Walter Adams studied approximately 10,000 such spectra in order to develop criteria for determining the surface temperature and luminosity of the stars. This spectroscopic determination of intrinsic brightness is necessary for the study of stars too far away for direct measurements of their distance and is even used to study stars in other galaxies. In dividing the stars into different luminosity groups, it was found that the spectra of some stars were too peculiar to be classified correctly. Some of these were the first known examples of the very old, metal-deficient stars formed in the early history of our galaxy. Hence, they are important in order to understand the origin of the elements.

Ultimately, special spectrographs were developed for the faintest stars and, when used with the 100-in. Hooker telescope on Mount Wilson, opened up new types of problems. The spectra of exploding stars (novae) showed the violence of these events, but the explosive catastrophes of supernovae revealed spectra that are not yet understood or even partially disentangled. At the same time, direct photographs taken through filters that isolated the light of different chemical elements showed to Walter Baade, one of the most skillful of observers, that the gas clouds of the Crab Nebula were expanding at 1,000 km a second from a center near which a supernova occurred in A.D. 1054. In addition, Baade found that some of the light from the inner portions of the nebula had a continuous spectrum, which he also observed to be polarized in a linear manner and slightly variable in appearance.

continued on page 361

A Gateway to the Future

A night on Palomar Mountain

By tradition each astronomer, when working at a large telescope, makes his own observations. Although he is surrounded by engineering marvels and advanced electronic technology, he has learned that making a critical and delicate observation is still, ultimately, a one-man struggle. His chief enemies in this enterprise are bad weather, malfunction of equipment, cold, and lack of sleep; he is faced, therefore, with more than just a scientific challenge. The romance and beauty of the night, of the half-seen, faint glow of starlight, promise excitement and mystery. The observing process is an irresistible adventure for me, even after 30 years. I am a telescope addict, in love with a 500-ton steel and glass monster.

Every few days a station wagon carries equipment, supplies, and one or two astronomers from the Carnegie and Caltech offices in Pasadena to Palomar. During the ride conversation about the weather assumes obsessive proportions. This is because even the most distinguished member of the Mount Wilson and Palomar staff can have no more than 25 nights a year of exclusive operation of the 200-in. telescope, and he can use only his assigned nights, even if they are cloudy. As the journey continues, city and suburbs and freeways are replaced by a country road up scrubby hills, and finally up the flat-topped 6,000-ft Palomar Mountain. The first sight of the silver bubble of the great dome atop the observatory startles even the most unromantic.

Inside the observatory it is cold and quiet but, in the first hours, desperately busy, as equipment is unloaded, mounted on the telescope, and tested. Each astronomer's project requires its own special technique and auxiliary apparatus. Some observers use a roomful of electronic equipment. Mine is simpler, consisting of the prime-focus spectrograph, to be mounted at the top of the Hale telescope, looking down on the giant 200-in. mirror. The "cage" of the telescope is a 6-ft-wide cylinder supported by thin steel fins in which the observer sits and where the instruments are placed. It is located at the principal focus, 55 ft above the mirror, and is reached by an elevator that creeps 60 ft up the curved inside of the dome. By late afternoon all is adjusted, the photographic plates have been cut to their correct size, and I can, at last, lean back inside the gray tube and enjoy the half light for a moment.

By 6 P.M. (11 hours after the morning's alarm clock) I am ready to begin work. Soon the stars begin to show through the opened slit of the dome. The objects I am to study, with priorities and technical specifications, are listed on a printout from a computer; before me are star charts and the photographic plates.

Down below the "night engineer" starts the generators, pumps, and telescope drive. Through the intercom his voice rises: "Are you ready, Dr. G.?" "Yes," I reply. "Let's begin with finding star number 32; after I've focused we'll go to the object." Relays bang, the motors roar through the loudspeaker, and the tube tilts downward and to the east, toward my celestial object. In the cage gravity goes mad, gimbaled boxes swing, and I furiously crank my observing chair to a level position from which I can still reach the spectrograph and, hopefully, survive the next four hours. The tube lurches as the brakes lock on, and small motors hum as they operate to achieve fine settings. Through the eyepiece I see a blue disk which, as I set the focus, sharpens into a star. If I am lucky, I have a dazzling point of light to center on the spectrograph slit, but if the seeing is poor, only a jumping blob.

"Good," I tell the engineer. "We've centered and focused. Now let's go to the object, R. Monocerotis." The telescope slides a few degrees; I look down the tube at a black pool filled with tiny lights, the mirror—55 ft away—catching starlight. Then, in the eyepiece appears a strange, white glow, shaped like a comet; at its tip is a star being born. My view is as old as civilization; the light I am seeing left the object 5,000 years ago.

A bustle of final settings, calibrations, data for the observing record; I pull out the camera-cover slide and the exposure begins. Then silence, only the distant pumps, and the passage of time. The telescope is turning 15 ft an hour, to follow a star 30 million billion mi away! The star stays frozen on the spectrograph slit, but every five minutes I check and reset the fine motions of the telescope, perhaps a thousandth of an inch, to maintain centering. I retilt the seat when I climb on it to look out at the nearby sky; 42° F feels cold if you sit still near midnight. What do I think of? Usually of nothing, hypnotized by the dulling reality of chill and fatigue, or of what I might have done incorrectly, or about the next exposure. But sometimes I do think of what may be creating the dim glow that I am seeing through the telescope.

Then there is a flurry of activity at the end of the exposure—reloading the camera in the dark —and the ride in the cage to the next object. Another focusing, another faint star, this one a suspected white dwarf, near the limit of vision and hard to find. We start a new exposure, for two more hours, and I think about the superdense matter of the white dwarf. Meanwhile, I listen to my radio playing Mozart, who lived in a different world.

After midnight I climb out of the tube and descend in the elevator to the darkroom for lunch and to develop the plates. Although still wet, the plates show that the nebula spectrum was well exposed. The faint white dwarf gave a narrow streak of blackened silver grains that tells me something new. Then I again go up the elevator to the cage, to new objects and another four hours of viewing. At the end of the last exposure, as dawn begins, the telescope is set in a vertical position and the motors stop. It is a sudden relief, riding down the lurching elevator while the giant dome is closing, to be able to stand and feel the end of cramped muscles and nervous tensions.

As the sun comes up, I enter the completely darkened and quiet sleeping quarters, to sleep five hours until breakfast. At 1 P.M. I go to the darkroom again to prepare for the next night and to question my previous night's efforts. "Are these objects interesting? Shall I change the program?" The plates taken last night, the first of my four nights of this run, suggested something new. Tonight might be crucial; I will be more tired and I wish there were more time! Were I sensible, would I be an astronomer again? Of course, because next year will be even better; new objects discovered, new instruments developed, new ideas proposed. There is so much that is unknown. What were all those flying specks of light in the mirror? What new marvels are waiting?

continued from page 359

In 1968 and 1969 the Crab Nebula became one of the most exciting astronomical objects ever studied because at its center a faint star was identified with a strange source of radio signals emitted at short, regular intervals. A team of observers, headed by Jerome Kristian, using the 200-in. telescope on Palomar with elaborate photoelectric apparatus, confirmed the discovery made by astronomers at the University of Arizona that this source (a pulsar) also emitted optical signals at the same intervals as the radio signals.

The most advanced electronic technology was necessary for the observations of the spectrum of the short pulses of light emitted by the pulsar in the Crab Nebula. The development of a multichannel spectrometer by J. B. Oke at Caltech was the decisive factor; Oke built a spectrograph that spreads the light of different colors so widely that it is possible to place 33 photoelectric sensors at different wavelengths. An elaborate electronic system then permits simultaneous measurement of the light received in each of 33 wavelength bands. The signals from faint objects are so weak, however, that it is also necessary to subtract the background sky light emitted by our ionosphere. For the Crab Nebula it was even more important to subtract the background of nebular emission, which was successfully done. It thus became possible for the first time to obtain the spectrum of the faint pulsar with a time resolution of a few thousandths of a second.

Photography and photometry at the observatories

The concentration of research at the observatories has always been on the faintest objects observable at a given stage of technology, and the changes in techniques are well illustrated by the development of photography and photometry. The measurement of the positions of stars on photographic plates is an old and successful art. The 60-in. telescope on Mount Wilson was used for such positional astronomy, largely by Adrian van Maamen, who determined the motions of faint stars and their distances by taking many series of photographic plates.

The photographic plate has changed enormously in the last 50 years. At first sensitive only to blue and violet light, its range was extended to the yellow, red, and part of the infrared regions by the Eastman Kodak Research Laboratory. Much of this research was done in collaboration with Mount Wilson and Palomar astronomers, who wished to take photographs in light of different colors. New types of plates were tested at the 60-in. telescope, and the result was a mutually profitable development of an entire arsenal of plates of different wavelength sensitivity, contrast, and speed. Working in blue (photographic) and in yellow (photovisual) light, astronomers made fundamental determinations of stellar brightness with the 60-in. telescope. It was a remarkable achievement, although appreciable errors have since been found in the measurements of the faintest stars.

The development of the photocell and the photomultiplier tube introduced electronics into astronomy. These devices provided a sensitive means of measuring the brightness of individual stars at selected colors that were defined by suitable filters. The technology was developed at the University of Wisconsin by Joel Stebbins and Albert Whitford, who worked at the Mount Wilson and Palomar Observatories as staff associates and guest observers for many years. At first, pho-

A Gateway to the Future

toelectric observations were made at two colors and later at three to six colors, but this since has been greatly improved by a spectrum scanner. The photoelectric standards of brightness generally confirmed the old photographic work, showed its errors, and extended it to much fainter stars and to new color ranges.

Throughout the evolution of instruments, from the photographic plate (the only technology available when the telescopes at Mount Wilson and Palomar were built) to the most modern electronic data-processing equipment, the telescopes have provided the basic constant factor—great light-gathering power. Although improvements in plates and electronic techniques have each doubled the effective size of the telescopes, without large instruments and clear skies all the other sophisticated auxiliaries would be useless.

The challenge of extragalactic studies

It is for the study of galaxies beyond our own that the need for the largest possible astronomical instruments is most apparent. In the 1920s the study of our own galaxy by Harlow Shapley and of other galaxies by Edwin Hubble culminated in the realization that the universe seemed to be expanding. Controversies based on studies of the size of our galaxy (the Milky Way) were resolved when astronomers realized that dust in space absorbed a large fraction of the light. Once it became possible to use the reddening produced by this dust to estimate the total light loss, the distance to the center of the galaxy was found to be about 30,000 light-years.

From photographic studies of Cepheid variable stars, Hubble then established the distance to the nearest external galaxies and found it to be of the order of a million light-years. Then, because there are two different types of Cepheids, Baade discovered that the calibration of Cepheid luminosities from the period of light variation had been carried out incorrectly. Although the correction of these calibrations resulted in a doubling of the extragalactic distance scale, which we now believe to be reasonably accurate, there still remains an uncertainty of perhaps 30% in the so-called "Hubble constant." This constant, H_0, is used to measure the rate of increase of the red shift of remote galaxies with increasing distance. (In the red shift, spectral lines shift toward the red end of the spectrum as an object moves away from an observer.) As a value for the red shift, Hubble had used 540 kilometers per second per megaparsec (one megaparsec = 3.2 million light-years).

Stars, comets, and galaxies are revealed with sharp clarity in photographs taken by some of the instruments at Mount Wilson and Palomar. The Pleiades star cluster in the constellation Taurus (above) was photographed by the 48-in. Schmidt telescope at Palomar, as was the Comet Humason (opposite page, left), and the Great Andromeda Nebula (opposite, lower right). The 200-in. Hale telescope at Palomar photographed the Trifid Nebula in the constellation Sagittarius (opposite, top right) and the Dumbbell Nebula in Vulpecula (opposite, lower center).

In subsequent calculations based on observations of many more red shifts of galaxies in which Cepheids, bright supergiant stars, and bright gaseous nebulae were used as distance indicators, Allan Sandage of the Mount Wilson and Palomar staff arrived at a value of 75 kilometers per second per megaparsec for the Hubble constant. A value of $H_0 = 100$ kilometers per second per megaparsec is more or less conventionally adopted now, subject to frequent rediscussions by Sandage and others.

To obtain these red shifts requires a large telescope and an efficient spectrograph. Recently, an image-intensifier spectrograph has helped shorten exposures for faint galaxies, but that helps solve only part of the problem. The major difficulty is the determination of the distances by an independent method. The properties of stars are presumably determined by their mass, chemical composition, and evolutionary status. This assumed uniformity permits us to recognize stars in other systems whose luminosity is known from studies of similar stars in our own galaxy. But making such conclusions on the basis of stars in our galaxy led to errors several times in the past. The only genuinely safe method is to resolve and study stars that resemble the sun in distant galaxies. But at 10 megaparsecs (at which the red shift is only 1,000 km/sec) the sun would be invisible, at an apparent magnitude of 35. The faintest objects worked on with the 200-in. telescope are those at the 23rd magnitude, 60,000 times brighter than

stars at the 35th. Thus, only intrinsically bright and, therefore, rapidly evolving stars can be resolved and studied.

Future activities

While the ultimate limit of faintness may be reached only by observations with a large telescope in space, technology will meanwhile help our instruments on the ground to perform more effectively. There is no doubt that another telescope of 200-in. size or larger is needed in the northern hemisphere, presumably in southern California, Hawaii, or Arizona. In addition, the Carnegie Institution has begun to develop a new telescope site in Chile and is seeking funds (about $25 million) to construct a 200-in. instrument and auxiliaries there. One special pressure, population growth in the Los Angeles area, has already had adverse effects on the Mount Wilson telescopes. Because of city lights scattered from the upper atmosphere, the night sky has become so bright that the large reflectors on Mount Wilson are useless to study the faintest celestial objects. Even Palomar, 120 airline miles away, has brighter skies at night than are desirable. Because population growth will further pollute the atmosphere with haze, smog, and city lights, eventually a more remote site than Palomar may become a necessity.

The difficulties posed by population growth are among the least of the many unsolved, exciting problems in observational astronomy. We need new techniques and new, revolutionary ideas. The pioneering effort that led to the construction of large telescopes at Mount Wilson and Palomar was wisely concentrated on the best possible instruments in the best possible location. The present staff maintains the tradition of responsible use of the facilities and is planning for the future. The unexpected new types of astronomical phenomena discovered in recent years (pulsars, quasars, etc.) strongly emphasize the absolute necessity for critical experiments at this frontier of knowledge. In the effort to understand these new mysteries, the Mount Wilson and Palomar Observatories, with their young and imaginative staff, serve as a vital national resource.

FOR ADDITIONAL READING

Bowen, Ira S., "Completing the Atlas of the Universe," *The National Geographic Magazine* (August 1955).

Cooper, Henry S. F. Jr., "A Night at the Observatory," *Horizon* (Summer 1967).

Wright, Helen, *Explorer of the Universe* (Dutton, 1966).

AUDIOVISUAL MATERIALS FROM ENCYCLOPÆDIA BRITANNICA EDUCATIONAL CORPORATION:

Films: *The Story of Palomar; Charting the Universe with Optical and Radio Telescopes.*

Filmstrip: *The Mount Wilson and Palomar Telescopes.*

A Gateway to the Future
A House for Living Molecules

by Max Perutz At the Laboratory of Molecular Biology in Cambridge, Eng., scientists have found some of the answers to many of the basic questions about life. The author, a Nobel laureate and chairman of the laboratory, describes some of the ingenious, patient, and often tedious work by the staff that has been rewarded with many "firsts" and that has created exciting new fields of research. (Parts of this article are reproduced by permission of the Controller of Her Britannic Majesty's Stationery Office.)

After World War II a group of young physicists and chemists gathered in the physics department at Cambridge University around Sir Lawrence Bragg, one of the founders of X-ray crystallography, to study the structure of biological systems by X-ray diffraction. Included in this group were John C. Kendrew, Francis H. C. Crick, Hugh E. Huxley, and myself. At first we were interested mainly in the structure of proteins. Crick, a physicist by training, had taught himself genetics, a subject that we hardly discussed among ourselves until the young American biochemist James D. Watson walked into our laboratory in October 1951. Eighteen months later he and Crick made a discovery that was to revolutionize biology. They solved the structure of deoxyribonucleic acid (DNA), the chemical substance in the genes that

Crystals of biological systems have been magnified and photographed by special techniques that emphasize their geometric characteristics. X-ray diffraction of crystals of a bacterial enzyme (left) and of insulin (right) will reveal their molecular structures.

Courtesy, Brookhaven National Laboratory

controls heredity. Later in the same year Huxley and Jean Hanson discovered the sliding mechanism of muscular contraction, and I found a method of solving the structure of proteins by X-ray analysis. These successes suggested that our approach to biological problems had a promising future and that our research might flourish best if we had a laboratory of our own in which our structural methods could be combined with chemical and genetic methods.

The idea for the laboratory began to take shape during the following years when first Vernon M. Ingram and then Sydney Brenner joined us, the former bringing expertise in protein chemistry and the latter in the genetics of microorganisms. In 1954 Frederick Sanger, who was then working at the university's department of biochemistry, completed the first determination of the chemical structure of a protein, which won him the Nobel Prize for Chemistry in 1958. In 1957, when Kendrew had solved the first three-dimensional structure of a protein and Sanger had expressed his wish to join forces with us, we finally felt confident enough to put the idea for a Laboratory of Molecular Biology to the government agency that supported us, the Medical Research Council. They reacted very favorably.

In February 1962 we moved into our new building and were joined there by the physicist Aaron Klug and his colleagues from Birkbeck College, London, who worked on the structure of viruses, and by Hugh Huxley, who had worked at University College, London, for the preceding six years and had become famous for his research on muscle. The laboratory was formally opened by Queen Elizabeth II on May 28, 1962. It contained divisions of protein chemistry, molecular genetics, and protein crystallography (later renamed structural studies), and it had a population of about 40 graduates and an equal number of other staff members in a floor area of 32,000 sq ft. By January 1969 these numbers had grown to 90 each and the staff had just moved into a new extension, which is half as big as the original building and makes the laboratory the largest of its kind in the world.

The organization of the laboratory

The scientific staff at the Laboratory of Molecular Biology includes mathematicians who devise computer programs, electronic engineers who design computer-linked equipment, experimental and theoretical physicists, crystallographers, chemists, biochemists, and microbiologists. About half

364

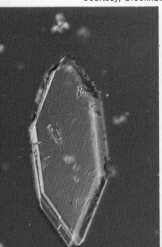
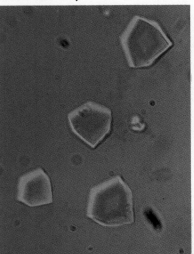

of our scientists are graduate students and young postdoctorates; many are from the U.S. The scientific population changes at the rate of 25% per year, which helps to keep us young and brings in new ideas. Most of the scientists have a technician to help them.

We have no hierarchy of any kind and no titles because these are liable to produce ill feelings, but we do have a constitution that is designed to give scientists the greatest possible freedom. A governing board consisting of the senior scientists in the laboratory decides only the broad lines of scientific policy, leaving the three divisions largely autonomous. Most research projects are carried out by groups of not more than six or eight scientists, and these research groups often include people from more than one division. This is important because success frequently depends on bringing different disciplines to bear on one problem.

Collaboration between different groups or divisions is catalyzed by a canteen where scientific discussions take place over cups of tea or coffee. As a further stimulus to collaboration, we begin each academic year with a week's symposium on the work of the laboratory, but we have no regular program of seminars. We hold seminars only when there is something interesting to report or when a visitor arrives with exciting news. Our laboratory is only two miles from the main science centers of Cambridge University, where several of us teach and where students can attend lectures, but we have no formal program of postgraduate training; in Britain this is generally left to the student's own initiative.

In our workshop, skilled instrument makers construct high-powered X-ray tubes and cameras for X-ray diffraction work. We have a medium-sized computer, which has been used to automate many of the tedious routine operations in X-ray crystallography. In addition, we have access to a larger computer. There are optical and electron microscopes, spectroscopes, amino acid analyzers, ultracentrifuges and fractionators of all kinds, machines for growing bacteria by the kilogram, and counters for detecting radioisotopes in quantities as small as 10^{-12} gram. We also have a library and a seminar room.

The structure of proteins

The chemical approach. The earliest and the most persistent efforts of the laboratory have centered around the study of proteins. Because proteins appeared to play a key role in the metabolism of all living cells, their structure seemed to many of us as one of the central problems of biology. The great question was how this problem might be solved. In the 1930s proteins were known to be giant molecules made up of 20 different kinds of amino acids linked together to form long chains, but their chemical structure and spatial architecture were obscure. Chemical methods for finding their amino acid composition were extremely laborious, and methods for finding the sequence of the different kinds of residues along the length of the chains did not exist.

In 1944, however, Sanger, then working at the Cambridge University department of biochemistry, introduced a chemical device that allowed him to determine the sequence of amino acids in small protein fragments of insulin. He combined the free end group of the amino acid chain with a colored compound; this labeled terminal amino acid could then be split off from the remainder of the chain and identified by partition chromatography, a method of separating chemical elements that had just been developed. The process could be repeated with the remaining amino acids in the chain until the complete sequence of the fragment was determined.

Sanger applied this method to the study of insulin because it was a pure protein of known amino acid composition. He first established that insulin consisted of two kinds of chains, one with 21 and the other with 30 residues, held together by sulfur bridges. In the course of 10 years he and his colleagues succeeded in the formidable task of determining the complete sequence of the amino acid residues in the two chains and the positions of the three sulfur bridges.

Sanger's elucidation was one of the milestones in protein chemistry. It established the fact that the amino acid residues really are arranged in a definite, genetically determined sequence; but disproved the widely held belief that this sequence was regular. It revealed the part played by sulfur bridges in the architecture of proteins and the chemical nature of species specificity. Most important of all, Sanger demonstrated that the complete formula for a protein can be determined by chemical methods and thereby stimulated a great volume of research all over the world.

The physical approach. The chemical constitution of proteins suggested that they were long threads or fibers, but the fact that most proteins behaved in solution as if they were spheres indicated that the long chains of amino acids must be coiled or folded. To understand their catalytic activity, it seemed essential to know how the chains were folded, but chemical methods by themselves could not reveal this. Also, the chains were 500 times thinner than the thinnest object a light microscope could reveal. It was at this

A Gateway to the Future

point that X-ray diffraction from crystals, or X-ray crystallography, suggested itself, a physical method widely used for finding the atomic arrangement of simpler chemical compounds.

In 1936, the structures that had been solved by X-ray diffraction were at least a hundred times smaller than the simplest enzymes; yet John Desmond Bernal, the crystallographer whom I joined as a research student in the physics department at Cambridge, inspired all around him with boundless optimism about the powers of the method. X-ray photographs of crystals of the enzyme pepsin that he and Dorothy Crowfoot had taken in 1934 had given diffraction patterns with sharp spots extending over a wide range of angles. Pepsin, however, proved too difficult a structure and, instead of pursuing it further, Bernal encouraged my plan to start X-ray studies of hemoglobin, the protein of the red blood cells. Unlike pepsin, crystals of horse hemoglobin had a type of symmetry that made them most favorable for X-ray analysis. Besides, horse hemoglobin was easy to come by and simple to crystallize.

In X-ray diffraction, X rays are scattered by the atoms they encounter. This interference causes the scattered rays to be diffracted, which means reinforced in some directions and weakened in others. When X rays strike disordered matter, such as a clot of blood, diffraction causes the

incident beam to be surrounded by diffuse halos that do not reveal anything about the atomic structure of the hemoglobin molecules in the clot. When X rays impinge on a hemoglobin crystal, however, the orderly arrangement of the hemoglobin molecules in the crystal creates a regular pattern of thousands of sharply defined diffracted rays. The strength of some of these rays and weakness of others provide a wealth of precise information about the atomic arrangement in the hemoglobin molecules. This is, however, only half of the information needed to solve the structure. The other half consists of the phases and gets lost in the process of recording.

In an X-ray diffraction pattern each spot can be regarded as the imprint of a stationary wave originating from some arbitrary reference point in the crystal. The phase is the distance of the nearest wave crest from that reference point. Since it cannot be measured directly, the atomic arrangement in crystals of simpler compounds often used to be guessed, at least in part, by combining chemical information with the crystal symmetry and a few striking features of the X-ray diffraction pattern. The solution of a protein structure, therefore, either had to be guessed or, if it was too complicated, a way had to be found of measuring the phases. This basic problem occupied Bragg, Kendrew, Crick, and myself for many years. Our

(Right) Two X-ray diffractometers with an X-ray tube between them. X rays diffracted from a crystallized specimen are scattered into patterns that are recorded on film (diagram, below). The pattern of a pepsin crystal (bottom, right) corresponds to the arrangement of molecules in the crystal.

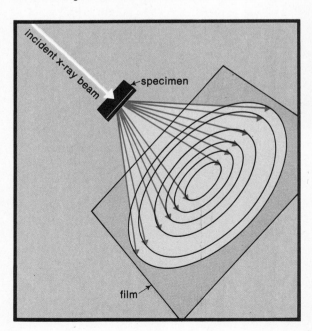

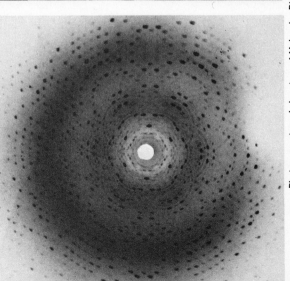

many approaches and disappointments are vividly described by Bragg in his lecture "First Steps in the X-Ray Analysis of Proteins" or, as he sometimes prefers to call it, "How Proteins Were Not Solved."

Hemoglobin and myoglobin. In 1951, however, the Dutch crystallographer J. M. Bijvoet pointed out that the phase problem could be solved in principle by measuring the X-ray diffraction pattern from three crystals having exactly the same atomic arrangement but with slight differences. Crystal 1 should contain the original compound under study; crystal 2, the same compound chemically modified so that one of the light atoms in each molecule, a hydrogen say, is replaced by a heavier one such as mercury; crystal 3, modified so that a different hydrogen atom is replaced by an atom of mercury. The presence of the heavy atoms would change the relative intensities of the spots in the diffraction pattern in a way that allowed the phases to be calculated.

In theory this seemed a hopeful approach to the problem of protein structure, but it was not clear at first how it could be applied in practice without disturbing the arrangement of the protein molecules. In 1953, Vernon Martin Ingram and I succeeded in preparing crystals with two atoms of mercury attached to each molecule of hemoglobin. When I developed the first X-ray diffraction picture I was thrilled to find that the molecular arrangement had remained constant and that the intensities of the spots had changed exactly as expected. At that moment I felt exuberantly confident that the structure of proteins would soon be solved.

Shortly afterwards, however, I obtained a picture of the molecule in projection on a plane and, to my great disappointment, the only information this gave me was its external shape, which Bragg and I had already worked out by another method. Owing to the great thickness of the molecule its internal structure did not reveal itself. Clearly, I had to solve the structure in three dimensions and to do this I needed another set of crystals with heavy atoms attached to a different pair of sites in each molecule. This proved very difficult and it took several years to find a solution.

In the meantime, Kendrew had made headway with the X-ray analysis of myoglobin, a simpler relative of hemoglobin that serves as an oxygen store in muscle. After a long search he and his colleagues found that myoglobin crystals contained several niches where compounds of gold, mercury, or platinum accommodated themselves without actually entering into chemical combination with the protein molecules or disturbing their arrangement in the crystal. This solved the phase problem and allowed them to calculate the distribution of electron density in a series of sections cut through the myoglobin molecule.

In many scientific investigations results accumulate undramatically. In X-ray crystallography, however, only after the measurements of thousands of diffracted spots have been combined into one grand mathematical synthesis does an image of the structure finally emerge. This first revelation of the structure of a protein molecule made up for many years of drudgery and frustration.

Kendrew's model was intensely exciting, even though it showed only the position of the hem (the red pigment that carries an atom of iron) and the general course of the polypeptide chain, but not the details needed to understand how myoglobin functions. To measure the intensities of about 5,000 spots required for the first image of myoglobin had seemed a backbreaking job, but improving the image so as to distinguish details of the individual amino acids involved the measurement of about a quarter of a million spots. It still seems incredible that this feat should have been accomplished in two years.

In the meantime, my colleagues and I had also surmounted the chemical problems at first encountered in preparing a series of heavy atom compounds of hemoglobin. In 1959 we obtained an excellent map showing the folding of the four chains and the positions of the hem groups. The chains were identical in pairs and each of them bore a strong resemblance to the single chain of myoglobin. In 1963 Hilary Muirhead and I discovered that the entire hemoglobin molecule changes its shape every time oxygen is taken up or released and that it is this change of shape that ensures its efficiency as a respiratory carrier. In 1967 Hilary Muirhead, Joyce Cox, Gwynne Goaman, and I advanced another step and solved the structure of the oxygen-containing form in sufficient detail to map the positions of nearly all the 574 amino acids and to construct a model showing the positions of its 10,000 atoms. We hope that this model will lead to an understanding of respiratory function in terms of the spatial arrangement of molecules (stereochemistry).

DNA and the genetic code

The most important event in the history of our laboratory has been the solution of the structure of DNA by Watson and Crick in 1953. Crick explained the discovery in his article "The Language of Life" in the *1969 Britannica Yearbook of Science and the Future.* It established that the pairing of complementary nucleotide bases, the four chemical side groups in the DNA molecule that attach to each other in a prescribed order, serves as the transmitter of chemical information in biological systems. Transmission of genetic information from parent to progeny and its translation into enzyme structure both depend on this principle.

The fact that enzyme function is genetically controlled, coupled with the knowledge that there is a definite sequence of amino acids in proteins, suggested that the sequence of the bases along the nucleic acid (DNA) chain ought to be collinear with the sequence of the amino acids in the corresponding protein chain. This is known as the sequence hypothesis and is one of the fundamental postulates of molecular biology. The form the genetic code might take at first seemed problematical because DNA contains only four different bases whereas proteins contain 20 different amino acids. Supposing two bases coded for one amino acid, then the number of possible pairs of bases is $4^2 = 16$, which is too few to code for 20 amino acids. If three bases coded for one amino acid, then the number of possible triplets is $4^3 = 64$, which would be too many.

In 1961, however, Crick, L. Barnett, Sydney Brenner, and R. J. Watts-Tobin proved that a group of three nucleotide bases (or, less likely, a multiple of three bases) coded for one amino acid. This meant that either the majority of the 64 possible triplets would have to be without meaning or that many amino acids must be coded for by more than one triplet. In addition, they showed that there are no commas (breaks or interruptions) between triplets coding for successive amino acids and that ambiguity is avoided by reading the sequence of bases from a fixed starting point. It had already been demonstrated that the code is nonoverlapping, *i.e.*, that separate triplets code for successive amino acids. Paradoxically, the sequence hypothesis took longer to prove than the unraveling of the general nature of the code, but it was finally confirmed in 1964 by genetic and biochemical experiments on virus-infected bacteria.

The actual triplets coding for each of the 20 amino acids were determined in the U.S. between 1961–67 by Marshall W. Nirenberg and Har Gobind Khorana (*see* Year in Review: HONORS, *Medical Sciences*), along with Severo Ochoa and others. Strangely, some amino acids are coded for by as many as six triplets, and others by only one. Of the triplets, 61 coded for amino acids but the remaining three appeared to spell nonsense. Researchers in our laboratory have since determined that all three nonsense triplets code for chain termination. Nonsense suggests that the synthesis of

the chain stops passively, but in 1968 Mark Steven Bretscher showed that chain termination is an active process. Its nature, however, was still obscure.

Translation of the genetic message. Most proteins in the cell are coded for by the DNA in the nucleus, the dense body enclosed in the cell. The proteins are made, however, in particles known as ribosomes located in the cytoplasm, the part of the cell outside the nucleus. An intermediary is necessary to transfer the information from the nucleus to the cytoplasm. Since it was known that ribosomes consist of both protein and ribonucleic acid (RNA), another complex substance found primarily in the nucleus, it was at first thought that the ribosomal RNA contained this transcript of the genetic message. In 1961, however, François Jacob and Jacques Monod in Paris pointed out that all the observations could be better explained if the ribosomes merely served as machines for the assembly of proteins and if the template was actually *another* RNA, which the French scientists called messenger RNA (m-RNA).

Brenner, Jacob, and M. Meselson tested this hypothesis and found that when a bacterium was infected by a virus an RNA transcript of the viral DNA attached itself to the ribosomes of the bacterial host. The bacterial ribosomes then manufactured viral protein. This experiment proved the nonspecificity of the ribosomes and the existence of m-RNA.

Another problem connected with the biosynthesis of proteins had arisen at an earlier stage. There is no stereochemical correspondence between amino acids and nucleic acid chains that would help amino acids to find their correct places on an RNA template. Crick suggested that this difficulty might be overcome if there were special activating enzymes that combined each amino acid with a special nucleotide adaptor. This adaptor would contain the "anticode" for the amino acid. The anticode, a triplet of bases, would find the right coding triplet on the m-RNA by complementary base pairing. Crick's hypothesis was borne out by the discovery in 1955–56 of the adaptor, transfer RNA (t-RNA), and of the necessary activating enzymes by M. B. Hoagland and by P. Berg in the United States.

In the early 1960s Sanger began to develop chromatographic methods for determining the sequence of bases in RNA. Transfer RNA, consisting of single chains of only 70 to 80 nucleotides, seemed the simplest material to begin with. When trying to isolate t-RNA for the amino acid methionine, he and Kjeld A. Marcker came across two different kinds: one carrying normal methio-

What is molecular biology?

Molecular biologists seek to understand the inheritance, development, and behavior of living organisms in terms of the atomic structure and interactions of certain large molecules that are common to all forms of life. The unity of life at the molecular level gives the subject coherence and great conceptual beauty.

The molecular approach to living things has developed in this century. Chemical reactions in living cells are catalyzed by enzymes. In the late 1920s physical chemists found that enzymes are protein molecules of definite size and structure. Since then one of the great achievements of molecular biology has been the determination of the structure of enzymes and the interpretation of their catalytic activity in precise atomic terms.

The transformation of genetics from an abstract to a molecular science began in the 1940s. Gregor Mendel, the father of genetics, had discovered in 1865 that specific genetic factors control such features as the color of flowers, but it had not been known how they exercise this control until George W. Beadle and Edward L. Tatum found in 1941 that one genetic factor, or gene, apparently determines one enzyme. The importance of DNA as the major constituent of chromosomes had been recognized in the 19th century, but later its role had become controversial. In 1944 the discovery that DNA extracted from a bacterium of one type could effect a permanent genetic change in a bacterium of another type proved that a hereditary factor could be isolated in the test tube as a distinct chemical entity.

Another important line of research was initiated in 1943 with the discovery that inherited variations in bacteria result from spontaneous genetic mutations and, three years later, by the discovery of genetic recombination in bacterial viruses. The rigorous methods of studying the genetics of microorganisms that developed from these discoveries paved the way for the analysis of genetic events at the molecular level, including the discovery of the genetic code.

The importance of RNA was first realized about 30 years ago but its functions were understood only recently when the intricate system of RNA and protein that constitutes the chemical machinery for the biosynthesis of enzymes was isolated in the test tube. This success led to the deciphering of the genetic code itself, which in its turn has opened an entirely new field of research in biology and medicine.

The practical applications of molecular biology are as yet in their infancy. For instance, inherited diseases and the action of antibiotics are beginning to be understood in molecular terms, but the diseases cannot yet be cured, nor can new antibiotics yet be designed. However, these applications and many others will come sooner than most of us think and, as Joshua Lederberg points out in his Feature Article, HUMANICS AND GENETIC ENGINEERING, we had better be prepared for them.

nine, and another carrying a methionine so modified that it was like a railway car with its front coupling blocked. This blocked amino acid could clearly form only the first amino acid of a growing chain, which suggested that it acts as the initiator of protein synthesis.

So far, this initiator has been found only in certain specialized bodies (organelles) in the cells of higher organisms. Only few enzymes, however, are made in these organelles. The mechanism of chain initiation of the majority of enzymes made in other parts of the cells of higher organisms is still unknown.

The mechanism of muscular contraction

The mechanism of muscular contraction has long been one of the fundamental problems to be studied by X-ray diffraction. At first it seemed obvious to suppose that muscle bears some resemblance to rubber, in which contraction is caused by random coiling of molecular chains. Such coiling, or any kind of systematic folding, should manifest itself by changes in the X-ray diffraction pattern. Soon after Hugh Huxley joined us, he began an X-ray study of wet muscle fibers under experimental conditions capable of revealing fine structure. Between 1950 and 1952 he found evidence of two interpenetrating kinds of filaments of submicroscopic dimensions, but, paradoxically, neither of these filaments seemed to shorten when muscle contracted.

The paradox was resolved in 1953 by Huxley and Jean Hanson while they were both working at the Massachusetts Institute of Technology, and, simultaneously and independently, by Andrew Fielding Huxley and R. Niedergerke at the Physiological Laboratory at Cambridge. Muscle was found to contract, not by a shortening of its protein chains, but by a sliding motion of the two interpenetrating sets of protein filaments. This concept was so new and revolutionary that few

A Gateway to the Future

workers in the field were willing to believe it. Stimulated by their scepticism, Hugh Huxley refined the methods of preparing specimens for electron microscopy and revealed the structure of muscle in a degree of detail never attained before.

Since then Huxley has studied the detailed mechanism of sliding. Striated (voluntary) muscle is divided into segments by a series of regularly spaced disks. Attached to each side of the disks are thin filaments, which consist mostly of the protein actin. Halfway between the two disks lies a set of thick filaments of the protein myosin. Huxley's photographs showed bridges extending from the filaments of myosin towards those of actin; these bridges might pull on the actin like a series of ratchets. To pull the actin filaments inwards, however, the two halves of the myosin filaments would have to pull in opposite ways. By dissolving myosin and allowing it to reaggregate into fibers, Huxley found that the myosin molecules grow outwards from the middle of the fiber so that the bridges at each end of the fiber point in opposite ways. Next he found that myosin molecules formed arrow-shaped bridges that pointed in opposite ways on the actin filaments attached to opposite sides of the membrane. Both the actin and myosin filaments, therefore, possess the polarity needed to allow the two halves of each segment to pull in opposite directions.

In the early days, evidence of the bridges actually moving was hard to obtain because it took 20 hours of exposure to get an X-ray diffraction picture from a live muscle. Thanks to new techniques, that time has been reduced to 20 minutes. These pictures suggest that the bridges in resting muscle form an orderly array, but that their arrangement in actively contracting muscle is more random, as might be expected if they moved backward and forward.

A precipitate of myosin cross-bridges attached to thin actin filaments from rabbit muscle (left) forms arrows that point away from the disk separating successive segments. At the right, note the disks between successive muscle segments and the regularly spaced cross-bridges that link the thick and thin filaments.

Photos, courtesy, Laboratory of Molecular Biology

Structure of small viruses

The present research in our laboratory by Klug and his colleagues on the structure of small viruses is a direct continuation of Bernal's X-ray studies in the late 1930s. Some of it, in fact, is still concerned with the same two plant viruses first examined by Bernal, tobacco mosaic and tomato bushy stunt. One is rod-shaped and the other spherical, and both consist of only RNA and protein. Between them they typify the simplest forms of living matter.

Bernal's work established that each individual particle of tobacco mosaic virus diffracted X rays as though it were a tiny crystalline rod made up of identical subunits regularly arranged along its length. The problem hibernated until 1952 when William Cochran and Crick developed a mathematical theory of diffraction from helical (spiral-shaped) chain molecules while testing a helical model of the protein chain. With the help of this theory, Watson found that the subunits are arranged along a helix with a pitch of 23 Å. Rosalind Franklin, working in Bernal's laboratory at Birkbeck College, London, where Klug joined her in 1954, determined that the virus consists of a long, helically wound filament of RNA, protected by a coat of small, identical, and helically arranged protein molecules.

Franklin and Klug's work stimulated Watson and Crick to formulate a general theory of virus structure in 1956. They argued that the amount of RNA present in a small virus is not enough to code for more than a very few protein molecules, so that it would be most economical, in terms of genetic information, if the coat of a virus were made of small protein molecules that are all alike.

This condition imposes certain geometrical restrictions. On a cylindrical surface, the protein molecules would have to grow in the form of a helix, but the theory imposes no geometric restriction on the pitch of the helix or the number of particles per turn. On the surface of a sphere, on the other hand, geometry shows that the molecules would aggregate only in multiples of 12, 24, or 60 and each type of aggregate would possess a different type of symmetry that could be detected by X-ray analysis. The symmetry predicted for a particle containing a multiple of 60 subunits was first detected in 1956 by D. L. D. Caspar in X-ray diffraction pictures of tomato bushy stunt virus. It has since been confirmed in all spherical viruses, including poliomyelitis and several others of medical interest.

At first, however, only the X-ray evidence agreed with the theory, while electron microscope data suggested that certain viruses are made up

370

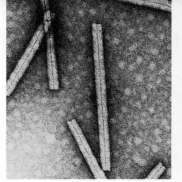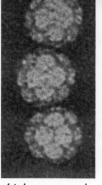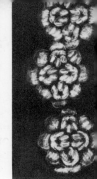

The fine cross striations in the rods of tobacco mosaic virus (left) are helical grooves between neighboring protein molecules. The geometric arrangement of protein subunits drawn according to the Casper-Klug theory (center) is confirmed in a micrograph of turnip yellow mosaic virus particles (right).

of numbers of subunits that are not multiples of 60. By an ingenious extension of the Watson-Crick theory, Caspar and Klug predicted that identical particles form solid surfaces by arranging themselves in patterns of pentagons and hexagons, thus establishing clusters that correspond to the apparent subunits seen in the electron micrographs.

The predicted patterns could not have been resolved by the techniques of electron microscopy used in the early 1950s. With the help of the method of negative staining, however, Klug and J. T. Finch have been able to verify that the subunits in all the small spherical viruses are arranged in accordance with one or the other of the predicted patterns, so that each virus can be assigned to a morphological class. Although protein subunits may be grouped into clusters, their number is a multiple of 60 in all cases.

The present and future of the laboratory

Now that the genetic code is known, Sanger and his group are developing methods for reading the genetic message itself. They hope to discover more about the mechanisms that control its transcription from gene to m-RNA and its translation from m-RNA to protein. The sequence of coding triplets that specifies the amino acid sequence of a protein may be preceded by a prefix and possibly followed by a postscript. Both of these may be concerned with control, but their nature and function are still unclear. Molecular biologists also suspect that the multiplicity of triplets that code for certain amino acids may serve to control the rate of protein synthesis.

In the long run work in genetics may lead to the design and synthesis of new kinds of enzymes and of the genes required to make them, and ultimately to their introduction into higher organisms. But first we must learn how protein chains of a given amino acid sequence fold up spontaneously to form a complex and uniquely ordered structure and how that structure determines a particular kind of catalytic activity.

Certain fields of molecular biology have become overcrowded, especially microbial biosynthesis and control. This was one of the reasons why Brenner and Crick switched research to growth and differentiation of higher organisms. Brenner has selected a small nematode worm that contains only 1,000 cells, has a life cycle of three and a half days, lives on bacteria, and is fully differentiated into skin, muscle, gut, and nerve cells. It possesses six pairs of chromosomes and repro-

duces either by self-fertilizing or by fertilization by sexually differentiated males. A large progeny can be raised from a single individual or crosses can be made of selected mutants, making this worm an ideal subject for genetic studies. At the moment the main interest is the growth of the nervous system and its genetic control.

One can foresee that the great unsolved problems of medicine, such as cancer and cardiovascular and degenerative diseases, may have to be approached by seeking an understanding of pathological events at the molecular level. This suggests that we should try to extend the frontiers of molecular biology towards medicine and the biology of higher organisms.

See also Year in Review: MEDICINE, *Medical Genetics;* MICROBIOLOGY; MOLECULAR BIOLOGY; ZOOLOGY.

FOR ADDITIONAL READING:
Bragg, Sir Lawrence, "First Stages in the X-ray Analysis of Proteins," *Reports on Progress in Physics,* 28:1–16 (1965).

Clark, B. F. C., and Marcker, K. A., "How Proteins Start," *Scientific American,* pp. 36–42 (January 1968).

Holley, R. W., "The Nucleotide Sequence of a Nucleic Acid," *Scientific American,* pp. 30–39 (February 1966).

Huxley, H. E., "The Mechanism of Muscular Contraction," *Scientific American,* pp. 18–27 (December 1965).

Kendrew, J. C., "Myoglobin and the Structure of Proteins," *Science,* pp. 1256–1266 (March 29, 1963).

Perutz, M. F., "The Hemoglobin Molecule," *Scientific American,* pp. 64–76 (November 1964).

Thompson, E. O. P., "The Insulin Molecule," *Scientific American,* pp. 36–41 (May 1955).

Watson, J. D., *The Double Helix* (Athenaeum, 1968).

Watson, J. D., *The Molecular Biology of the Gene* (Benjamin, 1965).

Oceanography

continued from page 305
the fact that the scientific study of the oceans and the proper use of the oceans is international in scope. Cooperative efforts at the international level through UN organizations, such as UNESCO and the Intergovernmental Maritime Consultative Organization, and through the international scientific unions, was expected to do much to lead the Decade to a successful program.

U.S. objectives. The U.S. government issued a report, "Our Nation and the Sea," prepared by the Commission on Marine Science, Engineering and Resources, which made more than 100 specific recommendations. If implemented in their entirety, these recommendations would completely restructure the organization of the marine sciences in the United States. The most far-reaching suggestion was that a "new civilian agency, which might be called the National Oceanic and Atmospheric Agency," should be formed "to be the principal instrumentality within the Federal Government for administration of the Nation's civil marine and atmospheric programs." This new agency would initially be composed of the U.S. Coast Guard, the Environmental Science Services Administration, the Bureau of Commercial Fisheries (with some parts of the Bureau of Sport Fisheries and Wildlife), the National Sea Grant Program, the U.S. Lake Survey, and the National Oceanographic Data Center.

The scope of this report was wide. It ranged over such diverse subjects as aquaculture, pollution control, the Barbados Oceanographic and Meteorological Experiment, the National Data Buoy System, improving marine fisheries, oil and mineral exploitation, uses of the continental shelf, polar exploration, oceanographic prediction, the world weather program, marine transportation, manned ocean habitats, coastal engineering, and the use of spacecraft to study the oceans.

Another area of concern is that of the United States' next objective in space. A report released by the National Academy of Sciences entitled "Useful Applications of Earth-Oriented Satellites" projected that space technology and space satellites would provide man with a better understanding of his planet. This would, in turn, yield better ways to forecast what occurs in the atmosphere and the oceans, to keep track of variations in resources, and to monitor and alleviate (and perhaps eliminate) atmospheric and oceanic pollution. Oceanographers participated in the development of this Earth Resources Program, and helped to conceive new ways of studying the oceans on a global basis from various types of satellites. The Nimbus satellites, for example, are capable of measuring certain quantities of the

Paris Match from Pictorial Parade

A French deep-sea diver practices new breathing techniques at about 700 ft. By strapping himself into a diving case specially designed to withstand the great pressures of the ocean depths, the diver is able to minimize the stress on his body. Electrodes located in his diving suit transmit all of his physiological reactions to technicians above.

ocean's surface as they orbit the earth twice each day, and the applications technology satellites (ATS) can watch nearly half the earth continuously and receive and transmit radio signals from and to any place they can see. One instrument on a satellite could conceivably do the work of many thousands of instruments on oceanographic buoys or on aircraft, except that the information gathered by a satellite instrument could be obscured by the atmosphere or by intervening rain and clouds. Considerable sophistication in the kinds of sensors and the use of the data would, therefore, be required if the ATS were to be used extensively.

The most promising solution to the prediction problem for oceanography and meteorology would involve collecting data on a global scale to provide initial information for computer-based atmosphere and ocean models. (See *Ocean Models,* below.) Buoys, satellites, and ships would all have to be used together as platforms for the wide variety of instruments that will be needed. The proper combination of these techniques so as to get the best data at the least cost posed a challenge for oceanographers.

In his Wexler Memorial Lecture, presented at the national meeting of the American Meteorological Society in New York in January 1969, Joseph Smagorinsky comprehensively outlined the scope of the meteorological and oceanographic prediction problem. He described the current status of computer-based meteorological prediction of atmospheric conditions (including winds, rains, and clouds) for five to ten days in the future. For the seven- to ten-day range, he showed that it was important to include realistically the effects of oceans on atmosphere. The construction of computer-based ocean models proved that the converse is also true: in order to predict changes in the oceans, it is necessary to include atmospheric effects.

The "Glomar Challenger." A fundamental thesis of marine geologists is that the sea floor contains the hidden secrets of the geological past. Since the days of A. Wegener, who first proposed the idea of continental drift in the 1920s, the sea floor has been probed and studied with ever-increasing effectiveness. As a part of these studies, the orientations of residual magnetism in the rocks of the ocean bottom have been mapped in great detail since the mid-1950s.

Among the many practical scientific achievements in the ocean sciences during 1968 and 1969 was the completion of one phase of a project called the Joint Oceanographic Institutions for Deep-Earth Sampling (JOIDES). In June 1966, JOIDES proposed, among other things, a Deep-Sea Drilling Project (DSDP), and the U.S. National Science Foundation (NSF) supplied the funds. Construction of a special ship was contracted, and by Aug. 11, 1968, the "Glomar Challenger" had completed its sea-trials and was prepared for the DSDP.

The "Glomar Challenger" was designed to orient, control, and rotate a drill string (a flexible drill pipe) in 20,000 ft of water. A computerized system of pulses from acoustic beacons on the ocean floor kept the ship stable while it was drilling with the string. After the drill pierced the ocean bottom, oceanographers lowered a core barrel down the inside of the drilling pipe. Samples were then drawn up through the pipe.

This method brought about impressive results. In January 1969 seven holes were drilled. Analysis of the magnetic data discovered in rocks taken out of the mantle and a study of the fossils of minute organisms affirmed the present theory of continental drift. North and South America are, indeed, drifting away from Europe and Africa at the rate of several centimeters per year.

Ocean models. A continuing area of development in meteorology has been the construction of computer-based models of the atmosphere for numerical weather prediction. These efforts started in the early 1950s with rather simple models and have been improved considerably since then. Electronic computers have already

revolutionized meteorology and are expected to do the same for physical oceanography. At the Geophysical Fluid Dynamics Laboratory of the Environmental Science Services Administration, Kirk Bryan and Michael Cox succeeded in producing realistic computerized models of the North Atlantic and the Indian oceans.

The North Atlantic model has yielded a circulation system caused by the stress of a mean wind over the ocean and by heating near the Equator and cooling in polar regions. It has successfully produced such known features of the ocean as a Gulf Stream, a Labrador Current, the gross temperature distribution of the North Atlantic, and something quite similar to the equatorial undercurrent. The Indian Ocean model is driven by seasonally varying winds and surface water temperatures. It has successfully produced many of the known climatological features of the Indian Ocean circulation, including strong ocean currents off Africa and the seasonal reversals of the currents that occur in the northern parts of the Indian Ocean.

A computer-programmed method for the study of the circulation of the world ocean became available in 1968 and it was clear that even more realistic models, allowing predictions of changes in the world ocean, would be developed. Developments during the next five to ten years may finally produce truly accurate detailed numerical descriptions of the currents, temperatures, salinities, and other physical properties of the world's oceans.

—Willard J. Pierson, Jr.

See also Feature Article: EXPLORING THE OCEAN FRONTIERS.

Physics

High-energy physics

The results of high-energy physics research in the period under review were more in the nature of a slow accumulation of new data and ideas than of spectacular breakthroughs. The first systematic experimental programs were carried out at two new accelerators, the 76-Bev (billion electron volt) proton accelerator at Serpukhov in the Soviet Union and the 20-Bev linear electron accelerator at Stanford, Calif. Each of these machines marked a substantial increase over previous accelerators in the highest energy available for the particles being accelerated.

A search for quarks. Perhaps the most exciting possibility for new experiments opened up by

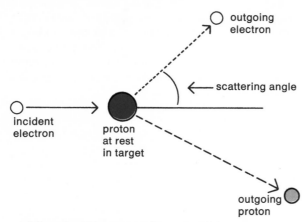

Elastic Electron-Proton Scattering

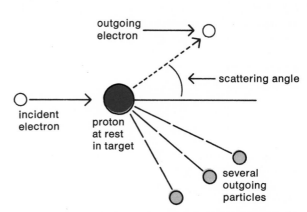

Inelastic Electron-Proton Scattering

the high energy of protons at the Serpukhov accelerator was the production of new particles with higher masses than those now known. Because of the Einstein relation $E = mc^2$ between rest mass and rest energy, the more massive a particle is, the more energy is required to produce it. At previous accelerators the maximum energy available was about 30 Bev, which allowed the production of pairs of particles whose rest energy was about 4 Bev each. At the Serpukhov accelerator pairs of particles with a rest energy of 6 Bev each can be produced. This is particularly relevant to the search for quarks, a still undiscovered set of three different particles.

According to one prominent theory, most of the known particles are made up of quarks, which is why physicists are interested in whether quarks can be produced. Because quarks have not been found at lower energy accelerators, some physicists have suggested that quarks are too massive to be produced by those machines. Accordingly, a search was made at the higher energies available at Serpukhov, but no quarks were found. If this result continues to be confirmed, it will probably mean that if quarks exist, their rest energy is greater than 6 Bev. Meanwhile, physicists await the completion in 1972 of the 200-Bev accelerator near Batavia, Ill., to search for more massive quarks.

Inelastic electron scattering. Experiments at the Stanford Linear Accelerator Center (SLAC) have for the most part been devoted to a study of electromagnetic interactions at high energy. The particles in the beam produced by this accelerator are positive or negative electrons. When they pass through matter, these electrons generate high-energy photons (gamma rays) so that beams of gamma rays are also available. Both electrons and photons are relatively simple par-

ticles, whose properties are well understood. It is, therefore, possible to use them as probes to study more complicated particles, such as protons. This is done by bombarding a target composed of protons with a beam of electrons and measuring what happens to the electrons and to the target protons. The technique is a modern version of the method that Lord Rutherford used in 1911 to discover the nucleus of the atom.

Two kinds of processes can occur in these experiments. It may happen that the electron and proton retain their identities and simply exchange some energy, with no other particles emerging. This is called elastic scattering. Alternatively, it is possible that the electron remains after the collision but the proton changes into several particles, one of which may still be a proton. In this case, we speak of inelastic scattering. Inelastic scattering really refers to many different processes, since the number and type of particles that can be produced in this way vary with the bombarding electron's energy and the angle at which the electron emerges relative to its direction when it collides (the scattering angle).

Independent experiments done in the past, in which electrons are scattered by other electrons, have shown that electrons have no detailed structure; therefore, whatever complexities occur in electron-proton scattering, whether elastic or inelastic, can be attributed to the structure of the protons. This is one advantage that such scattering experiments have over experiments in which protons scatter other particles, such as pi mesons. In the latter case both particles have complicated structures, and the results are, therefore, correspondingly more difficult to interpret.

Previous measurements of elastic electron-proton scattering at various laboratories showed that when high-energy electrons are scattered through large angles, the probability of scattering (scattering cross section) decreases very rapidly as the angle increases. If the proton charge were concentrated at one point, as the electron's charge seems to be, then the elastic scattering cross section would not decrease nearly so rapidly as it is observed to do. It was, therefore, inferred that the proton charge is smoothly distributed over its small radius of 7×10^{-14} cm and that there are no regions within the proton in which the charge is concentrated.

This tentative conclusion was cast into doubt as a result of the inelastic scattering experiments done in the past year at SLAC. These measurements indicated that the inelastic scattering cross sections do not decrease so rapidly with an increasing angle as do the elastic scattering cross sections, and, indeed, seemed to be consistent with the view that there are small, highly concentrated regions of charge within a proton. A model which tentatively seems to fit both elastic and inelastic electron-proton scattering has been proposed by several physicists. According to this model a proton does contain several concentrated charges which are not among the known elementary particles. When a high-energy electron hits a proton, the proton breaks up into these constituent objects, which have been named partons. The partons may rapidly recombine to make another proton, in which case the scattering will be elastic. Alternatively, they may recombine to make one or more other particles, with the same total charge as the proton, in which case the scattering will be inelastic. Because there are many more ways of recombining to make one or more new particles than of making a single proton, there should be much less elastic than inelastic scattering, as the experiments have shown. On the other hand, the partons must recombine in some way so that the total scattering, elastic plus inelastic, should behave as the scattering from several point charges, that is, should decrease slowly with the scattering angle, again in agreement with the experiments.

The reader will have noticed that the partons that are used to explain electron-proton scattering are similar to the hypothetical quarks discussed earlier. Whether the partons can truly be identified with quarks depends on a further study of their properties, such as their electric charge. Among the experiments that can be expected to clarify this question will be the scattering of high-energy gamma rays from protons, and the production of electron pairs when electrons are scattered by protons. We may expect such measurements to be done in the coming year. The results of these experiments can be compared

with predictions of the parton model and used to measure the electric charges of the partons. In this way it may be possible to infer the existence of quarks within the proton. It is likely, however, that most physicists will still await the production and detection of free quarks before being convinced of their existence.

Tests of CP invariance. Perhaps the most baffling problem being actively considered by high-energy physicists is the reason for the noninvariance of some particle interactions under CP symmetry. CP symmetry stands for the product of charge conjugation and parity symmetries, which may be described as follows. Under charge conjugation, all charges of particles (from positive to negative or vice versa), change sign while particle velocities and energies remain unaffected. Under parity, charges and energies are unaffected, while velocities change sign. Hence under CP, both charges and velocities change sign. Until 1964 it was believed that all particle reactions would proceed at the same rate if CP were applied to all particles involved in the re-

A superconducting magnet, the world's largest, is inspected at the Argonne (Ill.) National Laboratory. It will aid high-energy physicists by directing particles in accelerators into such viewing facilities as bubble chambers.

Courtesy, Argonne National Laboratory

action. This principle is known as CP invariance, and it was confirmed by experiments done until then. In that year, however, it was discovered that in the decays of a neutral particle known as K_2^0, CP invariance did not work. One example in which CP invariance does not hold in K_2^0 decay is that the two decays

$K_2^0 \rightarrow$ positive pi meson, negative electron, and antineutrino

and

$K_2^0 \rightarrow$ negative pi meson, positive electron, and neutrino

which should be equal by CP invariance, actually differ in rate by about one part in 400. Other observations of K_2^0 decay have also given small but definite violations of CP invariance.

Since the first discovery of the small CP noninvariance in K_2^0 decay, physicists have been trying to find other particle reactions for which this symmetry does not hold. Also, they have been looking for the underlying reason why CP invariance, which is so close to being an exact law of nature, breaks down where it does. Of course, these two searches are related, because each new occurrence of CP noninvariance would be a clue to the underlying cause, while any hypothesis about the reason for the noninvariance would suggest other places where it might or might not occur, and thus be a guide for new experiments.

Until recently there was no conclusive evidence for CP noninvariance in any reactions other than K_2^0 decay. In 1968, however, a result was reported by a group of physicists at Columbia University, which, if confirmed, would be an example of such a reaction. The Columbia group looked at the decay of a particle called η^0 (eta zero), discovered about eight years ago. This particle decays very rapidly. About 25% of the time it decays into three pi mesons, one of which is positively charged (π^+), one negatively charged (π^-), and one neutral (π^0). These three kinds of pi mesons are related particles with roughly equal masses. When charge conjugation is applied to the η^0 and π^0, they are unaffected, being neutral, while the π^+ and π^- are changed into one another. Suppose that some fraction of the η^0 mesons in a large sample decays into a π^+ with energy E_1, a π^- with energy E_2, and a π^0 with energy E_3. Then if CP invariance held for the decay, we would expect that an equal fraction of the sample would decay into a π^+ with energy E_2, a π^- with energy E_1, and a π^0 with energy E_3. In particular, this implies that there should be an equal number of decays in which the π^+ energy is greater than the π^- energy, and of decays in which the π^- energy is greater than the π^+ energy. Instead, the Columbia experiment indicated a small surplus of about 1.5% of decays in which the π^+ had the greater energy. The inconclusive nature of the experiment comes from the possibility that there is some error in measuring the pi meson energies, or that the result is a statistical fluctuation, which would disappear if a larger sample of decays were measured. Several groups of physicists, including the Columbia group, are planning new measurements of the η^0 decays.

The present result, if correct, is quite important for the theory of how the CP noninvariance occurs. The η^0 decay is thought to involve the electromagnetic interactions that also occur in electron-proton scattering, but not the weak interactions that occur in β decay (electron and neutrino emission) of nuclei. The K_2^0 decay involves both the electromagnetic and the weak interactions. Therefore, if both η^0 and K_2^0 decays exhibit CP noninvariance, it is likely that the underlying cause is that electromagnetic interactions are CP noninvariant. This hypothesis, if true, would have a number of other consequences, which have been the subject of experiments. Most of the experiments done to test this theory have given negative results; none were conclusive.

In early 1969, a group at Princeton University reported a result which would, if true, be another indirect confirmation of the hypothesis of CP noninvariance of electromagnetism. According to a well-tested and mathematically demonstrated principle called the TCP theorem, any interaction among particles that is not CP invariant will also not be invariant under time reversal; the converse will also be true. The meaning of time reversal invariance is the following. If we symbolize a reaction as

(1) $\qquad A + B \rightarrow C + D$

where A, B, C, and D refer to any four particles, then time reversal invariance would imply that the inverse reaction

(2) $\qquad C + D \rightarrow A + B$

should proceed at the same rate as (1). This relationship between a reaction and its inverse is sometimes known as the principle of detailed balance. In the Princeton experiment the reaction measured was

$$p + n \rightarrow d + \gamma$$

were p stands for proton, n for neutron, d for deuteron (or heavy hydrogen nucleus), and γ for a gamma ray. Their result was compared with previous measurements done elsewhere of the inverse reaction

$$\gamma + d \rightarrow p + n$$

at the same energy and scattering angle. The

A test model seeks to prove the feasibility of a "meson factory," a new type of linear proton accelerator that will produce beams thousands of times more intense than any other existing accelerator. Such a device should prove invaluable in studying the structure and dynamics of an atomic nucleus.

two measurements disagreed substantially with one another at some angles and energies. Because a gamma ray is involved, these reactions must proceed through the electromagnetic interaction, and, therefore, the result seems to imply a lack of time reversal invariance for this interaction. Thus, by applying the TCP theorem, this interaction is also not CP invariant. However, because of the difficulty of the experiment, which in this case comes from having to make sure that it is really a gamma ray that is being produced, it will also have to be repeated before physicists are convinced of the conclusion.

A theoretical analysis of the reaction studied in the Princeton experiment suggests that if the effect detected is real, there should be a substantial deviation from time reversal invariance in inelastic electron scattering experiments. A preliminary search for such a deviation was recently carried out at the Cambridge, Mass., electron accelerator, with negative results. A more detailed experiment was to be undertaken at SLAC. In this experiment electrons will be scattered from a polarized target. Whereas ordinarily the protons in a target are an equal mixture of two polarization states, in the forthcoming experiment there will be a surplus of one of the two states. It is then predicted that if time reversal invariance does not hold, the angular distribution of the scattered electrons and protons will

be different than in the scattering from unpolarized protons. A conclusive result for this experiment may be forthcoming by the end of 1969.

These experiments, and others which will examine the details of the K_2^0 decay, should go far to decide the question of how CP noninvariance comes about. If it is decided that the electromagnetic interaction is not the culprit, then it is likely that a new interaction, much smaller than any previously known, is responsible. In this case we expect that in all situations other than K_2^0 decay the effects of this new interaction will be very difficult to detect, and experimental physicists will have to devote themselves to looking for effects at the level of one part in a million or less. The author is confident that they will eventually develop suitable techniques for doing just that, with consequences that we cannot now foresee.

—Gerald Feinberg

Nuclear physics

The past year in nuclear physics resulted in a considerable increase in our understanding of the basic and complex structure of the nucleus of an atom. Interest was rapidly developing in many new regions of research, and appropriate particle accelerators for the study of these new frontiers were either being considered or are under construction.

Energy levels of nuclei. One of the more exciting developments within the last year was the appreciable increase in the understanding of the energy levels of many nuclei. This understanding was accomplished by means of the great improvement in measurement techniques that resulted from the new types of solid-state detectors, such as the germanium detector, and the increased capability of computers. The combination of more sophisticated experiments and theory merged together to a remarkable degree, making it possible to explain the energy levels of many nuclei with considerable accuracy.

The experimental nuclear physicist studies each of the various energy levels of a nucleus by measuring their special properties, characterized by what is called the spin and parity, and the manner of decay of each energy level. Actually, for each different level, or excited state, of a nucleus, there is only one configuration of the nucleons (electrons and protons) in the nucleus that can produce that particular level with its particular characteristics.

The nuclear physicist considers certain configurations of nucleons as closed shells in the sense that all of the particles comprising this closed system more or less share a common potential. (A potential, in an electric field, is a quantity roughly analogous to level or elevation in a gravity field). When only one nucleon is added to this closed shell configuration, it behaves as an independent particle and moves around in some type of simple potential rather than mixing in with the other nucleons in a collective fashion. As more and more nucleons are added to this closed shell configuration, the shell configuration gradually starts breaking down, permitting the newly added nucleons to interact in a more general way with the nucleons of the closed shell or core.

The shell configuration of the nucleus is considered in some cases to be spherical and in other cases to be deformed in the form of a flattened disk or elongated cigar. Besides these complex distortions, the nucleus also may be rotating and vibrating simultaneously. This description is considerably oversimplified, but it does give some idea of the complexities of the structure of a nucleus.

One of the ways that nuclei can be studied in terms of the various energy levels that characterize a given nucleus is by studying its decay products, particularly the electromagnetic or gamma rays emitted from a nucleus that is changing from a higher excited state to a lower energy level. In this case, the nucleus in an excited state is formed by some kind of nuclear reaction or decay process. The excited state then de-excites down through lower excited levels until finally it reaches the ground, or stable, state of the nucleus. The gamma rays emitted from the nucleus during this cascade process can be measured and correlated with other processes in order to gain information about the particular characteristics of the excited states involved.

The study of these decay processes was greatly facilitated in the last few years by the development of sensitive gamma-ray detectors made of pure germanium crystals that are specially treated with lithium. These new germanium-lithium counters increased the accuracy in the measurements of nuclear structure by factors of 10 to 100. Such highly accurate measurements, many of which were made within the last year, contributed tremendously to the general knowledge of nuclear structure and to the details and characteristics of the energy levels which comprise that structure.

Artificial heavy elements. The elements of the periodic table investigated most thoroughly from a theoretical point of view during recent months were those considerably heavier than the most heavy nuclei now known. The heaviest elements currently under experimental study were elements

104 and 105. Element 104 was studied by U.S. research groups at the University of California and by Soviet groups at Dubno. The two groups seemed to get different results in terms of the specific isotopes of element 104 that were observed. This heavy element was quite unstable, and various isotopes existed for only a few minutes down to a few seconds or less.

As the artificially produced elements became heavier and heavier, their lifetimes got shorter and shorter. In many cases, if the element was being produced by a nuclear reaction between a light and heavy nucleus, the resulting nucleus immediately fissioned into two or more pieces rather than remaining in the form of a new nucleus. This difficulty made it appear that moving beyond the present region of known heavy elements was a formidable or even impossible task. New calculations based on recent measurements, however, indicated that there was an "island" of stability of very heavy nuclei (mass of about 310) that appeared to be stable. In any event, the more measurements that were made and the more refined the calculations became, the more interesting this as yet undiscovered region of stability appeared. These very heavy nuclei, commonly called "supertransuranic," enticed both experimental and theoretical physicists and played a strong role in the future plans of both.

It appeared that supertransuranic nuclei might be made by the fusion of two fairly heavy nuclei that added up to the particular mass desired in the supertransuranic region or close to that mass. Another possibility was to fuse two heavy identical nuclei, such as those of uranium, which would then fission or fragment; one of these fragments would then form the new supertransuranic nucleus.

New particle accelerators. The new and unusual possibilities revealed by this work on heavy nuclei resulted in a number of new proposals for particle accelerators specifically designed to accelerate heavy ions (charged atoms) in order to study these nuclei. One of the new accelerators under construction was a large facility at Brookhaven National Laboratory in Upton, N.Y., that would normally be used to provide protons of up to 30 Mev energy, as well as many other types of particles for the study of nuclear structure. Special modifications would also allow nuclei as heavy as bromine-81 to be accelerated to hundreds of Mev in energy, which is sufficient for fusion with nuclei as heavy as uranium-235. This new facility may be one of the first accelerators in the world capable of fusing such large and heavy nuclei.

Recent work by a group at an accelerator at

Berkeley, Calif., where 10 Bev (billion electron volt) protons were allowed to strike a uranium target and produce whatever they would, led to the discovery of a number of new and interesting light nuclei which had an unusually large number of protons compared to the number of neutrons. These unusual nuclei were produced on rare occasions and were the result of the tremendous energy of 10 Bev, which literally explodes the uranium nucleus into many different pieces. This technique is not unlike smashing up large rocks with a hammer and studying the fragments to learn what they are made of, how they were made, how they differ from one another, and any other unusual characteristics, such as size and shape. These experiments contributed significantly to the interest shown by many other research teams throughout the country in the development of new types of accelerators which can accelerate heavy nuclei to the extent that not only fragmentation reactions are produced but fusion reactions occur; these latter reactions form nuclei considerably heavier than any of those now in existence or known.

Another new accelerator under construction is a "meson factory" at the Los Alamos (N.M.) Scientific Laboratory. This accelerator was designed to provide an exceptionally intense beam of protons at an energy of 800 Mev. These protons would interact with target nuclei and form profuse quantities of pi mesons, or pions, the particles normally used in the study of high-energy physics. In this case, the intent was to use the pions for the study of nuclear structures because their intensity would, for the first time, be sufficient to allow for precise and detailed nuclear structure measurements. Because a pion interacts with nucleons in a way that is different from the manner in which a nucleon interacts with another nucleon, physicists expected that the results would yield much new information about nuclear structure.

High-energy electron accelerators also can be used in the study of low-energy nuclear structure. In the latter situation the high-energy electrons excite the nucleus by means of photons or gamma rays that they produce. Such excitation permits the study of certain characteristics of the nucleus that would be extremely difficult or even impossible to study with the usual scattering techniques of low-energy nuclear physics. Along these lines one of the most recent developments was an electron linear accelerator that could be operated on a continuous basis with consequent increases in intensity of the electrons. This new development of an electron accelerator might well open up an entire new field of study in low-energy nuclear structure by means of scattering high-energy electrons from nuclei.

Some of the systematic studies of known nuclei utilizing research accelerators led to methods of predicting the mass and other characteristics of unknown nuclei. Some of these new calculations indicate that a nucleus resembling that of calcium, which normally has 20 neutrons and 20 protons, might exist in the form of calcium-70. Calcium-70 would have its normal 20 protons, but there would be 50 neutrons instead of 20. A calcium nucleus of this sort would be so different from any known radioisotope that this unusual nucleus, as well as other neighboring nuclei, would form a lightweight "island" of stability similar to the heavy supertransuranic island. It was not clear, however, how an accelerator could produce such a nucleus.

Another exciting possibility which may be accomplished in 1970 is the acceleration of protons or even heavy ions with a superconducting linear accelerator. The development of such an accelerator should immediately make possible sufficient energies of heavy ions to produce fusion reactions anywhere throughout the entire periodic table of elements. The modest cost of this kind of accelerator made it feasible for it to be added to many existing laboratories to extend their range of energies and experimental programs.

—H. E. Wegner

Solid-state physics

The past year might be characterized as one in which a high degree of basic understanding was achieved in certain areas of solid-state physics, such as semiconductors. In addition, increased attention was being paid to new areas of research where there is still little or no detailed theoretical understanding. The former areas are characterized by materials in which the one-electron band theory can be applied; the latter areas are those in which that theory breaks down and it has become necessary to develop new theories. (The one-electron band theory assumes that the wave functions of electrons are spread in an orderly manner throughout a crystalline solid and also that the interactions between the different electrons can be ignored.)

In this review the developments in materials where the one-electron theory applies will be examined first. This examination will be followed by a section describing developments where the band theory may not apply.

Covalent semiconductors and band theory. One characteristic of solid-state physics is the rather close connection that is often possible between basic work and applications. An example of this is the development of the Gunn oscillator (named for its discoverer, J. B. Gunn) for microwave generation. On investigating the current which passed through a gallium arsenide (GaAs) sample as increasing voltage was being applied, Gunn found that at a certain critical level the direct current decreased with increasing voltage. It was also found that high-frequency, or microwave, radiation was generated. As might be expected, the observation of this phenomenon caused considerable excitement. A number of possible explanations were put forth, but finally it was realized that the Gunn effect could be explained in terms of the quantum states (*see* below) predicted for GaAs by band theory.

The important feature of GaAs is the occurrence of states with quite different electronic properties. In one set of these quantum states the electrons can be accelerated easily by an external electric field. In the other set of states such acceleration is much more difficult to achieve. Band calculations showed that the latter states ("hard") were about 0.3 ev (electron volts) higher in energy than the former states ("easy"). Thus, when voltage was applied, the electrons were accelerated rather easily until they reached the energy level of the "hard" states; then their velocity actually decreased, causing a decrease in current. This reaction explained the drop in current with increasing voltage; however, in order to explain the generation of microwave radiation it was necessary to examine the spatial distribution of the charge carriers in GaAs. In so doing it was found that when the current decreased, the "hard" carriers were spatially localized in small domains near the cathode. The microwave radiation was produced by the movement of these domains across the GaAs sample to the anode, where they disappeared.

In the past year the emphasis in solid-state microwave devices has been on making practical Gunn effect microwave devices to replace the much larger and more clumsy microwave tubes used in radar and other applications. In addition, due to the interest inspired by the Gunn effect, different types of solid-state devices based on it are being developed and show considerable promise.

Understanding the Gunn effect was made possible in part by the considerable progress achieved in the calculations of the band structure of covalently bonded (bonded by means of shared electrons) semiconductors. This progress was important because once the band structure has been determined, the quantum states become

The atomic structure of a metal crystal (above) is revealed by an atom-probe field ion microscope (below), an instrument invented by Erwin Müller of Pennsylvania State University.
The fine detail visible through this microscope is of great value to those engaged in research to improve the characteristics of metals.

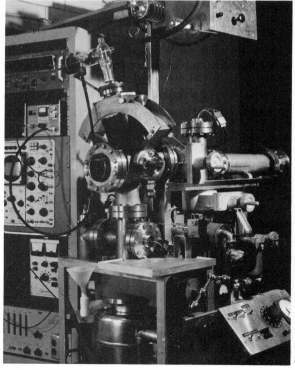

known and most of the electronic and optical properties of these semiconductors can, in principle, be calculated. The past year saw the ability to calculate and experimentally determine these quantum levels rise to a new high level. For example, a group at Stanford University and the Lockheed Aircraft Corp. Missiles and Space Division in Palo Alto, Calif., reported calculations and measurements on germanium, silicon, GaAs, gallium antimonide (GaSb), and gallium phosphide (GaP) in which agreement between experiment and theory of about ± 0.2 ev was obtained over an energy range of almost 20 ev. Such detailed knowledge can be important in understanding a wide range of optical and electric phenomena in these materials. For example, the color of a semiconductor is determined by the distribution in energy of the one-electron quantum states.

Another area in which strong advances were made concerned the preparation of semiconductor materials. New methods of fabrication of germanium and silicon, the original semiconductor materials, led to enormous advances in technology. Most striking was the development of integrated circuits, complete electronic circuits made economically on a single chip of silicon. Improved preparation of materials technology also made possible the use of binary compounds, such as GaAs or GaP, for specialized purposes. Examples included the above-mentioned Gunn microwave oscillators and also light emitters and electron emitters.

By changing the chemical composition of semiconductor alloy compounds, such as GaAs-GaP, it became possible to change their electronic and optical properties in a continuous manner. Thus, physicists found that the threshold voltage at which a Gunn device will oscillate can be reduced by adding GaP to GaAs to form gallium arsenide phosphide (GaAsP). Similarly, the wavelength or color of light produced by a semiconductor light emitter or laser can be varied by

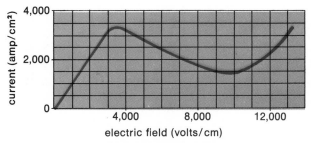

The Gunn effect demonstrates the temporary decrease in current with increasing voltage in gallium arsenide. The microwave radiation generated in this reaction led to the development of Gunn effect microwave devices.

varying the composition of an alloy such as GaAs-GaP.

This discussion has considered only the quantum states of electrons in solids. In addition, however, a solid is characterized by lattice vibrational states. These latter states determine the way in which atoms or ions of a solid move about their equilibrium positions in the latticelike arrangement of a crystal. For example, the vibrational states determine the speed with which sound moves through crystals and the way in which a crystal expands or contracts with changes in temperature. Just as it is necessary to understand and determine the electronic quantum states, it is necessary to understand and determine these vibration states if the properties of a crystal are to be well understood. Through the application of a number of techniques, including the use of lasers for studying the spectra of diffused light, considerable advances were made in the knowledge of lattice vibrations in solids during the past year.

New areas of research. In all of the above, systems were described which can be analyzed by applying the idealized one-electron band theory. As was illustrated in the preceding section, this theory has become highly developed and successfully applied to many materials; it has recently become increasingly clear, however, that it is not applicable to large groups of other materials. Much interesting solid-state work during recent months was associated with attempts to understand the properties of these other materials.

Several examples can be given of materials which cannot be treated by the simple one-electron band theory: (1) amorphous materials in which the atoms or ions of the crystal are not regularly arranged; (2) Mott insulators (named for Sir Nevill F. Mott, Cavendish Laboratory, Cambridge University, who did pioneering work on them) in which the interactions and correlations between the electrons are too strong to allow the one-electron theory to hold; and (3) certain alloys in which the electron interaction depends so strongly on the particular characteristics of the atom or ion occupying a given site that an average potential cannot be used.

Crystalline materials are characterized by an orderly, periodic arrangement of atoms. Amorphous materials, on the other hand, are characterized by a lack of any long-range, periodic order; that is, the atoms are arranged in a disorderly manner. A well-known example of an amorphous material is window glass. For crystalline material there are detailed theories explaining the optical, mechanical, and electrical properties. For the amorphous materials, however, no such theories exist.

Interest in the electrical properties of amorphous materials was heightened in recent months by a report from Stanford R. Ovshinsky in *Physical Review Letters.* This report described unusual electronic characteristics of certain amorphous materials. In materials composed of a mixture of such elements as silicon, germanium, tellurium, and arsenic, Ovshinsky reported that an increase in voltage above a certain minimum value would produce a drastic decrease in electrical resistance. In some cases the resistance would return to its original value as soon as the voltage was removed; in others, the new resistance state persisted even after the voltage was removed. The former behavior, called the "threshold effect," could be used to produce switches or active circuit elements; the latter phenomenon, called the "memory effect," could lead to devices that would be useful for storing information in computers.

The announcement by Ovshinsky produced considerable excitement as well as skepticism in the scientific community. Because of the lack of basic knowledge of this type of material and because of the preliminary nature of the practical work, it remained impossible to say whether or not one could expect devices of this type to have strong practical impact; however, it was clear that this would be an exciting area of research.

One of the earliest successes of the one-electron band theory was the prediction of the conduction of solids, that is, whether a given solid would exhibit metallic conduction or be an insulator or semiconductor. By the 1950s, however, it had become apparent that certain solids did not obey the predictions of band theory and that this was due to interactions between the electrons. For example, cobalt oxide and nickel oxide have electron arrangements that should cause them to be metals and, therefore, conduct electricity and heat. Instead, however, they are insulators.

More recently, other compounds were found which had insulator or semiconductor behavior at low temperatures and then changed abruptly into metallic conductors at a critical temperature. For example, in vanadium oxide (V_2O_3) the conductivity jumps by a factor of 10 million within a temperature range of much less than one degree. Because the occurrence of this behavior cannot be understood in terms of the conventional one-electron band theory, these materials, named Mott insulators, form an exciting area of new research that may lead to the development of new devices. The amount of interest and work in this field is expanding, and a number of tentative theories have been put forth. Thus, considerable progress can be anticipated.

Although little practical use is made of pure metals, rather extensive use is made of metal alloys (substances in which two or more metals are mixed together). In general, alloys are harder, stronger, and more durable than pure metals. A wide range of alloys has been developed. For example, various forms of steel are made by alloying with iron such elements as nickel, copper, vanadium, and carbon. Pure gold and silver are too soft to be used in jewelry; however, by alloying them with copper or other metals, sufficiently hard materials can be formed so that jewelry can be made.

Most of the alloys we use have been developed by trial and error rather than by the application of basic knowledge. In fact, our present basic understanding of alloys is quite meager. In order for solid-state physics to assist in developing new alloys and improving those that already exist, it is important to increase our basic knowledge of them. The past year has seen increased activity, both theoretical and experimental, aimed at achieving such knowledge. For a large and very important class, that of transition (such as iron and nickel) and noble (such as copper, silver, and gold) metals, encouraging preliminary success was attained. In particular, it was found that the electronic, magnetic, and optical properties of alloys are much more dependent on short-range rather than long-range effects. For example, a nickel atom in copper may have quite different magnetic properties, depending on whether or not it is surrounded by nickel or copper atoms. This again indicates that new theories must be developed if these alloys are to be properly understood.

—William E. Spicer

See also Year in Review: ELECTRONICS, *Semiconductors.*

Other developments in physics

An event of potentially great significance took place in June, when Joseph Weber and his colleagues at the University of Maryland announced that they had detected gravity waves, emanating probably from a massive object in our galaxy. If this discovery is confirmed by further research, it will furnish additional proof of Albert Einstein's General Theory of Relativity, which states, in part, that gravitational fields surrounding bodies in space should produce waves. Gravity waves are thought to be a form of energy similar to electromagnetic radiation and travel at about the speed of light. Solid aluminum cylinders, weighing about a ton each and set up 600 mi apart, were used as detectors.

Answers to many of the unsolved problems of physics and astronomy may be provided by gravity waves. Among these problems is that of the so-called missing matter in the universe, which has been postulated to account for the fact that the observed motions of stars in our galaxy show that they are under the gravitational influence of 40% more matter than can be seen. If the total amount of matter in the universe can be determined, scientists may be able to decide whether the universe is infinite or finite and whether or not it will expand forever or fall back into a condensed form. Another mystery that gravity waves might help clarify is the nature of quasi-stellar and pulsating radio sources (quasars and pulsars).

Science, General

The climate of science during the year was exemplified on Aug. 14, 1968, when almost identical letters were sent by Leland Haworth, director of the National Science Foundation (NSF), to several hundred U.S. university presidents. Since the federal government had become by far the largest benefactor of academic science in the world, and since the foundation was the only agency in the government specifically authorized to support basic research, the letters were read with more than routine interest. Their content was not calculated to generate enthusiasm among the recipients.

In the letters, Haworth explained that the imposition by Congress of a ceiling on government expenditures for fiscal 1969 (July 1, 1968, to June 30, 1969) had made it necessary for the foundation to impose a limitation on expenditures by those universities receiving foundation support. Then came the bad news: the total expenditures that each institution could charge to NSF. "This is the total available to you for the entire fiscal year for all grants in force," Haworth stated, "whether the grants were made in prior years or already awarded in FY [fiscal year] 1969 *and those that you may be awarded during the balance of FY 1969.*" [Author's italics.]

A realistic appraisal of the dependent relationship that had developed between academic science and the foundation then led the director to recognize that "it is not possible to forecast all contingencies and unusual circumstances at each institution with absolute accuracy." He added, however, that the foundation would not entertain

requests for adjustments in individual ceilings until the universities had had time to evaluate their effect—a period judged to be at least 90 days.

As it turned out, a surprisingly large number of universities needed considerably less than three months. In a second letter, Haworth wrote, "Although the 90-day period has not yet elapsed, information reaching the Foundation indicates the desirability of considering special adjustments sooner than originally contemplated." The "information" had reached the foundation through a number of sources, including the Congress. No single government action to date had so alerted the scientific community to the need for exploring the intricate network of the national political structure.

New York University group solicits signatures from passers-by on New York's Fifth Avenue as part of a March 4, 1969, protest against the "misuse" of science by government. The nationwide protest included work stoppages and discussions by scientists.

Neal Boenzi, The New York Times

Science and politics

The decrease in the growth rate of federal support of science during the later years of the Johnson administration had been substantial enough to provide a significant issue during the 1968 presidential campaign. It also brought about—for the first time—considerable en bloc participation by scientists and engineers in both parties.

The pervasive concern over the future of federal funding on the part of the scientific community induced both major 1968 candidates to issue pledges on the subject. As early as August, Republican Richard Nixon declared that "R and D should be among the highest priorities in any national budget; and that is where it will be in the next administration." Democrat Hubert Humphrey was equally reassuring: "Science and technology will have a strong voice in—and a strong commitment from—my administration. . . . Cutting back research is false economy."

Both candidates launched strenuous efforts to gain support from well-known scientists and engineers. According to the journal of the American Association for the Advancement of Science, the Democrats were more successful in attracting prestigious members of the scientific community, but the Republicans did better than they ever had before, especially among industrial scientists and engineers. Humphrey suffered from the anxiety many scientists felt over the war in Vietnam.

Johnson's last budget. As Pres. Lyndon Johnson prepared to retire from the leadership of the nation, the scientific community awaited with misgivings his last major presidential act—the fiscal 1970 budget. Straws in the wind fell in all directions, but most were not reassuring. In an August issue of *Scientific Research,* Donald F. Hornig, special assistant to the president for science and technology, assured his readers that "I cannot believe that we will really withdraw from . . . the supreme challenges of intellectual advance." But he then went on to say that the only "really meaningful way" for science to remain in the mainstream of American life was "by making real contributions to what the nation considers its most pressing problems."

The budget statement was released to the public on Jan. 16, 1969, and although funding for research and development remained on the flat growth curve of recent years (an increase from $16.8 billion to $17.1 billion), it was not as depressing as many had feared. The news was better for research scientists than for those in development. The budget provided for an increase of $350 million (from $5,057,000,000 to $5,406,000,000) in research expenditures, while expenditures for development were reduced $100 million (from $10.6 billion to $10.5 billion). Academic research was to be increased by $100 million in an unexpected move by the administration to restore the heavy cuts made in the fiscal 1969 budget for the NSF.

Science and the new administration. Shortly after his election, Nixon demonstrated that he at least meant to seek the help of the scientific community. In rapid succession, he named task forces to provide guidance in the related areas of scientific research, space exploration, and education, and named Lee A. DuBridge, the retiring president of the California Institute of Technology, as his special assistant for science and technology. As head of one of the handful of absolutely first-rank U.S. scientific institutions, DuBridge would have earned respect among his colleagues. Their delight with his appointment was enhanced even further by his distinguished career as a physicist, his deep appreciation of the importance that fundamental research held for the health and welfare of the nation, and a history of unflinching support of individual scientists who held unpopular views. At the press conference announcing DuBridge's appointment, Nixon acknowledged that he looked to his new special assistant to reduce the suspicion with which scientists tended to view the political domain.

The relationship between DuBridge and the president was under intensive scrutiny by the scientific community during the first 100 days of the new administration—not least because DuBridge's predecessor, Hornig, had been described by his own deputy as having been relegated to a

"I'm afraid this tips the balance of power in their favor."—Sidney Harris, RCA Electronic Age.

position of "secondary importance." One harbinger appeared on February 5 when, with DuBridge at his side, the president announced that he had "instructed the director of the Budget and the director of the National Science Foundation to increase immediately the expenditure ceiling for the National Science Foundation by 10 million dollars, in order to deal with the many serious disruptions which have occurred in academic programs of education and research."

Trouble appeared, however, in the last weeks of Nixon's first 100 days. After an extensive search for a distinguished scientist to replace the retiring Haworth as director of the NSF, the members of the National Science Board had congratulated themselves on being able to persuade Franklin Long, an outstanding physical chemist and vice-president for research and advanced studies at Cornell University, to accept the post. Following customary procedures for an appointment of such significance, the nomination had been approved by DuBridge as well as by the entire congressional delegation of New York State. An appointment was made for Long at the White House to give the president an occasion to announce the nomination publicly, although the imminence of the event had been common knowledge among the scientific leadership for weeks past. The effect was all the more shocking, therefore, when *Science* magazine, in mid-April, revealed that Long would not be named after all, that the decision had been made at the White House, and that the central reason was Long's opposition to the antiballistic missile (ABM) program.

The president candidly admitted that the Long appointment had been vetoed by members of the White House staff because of Long's "very sincere beliefs opposing the ABM." During the 10 days that followed there was grave concern among the scientific community that, although the president understood the value of an adequately funded research program, he had failed to appreciate how such a program could be vitiated by the intrusion of partisan politics. Moreover, there was a question over just how effective DuBridge had been in bringing these matters to the attention of the president.

Then, in one of those splendid about-faces that have so enlivened the U.S. political scene in recent years, the president suddenly announced, through his press secretary, that he had been wrong in his original decision, that he had authorized an invitation to Long to accept the post despite his opposition to the ABM, and that (since Long felt he could not now accept the appointment) neither partisan politics nor the ABM controversy would interfere with the choice of a new director. The nomination, announced in early summer, then went to William D. McElroy, chairman of the biology department at Johns Hopkins University.

Science and society

Even those most sympathetic toward the interests of science and technology were well aware that, although scientists and engineers might subscribe to the most conventional of value systems, the products of their endeavors did not necessarily promote those values. Concern was almost equally divided between those who feared the effect of technological advances on an unprepared society and those who looked toward the somewhat more distant horizons of biological engineering. (*See* Feature Article: HUMANICS AND GENETIC ENGINEERING.)

In the words of a science historian testifying before a U.S. Senate subcommittee, the adjustment of society to scientific advance had been "a rather slow and leisurely process, indeed more often than not an accidental process. I would contend," he added, "that no society can any longer afford this leisurely process of adapting to scientific and technological advance, but that society must anticipate and plan for the social integration of new discoveries." By 1969 it appeared that concern about such matters had spread from academic seminars to a more powerful forum—the U.S. Congress.

The most consistent voice in the House of Representatives belonged to Emilio Q. Daddario (Dem., Conn.), chairman of the Subcommittee on Science, Research and Development. Speaking to a group of scientists and engineers in his home state in early 1969, he enumerated a series of technological developments "that will change the fabric of society in the next generation." For some time, he said, "I have been concerned that events are moving at such a rapid rate that there is the chance that some action we take may have far-reaching implications to which we had not given proper consideration." In the Senate, parallel concerns were voiced by Walter F. Mondale (Dem., Minn.), who, on Feb. 17, 1969, reintroduced a joint resolution to create a National Advisory Commission on Health, Science and Society, with support from 18 other senators prominently associated with public-health matters.

The politicization of scientific institutions. Scientific societies in the U.S. have traditionally avoided political action, although scientists as individuals have come to play increasingly active political roles. There has been tacit agreement that professional societies cannot serve both as political arenas and as focuses for the advancement of disciplinary interests. In 1969, however, significant minorities within the societies began asking whether such diffidence had not become an anachronism.

One of the most carefully watched attacks on tradition occurred within the American Physical Society. When his letter attacking the war in Vietnam was rejected by the editors of the society's news magazine because its argument had no unique relevance to physicists, an associate professor at the University of California offered an amendment to the society's constitution that would have permitted members to vote on resolutions on "any matter of concern to the society," rather than only on matters of special relevance to the physical sciences. After more than a year of debate and a mail ballot in which more than half the membership participated, the amendment was defeated by a margin of two to one. Several hundred physicists then organized Scientists for Social and Political Action, charging that the American Physical Society and the government had "failed to alert the nation to the dangers . . . from the pollution of the air, water, and soil; to the growing menace of nuclear, chemical, and biological warfare; and to the wasting of vast sums of federal money on useless and even dangerous new weapons."

Although historically such activist groups had not thrived in the scientific community, there was no lack of initial enthusiasm in organizing them in the heated climate of 1969. The more classical scientific societies tended to withstand demands for their politicization, but many gave implicit recognition that their disciplines were not completely detached from public policy concerns. The establishment of senior committees to deal with such matters was under way or under discussion in the American Institute of Physics, the American Chemical Society, the American Institute of Chemical Engineers, the Ecological Society of America, and the American Institute of Aeronautics and Astronautics, as well as many other groups.

Controversy over military research. If there was a single matter on which a large fraction of the scientific community wanted to offer guidance and control, it was in the broad area of military research. Furthermore, it was becoming apparent that Congress, at least, was increasingly willing to listen. Eugene B. Skolnikoff, professor of political science at Massachusetts Institute of Technology, declared in *Science:* "The exciting and encouraging characteristic of the current ABM debate is that, for the first time since World War II, there is a major public challenge

of a complex technological project, and a refusal to accept the usual assurances that secret data and intelligence would justify the project."

That the challenge was indeed major was attested to by the caliber of those willing to take rather emphatic positions on both sides of the ABM controversy. Although there were a number of different aspects to the problem, the focus of the argument was whether or not the ABM system would work. Among those named by Secretary of Defense Melvin Laird as supporting it were two presidents of the National Academy of Sciences, presidential science adviser DuBridge, and such notable scientists as Gordon MacDonald, Edward Teller, and Eugene B. Wigner. Hostile to the plan was an array of former presidential science advisers—James R. Killian, George B. Kistiakowsky, Jerome Wiesner, and Hornig. Countering John Foster, the current director of defense research and engineering, was Herbert York, who held the same post under Pres. Dwight Eisenhower. Posed against the two Academy presidents was a telegram to President Nixon, signed by more than 100 members of the NAS, which declared "Neither a thin nor a heavy ABM system can provide effective protection against atomic attack." These arguments were attacked in turn by Frederick Seitz, NAS president, in testimony before the Senate Armed Services Committee.

As the battle raged, a small group of graduate students at MIT made plans to escalate the conflict. In late January it was proposed that academic scientists all across the nation leave their laboratory benches on March 4 to discuss government policies related to science. The proposal evoked angry responses from a number of senior scientists, who agreed with some of the students' concerns but not with their tactics, and caused a small band of countermilitants to announce plans to work overtime the same day. Nevertheless, the idea spread rapidly to other academic research centers. For the most part, speakers at the discussions were in basic agreement that both the nation and the world suffered because U.S. government policies provided considerably more support for research in weapons systems than in such areas as urban blight and social justice.

Although few expected any tangible by-products from the March 4 session, MIT announced two months later that a 22-man committee had been formed to examine the desirability of the institute's relationship to two semiautonomous laboratories carrying out classified research, and that no new programs of classified research would be accepted until October 1, when the panel was scheduled to report. A similar effect was evident at Stanford (Calif.) University in April, when a

"All we want is a non-lethal gas that will make the enemy feel friendly towards us, lay down their arms, and join us in a spirit of brotherhood and camaraderie."—Sidney Harris, Bulletin of the Atomic Scientists.

Wide World

Sheep, among several thousand killed near Skull Valley, Utah, in 1968 by a nerve gas tested at a nearby Army proving ground, served to illustrate scientists' fears of the dangers of chemical weapons development.

committee of students, faculty, and administrators recommended restraints on research undertaken by an affiliated institute, especially on programs involving chemical-biological warfare, counterinsurgency, and direct support of the war in Vietnam.

Concern over the environment. The anti-ABM movement in the scientific community was mainly organized by physicists. Meanwhile, the life scientists were beginning to organize more actively to counter present and future threats to the environment. They mobilized not only through their national professional societies but also in groups designed specifically to reach the public (such as the St. Louis Committee on Environmental Information) and in global multi-disciplinary efforts such as the International Biological Program. Like the physicists, they asserted their right to question policies concerning chemical and biological warfare, including the use of defoliants in Vietnam. And like the physicists, they found powerful new friends in the Congress.

One of these friends was Edmund S. Muskie, Democratic senator from Maine. In January 1969, for the third time, he submitted a resolution that would create a select Committee on Technology and the Human Environment to "provide a special forum for inquiry into the broad impact of science and technology on man's thinking, health, work, living habits, and his individuality over the next 50 years." He was joined by impressive co-sponsors, including Edward Kennedy (Dem., Mass.) and Fred Harris (Dem., Okla.).

Another co-sponsor was Gaylord Nelson (Dem.,

Wis.), who was also active on another front. In April he introduced two bills. One would create a Council on Environmental Quality within the Executive Office of the President "to appraise the environmental quality programs of federal, state, and local governments, and to formulate and recommend national policy to promote the improvement of the quality of the environment." The other would prohibit the interstate sale or shipment of DDT in the United States. DDT had proved to be one of the most effective pesticides in the history of agriculture. Part of its effectiveness, however, lay in its persistence, and it was chiefly this quality that appeared to threaten not only wildlife but also such commercially valuable species as the coho salmon of Lake Michigan. (*See* Year in Review: ENVIRONMENTAL SCIENCES.)

Scientific and engineering manpower

The reservoir of trained scientific and technical manpower available in the U.S. in 1969 was in a state of uncertainty. Affecting all manpower estimates was a change in military draft regulations that threatened a substantial percentage of graduate students. Of equal consequence were some rather surprising shifts in the career choices of young people.

The relevant changes in draft regulations were issued in 1968. They prohibited deferment for any first- or second-year graduate students, except in the medical fields. In addition, men in the 19–25

"Sorry, Wally. Let's say it was exploitation for exploitation's sake."—© *1969 Chicago Sun-Times.*

There was some reason to believe that the scientific professions were slipping even further behind the general trend. A decreasing proportion of college degrees were being awarded in the physical and biological sciences, mathematics, and engineering. There were also some interesting shifts among the technical fields themselves, as indicated in an analysis of doctoral degrees awarded in fiscal 1968, made by the Office of Scientific Personnel of the National Research Council. Whereas the total of all doctorates awarded had increased by 12.5% over fiscal 1967, those in the physical sciences had increased by only 7.1% while those in the life sciences had risen 18.1%. The social sciences, after a dramatic increase in 1967, had fallen back to a position slightly below the average. Engineering, too, had dropped.

The NSF reported that salaries of scientists were at least keeping pace with the cost of living. A survey of the National Register of Scientific and Technical Personnel showed a median annual salary of $13,200—up $1,200 from 1966. Economists, at $15,000, led the disciplines. Agricultural scientists were at the bottom with $11,000. Physicists did best in management of R and D: $20,800 per annum, compared with an average of $12,000 for a full year of teaching.

International developments

Proponents of substantial governmental support for scientific research frequently argue that there is a positive relationship between such support and economic growth, but this did not seem to hold true in all cases. Great Britain was spending nearly 3% of its gross national product on R and D—a higher proportion than any other country in Europe—but for the past decade it had had one of the lowest economic growth rates. Japan, which invested only 1.7% of its GNP in R and D, had one of the highest growth rates in the world.

A possible explanation for this emerged from a series of studies undertaken for the Directorate for Scientific Affairs of the Organization for Economic Cooperation and Development (OECD). In comparing academic research in Europe and the U.S., Joseph Ben-David, an Israeli sociologist, found that the science gap between the two originated in the latter part of the 19th century, when the U.S., unlike Europe, was able to adapt its university structure to the sudden growth in the capacity to produce scientific knowledge. The technological gap, he implied strongly, originates not in the higher levels of support for basic research in the U.S., but in its greater success in putting research to use.

age group were ordered for induction, oldest first. Since most of the young graduate students had been deferred from induction, their age made it likely that they would constitute the largest portion of the first groups to be drafted under the new regulations.

The effect on 1968–69 enrollment was less disastrous than had been anticipated, although many suspected that the inevitable had merely been postponed. A survey of graduate schools by the Stanford Research Institute in the fall of 1968 reported that only a little more than 10% of the respondents reported a "considerable" effect, while more than 50% reported that the effect was "not noticeable." Nevertheless, the Scientific Manpower Commission continued to warn in early 1969: "Unless present draft regulations are modified, the number of U.S. males now engaged in advanced scientific training in the nation's graduate schools will be substantially reduced during the coming months." The National Center for Educational Statistics reported in March 1969 that the number of full-time male students in their first year of graduate and professional study had declined 5% from 1967 to 1968, although demographic trends suggested an increase of 10% or more.

This view was also reflected in a memorandum by P. M. S. Blackett, president of the Royal Society, to the Select Committee on Science and Technology of Parliament. Focusing his attention on technological innovation, he found that the average unit size of those industries in the U.K. that could benefit from R and D was too small to permit them to hire a critical mass of qualified scientists and engineers. His solution: to encourage the reorganization of those segments of British industry into fewer, stronger units.

An OECD team studying science policy in the U.S.S.R. found that, although manpower did not seem to be a problem, successful research was not followed up by development except in a few high-priority fields. According to some estimates, Soviet research investments were double those in development—approximately the reverse of the U.S. situation. France, meanwhile, was suffering from a U.S. problem. The growth rate of its national science budget, which had been as high as 35% between 1966 and 1968, slackened to something like 4% in 1969. While certain fields, such as oceanography and computer technology, were protected, expenditures on the traditional disciplines were slashed 10 to 50%.

Support for West German science continued to grow. The 1969 federal research budget was double that of 1965, and plans were to double it again by 1972. Of the DM. 2,180,000,000 budget, DM. 1,036,000,000 was earmarked for oceanography, DM. 728 million for nuclear research, and DM. 368 million for aerospace research. Overall expenditures for R and D in West Germany in 1968 were approximately DM. 12 billion, 2.4% of GNP. According to the minister for scientific research, West Germany planned to reach the U.S. figure of 3% by 1970.

A report by Canada's Science Council indicated that in 1969, 10,760 Canadian students (out of a total of 58,300) would graduate with degrees in science, mathematics, or engineering. By 1977–78, the report predicted, the figure would be 20,000 out of 115,000. It was expected that the ranks of scientists in Canada would also be swelled by immigration. In terms of expenditures, if the Canadian research budget was to reach the goal of 3% of GNP by 1978, it would have to increase at a rate of 14.2% per year, compared with the 11% annual increase it had shown since 1957. The growth rate would have to be even better than this, the report pointed out, simply to fund R and D programs that could be carried out by the greatly increased number of scientists.

—Howard J. Lewis

See also Feature Article: TOWARD FUTURE GUIDANCE OF SCIENCE IN HUMAN AFFAIRS.

Transportation

Environmental factors, new concepts of urban form, and questions of public responsibility for social and cultural improvements offered new challenges to long-standing public investment policy for transportation in 1969. This policy, applied in varying degrees in all industrialized nations, was based upon the concept that transportation is an economic service and that the beneficiaries of the service should pay its cost. Although this policy has always been more theoretical than real, continued insistence on attempting to apply it has had the effect of holding back technological developments and transportation service innovations which otherwise probably would occurred. This was most notable in urban public transportation, but also has been a factor in certain types of air, rail, and water transport.

Urban mass transportation

The increased importance of urban mass transportation was recognized during 1968 and 1969 when the responsibility for this segment of transport in the United States government was transferred from the Department of Housing and Urban Development (HUD) to the recently established Department of Transportation (DOT). In its new home, the Urban Mass Transportation Administration (UMTA) was granted the same level of authority as the Federal Highway Administration, Federal Aviation Administration (FAA), and the Federal Railroad Administration (FRA).

Both in the U.S. and Europe, administrators of public transportation systems concentrated on improving bus service and constructing or improving the railway systems. In San Francisco and the adjacent bay area construction continued on the only completely new rail mass-transit system under way in the U.S. The UMTA provided the capital grant money for work on this project as well as providing part of the funds for extensions or improvements of rail rapid-transit systems in Chicago, Boston, New York, and Cleveland, O. A new rapid-transit line from downtown Cleveland to Cleveland-Hopkins Airport was opened for service in 1968. This was the first example of a rapid-transit line connected directly to an airport terminal.

For many years transportation engineers have concentrated primarily on improving methods of moving commuters into the central business districts of cities during the morning rush hours and back to the suburban residential areas in the evening rush hours. On the other hand, little attention has been focused on a new phenome-

Crowded waiting rooms, like this one at John F. Kennedy International Airport in New York, are becoming commonplace in the United States. The almost 200 million people who fly each year are placing a great strain on the technological and physical facilities of major airports.

non: the movement of industry from the cities into the suburbs. The cumulative effect of this industrial dispersal received widespread attention during 1968 and early 1969 as public attention focused on the economic requirements of the poor. Unlike the suburbanites, whose problem was to get into the city, the unemployed and underemployed portion of the population, largely Negro, had to be transported from their inner-city homes to the newly industrialized outlying areas, where many of their best job opportunities were located. Several studies and demonstration projects were undertaken during 1968 and 1969 in order to analyze and eventually deal with this transportation problem.

Ground transportation

Research and development in transportation services received new impetus during 1968 and 1969 because of growing needs for faster and safer systems. Both the UMTA and the FRA continued priority experimental activities in a variety of air-cushion vehicles and linear-induction motors for propulsion.

Linear-induction motors. The DOT was expected to complete the development of a 2,500 hp linear-induction motor, an engine with tremendous space-saving potentiality, by 1970. A linear-induction motor is like a regular rotary motor that has been sliced open and laid out flat. Both rotary and linear motors produce force by the interaction of a magnetic field and a current induced by the field. The movement of the rotor inside the stator of a rotary motor produces torque (a twisting force) which then must be transformed to thrust, usually through the form of gears connected to a wheel. The interaction of the magnetic field in a linear-induction motor,

however, produces thrust directly. Although there is need for additional research and development, the technological feasibility of the linear-induction motor was established. In fact, when it is perfected, the linear-induction motor, which is completely frictionless, will be able to be used to propel air-cushioned vehicles (craft that can hover and move about close to the earth's surface and which obtain most of their support from the layer of air between them and the surface).

The implication of successfully constructing linear-induction propulsion vehicles is potentially the most revolutionary of all technological experimentation in ground transportation. The combination of air-cushioned vehicles with linear-induction propulsion will solve a large portion of the problems of friction, noise, air pollution, and other undesirable factors of existing mass-transit systems. Air-cushioned vehicles have the potential for high speed, comfortable ride, rapid acceleration and deceleration, and economic efficiency. They could be completely automated and could operate at speeds up to 300 mph.

Computerized systems. The use of electronics and computers remained central to almost every technological development under way or being considered for improving transportation. Among the areas where they were being applied was the individual-response bus system, an attempt to combine the best features of bus and private automobile transportation in order to establish a service somewhat similar to that provided by limousines at many airports. A customer would telephone a command and control center and give the address where he wished to be picked up, his destination, and the time he desired to arrive. His call, along with similar ones received, would be fed into a computer, which, in turn, would direct a driver over a route pattern that

390

would minimize time and maximize the number of customers to be served. The cost per customer would be more than regular bus service but considerably less than driving and parking a private auto or using a taxicab. Actual field experiments were scheduled for 1970.

Another system being studied was one that was expected to reduce accident rates significantly. The "passing-aid" system uses electronic loops buried in blocks in the highway at 200-ft intervals. These loops detect the number of cars entering and leaving each 200-ft block in sequence and then relay to computers the number of vehicles, their speeds, and the direction of movement. A control computer polls each of the sensors at the same time and stores data on the number of vehicles and their average speed in each 200-ft link. The computer then calculates whether there is enough space for a passing maneuver for any given vehicle, plus a margin of safety, and tells the driver either to pass or wait.

A similar type of technology, an electronic route guidance system (ERGS), was developed and was expected to be field tested by 1970. The first ERGS would be able to direct drivers over static, predetermined routes to their destinations. The eventual goal would be to develop a dynamic system constantly updated with new traffic information on each road link so that any given driver could be directed to his destination using a least-time criterion regardless of the combinations of streets or roads. The necessary equipment for initial field testing was installed at two intersections in the Washington, D.C., area, and about 100 additional intersections were to be monitored late in 1969 and in 1970.

The system requires an induction loop in both the vehicle and the roadway, a destination encoder unit in the vehicle, a computer-decoder at each major intersection, and a display system in the vehicle to convey instructions to the driver. To operate the system a driver would dial his destination into the vehicle-based encoder. As the first electronically equipped intersection was passed, the induction loop in the roadway would pick up the destination code and transmit it to a computer, which would analyze the information and send back an instruction to the display panel in the vehicle for the driver to go straight, turn right, or turn left. The system would operate in the same sequence at each intersection until the vehicle arrived at its destination.

Aviation

Just as new systems were being developed for ground-transportation traffic control and direction,

similar and much more advanced systems were being implemented for air navigation.

Air traffic control. During 1969, the FAA started flight testing its new enroute traffic-control system, which permits fully computerized flight-data handling with alphameric displays (consisting of both letters and numbers) for the traffic controllers. The first unit went into operational testing at Jacksonville, Fla., during relatively light traffic hours. As the system is made fully operational and controllers are trained to use it, all of the FAA's 20 regional centers will install it. Completion of the system was set for 1973.

The implementation of the system was planned in phases, with the first phase involving the automatic computer processing of flight plans so that each controller working before his radar display will know where each plan calls for each aircraft to be at any given point in time. The next phase would provide for each aircraft to be equipped with a transponder which would give the controller the plane's identity and the altitude at which it was flying. In the past, this information has been transmitted verbally by the pilot.

The rapid growth in air transportation has outstripped the system's ability to handle it efficiently. The world's airlines in 1968 carried 261 million passengers, an increase of 19% in one year. The average annual rate of increase since 1950 has been 15%. A conservative growth-rate assumption of only 10% a year would mean that by 1990 worldwide air traffic would be seven and a half times the total in 1968. In addition to this tremendous passenger-traffic growth, air-cargo operations have tripled since 1963, and general aviation (private planes, business planes, etc.) has increased 50% during the same time span.

Jumbo jets. Complicating the airport congestion problem was the development of the jumbo jet. Flight tests started early in 1969 on the first of the Boeing 747s, and it appeared likely that commercial operation of the jets would begin late in 1969 or early in 1970. The jumbo jets were designed to carry between 360 and 490 passengers, depending upon their seating configuration. By 1970 they were scheduled to be produced and enter commercial service at the rate of three a week. Two other U.S. aircraft companies, McDonnell Douglas Corp. and Lockheed Aviation Corp., planned to begin producing jumbo jets in 1973.

STOL aircraft. Although top priority was placed on the development of large and fast jets and the resulting needs for airport and airway improvements, significant advances were made during 1968–69 in experimenting with short takeoff and landing aircraft (STOL) which can use runways and portions of air space that cannot be utilized by the big commercial jets. First scheduled operations of STOL flights were initiated in 1968, concentrating on short-flight commuter service. This type of operation was expected to grow significantly in 1969 and later years, and several major airlines experimented with STOL vehicles for short- and medium-length flights to serve regional markets.

Supersonic transports. Work on the design of the U.S. supersonic transport (SST) continued throughout the year, but at a rate which probably would not result in the testing of a prototype model until the mid-1970s, several years after the British-French Concorde and Soviet TU-144 were scheduled for commercial use. The Concorde and TU-144 had their first test flights in 1968. Testing of the Concorde was to be continued into 1970, with the first commercial operation expected in 1971. Little information was available on the testing program of the TU-144. Historically, Soviet transport planes have had very high direct operating costs, and if the TU-144 holds to this pattern, it probably would not be economically competitive with the Concorde or the projected U.S. plane.

The Concorde was designed to cruise supersonically at 1,400 mph. The U.S. SST, because of the planned extensive use of titanium, had a design speed of 1,800 mph. In addition, if the U.S. SST meets design specifications, it should have lower direct operating costs and carry more passengers than the Concorde. The latter, however, will be in operation for several years before the U.S. plane, and it will have the advantage of years of experience by the time its competitor goes on the commercial market.

Although there has been a rapid growth in the North Atlantic airline market between Europe and the U.S. for many years, some of the most spectacular increases have been on trans-Pacific routes. International passengers flown between Japan and the U.S., for example, rose from 160,-000 in 1956 to 1,200,000 in 1966—a 530% increase for the ten-year period.

Railroads

While the problems of aviation in 1968 involved, for the most part, dealing with the consequences of rapid growth, the problems of rail-passenger transportation involved attempts to slow down the continued decline. The number of people using intercity passenger trains grew fewer, and operating losses thus grew larger. As a result, many railroads were requesting, with increasing frequency, governmental permission to eliminate passenger service.

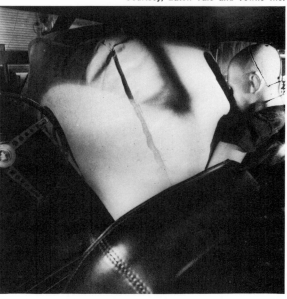

The Auto-Ceptor, a balloon that inflates in 1/25 of a second, can be concealed in the dashboard or steering wheel of a car. Designed by Eaton Yale and Towne Inc., it prevents a driver or passenger from striking the windshield or dashboard after a collision.

High-speed rail service. The most notable exception to this pattern was the high-speed rail service that was established between Washington, D.C., and New York City, and between Boston and New York City. The initial scheduling of the Penn Central railroad's new Metroliners reduced from four hours to three hours the traveling time between Washington and New York. Early in 1969, two nonstop trains were put into service between the two major cities, and the elapsed time was further cut to two and a half hours. Public reaction to the new service was encouraging.

The Washington–New York high-speed train service was expected to test a variation in the traditional train service of city center to city center sometime in 1970. It has long been known that in most cities only a relatively small percentage of airline passengers originate or terminate their trips in central business districts. As a result, DOT's High-Speed Ground Transport Program was to test whether suburban-to-city-center and suburban-to-suburban service will result in increased patronage of trains. A suburban station near Washington, for example, would feature parking space for patrons who wanted to drive to the station from their homes in suburban Washington, catch a train to New York, and return to the suburban station without ever going into the city. Similar service would be provided on the New York end of this experimental service.

—Lowell K. Bridwell

Steam engines and turbines

Because exhaust-emission-control devices can do little more than stabilize the present levels of air pollution, the search for alternative power units was intensified. Research into batteries and fuel cells did not yield the hoped-for breakthroughs. Suddenly, however, the steam engine became the object of enthusiasm as a possible alternative to the internal-combustion engine.

The steam engine, like the gas turbine and another hot-air device, the Stirling engine, burns fuel at a regular rate. With good design, this steady combustion could reduce significantly the level of air pollution. The high temperatures and pressures which occur during the explosionlike burning of fuel in a gasoline or diesel engine, on the other hand, result in the formation of many secondary compounds. The subsequent rapid cooling preserves these compounds, which constitute the basis of much of our air pollution.

Steam-driven buses and police cars were ordered for trial in California; buses with similar power units but using a high-molecular-weight fluid instead of water were expected to be tried in Dallas, Tex., and at least one of the automobile manufacturers experimented with the hot-air Stirling engine, a revival from the last century. One company was even working on the production of a steam-powered airplane.

Because all these alternatives, even the steam airplane, have been examined and abandoned before, one might well ask why steam engines should be feasible now if they were not so in the past. As a result of an enormous effort in the U.S. during the 1950s and 1960s to evaluate and develop small, efficient power plants for space and military purposes, the steam engine was found to be most suitable for many applications and, therefore, received much attention. With its possible antipollution characteristics also providing an impetus for research, the steam engine seemed likely to be the target of considerable development efforts in the future.

The threat of antipollution regulations was also one of the major factors leading to the announcement in 1968 that several manufacturers were firmly committed to the production of gas-turbine-powered highway trucks for the early 1970s. Although gas turbines seemed to have lost their chance of being used in automobiles because they were inefficient at low power levels and were too expensive to produce, they did appear to be a promising solution for the increasing power requirements of long-distance freight-hauling highway trucks.

—David G. Wilson

Veterinary medicine

During 1968 and 1969 the most fundamental problems that confronted the veterinary profession were related to the growing need to increase the human food supply through improved methods of animal production and disease control. Although not marked by spectacular developments as were other fields of medicine, the cumulative achievements of veterinarians represented substantial contributions to human welfare.

FAO and AID. Since its inception in 1945, the Food and Agriculture Organization of the United Nations (FAO), through its Animal Health Division, has attempted to diagnose the animal disease situation throughout the world and to expand its veterinary programs so that the control of animal disease and subsequently increased productivity could be most effective. Also, in certain countries, similar programs were carried on by the veterinary personnel of the U.S. Agency for International Development (AID). The efforts of both these agencies in Vietnam provided a good example of international cooperation.

Vietnam, in 1968, had about 15 native graduate veterinarians who served a livestock population of approximately five million cattle, hogs, and buffalo, as well as a large number of poultry. In all of these animals rinderpest, hemorrhagic septicemia, salmonellosis, hog cholera (swine fever), fowlpox, and Newcastle disease (of poultry) were widespread. With assistance from FAO, AID, and the Australian government, a national institute was established that was responsible for disease diagnosis and vaccine production. During 1968, the staff of the institute was doubled, and five AID veterinarians provided technical assistance. U.S. Army veterinarians also assisted the staff in the care of local livestock (including work elephants), and in the implementation of disease control programs.

Veterinary medicine and the world food supply. As of 1969, the U.S. had about 25,000 veterinarians, approximately half of whom were engaged primarily or solely in caring for small animals, while most of the rest were more or less directly involved in treating a livestock population of about 185 million. Although both the United Arab Republic and South Africa had a more favorable ratio of veterinarians to livestock numbers, there were nine African nations that had a total livestock population equal to that of the U.S. but at the same time had fewer than 100 veterinarians. To help correct this discrepancy, several of the highly developed nations provided technical assistance to emerging countries.

The immediate problem of increasing the avail-

A Vietnamese veterinarian inoculates a pig to protect it from hog cholera, a disease that is widespread in Vietnam. The Food and Agricultural Organization of the United Nations, along with various other agencies, provides technical assistance for animal disease control programs in Southeast Asia.

able food supply was probably more crucial than was generally realized. It was not sufficient merely to maintain present production levels in proportion to the population explosion, since at these levels half or more of the world's people were inadequately fed. It was estimated that the food supply in many countries must be doubled by 1975. The role of veterinarians in this effort included upgrading the productivity of native and imported domestic livestock and making available wild animals (antelope, elephant, hippopotamus, fish, etc.) as sources of animal protein.

Improved medical facilities. The methods employed in animal disease control varied according to the policies of the agencies involved in implementing them. In general, diseases indigenous to a particular country were kept in check by vaccination, while other diseases were eradicated by slaughtering affected and exposed animals. Thus, while vaccination for foot-and-mouth disease of cattle was widely practiced in South America and continental Europe, outbreaks that occurred in the U.S. and Great Britain were dealt with ruthlessly. An outbreak in England in 1967–68, for example, was wiped out in six months, but required the slaughter of more than 400,000 animals at a cost estimated to exceed £150 million ($360 million).

Although hog cholera has been indigenous to Britain and the U.S. for more than a century, the disease in Britain had to be eradicated by slaughter; and the U.S. was engaged in a similar program, except that vaccination was being phased out more gradually. The target date for full eradi-

cation was set at 1972, and as of 1969, 12 states were cholera-free. But the problem of keeping unvaccinated and, therefore, susceptible animals sufficiently isolated made it difficult for a state to maintain its disease-free status. The use of live vaccine was prohibited in 1968, and killed vaccines were expected to be outlawed in 1969. It was something of a paradox that the product designed to prevent the disease also served to perpetuate it by maintaining a reservoir of carrier animals. To circumvent this undesirable feature of vaccination, it was proposed early in 1969 to use a bovine viral diarrhea vaccine, since it had been demonstrated that it could produce a high level of immunity against hog cholera. This phenomenon of cross-immunity was used in dogs that had a maternally derived immunity to distemper vaccine. It was found that a strain of human measles could produce temporary immunity against canine distemper in these vaccine-resistant puppies.

Preventive medicine. The nature of veterinary practice itself has rapidly changed from a concept based primarily upon treatment of sick animals to one of preventive medicine. In 1968 and 1969 especially, emphasis was placed upon regular physical examinations for pet animals and on "preconditioning" livestock prior to sale. The latter involved treating the livestock with whatever medications and vaccines would be required for them to meet the stresses of transportation and the environmental conditions of their destination. In keeping with the preventive medicine concept, veterinary practice in many areas became more an advisory than a medical service, with herd health programs designed for individual situations and including such subjects as nutrition, environmental control, and breeding.

Other developments included the recognition of such specialties as bovine, equine, and zoo animal practice, radiology, opthalmology, pathology, and surgery. In the governmental area, the U.S. Federal Drug Administration's Bureau of Veterinary Medicine was engaged in a sweeping review of the effectiveness of veterinary drugs. Major improvements were also made in U.S. meat and poultry inspection programs, and the U.S. Department of Agriculture proposed a broad system for identification of individual animals sent to slaughter so that disease conditions, not evident in the live animal, could be traced to their source.

Since 1964, efforts of dog breeders to eliminate the widespread problem of hip dysplasia (a deformity of the hip) have resulted in the formation of the Orthopedic Foundation for Animals, which had the world's largest collection of pelvic radiographs. Two breeds each had more than 500 dogs certified free of hip dysplasia.

—J. F. Smithcors

Zoology

Throughout the world, zoologists continued to search for a fuller understanding of animal life in general and of mankind in particular. Some of the discoveries made during the past year revealed features peculiar to mankind or to certain groups of men that have evolved during the past ten million years or less. Other features were found that must have appeared earlier, since they are shared by other warm-blooded animals. Studies by zoologists also extended the perspective from which the long history of evolution can be appreciated. Additions to the classification of animals were made, and suggestions were offered for more rational ways to subdivide the animal kingdom. Zoologists, like other scientists, looked forward eagerly to the opportunity of examining samples collected by the first men to reach the moon in an attempt to determine whether life is limited to the planet earth.

Human adaptive physiology

For many years it has been known that oxygen molecules are carried from the lungs to other tissues in a loose linkage with the hemoglobin molecules in the red blood cells. Slight changes of acidity within the bloodstream, caused when carbon dioxide enters from the tissues and leaves through the lungs, facilitate this process. Recently, a team of biochemists at Columbia University identified an organic phosphate compound, 2,3-diphosphoglycerate, which regulates the release of oxygen to the tissues. The organic phosphate molecule attaches itself to the hemoglobin molecule when the oxygen has diffused to the tissues and becomes detached only when the red blood cell has returned to the lungs, where a fresh oxygen supply is available. This feature of the circulatory system apparently evolved long ago, since it is found in other warm-blooded animals besides man.

Differences of more recent origin among ethnic groups of mankind were discovered when patients were being treated with the drug pilocarpine at the Mulago Hospital in Kampala, Uganda. The drug caused European men to sweat more and lose greater amounts of sodium from their blood than women or men of other racial origins. European women produced significantly more sweat than their African—but not their Indian—counterparts, and lost sodium at about the same rate as European men and persons of Indian origin. Africans, particularly Bantu-speaking Ugandans, sweated significantly less and lost little sodium. These findings can be interpreted as

Fossil teeth found in Texas and dated from about 100 million years ago so closely resemble those of modern opossums, such as this one, as to suggest that marsupial and placental mammals began to evolve separately far earlier than most paleozoologists had previously believed.

Allan D. Cruickshank from National Audubon Society

showing that black Africans are better adapted to high temperatures and high relative humidity than white Europeans.

During the year, extensive testing was carried out on the relative intolerance to lactose (milk sugar) found among Asian peoples—a characteristic that has considerable bearing on plans to supplement the diet in less developed countries with surplus milk products from the West. Experience at the University of Chiangmai in Thailand led to specification of 14 g of lactose, about the quantity in half a pint of milk, as the maximum that could be taken daily without causing abdominal pains and diarrhea. (*See* Year in Review: FOODS AND NUTRITION.)

Nonhuman adaptive physiology

It has been found that, upon close inspection, the shells of edible cockles along the southern coast of Wales reveal fine lines that record the amount of growth each day. While a cockle is small and young, it remains in shallow water, partly buried in sediments on the bottom. There its activity is modified by the tide, and its growth is slowed by cold in winter. Later in life, after the large cockles have moved to deeper water, their shells show little indication of seasonal changes, although severe storms may inhibit them from feeding and enlarging their shells.

The great abysses of the ocean are still under the influence of the seasons, however. Despite the apparently uniform climatic conditions 10,000 to 15,000 ft below the surface, sea urchins and other echinoderms become sexually active in unison once a year. At similar depths in the North Atlantic Ocean off the Carolina coasts, the percentage of small isopod crustacean females carrying eggs increases from about 56% in August to a climax of around 95% in November. The same timing can also be seen in shallower water, to within 3,000 ft of the surface. The nature of this cyclic stimulus, however, remains to be discovered.

Night and day are obvious cues for animals in shallow water and on land. For years, light was believed to be the factor that inhibited hatchling sea turtles from emerging until after dark, when poor visibility and high humidity would give them some protection as they moved across the sand to the nearest waves. Recent tests, however, showed that temperature is the principal controlling factor, which explains why young turtles often emerge by day after a rain.

The pattern shown on an electroencephalogram taken during the hours when an animal is regularly inactive generally changes if the animal is actually asleep. Experimenters who reported no change in the brain waves of bullfrogs, and hence no true sleep, continued their research and discovered that tree frogs (*Hyla*) do show "electrographic correlates of behavior" that indicate sleep. From this, the scientists inferred that the active life of tree frogs is more complex than that of bullfrogs.

During 1968 the British magazine *Nature* published the suggestion that antlers in one or both sexes of deer evolved as a means of spreading skin with blood vessels over a large surface exposed to air, thereby cooling the blood. During the summer and prior to the breeding season, while blood is circulating through the skin (the "velvet") over the antlers, males might have a greater need for cooling because they are dispersing themselves over the available territory and therefore are more active during the day. Females, on the other hand, are more likely to spend their days hidden in the shade. This idea led to considerable controversy. It was pointed out that the antlers of deer in warm climates are actually smaller than those of deer in cooler zones, and that the fossil evidence shows extinct deer to have had larger antlers during cold periods than during warm ones. A vertebrate zoologist at the University of Calgary, Alta., stated that antlers evolved parallel to the rhinoceros's horn and the elephant's tusks. Functioning primarily as social adaptations, they are used for bluff and battle in determining dominance, as shields against attack by other individuals of the same species, as symbols of rank according to their size and display value, and as weapons against predators. However, the challenge to these older interpretations led to a reconsideration of their merits.

Man and his environment

One of the most pervasive and persistent medical problems in tropical countries is schistosomiasis, a group of diseases caused by the tiny flatworm known as a blood fluke or by its scientific name, *Schistosoma* (formerly *Bilharzia*). The worm reaches the human bloodstream when people wash themselves or their clothes in contaminated water, wade in it, or drink it. Recent research indicates that within a few days after each worm enters the blood, it changes its chemical nature to resemble the human cell. It mimics so well, in fact, that a person's own natural immune reactions fail to respond. Nor are there distinctive molecules left in the body surface of the worm for a drug to attack. Thus, it would appear that the best way to rid the tropics of this scourge is by full-scale use of modern methods of sewerage and water treatment. (*See* Year in Review: MEDICINE, *Pharmacology*.)

Many of the continuing problems in the less developed countries stem from the fact that the population is increasing at a faster rate than food production, industrialization, or education. Economists generally favor a lower rate of population growth, but they regard some increase as essential to the maintenance of an expanding economy. Recently, scientists at the General Electric Co. argued against this attitude in the *Journal of Biological Sciences*. According to their figures, an infant born in the less developed part of the world will consume $300 more in goods and services during its lifetime than it will contribute—an amount that can be saved by preventing its birth. They calculate that a birth-control program costing 30 cents per head of population annually would return the cost 13-fold in five years and 80-fold in 30 years.

A major outbreak of migratory locusts in the Sudan, Ethiopia, and the Arabian peninsula during 1968 showed that claims that these pests had been brought under control were premature. The United Nations program of reporting and poisoning small concentrations of locusts had been credited with preventing any major damage since

Suggestion that antlers, such as those of this blacktail buck, evolved as a cooling mechanism aroused considerable controversy in 1968. Most zoologists had interpreted antlers as a social adaptation.

Leonard Lee Rue from National Audubon Society

1963. However, one period of unusually generous rainfall sufficed to turn vast areas of semidesert green, leading to a sudden rise in insect numbers.

Farther south in Africa, zoologists discovered why native antelope, such as the Grant's gazelle and oryx, can survive a severe drought while domestic cattle die of thirst unless led to a good water hole every day or two. By following the antelopes day and night and recording what plants they ate and at what hour, the scientists learned that timing made the difference. Between midnight and early morning, when the antelopes fed, the night air cooled to almost 60° F, and the relative humidity rose to about 85%. Vegetation, particularly a favorite shrub (*Disperma*), absorbed moisture until the leaves were approximately 40% water, and by eating them the antelopes obtained all the water they needed. In the daytime, when the herdsmen let their cattle free to feed on the same plants, the hot sun and dry air quickly reduced the moisture in the leaves to around 1%. No practical way to use this information could be seen, since the herdsmen feared to let the cattle feed at night, when they were endangered by beasts of prey and rustlers.

In May 1968 an extraordinary bloom of single-celled planktonic organisms (*Gonyaulax tamarensis*) created havoc off the Northumbrian coast of Britain, a region where this phenomenon of "red tide" is almost unknown. No underlying cause was found to explain the appearance of the organisms, which turned the waters brightly luminous by night and brown by day and charged them with poisons. Fishes that schooled near the surface died and were cast ashore, and birds that ate the poisoned fishes also died. After 79 persons became seriously ill from eating cooked mussels that had picked up the poison, the British government prohibited all gathering of mussels, scallops, and cockles along this portion of the North Sea coast. The restrictions were continued until August 20, when the concentration of poison in shore waters had diminished to safe levels.

Paleozoology and evolution

Reexamination of something old during the year led to a new interpretation of the famous fossil of the earliest known bird, *Archaeopteryx lithographicus*, on public exhibit in the British Museum in London. The treasured specimen was fossilized in such a way that a natural cast of the inner surface of the brain case was preserved. Some years ago, the distinguished British anatomist G. R. de Beer made a plaster cast of this brain region and concluded from his examination that *Archaeopteryx*, for all its long tail and feathers, had a reptilian-type brain. Recently, however, a Stanford (Calif.) University zoologist borrowed de Beer's cast and reached a different conclusion. He identified as the midline of the brain a crease that was a few millimeters away from the one de Beer had chosen. While this difference would make the cerebral hemispheres larger than had been believed, they would be narrower than those of living birds but still avian. Similarly, the optic lobes, medial to and below the forebrain, would also be larger. Furthermore, he noted that reptilian brains do not ordinarily fill the cranial cavity and leave an imprint of the cleavage between fore- and midbrain, such as is seen in the cast of *Archaeopteryx*. His measurements led him to estimate a ratio of brain to body not far above the range shown by modern reptiles but definitely tending in the direction of modern birds.

Human evolution, the field of paleoanthropology, remained as controversial as ever, despite the remarkable assortment of human remains and tools and the improved techniques for assigning respectable dates to these fossils. Scientists attending the 1968 annual meetings of the prestigious British Association for the Advancement of Science in Dundee, Scot., spent considerable time reviewing the recent discoveries and new appraisals of ancient men and earlier hominoids. Some of the specialists placed the separation of the great apes (family Pongidae) from the human family (Hominidae) only five million years ago, and claimed that the earlier common ancestors were all knuckle-walkers like the modern gorilla. Others, using identical evidence, felt that the two families have been distinct for at least 14 million years, since before the end of the Miocene period. New measurements by the potassium-argon method yield a date of about 18 million years ago, in mid-Miocene, for the early hominoids *Proconsul* and *Kenyapithecus* found on Rusinga Island, Kenya. (*See* Feature Article: MAN IN AMERICA: THE CALICO MOUNTAINS EXCAVATIONS; Year in Review: ARCHAEOLOGY; BEHAVIORAL SCIENCES, *Anthropology*.)

Nonprimate fossils in recent collections gave a broader view of animal life in the past. Teeth from a mid-Cretaceous (about 100 million years ago) deposit in Texas so closely resemble those of modern opossums (Didelphidae) as to justify the belief that marsupial mammals were already distinct from placental ones at that time, and that the divergence between the two groups occurred earlier than had been thought. Impressions of soft-bodied coelenterates in early Silurian (about 435 million years ago) rocks were identified as new representatives of the class Dipleurozoa, pre-viously recognized only from Australian remains dated from Precambrian time, the earliest geologic period for which fossils have been found.

Zoogeography

During July 1968, zoologists discovered a breeding colony of northern fur seals (*Callorhinus ursinus*) on San Miguel Island, about 19 mi off Point Conception to the west of Santa Barbara, Calif. Of approximately 60 females accompanying the one adult male, five bore tags or tagging scars showing that they had been born on U.S. or Soviet islands in the Bering Sea. Some 40 young were still in baby fur. This was the first known instance of northern fur seals coming ashore to breed anywhere in the world except on the Pribilof Islands of Alaska and a few adjacent small islands in the Bering and Okhotsk seas. Fishermen, when questioned, said that seals of some kind had been on San Miguel Island two or three years previously, but they could not be sure that the ones they saw were northern fur seals, rather than the Guadaloupe fur seals whose territorial waters lie only a few hundred miles to the south off the coast of Baja California. The sudden extension of range by the northern fur seals could be regarded as a measure of the success achieved in conserving the Alaskan and Siberian herds.

Interest in the theory of continental drift and its possible implications for the dispersal of animals and plants continued at a high level. Geologists, armed with new measurements of spreading in the sea floors, of reversals of the earth's magnetic field, and of the orientation of magnetized materials in igneous rocks to which a date can be assigned, seemed more enthusiastic about continental drift than the biologists. (*See* Year in Review: EARTH SCIENCES, *Geophysics*.) Maps were being drawn to show probable groupings of land masses in the past, with computers being used to match the fit of one continent against another. The timing remained in dispute, however; for example, dates postulated for the origin of the Atlantic Ocean varied by many millions of years. Zoologists tended to agree with Philip J. Darlington, Jr. (*Biogeography of the Southern End of the World* [1965] and other writings) that alternative explanations can account more plausibly for the known features of modern zoogeography. During 1968 additional evidence in this vein was presented, based on the distribution of freshwater ostracod crustaceans (*Gomphocytere*) which are intolerant of salt water and desiccation and retain their eggs in a brood pouch until the young have hatched. The single species in Argentina, 13 in Africa, 2 in South

Australia, 1 in Tasmania, and 2 in New Zealand could have been dispersed on the muddy feet of shorebirds.

Zoologists and botanists intensified their studies of the geographic distribution of living things on the Pacific and Atlantic sides of Panama, in order to provide a sound basis for predicting the probable effect of connecting these waters through the proposed sea-level canal. New estimates were offered as to the rate at which mixing of the plants and animals of both oceans has been taking place through the present Panama Canal, principally in seawater taken on as ballast by empty cargo ships before entering the lock system and discharged after passage through the waterway. Although the land barrier provided by the Isthmus of Panama is recent in the geologic sense, the difference between the Pacific and Atlantic marine life is considerable. Differences that have evolved over the last ten million years could be obliterated in a few years, probably with a marked decrease in the variety of life on the Atlantic side.

Classification

In a bulletin published by the National Museum of Canada, Ottawa, Ont., a comparative anatomist proposed a modification of previous classifications of the world's bony fishes, of the class Teleostomi or Osteichthyes. Careful study of the branchiostegal skeleton, which supports the gills and gill covers, in living and fossil fishes led to the division of the 402 living and 157 extinct families into 4 subclasses: Dipneusti for the lungfishes; Crossopterygii for the lobe-finned fishes;

Actinopterygii for most of the ray-finned fishes previously in this subclass; and Branchiopterygii for perches, flatfishes, and some other families. Because of the complexity of the last two subclasses, supraordinal groups were proposed for them as well as orders and lower categories.

A far broader revision of the classification for living things was offered in *Science* by an animal ecologist at Cornell University, Ithaca, N.Y. He urged adoption of a five-kingdom system that would separate the blue-green algae and bacteria into the Monera, the unicellular and colonial algae and protozoans into the Protista, and would also place the fungi in a separate kingdom; the rest of the plants would remain in the Plantae and the rest of the animals in the Animalia. He elevated four categories of bacteria, five of protozoans, three of slime molds, and five of fungi to phylum level, bringing the total number of phyla to 52. As though this multiplication of a category that is supposedly a primary subdivision were not enough, three weeks later in the same journal a specialist at the University of North Carolina promoted recognition of the Gnathostomulida (including 45 species of worms) as a separate phylum, which would bring the total to 53. Half a century ago, most zoologists had need for far fewer categories and the educated layman was proud to know which plant was a cryptogam or a phanerogam, which animal a vertebrate or an invertebrate. Frustration over how to classify the one-celled organism *Euglena* seems to have led to complex categorizing of the natural world.

—Lorus J. Milne and Margery Milne

See also Year in Review: ENVIRONMENTAL SCIENCES.

Trumpeter swan family photographed on the nest. In 1968, after several years of protective measures, the population of these birds had risen from a 1931 low of 20 adults and 15 cygnets to a level high enough to permit removal of the species from the endangered list.

Harry Engels from National Audubon Society

A Scientific
View of Race
by Raymond W. Mack

The concept of race has been used to define groups with shared traits, ranging from skin color and head shape to language and religion. It has even been used to explain political dominance and to excuse social inequality. But is there any scientific basis for saying that humans can be divided into races at all? In undertaking to answer that question, a concerned sociologist sheds light on some shadowy corners of popular mythology.

Most citizens are confident of one of two things: (1) that there are differences among the human races in intelligence or in other inherited talents, or (2) that there are no such differences. One group of persons who do not hold to either conclusion with certainty consists of those scientists who study racial differences and their consequences: biologists, physiologists, students of genetics and of animal behavior, psychologists, sociologists, and physical and cultural anthropologists.

Questions about racial differences raise previous questions about both definition and measurement. Many scientists agree with Jerry Hirsch, professor of psychology and zoology at the University of Illinois, that the whole heredity-environment debate is a pseudo-question. Heritability estimates offer answers to questions concerning the development of a single individual, but the answers are based on test performances of a cross section of a population of individuals at a given point in time.

The meaning of a measured heritability, Hirsch points out, "is derived from the measurements of the expression of some trait by a certain set of genotypes in a certain set of environments. Statistical analysis of such measurements (based on very explicit additivity assumptions) then yields an estimate of the percentage of trait variance that is inferred to be related to the *additive* contemporary genetic variance. Such measurement naturally requires a perfectly balanced experimental design—all genotypes (or trait-relevant components) measured against all environments (or their trait-relevant components). Few, if any, behavioral studies have been so thorough, and certainly not any human studies."

Man the unclassifiable

An ideal scientific system of classification is one in which all the cases can be categorized—the system is exhaustive—and in which there is no overlap in the categories—the categories are mutually exclusive. In such a taxonomic system all cases are classified, and no one case can legitimately be classified in more than one of the categories. Because all human beings are members of one species, and because the various stocks in that species have been mixing with one another for thousands of years, scientists have no set of "racial" categories that are both exhaustive and mutually exclusive.

Biologists are concerned with genetic relationships, with those things that are hereditary. Religious beliefs do not come through the genes, nor can one inherit political ideologies, customs, or beliefs. So the biologists' classification of race is concerned only with factors of scientific interest to the biologist. He must deal only with those physical properties that may be transmitted through the genes. These include such characteristics as color of eyes, skin, and hair; form of nose, head, and hair; skeletal structure; and blood type.

Scientists would find it relatively easy to categorize men if their head forms came in two distinct shapes: round and square. It would be easy if three distinct nose forms could be found, or distinctly different skin colors of a small number and variety. But nature does

402

not oblige. Head shapes vary along a continuum from round to narrow and cannot be grouped into sharply different categories. Nose form, eye shape, hair type, hair color, and eye color also differ infinitesimally along a gradual scale, and skin coloring is almost infinitely divisible into variations along a color continuum.

A further problem is that the factors being measured are not associated with each other. A man with a round head may have black skin or white skin. A man with a ruddy complexion may have a flat nose or a sharp one. A man may have dark brown skin, a medium long head, dark eyes, straight hair, and a sharp nose.

Despite the fact that the number of possible combinations and permutations is enormous, physical anthropologists and biologists have somewhat arbitrarily divided mankind into three major categories: (1) the whites or Caucasoids, who were inhabitants of Europe, North Africa, and Southwest Asia, but who in recent centuries have spread over most of the globe; (2) Negroids, black or brown people, often having very curly hair, who originally were mostly Africans but now constitute a sizable proportion of the population of the Western Hemisphere; and (3) Mongoloids, yellow to brown people with straight, black hair, concentrated in Asia and the Pacific islands.

Scientists have also attempted, without notable success, to relate these three large categories, based heavily on skin color, hair type, and geographic distribution, to subcategories that take into account eye color, head shape, nose shape, eye form, hair color, and stature. Some scholars list subraces: the North Chinese; the Malays; the red Mongoloids or American Indians; the Nilotic Negroes; the Pygmies; the Nordics, the Alpines, and Mediterraneans of Europe; and so on. But at what point along the continuum of skin color do we make a cutoff, deciding that skin lighter than this will be Caucasoid and skin darker than this Mongoloid?

All human individuals differ from one another in various traits: stature, curl of hair, size of hand, length of toes, and so on. Clusters of similar features can be found distributed among a group of people who have lived together in some region for a long time in relative isolation from other groups. People who live in cool climates generally have lighter skin than those who live in the tropics. Many people in the Far East have coarse black hair. Europeans generally have softer, less tightly curled hair on their bodies than most Africans. Many of the millions of people in Asia (and some in Eastern Europe) have a skin fold over the inner corner of the eye that gives the eye the appearance of being slanted.

All of these are minor differences, less notable than, for example, the range of variation among black bears. Human beings are a single species; hence the basic body structure of men is the same all over the world. All human beings have the same kind of lungs, the same kind and number of bones, the same complex nervous systems, the same delicate sensory organs for tasting, smelling, touching, hearing, and seeing. All men have the same bloodstream and, while there

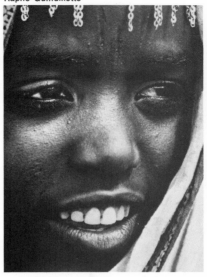

Myron Wood

are slight differences among individuals in blood chemistry, they are not related to skin color. A doctor handed a vial of type "O" blood has no way of ascertaining whether the donor was white or Negro, and no laboratory test of the blood can determine the donor's hair type, eye color, or other external physical traits.

The three major categories, then—Negroid, Mongoloid, and Caucasoid—are neither exhaustive nor mutually exclusive. The Australian aborigines, for example, with Negroid skin and Caucasoid hair, are sometimes classified as a fourth "race." The Mohaves of the American Southwest average nearly six feet in height; their neighbors, the Hopi, average five feet four inches. Both the longest human heads and the roundest are found among American Indian tribes. The tallest and the shortest people in the world, the Watusi and the Pygmy, live within a few miles of each other. Both have black skin and kinky hair, but some blond Norwegians also have kinky hair.

While slight differences have developed between groups living in relative isolation over a considerable period of time in various parts of the earth, the basic physical structure of all human beings is the same. Furthermore, differences within categories are greater than differences between them. The categories are based on gross averages. There is more difference between the lightest and the darkest Negroid, and between the lightest and the darkest Caucasoid, than between the lightest Negroid and the darkest Caucasoid. Even within a given geographic region, the differences are often as marked as the variations among the huge categories that are called "races."

Where inheritance ends and culture begins

There is more to this problem than the inability to construct a racial classification system that is exhaustive and the difficulty of defining categories that are mutually exclusive. Using these rough and approximate categories, is it possible to predict other biological characteristics? Are groupings such as Negroid, Mongoloid, and Caucasoid associated with differences in average intelligence, variations in athletic ability, gradations in musical talent, and meaningful differences in social relationships or culture? In short, does this classification scheme correlate with anything else? If so, approximate and error-laden though it may be, it would be useful to scientists in their attempts to classify and understand human behavior.

The only differences that have been established among the races are differences by definition. That is, we can say that Negroes *on the average* are darker than whites or Mongoloids; but being darker is only part of what we mean by being Negro. We have used the physical differences to define the racial boundaries. The question is whether there are systematic differences, by race, in such a basic cultural element as the language with which people communicate. There are not.

Any group of human beings can learn to speak any known human language. There is no better evidence of this than the contemporary English-speaking population of the United States. There we find Negroids, Mongoloids, and Caucasoids from all over the world who have learned in only a few generations to share a common culture and a common language. While many—whether Chinese-Americans or Hungarian-Americans—retain a few items from the culture of their grandfathers, all read the labels on the same frozen-food packages at the supermarket and cheer in the same language at a baseball game.

Nationality and race are also matters that bear no necessary relationship to one another. Again, the United States affords an example of a single nation made up of all the major racial stocks. Similarly, the Soviet Union combines in a single nation people ranging from the Mongoloid Eskimos of eastern Siberia to the swarthy residents of Turkestan to the blond Nordic Caucasoids in northwestern Russia.

Can a scientist determine a man's race from his religion or predict his religion from his race? No. As with language or any other learned behavior, any normal human being can learn the belief system of any religion. People sometimes speak of "the Jewish race," but there is no more a Jewish "race" than a Christian one. Judaism arose among Semitic Caucasoids in the Near East, people of the same race—and subrace—as the Arabs, who later spread their belief in Muhammad. But there are Chinese Jews, African Jews,

H. W. Silvester from Rapho Guillumette

405

European Jews, and American Jews. The American who wonders whether Jews are a race need only look at the blond, blue-eyed American Jews who came from north Germany and the swarthy, dark-haired American Jews who came from Turkey or Spain to be reminded that there are Mongoloid converts to Judaism living half way around the world from him, and that all these believers can hardly be considered a biological race. Islam, too, has made converts all over the world; and there are Japanese Christians, Nigerian Christians, and English Christians. We can classify people by the color of their skin, the length of their noses, the language they have learned, or the place of worship they choose, but these are four separate and distinct methods of grouping human beings, and the categories have no necessary relationship to one another.

But if Caucasoids are not a breed superior to Mongoloids and Negroids, how can we explain the European dominance of Asia and Africa for several centuries? A glance at the patterns of colonial expansion during the 17th, 18th, and 19th centuries seems to provide persuasive evidence of the superiority of the white race. The answer to this riddle is that one can easily believe in natural racial superiority—one needs only a profound ignorance of history.

Whatever the causes of the rise and fall of civilizations, race, over the span of human history, seems a poor explanation. The ancient Egyptians were a mixture of Negro and Semitic stocks. Kingdoms of Negroid Africans and Mongoloid Asians were at the forefront of civilization when Caucasoid Europeans were hunting in forests and living in caves. Even after Europeans had risen to the heights represented in ancient Greece and the Roman Empire, centuries followed during which Caucasoid Europeans were unable to defend themselves against the Mongoloid might of Attila and the Khans.

Various races and subraces have proved capable of expansion and consolidation of power when given fresh ideas in a favorable setting. As the sum of what men know has increased, each society has built on the knowledge of its predecessors and neighbors. This means that, in biological terms, any theory of human races that fails to appreciate the inseparability of gene complex and environment in the development of phenotype is scientifically worthless. Herbert G. Birch, research professor in the Albert Einstein College of Medicine at Yeshiva University, New York City, writes: "If the data of behavioral genetics permit us to draw any conclusions with respect to learning ability it is that learning ability is by no means a unitary strain, and that in different organisms different patterns of responsiveness, of motivation, of emotionality, and of antecedent history contribute substantially to determining which subgrouping will learn most effectively under conditions of different instruction and task demand. It appears, therefore, that a sober judgment would lead us to conclude that differences in learning achievements, whether measured by intelligence tests or by school achievement in human beings, represent the products of different degrees of goodness of

406

fit between the learner, the task, and in particular, the instructional mode."

To the extent that various tribes are in touch with one another, knowledge is diffused. There is a pyramiding of learning and skill. The discoveries, social inventions, technology, and organization of one society furnish a foundation for the building of the next. As time goes by, the arts and inventions pioneered by one people become the common property of their neighbors and of far-away tribes with whom they trade, and people of the next civilization are able to devote their imagination and energies to further advances in organization and application.

All organisms, including human beings, are programmed with perceptual systems such that an experience is prerequisite to a response, but the nature of the organism limits both the experiences and the responses that are possible. Peter Kilham and Peter H. Klopfer, of the department of zoology at Duke University, Durham, N.C., report research showing that yellow and black naïve chicks, reared with each other, show no consistent tendency to approach other chicks of the same variety. When reared with chicks of their own variety, however, they develop a preference for their own kind. This experiment demonstrates elegantly that, although a piece of information is transmitted genetically, it may nonetheless require an appropriate environment to manifest itself.

(Above) Frank Hurley from Rapho Guillumette;
(opposite page) courtesy, United Nations

These data are supported by Benson E. Ginsburg, professor of biology at the University of Chicago, and William S. Laughlin, professor of anthropology at the University of Wisconsin, who conclude that there is "a reciprocity or feedback between the genetic potential of a population and its social structure, such that not only does the former determine what the latter can be, but the latter exerts an important biological effect on the former." Potential behavioral adaptations do not in any way atrophy from disuse. Any genetically diverse population has the potential to replace another in the human species.

The power that comes from new knowledge has been the driving force in the creation of the great civilizations. Therefore, when a people is isolated from most advanced societies of its time, it is cut off from opportunities for rapid cultural growth. When African civilizations flourished, English and German tribes were unaware of them and remained relatively primitive. During the period when the Industrial Revolution was changing the social fabric of northwestern Europe and the United States, most Africans and Asians were completely isolated from these developments. The Maya Indians had a decimal system, but no wheel; the Romans had a wheel, but no concept of zero. Hence the Mayas made greater advances than the Romans in astronomy and mathematics; the Romans exceeded the Mayas in transportation and conquest.

The "race" of the underprivileged

People of every race have at one time or another achieved high place, held sway over their neighbors, and advanced in knowledge beyond what was generally known among other races at the time. But the question can still be raised whether, on the average, one race is not superior to the others. Again, a clue to the error in such an assumption can be found where members of several races participate in one society, as in the United States.

Seventy-five years ago, in the heyday of John L. Sullivan, it was widely held that the Irish were "born fighters," innately superior in prizefighting ability to representatives of other "races." As time passed and the Irish were able to climb the educational and economic ladders to assimilation in U.S. society, they were replaced in prizefighting by Italian-American champions and contenders. After a brief period of Italian dominance of the craft, Jews from Eastern Europe used prizefighting as a route to upward social mobility. (The occupation happens to be a good illustration because it requires a minimum of capital and formal education, and some of what it does require can be readily learned while growing up in the streets of a slum neighborhood.) The Jewish champions and contenders gave way to an era of Negro superiority, and the same phrases were used to describe Negroes that had been assigned to the Irish two generations before: "natural boxers," "hardheaded," "dumb but tough," and even "unfair competition because they're born with less feeling and the ability to take greater physical punishment." Currently, of course, Negroes are being displaced in the ring by Latin Americans. Racial differences may seem a good explanation for the behavior of members of a given group at a moment in time. With some historical perspective, a better explanation seems to be provided by an examination of the group's position in the social structure.

Equality and inequality *v.* identity and diversity

Theodosius Dobzhansky, professor of biology and genetics at Rockefeller University, New York City, brings us to the intersection of the biological and the sociological problem: "The inhabitants of different parts of the world are often visibly different, and the differences are in part genetic. This, in a nutshell, is the essence of race as a biological phenomenon. To be sure, any two persons, even brothers and sisters, also differ. Race differences are genetic differences between Mendelian populations, not between persons. And yet races differ in the same traits in which persons also differ. Difficulties arise because when a race or any other group is given a name, one is likely to assume that the individuals composing the group are alike or at least very similar. This is typological thinking, which befuddles not only the man in the street but some scientists as well. . . . Except for identical twins, everybody is biologically, genetically, different from

409

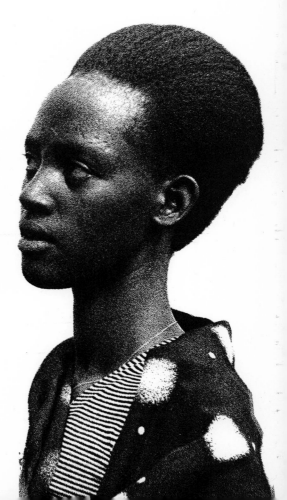

everybody else. Diversity should not, however, be confused with inequality. Equality and inequality are sociological, and identity and diversity are biological phenomena. Diversity is an observable fact; equality, an ethical precept. Society may grant or withhold equality from its members; it could not make them genetically alike even if this were desirable."

Dobzhansky's point is illustrated by social scientists' studies of the IQ and other measures of ability and achievement. On the average, U.S. Negroes score lower on such tests than U.S. whites. What we need to know is whether this is a racial trait or a difference attributable to the Negroes' position in U.S. society.

In U.S. Army tests of aptitude during World War II, Northern soldiers did better than those from the Southern states. Scientists would expect this, because education influences the results of such tests, and schools are, on the average, superior in the North. Northern Negroes excelled Southern Negroes; this would be expected because of the differing quality of the facilities for formal education. But when we know that (1) rural schools have lower standards and poorer facilities on the average than urban schools, and that (2) the quality of formal education in the Southern states is poorer than in the North, *and* that (3) most American Negroes have been born and reared in the rural South, how should we interpret the finding that Negroes average lower on test scores than whites? Is this a consequence of race (heredity) or of social structure (environment)?

410

The question is more complicated than it seems at first, for Negroes and whites in the United States simply do not share a comparable environment, even if we leave region and urban-rural differences out of it. A typical Negro child attending the same school with whites in a Northern city is not in the same environment as the whites: his parents had less formal education than most of the white parents, and education of inferior quality; he does not have the same things at home that the white children have; he lives in a poorer, more crowded neighborhood than the white children; his teachers treat him with less patience and sympathy than they give their white pupils; his fellow students exclude him from their evening homework sessions, especially if their parents insist. In short, he lives in an environment of discrimination. But because it is extremely difficult to compare racial abilities in a situation of experimental control, scientists cannot assert definitely that there are no differences in intelligence by race. When one addresses the policy implications of this statement, however, one does not see how it can be argued that we must wait until we know that potentialities are equal and then try to provide equal environments.

What we can do is contrast the performance of representatives of the two races in differing environments. Such a contrast casts doubt on any generalizations about race differences. Negro draftees from New York, Ohio, and Illinois averaged much better on Army literacy and aptitude tests than white soldiers from Georgia, Arkansas, and

Mississippi. We do not conclude from this that Northern Negroes are a smarter "race" than Southern whites. It simply means that where there are better opportunities, Negroes, like whites, profit from them.

Needed: a culture of opportunity

During the first half of the 20th century, scholars probably erred in overemphasizing the effect of heredity on the human condition while underemphasizing the enormous importance of the man-made part of environment: culture. In recent decades, cumulative social science research has pointed up man's ability to alter his natural environment. He changes his physical environment by engineering: he brings air conditioning to the tropics and central heating to colder climates. Man alters his psychological environment by psychological perception and by redefinition of social situations: what he cannot change, he rationalizes. Man alters his cultural environment through social organization: culture, being learned behavior, is changeable.

Psychologist Arthur R. Jensen, of the University of California at Berkeley, criticizes the environmentalist bias of some psychologists and social scientists: "All the major heritability studies reported in the literature are based on samples of white European and North American populations, and our knowledge of the heritability of intelligence in different racial and cultural groups within these popula-

412

tions is nil. For example, no adequate heritability studies have been based on samples of the Negro population of the United States." Joshua Lederberg, Nobel Laureate and professor of genetics at Stanford's School of Medicine, agrees, but challenges Jensen's views on the effect of racial alienation on intellectual development: "Jensen fails to see enough difference in early environments of children he believes to be in comparable economic strata, to account for later school difficulties. We must point out that 'comparable' groups have never been standardized even for simple physical health or for nutrition during pregnancy." (*See* Year in Review: BEHAVIORAL SCIENCES, *Psychology*.)

The flourishing of social research may have led to an exaggerated environmentalism on the part of social scientists. Instead of an either/or view of heredity versus environment, contemporary scientists are likely to stress the interaction of these two critical variables. Recent research demonstrates that people can benefit intellectually from improved nutrition. A sample of women of low socioeconomic status in New York City were given vitamin and mineral supplements during pregnancy. They gave birth to children who averaged eight points higher in IQ at four years of age than a control group of children whose mothers had received placebos during pregnancy. (*See* Feature Article: WHEN YOUNG CHILDREN GO HUNGRY: EFFECTS ON LEARNING AND BEHAVIOR.)

We know that representatives of all races are found throughout the range of intelligence: there are Negroid, Mongoloid, and Caucasoid geniuses, and there are Negroid, Mongoloid, and Caucasoid imbeciles. The best tests we have, controlling for regional differences, urban-rural differences, and other cultural influences, simply do not provide enough information to permit the conclusion that there are any innate differences in ability by race.

The only way we shall ever know whether equality of human achievement is possible is through providing equality of opportunity. Since we do not have genetic identity among human beings, we can provide equality of opportunity only by providing a diversified environment, a world of multiple opportunities affording outlets for the varied aptitudes of different-looking, different-feeling, and different-acting people.

FOR ADDITIONAL READING:

Fox, Robin, "Chinese Have Bigger Brains than Whites—Are They Superior?", *New York Times Magazine,* pp. 12 ff. (June 30, 1968).

Kluckhohn, Clyde, *Mirror for Man* (McGraw-Hill, 1949).

Mead, Margaret, *et al., Science and the Concept of Race* (Columbia University Press, 1968).

UNESCO, Department of Mass Communications, *What Is Race? Evidence from Scientists* (1952).

U.S. Commission on Civil Rights, *Racial Isolation in the Public Schools* (U.S. Government Printing Office, 1967).

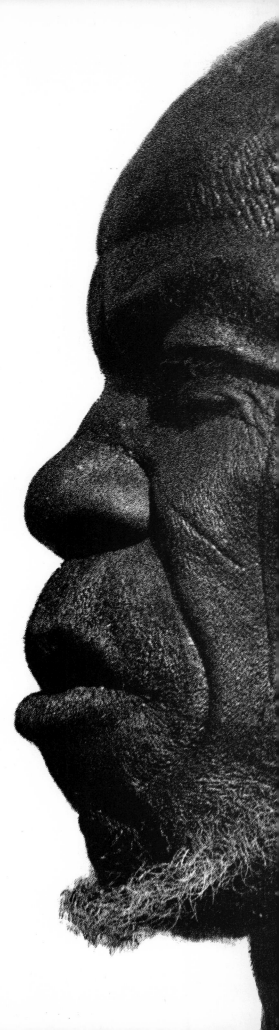

Physical Sciences in the Soviet Union
by Mikhail D. Millionshchikov

Though comparatively unknown in the West, Soviet physical scientists have a solid record of achievement. Their outstanding accomplishments, reviewed here by the vice - president of the Academy of Sciences of the U.S.S.R., are, in fact, influencing research throughout the world.

Soviet Russia inherited from czarism a severe economic, technical, and cultural backwardness. Thus, it was only natural that a new nation, which had set as its goal the creation of the most perfect social system within a short historical period, would find science a most attractive and practical tool. At the dawn of the Soviet state, therefore, in the most unfavorable conditions of the revolution, the civil war, and the first years of the reconstruction period, the principles for the organization of Soviet science under a socialist government were formulated.

The attention that was paid then and that has continued to be paid to science in the U.S.S.R. is in keeping with a fundamental tenet of Marxism-Leninism: science is the most dynamic and, historically, the most important long-range component of all man's efforts to remake his surroundings. Thus, it was recognized that a highly sophisticated system for applied scientific and technological research was necessary for economic and cultural development. Along with this encouragement for applied science, however, there has always been a parallel support in the U.S.S.R. for "pure science," research in the most fundamental concepts of mathematics, physics, chemistry, and biology. Basic research was recognized as the ultimate source for those developments that would eventually affect man and his environment most radically.

A Soviet research rocket bound for a probe of the upper atmosphere carries on the work of the Space Age, begun in 1957 when the U.S.S.R. launched Sputnik 1, the world's first artificial satellite.

V. Lebedev from APN

One of the many settlements where Soviet scientific workers live and work is the Sayan Mountains observatory. The facility is maintained on Mt. Munku-Sardyk near Mongolia by the Siberian branch of the Academy of Sciences of the U.S.S.R.

Such a bilateral approach must, of necessity, affect the management of science and the organization of research. In the U.S.S.R. research that has more or less concrete goals and that can, therefore, be planned in detail, is carried out by the institutions of the ministries and state committees. The management of research of a less concrete nature is the responsibility of the Academy of Sciences of the U.S.S.R., in Moscow. This work is conducted in the academy's institutes, in the science academies of the various union republics, and in institutions of higher learning. Over 700,000 scientific workers are employed by the more than 4,500 scientific institutions in the U.S.S.R., of which nearly 500 are affiliated with the Academy of Sciences of the U.S.S.R. and the science academies of the union republics.

Because of the rapid growth in the amount of current scientific research in the Soviet Union and the need to bring scientists into close contact with technology and industry, a certain amount of planned development is necessary even in fundamental research. To combine such planning with the broad, free nature of fundamental research is, obviously, a difficult problem, for which there is no ready solution. In the U.S.S.R. the management and planning of basic research is understood not as regimentation over the subject matter of research but as special support for certain indicated trends.

An important element in ensuring favorable conditions for scientific activity is the organization and dissemination of scientific information. One publishing house which functions under the aegis of the Academy of Sciences produces annually nearly 3,000 scientific titles. In addition, almost 1,700 titles are published each year by similar publishing houses in the union republics. Other publications include 240 scientific periodicals (of which 100 are devoted to specific disciplines) and nearly 200 journals of abstracts.

Soviet scholars studying animate nature have made significant contributions to world science, particularly in the physiology of nervous activity, in plant physiology, and in genetics. The social sciences also have been developing especially rapidly in the U.S.S.R. under the influence of new quantitative methods for studying society

Tass from Sovfoto

and the individual. Although Soviet efforts in the life and social sciences have been most impressive, they are much too numerous to include in this survey, which concentrates on the more notable achievements of the U.S.S.R. in the physical sciences, particularly those that have had worldwide implications.

The achievements in the physical sciences described in this article are not all-inclusive, but they do indicate the major trends in which Soviet scientists are engaged. Because science searches for that which is not yet known, the importance of certain revelations frequently does not become evident until after subsequent discoveries have been made. Thus, when describing such a broad subject as the physical sciences, no one is insured against the danger of omitting something that is potentially very important.

The tradition of excellence in mathematics

The contemporary position of Soviet mathematics is deeply rooted in a tradition of mathematical achievement that goes back to such eminent proponents as N. I. Lobachevski, P. L. Chebichev, and A. A. Markov. Following the work of these early scholars, a whole complex of mathematical trends has continued to develop in the Soviet Union. Especially outstanding achievements have been made in the analytic theory of numbers, the summation of trigonometric series, the theory of the so-called L-series, and the distribution of values of arithmetic functions. Fundamental results have been obtained, too, in the algebraic theory of numbers, in topology, and in the study of partial differential equations.

Computer technology has stimulated intensive efforts by Soviet mathematicians in the study of mathematical logic, particularly in the theory of algorithms. The theory of control systems has also been the subject of much investigation, and important results have been obtained in solving asymptotic problems in the synthesis of control systems. In addition, worldwide recognition has been earned for Soviet research on problems associated with probability theory, information theory, and the theory of random processes.

Substantial contributions concerning the general characteristics of functions, integrals, and sets that are not amenable to methods of classical analysis are being made by the Soviet school of mathematicians, founded by N. N. Luzin, which studies the functions of a real variable. Methods used for the functions of a real variable have also been applied to other divisions of mathematics. Soviet mathematicians have been credited, too, with significant findings resulting from their work in the theory of trigonometric and more general orthogonal sets and in the best approximations of the functions of a real variable. For the approximations of functions of a complex variable, a number of fundamental theorems with many ramifications have been proved by Soviet scholars.

In recent years notable results obtained in the study of the qualitative theory of differential equations have been applied to the theory of perturbations and automatic regulation. On the basis of methods worked out in the U.S.S.R. for investigating Hamiltonian systems, mathematicians were able to solve the classical problem of divergent series with small denominators, which has a number of important applications in physics and celestial mechanics. Methods for approximating solutions of non-Hamiltonian systems that are valid for long periods of time have also been developed by Soviet mathematicians.

Developments in astronomy and astrophysics

The current state of astronomy, which has as deep a tradition in the U.S.S.R. as mathematics, can be described as a "second youth." Its progress in recent years has been linked with the creation of large telescopes and sensitive radiation receivers, and especially with the emergence of radio astronomy as a means for studying the universe. Soviet astronomers are using these instruments for fundamental studies of the sun and planets, and for galactic and metagalactic observations.

In a number of Soviet observatories large telescopes provide high-quality observations of the fine details of stellar radiation. Among these instruments are the 2-m reflector in Shemakha and the 2.6-m reflector in the Crimean Astro-Physical Observatory. Another 2.6-m telescope is being erected in Armenia, and a reflector with a record mirror diameter of 6 m will be installed in the northern Caucasus. For the study of galaxies a 1-m Schmidt telescope is in use in Armenia, and large instruments for the study of the sun are located in the Crimea, outside of Moscow, and in Kislovodsk. New devices for radio astronomy include the first variable-profile antenna in Pulkovo, the 1-km × 1-km cross-shaped interferometer and the 22-m parabolic radio telescope in Serpukhov, and the two T-shaped radio telescopes and the antenna of the Distant Space Communications Center in the Ukraine.

Recent significant findings made by Soviet astronomers include the discovery of the supercorona of the sun and a series of radar observations that not only established the characteristics of the surfaces and atmospheres of the planets Venus, Mars, and Jupiter but also improved the accuracy of the astronomical unit and the orbital elements of the planets. Soviet studies of the evolution of stars and star clusters also have deservedly earned widespread fame. An especially notable series of studies on star associations concluded that the process of star formation may be continuing even in our time.

Notable Soviet astrophysical investigations have included study of the lines of hydrogen and the hydroxl radical (OH) in interstellar gas, and of the synchrotronic mechanism for the radiation of supernova remnants (*e.g.,* Crab nebula). In recent years, Soviet investigators have been using the concept of gravitational collapse to clarify the nature of quasars and radio galaxies.

The study of the near cosmos, which is a new stage in the development of astronomy (and also of geophysics), began with the launching of the earth's first artificial satellite by the U.S.S.R. in 1957. Soviet satellites and probes have since made possible the collection of data on the density of meteoric particles and meteorite streams, the composition of the upper atmosphere, and on the structure of the ionosphere and of the terrestrial magnetic field. One of the early Soviet satellites in 1958 was the first to register the outer radiation belt of the earth. The heaviest Soviet satellites, those of the Proton series, were designed to study the primary components of cosmic rays.

A more complex stage of investigations began with the sending of Soviet automated stations to the moon, Mars, and Venus to study the physical conditions on these bodies. With the aid of these devices a map was made of most of the far side of the moon; the extremely scant size or absence of a lunar magnetic field was established; the existence of the earth's hydrogen corona, which is formed by the hydrogen that constantly flows out of its atmosphere, was revealed; and the current of solar particles was discovered.

Novosti for Sovfoto

Each antenna of the cross-shaped radio telescope at Serpukhov (left) delivers signals received from space to a central monitoring area. Powerful equipment at Abastumani Observatory photographed the asteroid Icarus (the continuous trace of light, above) in June 1968.

Novosti from Sovfoto

International research projects are conducted in the experiment room at Serpukhov (above), site of the world's largest accelerator. At Melekess (facing page), remote control devices test the practicality of various applications of nuclear physics.

Elementary-particle and nuclear physics

Many of the aspects of contemporary research in nuclear physics in the U.S.S.R. first took shape at the Leningrad Physico-Technological Institute. Prior to World War II studies done at the institute by the first generation of Soviet nuclear physicists resulted in the development of an electric-drop model of the atomic nucleus and the first exchange theory of nuclear forces. Although this theory could not be proved experimentally inasmuch as pions had not yet been discovered, it did advance the study of the atomic nucleus. Other early work included the predicting of the magnetic moment of the neutron, the discovery of nuclear isomerism, and the discovery of spontaneous nuclear fission. In the 1930s, Cerenkov radiation of electrons, now widely known because of its application to elementary-particle physics, was discovered and interpreted in the Institute of Physics of the Academy of Sciences of the U.S.S.R. On the eve of the war, immediately after the discovery of neutron emission during the fission of uranium, Soviet physicists proved the possibility of a fission chain reaction and formulated a theory for it.

The urgent need of atomic physicists for sources of intense beams of charged particles with predetermined levels of energy was answered by the development of the principle of phase stability. This underlies the working of all large modern accelerators. Serious participation by Soviet physicists in this effort began after the construction in Dubno of two accelerators based on the phase-stability principle: a 680-Mev synchrocyclotron in 1949 and a 10-Bev proton synchrotron in 1957. With these accelerators as a base, the Joint Institute of Nuclear Research was formed in Dubno. The broad range of research in nuclear physics conducted there by scientists of the socialist countries has produced findings on the elastic and nonelastic interaction of nucleons with pions in energy ranges up to hundreds of Mev. Valuable quantitative information was also acquired on the birth processes of so-called strange particles, and the preservation of spatial parity in such processes was verified. Several types of resonances of elementary particles with very short life spans were also discovered.

In 1961, at the Institute of Theoretical and Experimental Physics, Moscow, a 7-Bev strong focusing proton accelerator was commissioned. It served as the model for the world's largest particle accelerator, the Serpukhov accelerator, which was designed to produce a 70-Bev proton beam and began operating in the autumn of 1967. A unique complex, the Serpukhov accelerator includes, in addition to the machine itself, which has a circumference of 1.5 km, a linear 100-Mev proton accelerator, an injector, a huge experiment room, and a number of auxiliary facilities. Nuclear physicists from many Soviet institutes are participating in investigations with this accelerator. Furthermore, they are collaborating with French scholars on the construction of a large liquid hydrogen bubble chamber with a volume of six cubic meters, and with scientists at the European Organization for Nuclear Research (CERN), in Geneva, in the creation of separated beams of particles in the accelerator. Also commissioned in 1967 was a 6-Bev electronic ring accelerator, in Yerevan, which was designed basically to study electromagnetic interactions of nuclear particles.

When attempting to increase the energies of particles, physicists today must consider the economic factor: the cost of an up-to-date accelerator is comparable to the budgets of some small governments. Since the mid-1950s, therefore, in the U.S.S.R. particular attention has been given to the search for new means of accelerating particles. At the present time, two methods appear most promising and economical. One of these, the colliding-beams method, is being investigated at the Nuclear Physics Institute of the Siberian branch of the Academy of Sciences of the U.S.S.R. in Novosibirsk. This method is based on the relativistic laws of the collision of charged particles, in which the effective energy of the interaction of the particles sharply increases at velocities approaching the speed of light. Two installations utilizing this principle are operating at Novosibirsk: one has colliding beams of electrons with an energy of 2 × 160 Mev; the other has colliding beams of electrons and positrons with an energy of 2 × 700 Mev.

The second method of accelerating nuclear particles is called collective acceleration. Originated by Soviet scholars, this method utilizes internal high-intensity fields in a plasma. All the physical and technical principles for such an accelerator have been formulated, and a model of one is being constructed in the Soviet Union. Experiments conducted in Dubno showed that such accelerators could increase the energy of protons nearly 1 Bev/m. The most effective contemporary accelerators, on the other hand, provide an energy increase of no more than 50 Mev/m.

Much consideration has also been given in the U.S.S.R. to atomic nuclear research. Scientists are attempting to work out a complete theory for describing the characteristics of atomic nuclei from a single point of view. Of special interest are the studies on the synthesis of transuranium elements. A broad range of research conducted in Dubno with the specially constructed high-current, heavy-ion accelerator resulted in the synthesis of a number of isotopes of element 102 (nobelium) and the discovery and study of element 104, for which the name "kurchatovium" has been proposed.

The growing interest in plasma physics

In the U.S.S.R., as in a number of other countries, there is a growing interest in plasma physics, the study of balanced mixtures of free ions and electrons. This recent development is associated not only with the fact that the physical characteristics of plasma appear in a wide range of cosmic phenomena, but also that plasma plays a

Camera Press-Pix

Tokamak-3 is one of several promising Soviet techniques for obtaining stable high-temperature hydrogen plasma for thermonuclear uses.

role in solving a most important contemporary problem, controlled thermonuclear fusion. It is also involved in the problem of the direct transformation of thermal energy into electrical energy. Plasma physics had its most rapid development in the 1950s, after the principle of thermomagnetic isolation for obtaining controlled thermonuclear reactions had been formulated in the U.S.S.R. More recently Soviet scholars developed the theory of the nonlinear waves in plasma and made basic contributions to the theory of the instability and stochastic processes in plasma.

A number of Soviet investigations in the stabilization of plasma in magnetic traps and in the turbulent heating of plasma have won the deserved recognition of the world scientific community. Scientists in the U.S.S.R. discovered, investigated in detail, and stabilized (for low-density plasma) the "groove instability" of rarified plasma, which was predicted by both Soviet and U.S. physicists. The possibility of stabilizing this instability also led to an intensive search for new types of magnetic traps to contain thermonuclear processes. In recent years toroidal installations of the Tokamak type have been used to obtain high-temperature, sufficiently dense plasma.

One immediate application of plasma physics has been the magnetohydrodynamic (MHD) transformation of thermal energy into electrical energy. Soviet investigations of the fundamental characteristics of low-temperature plasma have led to the development of MHD generators, and a semi-industrial power plant with a 30 kw MHD generator has been commissioned.

Courtesy, V. Peshkov,
USSR Academy of Sciences

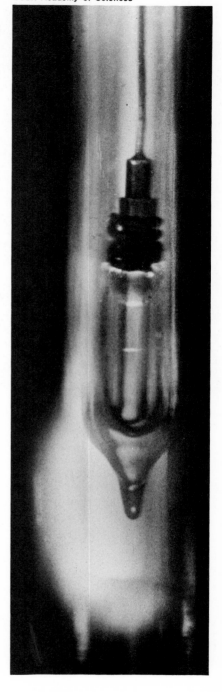

Revolutionary advances in solid-state physics

In recent decades, the influence of solid-state physics on scientific and technical progress and its role in improving experimental methods have been comparable to the revolutionary transformations in engineering engendered by the achievements of nuclear physics. One of the most important principles underlying solid-state physics is the notion that any weakly excited state of a macroscopic body can be regarded as the sum total of separate elementary excitations, or quasi particles, whose properties can be determined by observing the thermal, magnetic, electrical, and other characteristics of solids. Working with this approach, Soviet scientists had the honor of introducing the first quasi particles, the phonons (sound quanta in a crystal lattice), and the concepts of two others: the exciton, a specially excited state of electrons in a crystal lattice; and the polaron, a conducting electron in an ionic lattice. It was the eminent Soviet physicist L. D. Landau who formulated the general principles for classifying quasi particles according to their statistical characteristics. Landau was also the first to apply the concept to the theory of liquid helium II, and, as a result, to explain the phenomenon of superfluidity, which was discovered in the U.S.S.R. in the 1930s.

Theoretical physicists at Kharkov have used the concept of quasi particles as conductivity electrons to enhance knowledge of such electronic properties of metals as the galvanomagnetic phenomenon and the anomalous spin-effect. Data from this work also provided exhaustive information on the energy distribution of the conductivity electrons. Also connected with the characteristics of the quasi particles is the concept of superconductivity. Much of the current interest in this phenomenon has been based on Soviet efforts to develop the theory of the "hard" superconductors that has found practical application in the form of superconducting alloys.

Research on semiconductors occupies a special place in the work of solid-state physicists in the U.S.S.R. In fact, it was the work begun by A. F. Ioffe and his associates in the late 1920s, far earlier than in other laboratories of the world, that laid down the foundations for the contemporary physics of semiconductors. This research has led to the creation of semiconductor thermoelectric generators, one of which was developed several years ago in the Soviet Union to transform nuclear heat into electrical power. The world's first

Tass from Sovfoto

*Soviet physicist V. Peshkov
photographed his separation of two
helium isotopes (above). At 0.5°
helium-3 is seen above
the separation in the tube; helium-4
settles below the line. Uppermost
line is the liquid level. At left,
an effort to create high-temperature
plasma utilizes the oscillation
of a laser ray on neodymium glass.*

reactor-converter, this generator consists of a high-temperature reactor operating on fast neutrons and a silicon-germanium thermo-electric converter. It is intended as the prototype for autonomous nuclear power units that are transportable.

One of the greatest achievements of semiconductor physics in recent years has been the development of various quantum generators (masers and lasers), the importance of which for the progress of communications, meteorology, navigation, medicine, and other fields can scarcely be exaggerated. A series of fundamental studies in quantum electronics carried out in the U.S.S.R. in the 1950s laid the foundation for the manufacture of lasers.

Another significant achievement in physics in the last 20 years was the discovery in the U.S.S.R. of the phenomenon of electronic paramagnetic resonance, which gives the same information about energy levels in a solid as normal optics gives about the energy levels of an individual atom. The development of relatively simple, accurate instruments to investigate paramagnetic resonance has made this study popular among chemists, biologists, and others.

The practical contributions of the earth sciences

Because there is great physical diversity within the borders of the U.S.S.R., it is only natural that Soviet scientists should be very interested in the earth sciences and that their contributions should be important ones. Two prominent Soviet scholars, V. I. Vernadski and A. E. Fersman, have been credited with major contributions in the development of modern geochemistry, which studies the history of the chemical elements in the earth's crust and their behavior under various natural thermodynamic and physico-chemical conditions. Theoretical work by Soviet scientists has also provided a foundation for spatial, or three-dimensional, geodesy, which has significantly simplified the task of accurately determining the earth's configuration. Studies on the registration and interpretation of short-period oscillations (those lasting for seconds or fractions of seconds) of the earth's electromagnetic field have led Soviet geophysicists to theorize the existence of two types of magnetohydrodynamic oscillations in the earth's magnetosphere.

A network of more than 100 seismic stations with the most modern equipment and a tsunami warning service provide the base for Soviet seismological research. A method for deep seismic sounding developed in the U.S.S.R. has played an important role in the study of deep crustal structures and has provided knowledge that is valuable for predicting earthquakes. Working with theories of the processes taking place in seismic foci, Soviet seismologists were the first to propose a model of an earthquake as a mechanical dislocation.

The Soviet Union has obtained abundant data on the structure of the deep strata of the earth's crust and upper mantle, on the composition and dynamics of the ocean waters, and on the laws governing many phenomena in the atmosphere generally, and the troposphere in particular. Radioactive methods for determining the absolute age of rocks and ores have been developed widely and used to explain the chronological sequence of magmatic processes, and to decipher the most ancient pages of the history of the earth. Studies with stable isotopes of oxygen have yielded answers to a number of problems associated with the temperature conditions of various geological processes and with the evolution of the earth's climate.

With the help of geophysics and geochemistry, Soviet geologists have formulated theories about paragenesis (the natural formation of minerals and the rocks that are associated with them) and have established principles for the origin of rocks (petrogenesis) under various conditions. A set of methods devised in the U.S.S.R. is being used as the basis for making international tectonic maps of the earth's major structural features.

For biostratigraphic purposes, a tremendous amount of work has been done in the Soviet Union on microscopic fossil remains (Foraminifera, Radiolaria, ostracods, algae, spores, and plant pollen). The possibility of using algal structures to separate and compare pre-Cambrian strata that is more than 500 million years old has been proved for the first time. Methods for correlating sections of strata have permitted comparisons of the most recent geological events that have occurred over the entire land mass from Europe to the Pacific Ocean. The recently published 15-volume work on the fundamentals of paleontology provides a new taxonomy of all fossil organisms.

Considerable success has also been achieved in the study and classification of magmatism (including vulcanism), metamorphism, and of ore formation. In the mid-1950s Soviet scholars began to work on an explanation of the general laws of mineral distribution as a means for detecting deeply bedded, "blind" deposits. Discoveries in the last ten years of the diamonds of Yakutia, of the largest oil- and gas-bearing area in western Siberia, of rich gas deposits in Central Asia and in the basin of the Vilyuy River, and of a number of other minerals have been the direct consequence of scientific predictions resulting from these studies.

Carrying on a tradition in chemistry

Chemical research in the U.S.S.R. is influenced not only by industrial need but also by the impressive legacy of such noted compatriots as D. I. Mendeleyev, A. M. Butlerov, and N. Zinin. In addition, in the late 1920s and early 1930s many prominent Soviet chemists were also eminent physicists. This circumstance played a positive role in the development of the new trends in contemporary chemistry: chemical kinetics, catalysis theory, electrochemistry, adsorption theory, and physico-chemical mechanics.

In the kinetics of chemical reactions, a theory developed in the

Methods for speeding up chemical reactions of all kinds and for using them in industry are investigated at the Institute of Catalysis of the Siberian branch of the Academy of Sciences in Novosibirsk.

Novosti from Sovfoto

A spectacular display of northern lights flashes above the Yakutsk laboratories. Cosmic rays and other phenomena are studied easily in the clear, cold atmosphere.

Camera Press-Pix

U.S.S.R. to explain chain reactions from a single point of view has been applied to the analysis of basic chemical reactions, such as oxidation, cracking, polymerization, and halogenation. Furthermore, while studying the nature of active centers and of elementary processes in an effort to substantiate the theory, Soviet chemists made important findings on the roles of hydroxyl radicals and hydrogen atoms.

In work on heat theories and mechanisms of combustion and detonation, Soviet chemists have consistently taken into account the kinetics of chemical reaction, heat transfer, and diffusion. Their research on catalysts has concentrated on the mechanism of heterogeneous organic catalysis and has produced a multiplet theory of catalysis that has received widespread recognition.

In electrochemistry, significant successes have resulted from studies of the double layer, the influence of adsorption on the kinetics of electrode reactions, the role of diffusion factors, hydrogen overvoltage, corrosion, and passivity. On the basis of these works, the mechanism and kinetics were established for such electrode processes as the evolution of hydrogen, the evolution and reduction of oxygen, the reduction of a number of anions and organic compounds, the dissolution of metal in acids, and the passivity of metals.

Developments in colloid chemistry and the physical chemistry of surface phenomena have led to the emergence of a special field, physicochemical mechanics. Studies in this area have produced new ideas about the spatial structures that arise in dispersed and colloidal systems, established the rheological features of the various structures, measured directly the van der Waals forces as a function of distance, and worked out the influence of the surface of a lyophilic solid on the structure of adjoining layers of liquid.

As a result of Soviet research in organic chemical compounds and their catalystic transformations, the laws of the internal conversion of acetylene and diene hydrocarbons, as well as the hydrogenation, dimerization, and polymerization of the latter, were discovered. The catalytic conversions that have been worked out include cracking with aluminum chloride, aromatization of cyclanes, and cyclization and aromatization of alkanes into alkenes and dienes. This work also provided a method for producing synthetic rubber.

Of great importance have been the studies of carbon compounds reacting with elements that are typically inorganic in nature—both metals and nonmetals. Fundamental results obtained in the U.S.S.R. include the synthesis of metallo-organic compounds on a base of double diazonium salts. Practical applications include the production of antidetonators, insecticides, and flotation agents. A major independent trend paralleling this has been the chemistry of silicoorganic compounds and their polymers. Soviet chemists have created silicon polymers with molecular chains that include silicon, oxygen, and aluminum. Because of their high heat resistance, these polymers have found widespread application.

Toward Future Guidance of Science in Human Affairs

by Christopher Wright

In a technocratic world, man has tended to view scientific discovery as an inevitable process to which society must adjust. Not so, says the director of Columbia University's newly founded Institute for the Study of Science in Human Affairs. Science must be put into perspective, and to do this we need new knowledge of how science and society interact.

"Science," as we know it today, is a relatively recent phenomenon for which we have yet to evolve adequate mechanisms for accommodating it to other human affairs. What we might call "the scientific enterprise" has given rise to many of the most subtle and specialized of human activities. Such increased specialization of function is, indeed, one characteristic of the evolution of a biological or social organism, but only if it is accompanied by the development of integrative mechanisms for coordinating and guiding the activities of the parts. For the scientific enterprise, however, such integration has been far outpaced by the growth of specialized research and the technologies that arise from it. The issue today is whether integration is feasible and, if so, how scientists might adjust to it.

We must assume that the world of the future will be man-made, or at least man-decided. We must also assume that man will survive only if he wills it and, through his social institutions, makes the appropriate choices. The character of the choices to be made concerning science is especially important. Must they be basic and irrevocable, and must they be made by a few men in private, as Lord Snow suggested a few years ago in connection with decisions involving weapons of mass destruction? Must they be made by scientists themselves? Or can the choices be of a more open, piecemeal, and revocable nature? The answers to such questions depend on the availability of detailed knowledge concerning the possible effects of

428

constraints on and guidance of science and the potentially revolutionary interactions of science with human affairs. This is knowledge that we do not yet possess.

The perils of scientific research

In the *1969 Britannica Yearbook of Science and the Future,* René Dubos noted that science clearly contains both perils and promises for man. It is equally clear that the perils will far outweigh the promises unless procedures can be devised that will integrate science with other human concerns while at the same time preserving its vitality. Yet the obstacles confronting any alternative approaches to scientific research and development are formidable. If these obstacles are to be overcome, they must first be recognized and widely understood.

The trial-and-error methods of unplanned scientific development are now more likely to lead to disaster than to success, and some of the applications of science that may become technically feasible in the near future, such as the alteration of ecological, geophysical, or atmospheric processes, no longer permit of experimentation without inviting serious—perhaps irreversible—consequences. Nor should the intellectual and social effects of scientific revolutions be underestimated. Galileo and Copernicus were attempting to discover the workings of the solar system, but a side effect of the remarkable unity and simplicity that they introduced into astronomy in the 16th and 17th centuries was the exacerbation of the severe theological and social strains of the time.

As late as the 18th century, the scientific enterprise still was not isolated from other human endeavors. The philosophers and leaders of the Enlightenment seemed capable of integrating scientific knowledge with other knowledge when it was appropriate to do so, and of making public policy judgments against that background. Today, however, no lone individual or group of individuals can play a similar role. Avoiding or eliminating the disproportions and gaps between scientific and other human interests requires a battery of institutional mechanisms—educational programs, panels of scientists, legislative committees, budgetary planning, and many others—whose functions are commonly misunderstood and which scientists frequently regard with considerable suspicion.

Historically the scientist has sought—or has claimed that he was seeking—objective truth, without regard to the consequences of his discoveries. His justification, which has generally been accepted by nonscientists, has been that, in the long run, expansion of the total fund of knowledge will work toward the ultimate well-being of mankind. Thus, efforts to locate science within an overarching humanistic context and to guide it toward socially desirable goals have been viewed as degrading to science and destructive of its special objectivity; parochial at best and, at worst, threatening to the process

429

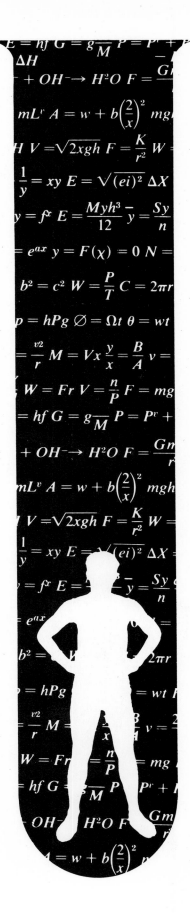

of independent and unbiased scientific inquiry. This attitude has inhibited a full understanding of the nature of science and the development of useful science policies.

The power of scientific thought comes from the recognition of uniformities and the development of general theories concerning these uniformities that have both broad and specific applicability. Yet this body of knowledge is essentially self-contained. Scientific knowledge, in and of itself, does not explain how science should contribute to the fulfillment of human values and social goals. Are certain values and goals to be favored simply because their attainment is scientifically feasible? Must intellectual revolutions in science also lead to social revolutions or, conversely, to extreme social reactions? Where might science lead us and must we follow? Today these and other questions are being asked with increasing concern. This fact alone suggests that the inherent tendency of scientific inquiry to upset established knowledge may become a source of social conflict between those persons and institutions that are most fully committed to science and those that remain more detached from it.

New forces of science

In less than 400 years science as an enterprise has evolved from the personal intellectual interest of a few individuals to a major force in society. In the United States alone, for example, there are over half a million scientists and a million engineers. They are chiefly responsible for the use of over $15 billion a year in research and development funds from the federal government, as well as somewhat lesser amounts from other sources. Although only about 10% of these funds are used for fundamental research, elaborate systems of training, publication, and information retrieval have been devised that almost guarantee significant results. The scientific establishment cannot be considered as monolithic, however. Methods, personnel, and institutions—even the boundaries of science itself—vary according to the kind of knowledge available or being sought.

Every area of science has the capacity to expand through a self-reinforcing application of increasingly refined methods to the problems at hand. The study of subatomic particles, for example, leads to the building of high-energy accelerators, which leads to the discovery of new particles, which leads to the building of bigger and more complex accelerators that attract more specialized scientists into the field, and so on. Through such processes, prodigious advances were made in physics and chemistry during this century, while the biological sciences remained relatively stagnant until their recent infusion of techniques and personnel from the other disciplines. Such patterns might be interpreted to imply an inevitable sequence in the unfolding of knowledge. They can also be interpreted to suggest the possibility that the techniques of science, as distinct from the great men of science, could be consciously directed toward important but neglected areas of inquiry rather than toward those that are advancing most rapidly.

Political decisions concerning the allocation of resources among the various fields of scientific research usually have been made with the awareness that significant new knowledge might be gained and that such knowledge might have social applications, although these cannot always be specified in advance. Little attention has been paid, however, to the possible secondary consequences of such applications, or to the relative advantages of new knowledge in one field of science as compared with another. Today, the selection of subjects for scientific inquiry has become a political and social issue, and with it questions arise concerning the general direction of such inquiries and the rates at which science might develop and be applied.

Furthermore, the scientific enterprise itself has problems that suggest the need for deliberate guidance of science, as well as an awareness on the part of scientists of the need for restraint, if not constraint. For one thing, the particular human and material resources that science requires are not unlimited and may already be overextended. It has become a commonplace to point out that a large percentage of all the scientists who have ever lived are alive today. The growth of modern science has been such that the same statement would probably have been true at any time in the past 300 years, although in the past the absolute number of persons involved was much smaller. There is, however, no prospect that the same rate of expansion can continue indefinitely. It is also true that each additional increment of scientific knowledge has required proportionately greater investments of talent and equipment, although it is not obvious that this must always be so.

There is still a tendency to view science as a free intellectual activity capable of yielding earthshaking discoveries. Scientists are regarded as nature's agents and, indeed, fundamental scientific inquiry would probably be severely hampered if practicing scientists were to see themselves differently. Nevertheless, it is no longer possible—even if it were desirable—to foster science as a purely intellectual exercise, a gemstone to be admired but kept isolated from technology and from other cultural and social activities. It does not follow, however, that society must necessarily adjust to revolutions in science, or that scientific discoveries must lead inevitably to particular applications, whether or not those applications are beneficial.

Constraints and guidance

The very idea of giving guidance to science in the context of human affairs is controversial, since "guidance" implies an external judgment. Of course science, like all human activities, has in reality been

constrained and to some extent guided by economic, social, and political circumstances. The science policies now being developed in some of the advanced countries (described in an impressive set of reviews prepared by the Organization for Economic Cooperation and Development) tend, in fact, to relieve some of these constraints. Specific scientific work cannot be fully planned from the outset, let alone from the outside, but planning the resources and rewards available for scientific work certainly is possible. Some major scientific programs and teams of investigators are being provided with protection and independence comparable to that previously enjoyed only by single investigators, who had few requirements other than to be left alone.

Providing the prerequisites for a given scientific inquiry is, however, quite different from the act of choosing among many possible lines of inquiry. Yet every decision to support a given project implies the rejection—whether deliberate or not—of other projects. Many factors influence these choices, and they cannot be separated from the intellectual, economic, and technological environment in which they are made. Thus, the desire to make full use of persons especially skilled in building and operating high-energy accelerators and space probes has been a significant factor in decisions to support scientific inquiries using these expensive devices. In the political atmosphere that has prevailed since the end of World War II, military applications of new scientific discoveries have tended to be exploited more rapidly than their nonmilitary counterparts, although historically there used to be remarkably little military innovation between wars.

Many of the facts of science need not be uncovered through just one kind of experiment or through one inevitable sequence of discoveries. We tend to forget the premature efforts, the failures, and the "if's" of history and to conclude that what has been done in science needed to be done when it was done, and that what can be done should be done. Yet many fundamental experiments in physics or biology could be deferred and performed more economically later through the use of new, independently developed techniques. Even more important, we have reached a point where testing a scientific theory with the techniques at hand may have irreversible global effects. The use of high-altitude nuclear explosions to test theories about the earth's radiation belt, for example, could well have had such consequences.

The choice of priorities and policies with respect to the sciences can no longer be made solely on the basis of considerations internal to science, of unsubstantiated opinions, or of the laissez-faire processes of the marketplace. Even now, weight is being given to other factors, including prestige, competition, stability, possible short-term applications (especially in matters of health or defense), and geographic distribution. The forces currently guiding science and the assumptions upon which they operate have yet to be studied in detail. Yet, though present-day efforts to guide the development of science may still be very crude, they do show that certain judgments are possible and may have a social purpose uncharacteristic of the sciences themselves.

Approaching the future

Some pragmatic searches for guidelines are now under way. In the U.S. Congress, for instance, subcommittees led by Rep. Emilio Daddario of Connecticut and Sen. Edmund Muskie of Maine, among others, have been considering ways to assess new technologies, their social and economic implications, and their relationship to basic and applied research. These investigations are not intended to forecast new technologies; rather, they assume that the assessments themselves can and should influence the pattern of development. Their aim is to avoid regrettable, irreversible commitments to new technologies and to minimize trial-and-error social experimentation. The supersonic transport, anti-ballistic missile systems, and pesticides are only three technologies for which valid methods of appraisal are needed. (*See* Year in Review: SCIENCE, GENERAL.)

Because of the close relationship that has developed in this century between science and technology, the concept of technological assessment implies assessment of science as well. Typically, scientists have assumed an apolitical stance, insisting that science needs no guidance and resisting even minimal efforts to provide it. Yet some form of mediation between science and other human affairs seems both inevitable and necessary. Political processes must somehow balance the interests of the scientific community and those of the larger society.

Knowledge of science affairs

We must assume that substantial knowledge of how the sciences interact with other areas of human concern—which we will call the knowledge of science affairs—will increase popular agreement about the value of science and lessen the need for ad hoc political adjustments to scientific discoveries. At times, perhaps, a society should be compelled to adapt to new scientific developments, but we do not now possess the knowledge that would help us identify such situations. Nor can we take it for granted that we will spontaneously acquire this knowledge before science has advanced to the point where the opportunities for choice are reduced or preempted. Even when it is widely known that scientists are pursuing a certain line of inquiry—as, for example, in the present study of the mechanisms of human reproduction—we tend to ignore or discount its social implications until the possibility of practical applications of the research has become a reality. (*See* Feature Article: HUMANICS AND GENETIC ENGINEERING.)

433

In some instances, knowledge of science affairs might lead to the conclusion that the implications of a given line of scientific inquiry should be thoroughly investigated before the inquiry itself is popularized or even pursued. This is not an indirect argument for ignorance or the suspension of scientific investigation. Rather, the problem is one of balancing knowledge of science with knowledge of its implications and of society's influence on science. In formulating national priorities, for example, it might be appropriate to consider the relative advantages of giving greater encouragement to a science such as ecology and relatively less to a science such as physics. For while emphasis on ecology might lead to some difficult adjustments among existing interests, intensive study in this field is inherently unlikely to generate unanticipated and unwanted long-range side effects. Physics, on the other hand, might be easier to pursue now, because a large and active physics "establishment" is already in existence, but it is far more likely to result in unexpected and less controllable applications.

Knowledge of science affairs emerges from two rather distinct types of inquiry: one concerned with the historical, philosophical, and sociological aspects of science itself; the other with the ways science affects—and is affected by—technology, politics, economics, international relations, and similar aspects of human affairs. Taken together, these two lines of inquiry help us to understand the significance of specific scientific developments, the prerequisites for science, and the characteristics of its methods, personnel, and institutions. They provide guidelines for identifying the points at which critical policy decisions affecting the future of a science may be made, the criteria most appropriate for making such decisions, and the organizations most needed to utilize this kind of knowledge.

We can learn much by studying examples of the use or apparent misuse of scientific advances. A few characteristic situations can be viewed in these terms. In one type, the sciences contribute to competitive conditions, as in the nuclear arms race, in prestige-laden ventures into outer space, and in industrial rivalries. In another, the sciences help lead the way toward mutually advantageous cooperative efforts, as in such programs as the International Geophysical Year. In yet another, science is instrumental in refashioning our partially man-made world—for instance, through new-found controls over man's life-span and mental capacity. Some scientific efforts, such as those concerned with nuclear energy, may of course be considered in more than one of these contexts simultaneously. But studies of all these types of situation will yield knowledge of science affairs and the institutions concerned with developing or applying such knowledge.

Institutional developments

Clearly, our present capacity for carrying out large-scale scientific and technological programs is much greater than our capacity for studying either the purposes or the consequences of such programs. Research and development accounts for a sizable portion of the federal budget, but probably less than 1% of this money is used to study where and how the rest of it should be spent.

In the U.S. the need for presidential involvement in critical decisions concerning new weapons and defense systems has become apparent over the last two decades. The presidential decisions to attempt a manned lunar landing by 1970 and to build a 200 billion electron volt accelerator requested by physicists, at a cost of well over $100 million, represent comparable involvement in nonmilitary fields. As the nation's top-level policy makers have become increasingly engaged in providing guidance to research and development programs, their need for knowledge that will enable them to make decisions rationally has become more and more apparent. Despite this, the development of institutional capabilities for systematically supplying policy makers with this knowledge has been remarkably slow.

Some progress has been made. Several recent institutional developments have served to broaden the considerations used in assessing scientific and technical undertakings. Thus, possible lines of basic research are being assessed in terms of their relevance to higher education partly because the National Science Foundation and its National Science Board have assumed some major responsibilities in both science and education since their creation in 1950. The possible effects of new military technologies on arms control agreements and other international activities have received more consideration since the establishment in the early 1960s of the Arms Control and Disarmament Agency and related offices in the U.S. Department of State.

A little over a decade ago even the president had no regular access to advice and information about science affairs. Since that time, science advisory committees and offices for science and technology have been established in the Executive Office of the President, in many federal departments and agencies, in some state governments, and in the National Academy of Sciences and other professional organizations (although even today Congress, despite its vast decision-making powers, has no regular sources of independent advice).

The creation of such units in the United States and, to a lesser extent, in other countries has helped to meet the need. This institutional growth, however, has brought into clearer focus the scarcity of relevant information and analysis of the kind these agencies are designed to supply, as well as a shortage of the skilled personnel required to provide such information. The lack is perhaps most critical outside the United States, where science resources are relatively less abundant and the need to husband them is correspondingly greater.

435

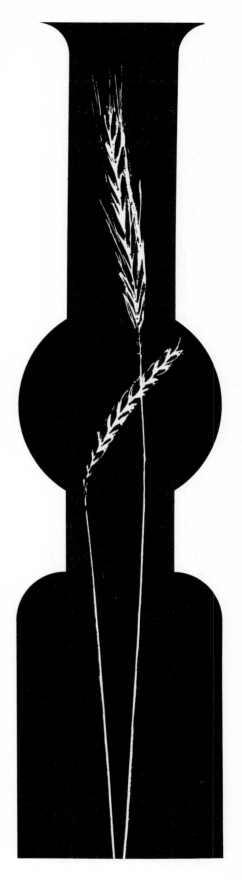

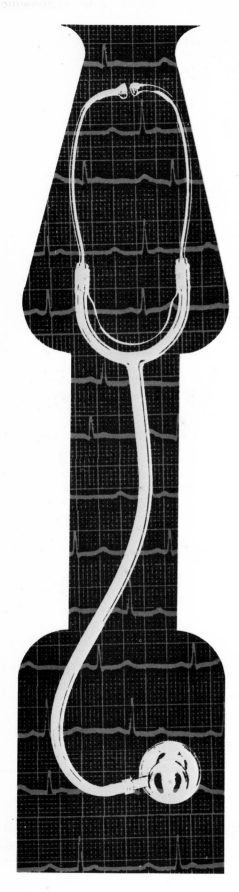

The task of improving the rationality of public policies involving science is awesome. The present keen interest in technological forecasting and in social projections to the year 2000 can, perhaps, be accounted for partly by a desire to make this task more manageable by delimiting the future and thus bypassing the need for truly fundamental understanding. The major effect of such forecasting, however, may well be to advance the view that man makes the future; to see the alternatives is to realize that choices are possible, if sufficient knowledge can be obtained to make such choices intelligently. But public understanding of science alone is not sufficient. Clearly, scientists and other scholars must collaborate in developing knowledge of science affairs, and new institutional mechanisms will have to be established for this purpose.

If the new agencies are to bring some order to science affairs, then there is just as urgent a need for a further evolution of the universities so that they will be able to supply the knowledge and talent that the agencies must have if their work is to be meaningful. This evolution is progressing slowly. Although the many specialized departments in universities provide a home for scientists engaged in basic research and a training ground for future researchers, the development of integrative studies that would explore the social significance of these activities is only beginning. About 20 U.S. universities, most notably Harvard and Columbia—where the Institute for the Study of Science in Human Affairs was set up in 1966— are now actively working in this field. Continued evolution of the universities and of society itself requires that the proliferation of specialized activities be supplemented by many more such cross-disciplinary programs, designed to establish the relevance of one specialty to another and to effect appropriate connections between them. It remains to be seen whether present institutions of higher education are capable of meeting this challenge.

FOR ADDITIONAL READING:

Dubos, René, *So Human an Animal* (Scribner, 1968).

Ferkiss, Victor C., *Technological Man: The Myth and the Reality* (George Braziller, 1969).

Greenberg, Daniel S., *The Politics of Pure Science* (The New American Library, 1969).

Price, Don K., *The Scientific Estate* (The Belknap Press of the Harvard University Press, 1965).

Shils, Edward (ed.), *Criteria for Scientific Development: Public Policy and National Goals* (a selection of articles from *Minerva,* Massachusetts Institute of Technology Press, 1968).

Current issues about science affairs are regularly reported or discussed in the "News and Comment" section of *Science,* the weekly publication of the American Association for the Advancement of Science, and on a more highly selective basis in the science section of the *Saturday Review.*

Index entries to feature and review articles in this and the previous edition of the *Britannica Yearbook of Science and the Future* are set in boldface type, *e.g.,* **Astronomy.** Entries to other subjects are set in light-face type, *e.g.,* Radiation. Additional information on any of these subjects is identified with a subheading and indented under the entry heading. The numbers following headings and subheadings indicate the year (bold-face) of the edition and the page number (lightface) on which the information appears.

Astronomy 70–119; **69**–247
 honors **70**–251; **69**–257
 Mt Wilson and Palomar Observatories: Two Rooms with a View **70**–356
 photography **69**–16
  new film **69**–354
 A Space Age Goal: Exploring the Solar System **69**–61
 spacecraft navigation **70**–184
 X-ray Astronomy **69**–176

All entry headings, whether consisting of a single word or more, are treated for the purpose of alphabetization as single complete headings and are alphabetized letter by letter up to the punctuation. The abbreviation "il." indicates an illustration.

Acknowledgments

Book design by Lawrence Levy

34–53	Illustrations by Bunji Tagawa
80–97	Illustrations by David Beckes
178–191	Illustrations by Dick Fickle
192	Illustration by Bill Neebe
194 & 199	Illustrations by William A. Norman
202–225	Illustrations by Ron Despeaux
306–319	Photographs by Bill Arsenault
320–329	Illustrations by Ron Bradford
330–343	Illustrations by Ardy Kazarosian
400–413	Designed by David Lawrence
428–436	Designed by David Lawrence